Harden's

UK Restaurant Survey 2015

"The UK's most helpful and informative guide"
The Sunday Times

0 RESTAURANTS

ISBN 978-0-9929408-9-1

British Library Cataloguing-in-Publication data: a catalogue record for this book is available from the British Library.

Printed in the UK by Advent Printing

Research assistants: Sarah Ashpole, Clare Burnage, Daniel O'Mahony, Clodagh Kinsella, Wayne Tuckfield
Assistant editor: Karen Moss
Designers: (text) Paul Smith, (cover) Margaret Vanschaemelhout

Harden's Limited
Golden Cross House, 8 Duncannon Street
London WC2N 4JF

Would restaurateurs (and PRs) please address communications to 'Editorial' at the above address, or ideally by email to: editorial@hardens.com

THE SUNDAY TIMES

The UK's 100 Best Restaurants

1 Fraîche, Oxton

2 Le Manoir aux Quat' Saisons, Great Milton

3 L'Enclume, Cartmel

4 The Ledbury, London W11

5 Mr Underhill's, Ludlow

6 Restaurant Sat Bains, Nottingham

7 Rasoi, London SW3

8 Harry's Place, Great Gonerby

9 Gidleigh Park, Chagford

10 Waterside Inn, Bray

11 Restaurant Martin Wishart, Edinburgh

12 The Pass Restaurant, South Lodge Hotel, Horsham

13 Martin Wishart, Cameron House, Loch Lomond

14 Simon Radley, The Chester Grosvenor, Chester

15 Restaurant Nathan Outlaw, The St Enodoc Hotel, Rock

16 Le Gavroche, London W1

17 One-O-One, Sheraton Park Tower, London SW1

18 The Castle Terrace, Edinburgh

19 Yorke Arms, Ramsgill-in-Nidderdale

20 Kitchen Table, London W1

21 Midsummer House, Cambridge

22 Kai Mayfair, London W1

23 21212, Edinburgh

24 Northcote, Langho

25 Fera at Claridge's, Claridge's Hotel, London W1

1
2
3
4

THE SUNDAY TIMES

The UK's 100 Best Restaurants

26 Raby Hunt, Summerhouse

27 The Latymer, Pennyhill Park Hotel, Bagshot

28 Pied à Terre, London W1

29 The Fat Duck, Bray

30 Hedone, London W4

31 Drakes, Ripley

32 The Neptune, Old Hunstanton

33 Bath Priory Hotel, Bath

34 Pétrus, London SW1

35 The Square, London W1

36 Tyddyn Llan, Llandrillo

37 Zuma, London SW7

38 Murano, London W1

39 The Five Fields, London SW3

40 Hambleton Hall, Hambleton

41 The Dining Room, Whatley Manor, Easton Grey

42 The Greenhouse, London W1

43 Andrew Fairlie, Gleneagles Hotel, Auchterarder

44 Hakkasan, London W1

45 Checkers, Montgomery

46 L'Ortolan, Shinfield

47 Koffmann's, The Berkeley, London SW1

48 Marianne, London W2

49 Nobu, Metropolitan Hotel, London W1

50 Le Champignon Sauvage, Cheltenham

THE SUNDAY TIMES

The UK's 100 Best Restaurants

51 André Garrett At Cliveden, Cliveden House, Taplow

52 La Petite Maison, London W1

53 The Harrow at Little Bedwyn, Marlborough

54 Fischers at Baslow Hall, Baslow

55 The Peat Inn, Cupar

56 Roka, London W1

57 The Terrace, Montagu Arms Hotel, Beaulieu

58 Benares, London W1

59 L'Atelier de Joel Robuchon, London WC2

60 Seven Park Place, London SW1

61 The French Restaurant, Midland Hotel, Manchester

62 Artichoke, Amersham

63 Read's, Faversham

64 Wiltons, London SW1

65 Theo Randall, InterContinental Hotel, London W1

66 Min Jiang, The Royal Garden Hotel, London W8

67 The Kitchin, Edinburgh

68 Pollen Street Social, London W1

69 Purnells, Birmingham

70 Amaya, London SW1

71 Holbeck Ghyll, Windermere

72 Scott's, London W1

73 Texture, London W1

74 Bohemia, The Club Hotel & Spa, Jersey

75 Alyn Williams, Westbury Hotel, London W1

The UK's 100 Best Restaurants

76 Hand & Flowers, Marlow

77 Story, London SE1

78 HKK, London EC2

79 Chez Bruce, London SW17

80 Loves, The Glasshouse, Birmingham

81 Marcus, The Berkeley, London SW1

82 Lucknam Park, Luckham Park Hotel, Colerne

83 Sushi Tetsu, London EC1

84 Dinner, Mandarin Oriental, London SW1

85 The Three Chimneys, Dunvegan

86 Hunan, London SW1

87 Gordon Ramsay, London, SW3

88 The Ritz Restaurant, The Ritz, London W1

89 The River Café, London W6

90 Galvin La Chapelle, London E1

91 Seafood Restaurant, Padstow

92 The Clove Club, London EC1

93 Tamarind, London W1

94 Lumière, Cheltenham

95 Wilks, Bristol

96 The Pipe & Glass Inn, Beverley

97 Hibiscus, London W1

98 Samuel's, Swinton Park Hotel & Spa, Masham

99 Freemasons at Wiswell, Wiswell

100 La Trompette, London W1

Eat Well

If you care about where your food comes from, whether your waiter is paid a fair wage or how the restaurants you eat in are reducing the amount of food they waste, then look out for the Sustainable Restaurant Association's (SRA) ratings next to the listings in this guide.

The SRA is a not for profit body helping restaurants achieve greater sustainability. Members are scored across three main categories: Sourcing, Environment and Society, so you can easily identify those restaurants doing great things like sourcing seasonably, supporting local producers, using high welfare meat and dairy and ensuring fish stocks aren't endangered.

The One, Two or Three Star rating you'll see at the bottom of a restaurant's listing will also give you a guide as to how well it manages its waste, energy and water and how committed it is to supporting its local community.

So you when you choose to eat in a restaurant boasting the SRA stars you can rest assured your meal isn't costing the earth.

All of the restaurants in the guide with SRA stars have completed the rating in the last 12 months.

> *We're proud to support the SRA, and hope that by adding SRA Sustainability Ratings to the restaurants we include, we can help set diners' expectations as to which of their choices will ensure the trade thrives for decades, and hopefully centuries to come.*
>
> **– Harden's**

SRA One Star - Good Sustainability
SRA Two Stars - Excellent Sustainability
SRA Three Stars - Exceptional Sustainability

Among the winners at the Sustainable Restaurant Awards in February 2014 were:

cafe-ODE - Sustainable Restaurant of the Year
Grain Store - London Sustainable Restaurant of the Year
Lussmanns - Sustainable Small Group of the Year
River Cottage - SRA Award for Sourcing
Carluccio's - Sustainable Innovation Award
Belmond Le Manoir aux Quat'Saisons - Sustainable Hotel Restaurant of the Year
The Gate, Islington - Most Improved Sustainability

CONTENTS

Fischer's

Patty & Bun

RATINGS & PRICES

Ratings

Our rating system does not tell you – as most guides do – that expensive restaurants are often better than cheap ones! What we do is compare each restaurant's performance – as judged by the average ratings awarded by reporters in the survey – with other similarly-priced restaurants.

This approach has the advantage that it helps you find – whatever your budget for any particular meal – where you will get the best 'bang for your buck'.

The following qualities are assessed:

F — Food
S — Service
A — Ambience

The rating indicates that, ***in comparison with other restaurants in the same price-bracket***, performance is…

5 — Exceptional
4 — Very good
3 — Good
2 — Average
1 — Poor

NEW IN 2015!

Regular readers take note: we've turned our marking system on its head.

5 is the new 0!

In the **UK section**, some restaurants are worth a mention but, for some reason (typically low feedback) we do not think a rating is appropriate. These are indicated as follows:

T —Tip

Prices

The price shown for each restaurant is the cost for one (1) person of an average three-course dinner with half a bottle of house wine and coffee, any cover charge, service and VAT. Lunch is often cheaper. With BYO restaurants, we have assumed that two people share a £7 bottle of off-licence wine.

Telephone number – *all numbers are '020' numbers.*

Map reference – *shown immediately after the telephone number.*

Full postcodes – *for non-group restaurants, the first entry in the 'small print' at the end of each listing, so you can set your sat-nav.*

Website and Twitter – *shown in the small print, where applicable.*

Last orders time – *listed after the website (if applicable); Sunday may be up to 90 minutes earlier.*

Opening hours – *unless otherwise stated, restaurants are open for lunch and dinner seven days a week.*

Credit and debit cards – *unless otherwise stated, Mastercard, Visa, Amex and Maestro are accepted.*

Dress – *where appropriate, the management's preferences concerning patrons' dress are given.*

Special menus – *if we know of a particularly good value set menu we note this (e.g. "set weekday L"), together with its formula price (FP), calculated exactly as in 'Prices' above. Details change, so always check ahead.*

'Rated on Editors' visit' – *indicates ratings have been determined by the Editors personally, based on their visit, rather than derived from the survey.*

SRA Star Rating – *the sustainability index, as calculated by the Sustainable Restaurant Association – see page 8 for more information.*

For the third year, we're pleased to bring you what we believe to be the UK's most useful restaurant guide in its new 'glovebox' format. As ever, it is written 'from the bottom up' – we don't dictate the establishments listed, but base the selection on the results of our unique annual survey of thousands of restaurant-goers, in which you are most welcome to take part. (Further details of this are given overleaf.)

This guide includes the full content of our separately-published London guide, as well as coverage of cities, towns and villages across the whole of the UK. We recognise that the result is a guide somewhat skewed to London. We urge readers, though, to think of this extensive London coverage as a bonus rather than a defect. After all, our out-of-London coverage alone is broadly equivalent to the total content of the UK's longest-published UK guide, The Good Food Guide (including the restaurants of the metropolis).

It is certainly no longer true, as one could have said as recently as five years ago, that large areas of the UK are pretty much restaurant deserts, devoid of almost anything of interest to the discerning visitor. This ongoing transformation is perhaps most obvious in the great regional centres – even Manchester, a 'second city' which has been a laggard until very recently, seems finally to be getting its act together!

We urge all our readers to help us do even better justice to the restaurant scene outside the capital. If you think your area is under-represented, the answer is largely in your own hands – take part in our annual survey, and make sure your friends do too!

We are very grateful to each of our thousands of reporters, without whose input this guide could not have been written. Many reporters express views about a number of restaurants at some length, knowing full well that – given the concise format of the guide – we can seemingly never 'do justice' to their observations. We must assume that they do so in the confidence that the short – and we hope snappy – summaries we produce are as fair and well-informed as possible.

You, the reader, must judge – restaurant guides are not works of literature, and should be assessed on the basis of utility. This is a case where the proof of the pudding really is in the eating.

Our relationship with the Sunday Times continues to develop. For the fifth year, we are pleased to record, in the front section of the guide, the list we prepare for them of the Top 100 restaurants in the UK. As the years roll on, the risers and fallers – and the 'stayers' – in this tabulation are taking on an interest all of their own.

All restaurant guides are the subject of continual revision, and the more input we have, the more accurate and comprehensive future editions will be. If you are not already signed up, please do join the www.hardens.com mailing list – we will then ensure that you are invited to take part in future surveys.

Richard Harden **Peter Harden**

HOW THIS BOOK IS ORGANISED

The guide begins in *London*, and contains the full text of the guide already published as *London Restaurants 2015*. Thereafter, the guide is organised strictly alphabetically by location, without regard to national divisions – Beaumaris, Belfast and Birmingham appear together under 'B'.

For *cities and larger towns*, you should therefore be able to turn straight to the relevant section. In addition to the entries for the restaurants themselves, cities which have significant numbers of restaurants also have a brief introductory overview.

In *less densely populated areas*, you will generally find it easiest to start with the relevant map at the back of the book, which will guide you to the appropriate place names.

If you are looking for a specific restaurant, the alphabetical index at the very back of the book lists all of the restaurants – London and UK – in this guide.

YOUR CONTRIBUTION

This book is the result of a research effort involving thousands of 'reporters'. As a group, you are 'ordinary' members of the public who share with us summary reviews of the best and the worst of your annual dining experiences. This year, over 6,250 of you gave us some 65,000 reviews in total.

The density of the feedback on London (where many of the top places attract several hundred reviews each) is such that the ratings for the restaurants in the capital are almost exclusively statistical in derivation. (We have, as it happens, visited almost all the restaurants in the London section, anonymously, and at our own expense, but we use our personal experiences only to inform the standpoint from which to interpret the consensus opinion.)

In the case of the more commented-upon restaurants away from the capital, we have adopted an essentially statistical approach very similar to London. In the case of less-visited provincial establishments, however, the interpretation of survey results owes as much to art as it does to science.

In our experience, smaller establishments are – for better or worse – generally quite consistent, and we have therefore felt able to place a relatively high level of confidence in a lower level of commentary. Conservatism on our part, however, may have led to some smaller places being under-rated compared to their more-visited peers.

LONDON INTRODUCTION & SURVEY RESULTS

SURVEY MOST MENTIONED

RANKED BY THE NUMBER OF REPORTERS' VOTES

These are the restaurants which were most frequently mentioned by reporters. (Last year's position is given in brackets.) An asterisk* indicates the first appearance in the list of a recently-opened restaurant.

1 J Sheekey (1)
2 Scott's (3)
3 Le Gavroche (2)
4 Clos Maggiore (4)
5 The Ledbury (8)
6 The Delaunay (11)
7 Chez Bruce (6)
8 Pollen Street Social (10)
9 Dinner (7)
10 The Wolseley (9)

11 Brasserie Zédel (5)
12 Gymkhana*
13 The Cinnamon Club (17)
14 Galvin La Chapelle (20)
15 The Square (12)
16 Bleeding Heart (16)
17 The River Café (19)
18 Bocca Di Lupo (23)
19 La Trompette (13)
20 Pied à Terre (40)

21 Medlar (13)
22= La Poule au Pot (21)
22= Marcus (15)
24= The Berners Tavern (-)
24= Benares (23)
26 Galvin Bistrot de Luxe (18)
27 Zucca*
28= Gauthier Soho (38)
28= Trinity (28)
30= Grain Store*

30= Le Caprice (20)
32 Zuma (34)
33 Gordon Ramsay (30)
34 The Ivy (26)
35 Andrew Edmunds (37)
36= Tayyabs (35)
36= The Anchor & Hope (-)
38 Terroirs (33)
39 Yauatcha (-)
40 Amaya (25)

J Sheekey

Gymkhana

Grain Store

Zuma

Top gastronomic experience

1. The Ledbury (2)
2. Le Gavroche (1)
3. Dinner (3)
4. Chez Bruce (4)
5. Pollen Street Social (5)
6. Pied à Terre (10)
7. Gordon Ramsay (-)
8. The Square (8)
9. Marcus (6)
10. Medlar (9)

Favourite

1. Chez Bruce (1)
2. J Sheekey (5)
3. Clos Maggiore (-)
4. The Ledbury (8)
5. Le Gavroche (2)
6. The River Café (10)
7. The Delaunay (6)
8. Le Caprice (4)
9. Pollen Street Social (9)
10. The Wolseley (3)

Best for business

1. The Wolseley (1)
2. The Delaunay (3)
3. The Square (2)
4. Galvin La Chapelle (4)
5. Bleeding Heart (6)
6. The Don (5)
7. Coq d'Argent (-)
8. Scott's (8)
9. L'Anima (7)
10. Pollen Street Social*

Best for romance

1. Clos Maggiore (1)
2. La Poule au Pot (2)
3. Andrew Edmunds (3)
4. Bleeding Heart (4)
5. Le Gavroche (5)
6. Chez Bruce (7)
7. Galvin at Windows (6)
8. Galvin La Chapelle (-)
9. The Ledbury (-)
10. Gauthier Soho (-)

Best breakfast/brunch

1. The Wolseley (1)
2. The Delaunay (2)
3. Duck & Waffle (8)
4. Riding House Café (5)
5. Roast (3)
6. Colbert*
7. Cecconi's (3)
8. 3 South Place*
9. The Pantechnicon (-)
10. Balthazar*

Best bar/pub food

1. The Anchor & Hope (1)
2. Bull & Last (2)
3. Harwood Arms (3)
4. The Jugged Hare*
5. Canton Arms (7)
6. The Gun (8)
7. Ladbroke Arms (10)
8. Pig & Butcher*
9. Truscott Arms*
10. Thomas Cubitt (4)

Most disappointing cooking

1. Oxo Tower (Rest') (1)
2. Dinner (6)
3. Colbert (5)
4. The Ivy (8)
5. Gordon Ramsay (3)
6. Le Gavroche (-)
7. Balthazar (2)
8. Marcus (-)
9. Alain Ducasse (9)
10. Dabbous*

Most overpriced restaurant

1. The River Café (3)
2. Oxo Tower (Rest') (1)
3. Dinner (4)
4. Gordon Ramsay (2)
5. Marcus (7)
6. Alain Ducasse (5)
7. Le Gavroche (8)
8. Cut (6)
9. Balthazar*
10. Pollen Street Social (10)

SURVEY HIGHEST RATINGS

FOOD

£85+

1. The Ledbury
2. Rasoi
3. Pied à Terre
4. Le Gavroche
5. One-O-One

£65-£84

1. The Five Fields
2. Hedone
3. Chez Bruce
4. Zuma
5. HKK

£50-£64

1. Sushi Tetsu
2. Moro
3. Dinings
4. Sukho Fine Thai Cuisine
5. Gauthier Soho

£40-£49

1. Sushi-Say
2. Lamberts
3. Jin Kichi
4. Brawn
5. Donostia

£39 or less

1. Pitt Cue Co
2. Ragam
3. Mangal I
4. Santa Maria
5. Silk Road

SERVICE

£85+

1. Le Gavroche
2. The Ledbury
3. Bubbledogs KT
4. Fera at Claridge's
5. Pied à Terre

£65-£84

1. The Goring Hotel
2. The Five Fields
3. Chez Bruce
4. Trinity
5. Petersham Hotel

£50-£64

1. Sushi Tetsu
2. Oslo Court
3. Otto's
4. Gauthier Soho
5. Clos Maggiore

£40-£49

1. Lamberts
2. Donostia
3. Pentolina
4. Sushi-Say
5. Yming

£39 or less

1. Paradise Hampstead
2. Boqueria
3. Kaffeine
4. Morito
5. Blanchette

AMBIENCE

1. The Ritz Restaurant
2. Bubbledogs KT
3. Galvin at Windows
4. Oblix
5. Le Gavroche

1. Petersham Hotel
2. The Berners Tavern
3. Rules
4. Criterion
5. The Goring Hotel

1. Clos Maggiore
2. The Wallace
3. L'Aventure
4. La Poule au Pot
5. Randall & Aubin

1. Andrew Edmunds
2. St Johns N19
3. Brawn
4. José
5. The Depot

1. Brasserie Zédel
2. Carom at Meza
3. Churchill Arms
4. Princi
5. The Begging Bowl

OVERALL

1. The Ledbury
2. Bubbledogs KT
3. Le Gavroche
4. Fera at Claridge's
5. Pied à Terre

1. The Five Fields
2. The Goring Hotel
3. Chez Bruce
4. Scott's
5. Galvin La Chapelle

1. Sushi Tetsu
2. Clos Maggiore
3. L'Aventure
4. Randall & Aubin
5. J Sheekey Oyster Bar

1. Lamberts
2. Donostia
3. Brawn
4. Sushi-Say
5. José

1. Carom at Meza
2. The Begging Bowl
3. Pitt Cue Co
4. Paradise Hampstead
5. Meat Mission

SURVEY BEST BY CUISINE

These are the restaurants which received the best average food ratings (excluding establishments with a small or notably local following).

Where the most common types of cuisine are concerned, we present the results in two price-brackets. For less common cuisines, we list the top three, regardless of price.

For further information about restaurants which are particularly notable for their food, see the cuisine lists starting on page 172. These indicate, using an asterisk*, restaurants which offer exceptional or very good food.

British, Modern

£50 and over
1 The Ledbury
2 The Five Fields
3 Hedone
4 Chez Bruce
5 Fera at Claridge's

Under £50
1 Lamberts
2 The Dairy
3 10 Greek Street
4 40 Maltby Street
5 Rochelle Canteen

French

£50 and over
1 Pied à Terre
2 Le Gavroche
3 Pétrus
4 Gauthier Soho
5 The Square

Under £50
1 Brawn
2 Casse-Croute
3 Brula
4 Comptoir Gascon
5 Toasted

Italian/Mediterranean

£50 and over
1 Murano
2 Zucca
3 Al Boccon di'vino
4 Olivomare
5 Theo Randall

Under £50
1 Santore
2 Opera Tavern
3 Pizza Metro
4 Dehesa
5 Le Querce

Indian & Pakistani

£50 and over
1 Rasoi
2 Babur
3 Amaya
4 Gymkhana
5 Benares

Under £50
1 Ragam
2 Indian Rasoi
3 Ganapati
4 Indian Zing
5 Roots at N1

Chinese

£50 and over

1. Kai Mayfair
2. HKK
3. Hunan
4. Min Jiang
5. Royal China Club

Under £50

1. Silk Road
2. A Wong
3. Yipin China
4. Mandarin Kitchen
5. Yming

Japanese

£50 and over

1. Sushi Tetsu
2. Zuma
3. Dinings
4. Chotto Matte
5. Sushisamba

Under £50

1. Sushi-Say
2. Pham Sushi
3. Jin Kichi
4. Koya
5. Bone Daddies

British, Traditional

1. Scott's
2. St John
3. St John Bread & Wine

Vegetarian

1. Ragam
2. Ganapati
3. Mildreds

Burgers, etc

1. Meat Mission
2. Opera Tavern
3. Bar Boulud

Pizza

1. Santa Maria
2. Oliveto
3. Pizza Metro

Fish & Chips

1. Toff's
2. The Fish & Chip Shop
3. The Sea Shell

Thai

1. Sukho Fine Thai Cuisine
2. The Begging Bowl
3. Churchill Arms

Steaks & Grills

1. Carom at Meza
2. The Guinea Grill
3. 34

Fish & Seafood

1. One-O-One
2. Scott's
3. J Sheekey

Fusion

1. Bubbledogs KT
2. Eight Over Eight
3. L'Etranger

Spanish

1. Moro
2. Donostia
3. José

Turkish

1. Mangal I
2. Fez Mangal
3. Kazan

Lebanese

1. Maroush
2. Fairuz
3. Yalla Yalla

TOP SPECIAL DEALS

The following menus allow you to eat in the restaurants concerned at a significant discount when compared to their evening à la carte prices.

The prices used are calculated in accordance with our usual formula (i.e. three courses with house wine, coffee and tip).

Special menus are by their nature susceptible to change – please check that they are still available.

Weekday lunch

£95+ Alain Ducasse
Quattro Passi

£85+ Le Gavroche

£70+ The Goring Hotel
Hedone

£65+ L'Atelier de Joel Robuchon
Dinner
The Greenhouse
Hélène Darroze
Marianne
Rib Room

£60+ The Ledbury
Sketch (Lecture Rm)

£55+ Ametsa
Club Gascon
Galvin at Windows
Gordon Ramsay
Hibiscus
Pétrus
Seven Park Place
The Square
Texture

£50+ Alyn Williams
Aqua Shard
Babbo
Bibendum
The Clove Club
Coya
The Ivy
Murano
One-O-One
Pied à Terre
Poissonnerie de l'Avenue
Pollen Street Social
Roast
Savoy Grill
Story
34
Thirty Six
Trinity
Typing Room

£45+ Amaya
L'Autre Pied
Babylon
The Bingham
Cambio de Tercio
The Cinnamon Club
Dabbous
Daphne's
L'Etranger
Franco's
Galvin La Chapelle
Gauthier Soho
The Glasshouse
Hunan
Landmark (Winter Gdn)
Medlar
Quilon
Rules
J Sheekey
Tamarind
La Trompette

£40+ The Abingdon
The Avenue
Bam-Bou
Belvedere
Cheyne Walk Brasserie
Chor Bizarre
Garnier
Hix
Kitchen W8
Lima
Little Social
Le Pont de la Tour
La Poule au Pot
Spice Market
Trishna
Les Trois Garçons

£35+ The Almeida
L'Aventure
Bradley's
Christopher's
The Dock Kitchen
Entrée
Essenza
Frantoio
Frederick's
Galvin Bistrot de Luxe
High Timber
Magdalen
Massimo
Merchants Tavern
Mon Plaisir
Outlaw's Seafood and Grill
Quaglino's
Quantus
Racine
Red Fort
Suk Saran
Sukho Fine Thai Cuisine
Trullo
The Victoria

£30+ The Anchor & Hope
Buen Ayre
La Buvette
Chapters
City Miyama
Fairuz
Gilgamesh
Hereford Road
The Hoxton Grill
Jamie's Diner
Joe Allen
Kensington Wine Rooms
The Light House
Market
Mazi
Odette's
Orso
Le P'tit Normand
Sam's Brasserie
Smiths (Dining Rm)
Sonny's Kitchen

£25+ Augustine Kitchen
Camino
Chez Patrick
Elephant Royale
Mill Lane Bistro
The Palmerston
Pearl Liang
Yming

£20+ Olley's
Le Sacré-Coeur

£15+ Apulia
Cellar Gascon
El Pirata
Sticky Fingers
Tentazioni

Pre/post theatre (and early evening)

£80+ The Ritz Restaurant

£65+ Atelier de Joel Robuchon
Oxo Tower (Rest')
Tamarind

£55+ Benares

£50+ Bentley's
Koffmann's
Oxo Tower (Brass')
Wild Honey

£45+ L'Autre Pied
Boulestin
Le Caprice
Daphne's
Gymkhana
Homage
MASH Steakhouse
Santini
Savoy Grill
Veeraswamy

£40+ The Avenue
Belvedere
Hix
The Jugged Hare
Lima
Quaglino's
Spice Market

£35+ The Almeida
Baltic
Christopher's
L'Escargot
Franco's
Latium
Massimo
Orso
The Portrait
Red Fort
Sarastro

£30+ Boulevard
Le Garrick
Gay Hussar
Mon Plaisir
The Noodle House

£25+ Café des Amis
Moti Mahal
Skylon Grill
Yming

Sunday lunch

£85+ Rib Room

£55+ Medlar
Petersham Hotel
Roast
Trinity

£50+ The Glasshouse
Kitchen W8
Odette's
Orrery
La Trompette

£45+ Bradley's
Coq d'Argent
Galvin La Chapelle
Hix
J Sheekey

£40+ A Cena
Blueprint Café
The Botanist
Café Bohème
Charlotte's Bistro
Le Cigalon
Foxlow
Kaifeng
Maggie Jones's
Sam's Brasserie

£35+ Babur
Elephant Royale
Entrée
First Floor
The Wharf

£30+ Les Associés

THE RESTAURANT SCENE

The bull run continues

This year we record a restaurant scene in overdrive. Not only was the openings figure, at 148, very high by historical standards, but the figure for closings, 47, was the lowest this millennium. One should always beware of talk of 'smashing' records, but the level of net openings this year (openings minus closings) – at 98 – is nearly a third higher than the previous record of 75, noted in our 2006 guide.

The ratio of openings to closings tells a similarly robust story. At around 3:1, the ratio is now double what it was at the low point in the cycle, three years ago. Can a 'bull run' like this go on for very much longer? Since our first guide back in 1992, a year-to-year upswing in the ratio has never gone on for more than three consecutive years, so we are very likely now set for some loss of momentum (which is of course a very different thing from an actual reverse).

We are very conscious that the restaurant scene is now getting so big that the bar for registering on the critical appraisal 'radar' has risen in recent years: there are certainly openings which would have seemed of some significance a decade ago which today pass largely unnoticed.

So quickly can the dining out scene change that restaurant years are more like dog years than human ones. Many people who have come to London in the past half-decade think that it is normal and natural for this to be regarded as one of the great dining out cities of the world, not realising just how recently this situation has come to pass – 20 years ago the proposition would rightly have been derided, and even a decade ago it would have sounded very much like boosterism.

It is a paradox that now, in the year when the London restaurant scene can finally and indubitably be said to have 'arrived', Harden's is the only 'comprehensive' guide which has survived long enough to chronicle it, and we lament the apparent passing of the Time Out guide – the only comprehensive London-specific guide in publication longer than this one.

Every year, we choose what to us seem to be the most significant openings of the year. This year, our selection is as follows:

Chiltern Firehouse	City Social
Fera at Claridge's	Kurobuta
Lyle's	Merchants Tavern
The New Angel	The Palomar
The Typing Room	Uni

East – the new West

It is a sign of a new normality that these picks are equally divided between 'East' and 'West' postcodes. Go back a decade, and the East was unrepresented on this list; go back five years, and we would have spotted only a single star there. And it is not just at the top end of the market that an equivalence between East and West is becoming a feature of the market: even Peckham, an historically deprived area in the SE corner of the city, is beginning to show signs of restaurant life!

Interesting restaurants are not only popping up everywhere, they come progressively in every national flavour, and indeed nowadays often a subdivision of a national flavour. A decade ago, we usually described restaurants as, say, 'Italian'. Nowadays they are often Sardinian, Sicilian, Puglian, Neapolitan... And all the (larger) continents, in the last few years including South America, are now represented.

'Trends' do not seem radically to have changed of late. Most obvious is the continuing fetishisation of New York City as the first port of call for anyone looking for so-called inspiration for any 'new' sort of restaurant concept, and the continuing obsession for meat-led restaurants. Perhaps the message that excessive meat consumption is bad both for the individual and the planet will finally get through? One day!

Also imperishable, but over a much longer timescale, seems to be the appeal of some of the fast food classics, and in particular the pizza and the hamburger, both of which are in the process of re-invention by a new generation. It is difficult, though, to say that there is really anything new in this – the first London craze for hamburgers kicked off with the opening of the first Wimpy bar... in 1954.

One area where progressive change definitely is apparent is the continuing move away from the idea that quality dining out is a knife-and-fork activity, usually consisting of three courses – witness the opening of *Fera* at that supposed bastion of the Establishment, Claridge's. If there has been one single decisive shift of recent years, it is that small plates – considered radical a decade ago – now seem very much here to stay.

Prices

The average price of dinner for one at establishments listed in this guide is £49.46 (compared to £47.68 last year). Prices have risen by 2.7% in the past 12 months. This is a little less than last year's rise, and broadly in line with inflation as recorded by the Retail Price Index.

OPENINGS AND CLOSURES

Openings (148)

L'Amorosa
Andina
L'Anima Café
The Ape & Bird
Apulia
Arabica
Artusi
Assunta Madre
Augustine Kitchen
Bar Esteban
Barnyard
Beast
Bibo
Bilbao Berria
Bird
Blackfoot
Blanchette
Blind Pig
Bo Lang
Bobo Social
Bocconcino
Bonnie Gull Seafood Café
The Brackenbury
Bravas
Bubba Gump Shrimp Co.
Buddha Bar London
Bunnychow W1, E1
Café Murano
Café Pistou
The Camberwell Arms
Canvas SW1
Chez Abir
Chicken Shop SW17
Chicken Shop & Dirty Burger
The Chiltern Firehouse
Chotto Matte
City Barge
City Social
The Clink
Clutch
Colony Grill Room
Compagnie des Vins Surnaturels
Cornish Tiger
DF Mexico
Dip & Flip
Dirty Bones
Dishoom N1
Drakes Tabanco
Dub Jam
East Street
Eat 17
Edwins
Eelbrook
8 Hoxton Square
Ember Yard
Ergon
Er Mei
Fera at Claridge's
Fischer's
Flat Iron WC2
GB Pizza Co.
Gin Joint
Les Gourmets des Ternes
Granger & Co. EC1

DF Mexico

Greenberry Cafe
Ham Yard Restaurant
Heddon Street Kitchen
Hill & Szrok
Hixter
Holborn Dining Room
Homeslice
House of Ho
Hubbard & Bell
Ibérica EC1
Ippudo London
Jamaica Patty Co.
Jamie's Diner
Kurobuta
Lima Floral
Linnea
The Lobster House
London House
Lyle's
M
Marani
Margaux
Merchants Tavern
Meza SW17
The New Angel
New Tom's
The Noodle House
Olympic
On the Bab
Pachamama
The Palomar
Parlour
Patty & Bun EC2
Pavillion
Peckham Bazaar
Penkul & Banks
Peyote
La Polenteria
Pond
Primeur
Q Grill
Quattro Passi
Rabbit
Rabot 1745
Raw Duck
Red Dog SW4
Rextail
Rivea
Rocket WC2
Roka W1, WC2
The Rooftop Café
Rotorino
Rugoletta
Salvation in Noodles
Sea Containers
Shoryu Ramen, Kingly Ct
Source
Spring
Strand Dining Rooms
TED
The Terrace
Ting
Tonkotsu E8
Toto's
Tredwell's
Truscott Arms
21 Bateman Street
Typing Room
Uni
Vapiano SE1
Verden
Villandry SW1
Villiers Coffee Co
Vivo
Whyte & Brown
Wright Bros E1
Yard Sale Pizza
Zest

Closures (47)

Albannach
Anglo Asian Tandoori
Apsleys
L'Art du Fromage
Assiette Anglaise
Automat
Bangalore Express
Beard to Tail
Bincho Yakitori
Bo London
Brompton Bar & Grill
Il Calcio SW5
Cape Town Fish Market
Le Cercle
Chabrot Bistrot des Halles
Chez Marcelle
Choys
Chuen Cheng Ku
Cotidie
Downtown Mayfair
E11even Park Walk
Empress of Sichuan
Fire & Stone E1
Giaconda Dining Rooms
Gran Paradiso
Jenny Lo's Tea House
Ken Lo's Memories of China W8
Lola & Simón
Mango & Silk
Mao Tai
Morgan M
Mr Wing
Naamyaa Café
One Blenheim Terrace
Osteria dell'Arancio
The Palm
Pissarro
Porters English Restaurant (Jan '15)
Refettorio
Solly's
Thatched House
Toku
Tom Aikens
Tom's Deli
Uli
Verru
Viajant

How should I use this guide?

You will often wish to use this guide in a practical way. At heart, the issue will usually be geographical – where can we eat near…? To answer such questions, the Maps (from page 224) and Area Overviews (from page 186) are the place to start. The latter tell you all the key facts about the restaurants – perhaps dozens of 'em – in a particular area in the space of a couple of pages. These Area Overviews are unique, so please do spend a second to have a look!

This section, though, is about seeking out restaurants for the joy of it – a few thoughts to lead you to London's best restaurants for particular types of events, or to lead you down byways you might not otherwise have considered.

What makes London special?

Cosmopolitanism has always been part of London's make-up, but in recent years this diversity has more and more been allied with quality. A 'virtuous' circle has set in, with London becoming an acknowledged destination for chefs and restaurateurs from all over the word, which has further reinforced the capital's name as the 'place to be', which has then sucked in further talent. This process has now gone on for long enough that London is often identified (and not just by Londoners) as one of the world's great restaurant cities.

This process has been accompanied and in part sustained by another virtuous circle – a greater interest in dining out by the capital's under-35s than was traditionally the case. This has encouraged a greater provision of dining out opportunities suited to that demographic. Younger people being, generally speaking, more novelty-seeking than silver haired types, the whole restaurant scene has become much buzzier.

The result is that there is no restaurant scene in the world today which is more exciting – and deservedly so – than the one we enjoy in London.

Which is London's best restaurant?

In a restaurant scene as diverse and interesting as London's, 'best' – more and more – means different things to different people, so it gets ever harder to give a single answer. If the question is translated to mean 'which is the best grand French restaurant in town', the answer is pretty clearly – still! – *Le Gavroche*. London's original grand restaurant of recent times has been performing particularly strongly of late. If you're looking for a more modern – and informal – take on the grand dining experience, *The Ledbury* is probably the place to go. For other truly tip-top suggestions, please use the lists on pages 20-21.

What about something a little more reasonably priced?

There is a reason that *Chez Bruce* has just been voted London's favourite restaurant for an amazing 9th consecutive year – if you're looking for a top quality all-round experience at a level which, if not inexpensive, is less than ruinous, it is a destination it's hard to beat. The only downside is that you have to make the schlep to Wandsworth to enjoy it.

A step down in the price-and-grandeur stakes, how about the excellent *Lambert's*... but that's even further out, in Balham. Just too far? A formula rather similar to Chez Bruce (if not yet quite as good) can be enjoyed, somewhat more conveniently for many people, at Chelsea's rising *Medlar*. Or, for an all-round foodie treat of a much trendier type, head to Shoreditch's former Town Hall, now home to *The Clove Club*.

What about some really good suggestions in the heart of the West End?

It is becoming less the case than once it was that you need to head out of the West End for a really good meal without breaking the bank. Witness such possibilities as *Little Social*, cutely hidden away in Mayfair, and *Gauthier Soho*. You have to ring for entry to the latter's townhouse premises, adding to the sense of occasion.

What about a big night out?

Sometimes, of course, the food is just part of the package, and you're looking for theatre and people-watching as much as a meal. The obvious choice for such a trip, especially if you are entertaining visitors from out-of-town, is *The Wolseley* – the food may not be that remarkable, but the 'package' – which includes a remarkable Edwardian interior and a location right next to the Ritz – is very hard to beat. The food may not be earth-shattering, but no one seems to mind.

Other West End establishments offering a grand all-round formula, of which the food is just one part of the whole, albeit an important one, include such stand-outs as *Scott's* (Mayfair), *Le Caprice* (St James's), *The Delaunay* (Covent Garden) and *J Sheekey* – the long-established fish restaurant, hidden-away in Theatreland, which was once again this year the survey's most commented-on restaurant.

Small is beautiful

Much of the gastronomic excitement of recent years has come from 'tapas' specialists, inspired not just by Spain but by SW France and beyond. Such concepts have brought sophisticated yet affordable formats to the heart of the West End. *Barrafina* represents the classic tapas ideal, with outfits such as *Bocca di Lupo, Ceviche, Copita, Dehesa, Lima* and *Salt Yard* all offering their own variations on the theme.

What about British cooking?

Until recently, the idea of British restaurants (other than simple grill or roast houses) was pretty much unknown, as most restaurants were French or Italian, or, in more recent times, Indian or Chinese.

It was the Smithfield restaurant *St John*, established in 1994, whose dedication to old-fashioned (and usually offal-heavy) British cooking captured the zeitgeist and re-awakened an interest in traditional food culture. Other notable British restaurants often trace their roots back to St John, including *Magdalen* (South Bank), *Great Queen Street* (Covent Garden), *Hereford Road* (Bayswater) and, of course – currently best of all – *St John Bread & Wine* (Shoreditch).

A couple of years ago, the trend reached a zenith, at least in a media-friendly sense, with the opening of Heston Blumenthal's good-but-pricey *Dinner* (Knightsbridge). But a lot of the 'British' cooking is taking place in gastropubs…

What are gastropubs?

Essentially, bistros in pub premises. They come in many styles. What many people think of as the original gastropub (*The Eagle*, 1991) still looks very much like a pub with a food counter. Few of the best gastropubs are particularly central. The handy location of the *Anchor & Hope*, on the South Bank, is part of the reason for its great popularity. Other stars include the *Bull & Last* (Kentish Town), the *Canton Arms* (Stockwell) and the *Harwood Arms* (Fulham).

Isn't London supposed to be a top place for curry?

Many visitors come to London wanting to 'try Indian'. The choice of 'Indians' – a term including Pakistani and Bangladeshi restaurants in this context – is so great, however, that you then need to decide what sort of Indian you want to try.

You want value? Two top names in the East End (and hence relatively accessible from central London) are almost legendary 'experiences' – the *Lahore Kebab House* and *Tayyabs*. The predominantly veggie *Rasa* group also includes some very good value options. Or, for an immersive experience, go down to Tooting, and check out a fixture like *Sree Krishna*.

At the other end of the scale (and, for the most part, right in the heart of town) are the 'nouvelle Indians', where spicy dishes are presented with a heavy European influence. *Amaya, Benares, The Cinnamon Club, The Painted Heron, Quilon, Rasoi, Trishna, Veeraswamy* and *Zaika* are all examples of plush restaurants just as suited to business (and in many cases romance) as their European price-equivalents.

In fact, wherever you are in London, you should be in reach of an Indian restaurant of more-than-average note – search out the asterisked restaurants in the Indian and Pakistani lists commencing on pages 181 and 182 respectively.

Any money-saving tips?

- If you have the luxury of being in charge of your own timetable, there are some extraordinary bargains to be had simply by lunching rather than dining, and the more reasonably priced menus often available at the lunch service give you the opportunity to check out establishments which might otherwise be simply unattainable. See the spread on pages 22 and 23.

- Think ethnic – for a food 'experience' at modest cost, you're likely to be better off going Indian, Thai, Chinese or Vietnamese (to choose four of the most obvious cuisines) than English, French or Italian. The days when there was any sort of assumption that ethnic restaurants were – in terms of comfort, service and décor – in any way inferior to European ones is long gone, but they are still often somewhat cheaper.

- Don't assume the West End is the obvious destination. It is becoming less and less true anyway that the best and most interesting London restaurants are necessarily to be found within the confines of the Circle Line, so don't be reluctant to explore! Use the maps at the back of this book to identify restaurants near tube stations on a line that's handy for you.

- If you must dine in the West End, try to find either pre-theatre (generally before 7 pm) or post-theatre (generally after 10 pm) menus. You will generally save at least the cost of a cinema ticket, compared to dining à la carte. Many of the more upmarket restaurants in Theatreland do such deals. For some of our top suggestions, see page 23.

- Use this book! Don't take pot luck, when you can benefit from the pre-digested views of thousands of other diners-out. Choose a place with a **5** or **4** for food, and you're very likely to eat much better than if you walk in somewhere 'on spec' – this is good advice anywhere, but is most particularly so in the West End.

- Once you have decided that you want to eat within a particular area, use the Area Overviews (starting on p186) to identify the restaurants that are offering top value. We have gone to a lot of trouble to boil down a huge amount of data into the results which are handily summarised in such lists. Please use them! You are unlikely to regret it.

- Visit our website, www.hardens.com for the latest reviews, news and offers, and to sign up for our annual spring survey.

Rotorino

Heddon Street Kitchen
Chiltern Firehouse
Polpetto

LONDON DIRECTORY

A Cena TW1 £50 333
418 Richmond Rd 8288 0108 1–4A
A "better-than-average local", just south of Richmond Bridge in St Margarets, with an "ever-changing Italian menu", and a "top wine list" too. / TW1 2EB; www.acena.co.uk; @acenarestaurant; 10 pm; closed Mon L & Sun D; booking: max 6, Fri & Sat.

A Wong SW1 £34 433
70-71 Wilton Rd 7828 8931 2–4B
"Extraordinarily good dim sum" are a highlight of the "wacky" and "exciting" dishes on offer at this "canteen-style" Chinese yearling, five minutes' walk from Victoria. / SW1 1DE; www.awong.co.uk; @awongSW1; 10.15 pm; closed Mon L & Sun.

Abbeville Kitchen SW4 £50 342
47 Abbeville Rd 8772 1110 10–2D
"An amazing neighbourhood spot!" – Clapham locals are delighted with this "welcoming" and "reliable" two-year-old, which offers "generous portions" of "yummy" fare from an "ever-changing" menu; a "delicious brunch" is a highlight. / SW4 9JX; www.abbevillekitchen.com; @abbevillek; 10.30 pm, Sun 9.30 pm; Mon-Thu D only, Fri-Sun open L & D.

Abeno £41 332
47 Museum St, WC1 7405 3211 2–1C
17-18 Great Newport St, WC2 7379 1160 4–3B
"Interesting", "authentic" and "consistently tasty"; okonomi-yaki – which is to say fancy Japanese omelettes – are the stock-in-trade of these "courteous" West End cafés; all those tabletop barbecues, though, can make the atmosphere rather "smelly". / www.abeno.co.uk; 10 pm-11 pm; WC2 no booking.

The Abingdon W8 £63 334
54 Abingdon Rd 7937 3339 5–2A
In the sleepy residential backwoods of Kensington, a "great gastropub with reliable food, friendly service and a decent wine list"; it may be no bargain, but it's a "jolly" sort of place, on which feedback is impressively consistent. / W8 6AP; www.theabingdon.co.uk; 10.30 pm, Fri & Sat 11 pm, Sun 10 pm; set weekday L £40 (FP).

Abokado £17 244
Branches throughout London
"Great for healthy lunches" – this sushi-and-more snack chain inspires consistently upbeat reports. / www.abokado.com; 7.30 pm Mon-Fri, NW1 9 pm, 5 pm Sat & Sun; no Amex; no booking.

About Thyme SW1 £54 342
82 Wilton Rd 7821 7504 2–4B
"Caring" staff and "satisfying" Spanish-influenced food have made a bit of a name for this "always-buzzy" stalwart of the west-Pimlico wasteland; prices are quite high, though, and some meals this year seemed rather "rough and ready". / SW1V 1DL; www.aboutthyme.co.uk; 10.30 pm; closed Sun.

L'Absinthe NW1 £45 232
40 Chalcot Rd 7483 4848 8–3B
"An unfailing welcome" helps underpin local support for this "crowded" but "enjoyable" corner bistro, in Primrose Hill; critics, though, say it's "pricey" for food that's "only fair", and feel its "rather static" formula is "in need of a facelift". / NW1 8LS; www.labsinthe.co.uk; @absinthe07jc; 10 pm; closed Mon, Tue L, Wed L & Thu L.

Abu Zaad W12 £23 332
29 Uxbridge Rd 8749 5107 7–1C
"Don't be put off by the location" on a "drab stretch of the Uxbridge Road" – there's "terrific-value, hearty Syrian food" to be had at this "elaborately decorated" café, where "fantastic, freshly squeezed juices" compensate for the lack of alcohol. / W12 8LH; www.abuzaad.co.uk; 11 pm; no Amex.

Adams Café W12 £31 254
77 Askew Rd 8743 0572 7–1B
"Greasy spoon by day, North African grills and tagines by night" – the enduring recipe for success at this "real" Shepherd's Bush local, where the personable owners always ensure a "happy atmosphere"; licensed nowadays, but you can still BYO. / W12 9AH; www.adamscafe.co.uk; 10 pm; closed Sun.

Addie's Thai Café SW5 £32 332
121 Earl's Court Rd 7259 2620 5–2A
"Fine Thai street food-style cuisine", with "authentic flavours", helps fuel the buzz at this simple Earl's Court staple. / SW5 9RL; www.addiesthai.co.uk; 11 pm, Sun 10.30 pm; no Amex.

The Admiral Codrington SW3 £53 222
17 Mossop St 7581 0005 5–2C
This "enjoyable" backstreet spot ('The Cod') has long been one of Chelsea's more popular boozers, and it can still get "very noisy"; it has a large and airy dining room, where the food is "generally good". / SW3 2LY; www.theadmiralcodrington.co.uk; @TheAdCod; 10 pm, Thu-Sat 11 pm, Sun 9.30 pm.

Afghan Kitchen N1 £26 4 2 1
35 Islington Grn 7359 8019 8–3D
A tiny central Islington café whose mega-cramped, "spartan" interior doesn't detract from the appeal of its "delicious" and "interesting" dishes. / N1 8DU; 11 pm; closed Mon & Sun; no credit cards.

Aglio e Olio SW10 £42 3 3 2
194 Fulham Rd 7351 0070 5–3B
"Loud and proud!"; this "reverberative", "chaotic" and "fun" canteen, by the Chelsea & Westminster Hospital, offers "fresh-tasting pasta" at "great-value prices", and with "skill and enthusiasm" too. / SW10 9PN; 11.30 pm.

Akari N1 £39 4 2 3
196 Essex Rd 7226 9943 8–3D
The exterior may look "just like an old Islington boozer", but this is in fact "a wonderful family-run Japanese"; don't just order sushi – "the warm dishes are fantastic", and "they have Asahi on tap" too. / N1 8LZ; www.akarilondon.co.uk; 11 pm; closed Mon, Tue-Fri D only, Sat & Sun open L & D; no Amex.

Al Duca SW1 £46 2 2 2
4-5 Duke of York St 7839 3090 3–3D
Notably "unpretentious" by St James's standards (and "not overpriced either"), a "reliable" and "usefully located" Italian that comes recommended for lunch, business or pre-theatre. / SW1Y 6LA; www.alduca-restaurant.co.uk; 11 pm; closed Sun.

Al Forno £38 2 4 4
349 Upper Richmond Rd, SW15 8878 7522 10–2A
2a King's Rd, SW19 8540 5710 10–2B
"Your classic friendly local Italian", in "rustic style, circa 1980" – these "buzzy" joints are "pretty basic", but their "charming" service and "reasonable prices" make them "good with friends" and family. / SW15 11 pm; SW19 11.30 pm, Sun & Mon 10.30 pm.

Al Hamra W1 £55 3 2 2
31-33 Shepherd Mkt 7493 1954 3–4B
Three decades in business, this "typically Middle Eastern" Shepherd Market spot long predates the trendification of Mayfair, but fans insist it still offers "the best Lebanese food in town"; others aren't so sure, but the outside tables are certainly a charming sunny day destination. / W1J 7PT; www.alhamrarestaurant.co.uk; 11.30 pm.

Al Sultan W1 £46 3 2 1
51-52 Hertford St 7408 1155 3–4B
"The food is consistently very good", at this long-established Lebanese, near Shepherd Market; the ambience is "rather sterile" though, and it's often "let down by sloppy service". / W1J 7ST; www.alsultan.co.uk; 11 pm.

Al-Waha W2 £47 3 2 1
75 Westbourne Grove 7229 0806 6–1B
For fans, this Bayswater Lebanese remains "the best Eastern Mediterranean place in town", and its "fresh" fare continues to be a general crowd-pleaser; this year's survey, though, also recorded the occasional let down. / W2 4UL; www.alwaharestaurant.com; 11 pm; no Amex.

Alain Ducasse Dorchester W1 £121 2 3 2
53 Park Ln 7629 8866 3–3A
"How this got three Michelin stars, I really don't know!" – the tyre man's enduring esteem for the Gallic über-chef's "bland foodie temple" in Mayfair – with its "unchallenging and stratospherically overpriced" food – is quite unfathomable; on the plus-side, however, the all-in set lunch is "a steal". / W1K 1QA; www.alainducasse-dorchester.com; @Chefalinducase; 9.30 pm; closed Mon, Sat L & Sun; jacket; set weekday L £96 (FP).

Albertine W12 £34 2 4 4
1 Wood Ln 8743 9593 7–1C
"An oasis of calm that deserves our continued support"; this cute old Shepherd's Bush wine bar "boldly resists the rise of Westfield over the road", and "continues a tradition of simple but tasty food, with a fine selection of wines by the glass". / W12 7DP; 10.30 pm; closed Sat L & Sun; no Amex.

Albion £45 2 2 2
NEO Bankside, Holland St, SE1 7827 4343 9–3B
2-4 Boundary St, E2 7729 1051 12–1B
The newer, South Bank, branch of Sir Terence Conran's café duo has been "a welcome addition to the still underserved area round Tate Modern" – "ideal for a pre-gallery lunch or brunch"; the "barren but stylish" Shoreditch original has its fans too, especially for breakfast. / 11 pm.

The Albion N1 £45 2 2 4
10 Thornhill Rd 7607 7450 8–3D
An Islington boozer serving "dependable pub fare"; "I visit over and over again, for the great atmosphere, and fantastic beer garden", says one fan. / N1 1HW; www.the-albion.co.uk; @thealbionpub; 10 pm, Sun 9 pm; SRA-2 stars.

Ali Baba NW1 £23 3 2 2
32 Ivor Pl 7723 5805 2–1A
"Excellent, if you like the atmosphere of a Cairo café"… this quirky family-run Marylebone BYO

(behind a take-away) looks "tired", but it's "faithful" to the real thing, offering decent Middle Eastern cooking. / NW1 6DA; midnight; no credit cards.

Alloro W1 **£62** 242
19-20 Dover St 7495 4768 3–3C
"Buzzy without being noisy", this "upmarket" Mayfair Italian makes "a great spot for a business lunch"; the food is "solid" too, if "nothing special", given the prices. / W1S 4LU; www.alloro-restaurant.co.uk; 10.30 pm; closed Sat L & Sun.

The Almeida N1 **£58** 222
30 Almeida St 7354 4777 8–2D
It's "more than adequate for pre- or post-Almeida Theatre" (opposite), but this large D&D Group venture, in Islington, again incites rather ambivalent commentary – its "noisy" interior can seem "characterless", and its contemporary cooking is "well presented" but a trifle "boring". / N1 1AD; www.almeida-restaurant.co.uk; 10.30 pm; closed Mon L & Sun D; set weekday L & pre-theatre £38 (FP); SRA-2 stars.

Alounak **£30** 323
10 Russell Gdns, W14 7603 1130 7–1D
44 Westbourne Grove, W2 7229 0416 6–1B
"An incredibly cheap, good, authentic and reliable BYO Iranian!" – one reporter neatly captures all the plus points of these "always-buzzing" Bayswater and Olympia cafés. / 11.30 pm; no Amex.

Alquimia SW15 **£54** 342
Putney Wharf 8785 0508 10–2B
By the river at Putney Wharf, a sizeable yearling tipped as just the spot for "a wide selection" of "authentic" tapas; lovely al fresco tables in summer. / SW15 2JX; www.alquimiarestaurant.co.uk; @AlquimiaRestUK; 11.30 pm, Sun 10.30 pm.

Alyn Williams
Westbury Hotel W1 **£82** 442
37 Conduit St 7183 6426 3–2C
"A hidden gem!"; with Alyn Williams's "superbly executed" cuisine, "interesting" wines, and service that's "so charming", this "swish" Bond Street hotel dining room deserves a wider following; the catch? – atmosphere is "slightly lacking". / W1S 2YF; www.alynwilliams.com; @Alyn_Williams; 10.30 pm; closed Mon & Sun; jacket; set weekday L £54 (FP).

Amaya SW1 **£78** 543
Halkin Arc, 19 Motcomb St 7823 1166 5–1D
"Amazing and free from cliché" – this "unmatchable" Belgravian offers a "refined" tapas-style formula that puts it among the capital's very best subcontinentals; the interior is pleasingly "upscale" too (though "it's best not to sit next to the grill"). / SW1X 8JT; www.amaya.biz; 11.30 pm, Sun 10.30 pm; set weekday L £46 (FP).

Ametsa with Arzak Instruction
Halkin Hotel SW1 **£85** 231
5 Halkin St 7333 1234 2–3A
"Why isn't it booked out nightly?", ask fans of Juan Mari Arzak's Basque export to Belgravia, and its "creative, indulgent and beautiful" cuisine; the mega-"bland" interior doesn't help though, and a large minority of reporters just feel that the food is "surprisingly poor, given the pedigree". / SW1X 7DJ; www.comohotels.com/thehalkin/dining/ametsa; @AmetsaArzak; 10 pm; closed Mon L & Sun.

Amico Bio **£38** 222
43 New Oxford St, WC1 7836 7509 4–1C
43-44 Cloth Fair, EC1 7600 7778 9–2B
Though they offer potentially "interesting" Italo-veggie fare, these Bloomsbury and Smithfield bistros can fail to live up – "the food sounded so promising, but it was surprisingly dull". / EC1 10.30pm; EC1 closed Sat L & Sun; no booking.

L'Amorosa W6 NEW **£42**
278 King St 8563 0300 7–2B
Lola & Simon (RIP) was a cute little café on Hammersmith's trafficky main drag; Andy Needham – for 15 years head chef at Belgravia's Zafferano – opened a new neighbourhood Italian on the site as this guide went to press. / W6 0SP; www.lamorosa.co.uk.

Anarkali W6 **£34** 332
303-305 King St 8748 1760 7–2B
"Hasn't changed for years" – no bad thing, as this veteran Hammersmith Indian continues to offer "consistently good food and friendly service". / W6 9NH; www.anarkalifinedining.com; midnight, Sun 11.30 pm; no Amex.

The Anchor & Hope
SE1 **£48** 533
36 The Cut 7928 9898 9–4A
"Number one for pub food in London"; for the 9th year this "convivial" South Bank boozer – with its "hearty" but "superbly precise" British cooking – remains "the benchmark for gastropoub eating"; if only it weren't "so horribly hard to get a table" – expect to queue and share tables. / SE1 8LP; www.anchorandhopepub.co.uk; @AnchorHopeCut; 10.30 pm; closed Mon L & Sun D; no Amex; no booking; set weekday L £30 (FP).

Andina E2 NEW **£35** 4 3 4
1 Redchurch St 7920 6499 12–1B
"Unique flavours focussed on nutritious ingredients from Peru" help win a thumbs-up for this "trendy" Shoreditch newcomer; "the clubby downstairs is the place to sit". / E2 7DJ; www.andinalondon.com; 11 pm.

The Andover Arms W6 **£40** 2 4 4
57 Aldensey Rd 8748 2155 7–1B
"A solid clientele of male pint-drinkers" only adds to the "classic friendly local atmosphere" of this Hammersmith backstreet boozer; "Sunday roast (book) is a highlight" of the "solid" and "uncomplicated" pub grub. / W6 0DL; www.andoverarms.co.uk; @theandoverarms; 11.30 pm; no Amex.

Andrew Edmunds W1 **£46** 3 4 5
46 Lexington St 7437 5708 3–2D
"Unique" and "utterly charming", this ancient candlelit Soho townhouse remains one of London's most prodigiously popular bolt-holes; "squashed" it may be, and the "extraordinary" wine may outshine the cuisine ("reasonably priced" as it is)… but "if you only have eyes for your date, this is the place!" / W1F 0LW; www.andrewedmunds.com; 10.45 pm, Sun 10.30 pm; no Amex; booking: max 6.

The Angel & Crown WC2 **£45** 2 2 3
58 St Martin's Ln 7748 5244 4–3B
"A real open fire in the dining room" (rarely found in central London) is a particular feature of this Covent Garden boozer; otherwise, however, by the top standards of the Martin ('Gun' etc) brothers' stable, it's a bit of a damp squib. / WC2N 4EA.

Angels & Gypsies Church Street Hotel SE5 **£42** 2 2 3
29-33 Camberwell Church St 7703 5984 1–3C
"Wonderful, wonderful tapas, and a laid-back attitude" have put this "lively" modern tapas bar, in Camberwell, firmly on the map; even fans, however, may complain of "creeping prices". / SE5 8TR; www.angelsandgypsies.com; @angelsngypsies; 10.30 pm, Fri & Sat 11 pm.

Angelus W2 **£74** 3 5 4
4 Bathurst St 7402 0083 6–2D
Thierry Tomassin "is a great host", and he has assembled "an amazing wine selection" at this "cosy" and "animated" pub-conversion, near Lancaster Gate; the prices "all add up" though, and while the "classic" Gallic cuisine can be "excellent", it can also "under-deliver". / W2 2SD; www.angelusrestaurant.co.uk; 11 pm, Sun 10 pm.

Angler South Place Hotel EC2 **£73** 3 3 4
3 South Pl 3215 1260 12–2A
The "superb view and splendid terrace" seal the appeal of D&D Group's "stunning" top-floor room, over a trendy hotel "in the heart of the City"; aside from the "eye-watering prices", it's a "good all-rounder", where fish dishes in particular are "top-notch". / EC2M 2AF; www.anglerrestaurant.com; @southplacehotel; 10 pm; closed Sat L; max 14; set dinner £53 (FP).

The Anglesea Arms W6 **£50** 4 2 4
35 Wingate Rd 8749 1291 7–1B
Much to the relief of Brackenbury Village regulars, this acclaimed gastropub finally reopened in mid-2014, under the management of the old chef; early reports say its "ambitious" food and "wonderful and welcoming" ambience are just the same as ever. / W6 0UR; www.angleseaarmspub.co.uk; @_AngleseaArmsW6; 10 pm, Sun 9 pm; closed weekday L.

The Anglesea Arms SW7 **£48** 2 2 4
15 Selwood Ter 7373 7960 5–2B
"Enjoy a few ales on the terrace first", if you make a summertime visit to this "charming" South Kensington pub; the restaurant is "nothing fantastic, but portions are large. the food's OK, and you can usually get a table". / SW7 3QG; www.angleseaarms.com; @angleseaarms; 10 pm, Sun 9.30 pm.

L'Anima EC2 **£74** 3 3 3
1 Snowden St 7422 7000 12–2B
Undoubtedly "very classy", if also a bit "cold" and "noisy", this "upmarket" City Italian is an impressive all-rounder, and very popular for business entertaining; some critics, though, do feel it "lacks the spark it had when it opened". / EC2A 2DQ; www.lanima.co.uk; 11 pm, Sat 11.30 pm; closed Sat L & Sun.

L' Anima Café EC2 NEW **£45** 3 4 3
1 Snowden St 7422 7000 12–2B
Near the grand City-fringe Italian of the same name, a large contemporary-style café-pizzeria-

trattoria; some of the food is of very high quality, and some of the prices are very reasonable too. / EC2A 2DQ; Rated on Editors' visit; 10.30 pm, Sat 11 pm; closed Sun.

Annie's **£46** 234

162 Thames Rd, W4 8994 9080 1–3A
36-38 White Hart Ln, SW13 8878 2020 10–1A

"Boudoir-chic decor" helps create a "fantastic" atmosphere at these Barnes and Strand-on-the-Green family-favourites, where brunch is a highlight of cuisine that's generally rather "so-so". / www.anniesrestaurant.co.uk; 10 pm, Sat 10.30 pm, Sun 9.30 pm.

Antepliler **£35** 322

139 Upper St, N1 7226 5441 1–1C
46 Grand Pde, N4 8802 5588 1–1C

"Tasty, plentiful dishes, fast service and decent prices" – such are the virtues of these modern Turkish establishments, in Islington and Newington Green. / www.anteplilerrestaurant.com; 11 pm.

The Anthologist EC2 **£42** 343

58 Gresham St 468 0101 9–2C

"A please-all menu, but none the worse for that" – this large and comfortable bar-restaurant, near the Guildhall, is a handy, very versatile standby, and it's open all day too. / EC2V 7BB; www.theanthologistbar.co.uk; @theanthologist; 10 pm; closed Sat & Sun; SRA-3 stars.

Antico SE1 **£48** 443

214 Bermondsey St 7407 4682 9–4D

This Bermondsey Italian two-year-old is "a very laid-back but comfortably romantic venue", serving up "thoughtful" and "very well-executed" cooking; "the only downside is that it's very noisy". / SE1 3TQ; www.antico-london.co.uk; @AnticoLondon; 10.30 pm; closed Mon.

Antidote W1 **£57** 543

12a Newburgh St 7287 8488 3–2C

"Astoundingly good" – the food in the upstairs room of this relaunched Soho wine bar can come as a "surprise"... until you learn that it is now overseen by Hedone's Mikael Jonsson; on the ground floor, you get "fantastic biodynamic and natural wines" too. / W1F 7RR; www.antidotewinebar.com; @AntidoteWineBar; 10.30 pm; closed Sun; max 8.

Antipasto & Pasta SW11 **£41** 342

511 Battersea Park Rd 7223 9765 10–1C

"A great local eatery serving no-nonsense Italian food"; this age-old Battersea fixture never waivers and, as ever, its "half-price nights are an added bonus". / SW11 3BW; 11.30 pm, Sun 11 pm; need 4+ to book.

The Ape & Bird WC2 NEW **£46**

142 Shaftesbury Ave 7836 3119 4–2B

In a rare misstep, Russell Norman launched a "very ordinary" Theatreland gastropub in early-2014; later in the year, however, it was relaunched in more 'Polpo' style, so we'll hold off on a rating until next year. / WC2H 8HJ; www.apeandbird.com; @ApeandBird.

Apollo Banana Leaf SW17 **£20** 511

190 Tooting High St 8696 1423 10–2C

This Tooting shop-conversion may look "really grotty" (and "don't expect service with a smile"), but "it's all about the food here" – "real" Indian ("not a Korma in sight!") at "unbeatable" prices; BYO. / SW17 0SF; www.apollobananaleaf.com; 10.30 pm; no Amex.

Apostrophe **£18** 333

Branches throughout London

"A bit different" from the sandwich-shop norm – these Gallic-owned outlets offers sarnies that are "a cut above", plus "excellent" coffee and "thick hot chocolate to die for". / www.apostropheuk.com; most branches 6 pm, Sat 5.30 pm; no booking.

Applebee's Café SE1 **£43** 322

5 Stoney St 7407 5777 9–4C

"Brilliant fish straight from the fresh fish counter" (grilled or fried) is the promise at this "no-nonsense and fun" Borough Market outfit. / SE1 9AA; www.applebeesfish.com; @applebeesfish; 10 pm, Fri 10.30 pm; closed Sun; no Amex.

Apulia EC1 NEW **£38** 331

50 Long Ln 7600 8107 9–2B

"Genuine", "friendly" and "reasonably-priced", this family-run Italian newcomer, near Smithfield Market, is quite a hit with most reporters; the decor is "bare" and "unstyled", though – perhaps to a fault. / EC1A 9EJ; www.apuliarestaurant.co.uk; set weekday L £19 (FP).

aqua kyoto W1 **£75** 222

240 Regent St (entrance 30 Argyll St) 7478 0540 3–2C

The Japanese-fusion section of this nightclubby operation, six floors above Regent Street, wins praise for its views, cocktails and Asian-inspired cuisine; reports are inconsistent, though, with a minority noting a "poor" ambience and "ridiculous" prices. / W1B 3BR; www.aqua-london.com; @aqualondon; 10.30 pm; closed Sun D; booking: max 6.

aqua nueva W1 **£66** 222
240 Regent St (entrance 30 Argyll St) 7478 0540 3–2C
Near Oxford Circus, a "fancy" nightclub-style Spanish rooftop operation, with surprisingly striking outside space; the food can be good but the staff sometimes act "like they're doing you a favour" – one reason, perhaps, the place inspires little survey commentary. / W1B 3BR; www.aqua-london.com; @aqualondon; 10.30 pm; closed Sun.

Aqua Shard SE1 **£81** 114
Level 31, 31 St Thomas St 3011 1256 9–4C
"Go for cocktails, and give the restaurant a miss!" – the Shard's 31st-floor restaurant is a bad case of: "stunning view, shame about the food" (or, to put it another way, the 'Oxo Tower Syndrome' Strikes Again!). / SE1 9RY; www.aquashard.co.uk; @aquashard; 10.30 pm; set weekday L £54 (FP).

Arabica Bar and Kitchen SE1 NEW **£44** 343
3 Rochester Walk 3011 5151 9–4C
Unusually stylish by Lebanese restaurant standards, this Borough Market newcomer is a "friendly" and "buzzy" sort of place where the food, on our early-days visit, was always competent, and sometimes better. / SE1 9AF; Rated on Editors' visit; www.arabicabarandkitchen.com; 10.30 pm; closed Sun.

Arbutus W1 **£50** 442
63-64 Frith St 7734 4545 4–2A
"Rarely-made classic dishes" (featuring "cheaper cuts and offal") and "interesting wines by the glass and carafe" has won acclaim for this "keenly priced" Soho favourite; its "plain" interior is "not the most comfortable", though, and can get "very noisy" at peak times. / W1D 3JW; www.arbutusrestaurant.co.uk; @artutus; 10.45 pm, Fri & Sat 11.15 pm, Sun 10.30 pm.

Archduke Wine Bar SE1 **£52** 222
Concert Hall Approach, South Bank 7928 9370 2–3D
"For meeting up with friends before a South Bank concert", this outpost of the 'Black & Blue' steak 'n' burger chain – under the arches by the Festival Hall – is certainly hyper-convenient; otherwise, though, it's "nothing special", and "expensive for what it is". / SE1 8XU; www.blackandbluerestaurants.com; 10.30 pm, Sun 10 pm.

Ark Fish E18 **£42** 542
142 Hermon Hill 8989 5345 1–1D
"Fish 'n' chips, yes, but brilliantly fresh fish superbly cooked" – this no-bookings South Woodford spot is arguably "east London's best fish place", and "worth every penny". / E18 1QH; www.arkfishrestaurant.co.uk; 9.45 pm, Fri & Sat 10.15 pm, Sun 8.45 pm; closed Mon; no Amex.

Artigiano NW3 **£46** 333
12a Belsize Ter 7794 4288 8–2A
A "quintessential" neighbourhood Italian, in Belsize Park, where the "solid" cooking includes a "great selection of fish". / NW3 4AX; www.etruscarestaurants.com; @artigianoesp; 10 pm; closed Mon L.

L'Artista NW11 **£35** 244
917 Finchley Rd 8731 7501 1–1B
Under the arches by Golders Green tube, this jolly Italian has long been a local favourite, especially for parties – the "obliging" staff "love making a fuss of you", "kids can make as much noise as they like", and the pizza and pasta come "in really good portions". / NW11 7PE; www.lartistapizzeria.com; 11.30 pm.

L'Artiste Musclé W1 **£44** 224
1 Shepherd Mkt 7493 6150 3–4B
It's a little bit of a "cliché", but the "Paris-in-London" charms of this pint-sized Shepherd Market bistro still make it an "enjoyable" destination; the cooking may be "unremarkable", but it's "reliable" too. / W1J 7PA; 10 pm, Fri-Sun 10.30 pm.

Artusi SE15 NEW **£45** 432
161 Bellenden Rd 3302 8200 1–4D
"Another excellent Peckham opening!" – this "tiny" Italian may be "a little overhyped" locally, but it "astonishes" its fans with an "interesting" menu using "super-fresh ingredients"; shame it can seem a touch "vibeless". / SE15 4DH; www.artusi.co.uk; @artusipeckham.

Asadal WC1 **£40** 322
227 High Holborn 7430 9006 2–1D
An implausible dining room to find beneath Holborn tube, offering "a reliable, traditional Korean dining experience"; shame the service is rather lacklustre. / WC1V 7DA; www.asadal.co.uk; 10.30 pm; closed Sun L.

Asakusa NW1 **£36** 522
265 Eversholt St 7388 8533 8–3C
"A veritable Aladdin's cave of delicious Japanese food", and at "surprisingly low" prices too; it may

look "like a rundown old caff" and have "chaotic" (if "friendly") service, but this "nondescript" spot, near Euston Station, is "awesome". / NW1 1BA; 11.30 pm, Sat 11 pm; D only, closed Sun.

Ask **£41** 222
Branches throughout London
"Unexciting, but adequate for a basic meal", these "standard" pizza-and-pasta operations are a paradigm of your "typical chain restaurant". / www.askcentral.co.uk; most branches 11 pm, Fri & Sat 11.30 pm; some booking restrictions apply.

Assaggi W2 **£75** 442
39 Chepstow Pl 7792 5501 6–1B
"Some of the best Italian food in London" made "with real love", plus "terrific" service, has won renown for this "noisy" room above a Bayswater pub, where "even after so many years, it's still not easy to get a table"; perhaps it "used to be better value", but most reporters feel "it still hits the right notes". / W2 4TS; 11 pm; closed Sun; no Amex.

Les Associés N8 **£46** 342
172 Park Rd 8348 8944 1–1C
"Tiny, charming and genuine" – it's not much to look at, but this unassuming Crouch End Gallic stalwart still impresses reporters... even if it "does need a lick of paint". / N8 8JT; www.lesassocies.co.uk; @lesassociesn8; 10 pm; closed Mon, Tue L, Sat L & Sun D; 24 hr notice for L bookings; set Sun L £33 (FP).

Assunta Madre W1 NEW **£83** 322
9-10 Blenheim St 3230 3032 3–2B
On the former site of Semplice (RIP), a Mayfair offshoot of a restaurant in Rome; most early-days supporters do praise its "excellent fresh fish", but not everyone's convinced, and it can seem "seriously overpriced". / W1S 1LJ; www.assuntamadre.com; @assuntamadre; 10.30 pm.

Atari-Ya **£32** 521
20 James St, W1 7491 1178 3–1A
1 Station Pde, W5 8896 3175 1–3A
31 Vivian Ave, NW4 8202 2789 1–1B
75 Fairfax Road, NW6 7328 5338 8–2A
The branches are "not the most glamorous", but the cafés run by these Japanese food importers serve "wonderful, expertly prepared sushi" that's some of the best in town ("and that includes the Nobus of the world!"). / www.atariya.co.uk; W1 8 pm, NW4 & NW6 9.30 pm, W9 9 pm; NW4, NW6 closed Mon.

L'Atelier de Joel Robuchon WC2 **£86** 333
13-15 West St 7010 8600 4–2B
"Delightful and meticulous" delicacies – eaten on high stools, many beside the open kitchen – help justify the vertiginous prices (the "steal of a set lunch" aside) at this "glamorous" Covent Garden outpost of the Parisian über-chef; as the formula dates, though, reporters find the place increasingly "overrated". / WC2H 9NE; www.joelrobuchon.co.uk; @latelierlondon; midnight, Sun 10 pm; no trainers; set weekday L & pre-theatre £67 (FP).

Athenaeum Athenaeum Hotel W1 **£80** 333
116 Piccadilly 7499 3464 3–4B
"Very good quality, for a hotel restaurant" – this handily-sited dining room ('twixt Hyde Park Corner and The Ritz) is especially worth knowing about for the "great-value set lunch"; "great afternoon teas" too. / W1J 7BJ; www.athenaeumhotel.com; 10.30 pm.

The Atlas SW6 **£45** 444
16 Seagrave Rd 7385 9129 5–3A
This "great backstreet pub", near Earl's Court 2, "continues to be a shining light in the desert of north Fulham"; it boasts a "textbook film-set Victorian interior", but "it's the kitchen that continues to draw the crowds", with its "really polished" Mediterranean-inspired cuisine. / SW6 1RX; www.theatlaspub.co.uk; @theatlasfulham; 10 pm.

The Attendant W1 **£13** 444
27a, Foley St 7637 3794 2–1B
"How surreal to have London's richest and most flavoursome coffee in an ex-public loo!"; so say fans of this "wonderful conversion" – a year-old café in Fitzrovia. / W1W 6DY; www.the-attendant.com; @Attendantcafe; 6 pm, Sat 5 pm; L only, closed Sun.

Aubaine **£58** 111
31 Dover St, W1 7368 0955 3–3C
4 Heddon St, W1 7440 2510 3–2C
Selfridges & Co, 400 Oxford St, W1 7318 3738 3–1A
260-262 Brompton Rd, SW3 7052 0100 5–2C
37-45 Kensington High St, W8 7368 0950 5–1A
Fans insist these Gallic bistro-cafés offer "excellent" breakfasts in a "cosy" but "lively" setting; more generally, though, reporters feel the food is "uninspiring", service "struggling" and prices "scandaludicrous". / www.aubaine.co.uk; @balanslondon; SW3, SW19 10 pm, Sun 9.30 pm; Heddon St 11 pm, Oxford St 9 pm, Sun 6 pm, W8 10 pm, Sun 6 pm, Dover St 10 pm, Sun 9.30 pm; W8 no booking.

Augustine Kitchen SW11 NEW **£45** 4 4 1
63 Battersea Bridge Rd 7978 7085 5–4C
"Poorly located in a row of shops", this is a Battersea newcomer "you could walk straight past"; "it deserves to do well" though – staff are "fun", and the French cooking is "delicious, and phenomenally well priced". / SW11 3AU; www.augustine-kitchen.co.uk; @augustinekitchen; 10.30 pm; closed Mon & Sun D; set weekday L £27 (FP).

Aurora W1 **£50** 3 3 4
49 Lexington St 7494 0514 3–2D
It's a mistake to overlook this "small and cosy" Soho stalwart whose "romantic" attractions include "a lovely quiet patio offering a few tables hidden away at the back"; the menu's only short, but "all the choices are appealing". / W1F 9AP; www.aurorasoho.co.uk; 10 pm, Wed-Sat 10.30 pm, Sun 9 pm.

L'Autre Pied W1 **£80** 4 4 2
5-7 Blandford St 7486 9696 2–1A
"Colours, tastes and textures are beautifully combined" to create "exciting and delicious" dishes, at Pied à Terre's Marylebone offshoot; shame about the interior, though – critics say it has "all the ambience of a railway café". / W1U 3DB; www.lautrepied.co.uk; 10 pm; closed Sun D; set weekday L & pre-theatre £49 (FP).

L'Aventure NW8 **£60** 4 5 5
3 Blenheim Ter 7624 6232 8–3A
Few restaurants can equal the ultra-"cute" charm or longevity of this St John's Wood "classic", run – "with a high degree of Gallic authority" – by chef-patronne Catherine Parisot; her cuisine bourgeoise is "reliably divine" too. / NW8 0EH; 11 pm; closed Sat L & Sun; set weekday L £36 (FP).

The Avenue SW1 **£54** 1 3 3
7-9 St James's St 7321 2111 3–4D
"Oh dear, what went wrong?"; the staff may be "charming and hard working", but the post-relaunch food at this longtime St James's business favourite is too often "dreadful" – "how can you have an American place that screws up steak or brownies?" / SW1A 1EE; www.avenue-restaurant.co.uk; @avenuestjames; 10.30 pm; closed Sat L & Sun; set weekday L £42 (FP); SRA-2 stars.

Axis One Aldwych Hotel WC2 **£63** 2 2 3
1 Aldwych 7300 0300 2–2D
This impressive-looking Covent Garden basement offers a "good-value pre-theatre set menu", and its film-and-dinner deals attract "appreciative regulars"; otherwise, however, feedback is modest in volume, and rather lacklustre. / WC2B 4RH; www.onealdwych.com; @OneAldwych; 10.30 pm; closed Mon, Sat L & Sun.

Azou W6 **£42** 4 4 4
375 King St 8563 7266 7–2B
"A real gem, in a forest of competition"; this small, sweet café on Hammersmith's main drag serves tagines "you will want to eat time and time again". / W6 9NJ; www.azou.co.uk; @azourestaurant; 11 pm.

Ba Shan W1 **£49** 4 1 2
24 Romilly St 7287 3266 4–3A
Just over the road from its famous Soho parent, Bar Shu, this "not especially friendly" Soho pit stop is nonetheless "worth going back to" for its "bright, chilli-rich and zingy" dishes, from Hunan. / W1D 5AH; www.bashanlondon.com; 11 pm, Fri & Sat 11.30 pm.

Babbo W1 **£79** 2 2 2
39 Albermarle St 3205 1099 3–3C
A small restaurant near The Ritz, hailed by fans as a "true Italian" – "passionately run" and with "mouthwatering" cuisine; it also has its critics, though, who say "don't bother going" – "it's too expensive for what it is!" / W1S 4JQ; www.babborestaurant.co.uk; @BabboRestaurant; 11 pm, Sun 10.30 pm; closed Sun L; set weekday L £51 (FP).

Babur SE23 **£51** 5 4 3
119 Brockley Rise 8291 2400 1–4D
"It's curry Jim, but not as we know it!"; this "fabulously inventive" Honour Oak Park fixture is "in a different league from your standard Indian" and – despite a fractional slip in ratings this year – remains one of SE London's top destinations. / SE23 1JP; www.babur.info; @BaburRestaurant; 11.30 pm; set Sun L £35 (FP).

Babylon Kensington Roof Gardens W8 **£72** 2 4 4
99 Kensington High St 7368 3993 5–1A
"Extraordinary to have trees, streams and flamingos, up above Kensington High Street!" – these "cool" ("blingy") 8th-floor dining rooms, overlooking the roof gardens, make "such a romantic summer location"; perhaps best to visit for lunch, when there's a "very good-value 3-course set option". / W8 5SA; www.virgin.com/roofgardens; 10.30 pm; closed Sun D; set weekday L £46 (FP); SRA-3 stars.

Il Bacio **£43** 322
61 Stoke Newington Church St, N16 7249 3833 1–1C
178-184 Blackstock Rd, N5 7226 3339 8–1D
A "staple" in both Stoke Newington and Highbury – these "trusted locals" serve "proper Italian pizza", plus a range of "good-value" Sardinian dishes. / www.ilbaciohighbury.co.uk; 10 pm-11 pm; Mon-Fri L; no Amex.

Baker & Spice **£41** 222
54-56 Elizabeth St, SW1 7730 5524 2–4A
47 Denyer St, SW3 7225 3417 5–2D
20 Clifton Rd, W9 7289 2499 8–4A
Curiously, it's the "lovely" salads (sold by weight) at this chichi café/bakery chain which have inspired the most commentary of late; even fans, though, rail at the "exorbitant" prices. / www.bakerandspice.uk.com; 7 pm, Sun 6 pm; closed D; no Amex; no booking.

Balans **£48** 243
60-62 Old Compton St, W1 7439 2183 4–3A
Westfield, Ariel Way, W12 8600 3320 7–1C
214 Chiswick High Rd, W4 8742 1435 7–2A
187 Kensington High St, W8 7376 0115 5–1A
Westfield Stratford, E20 8555 5478 1–1D
"Loud, cheerful, and served up with a little bit of flirtation" (especially if you're male and gay) – the late-night, heart-of-Soho original of this small diner chain is "great for breakfast any time". / www.balans.co.uk; midnight-2 am; 34 Old Compton St 24 hrs, E20 11pm; some booking restrictions apply.

The Balcon
Sofitel St James SW1 **£59** 223
8 Pall Mall 7968 2900 2–3C
Just off Trafalgar Square, this "grand" brasserie, in a "fancy" French hotel, is just the job for a business lunch or "decent pre-theatre" bite; for more serious dining, though, the cuisine can seem rather "ordinary". / SW1Y 5NG; www.thebalconlondon.com; 10.45 pm, Sun 9.45 pm.

Bald Faced Stag N2 **£48** 333
69 High Rd 8442 1201 1–1B
A popular gastropub that spans the range from "casual eats" – "ideal if you're going to a movie at the Phoenix in East Finchley" – to an "excellent Sunday lunch". / N2 8AB; www.thebaldfacedstagn2.co.uk; @thebaldfacestagn2; 10.30 pm, Sun 9.30 pm.

Balthazar WC2 **£64** 124
4-6 Russell St 3301 1155 4–3D
"Ridiculous prices for ordinary food", and "sloppy" service too – for far too many reporters, Keith McNally's "hyped" and "Disney-esque" NYC-Gallic brasserie import "just doesn't cut the mustard". / WC2E 7BN; www.balthazarlondon.com; @balthazarlondon; Mon-Thu 11.30 pm, Fri & Sat 11.45 pm, Sun 10.30 pm .

Baltic SE1 **£53** 323
74 Blackfriars Rd 7928 1111 9–4A
"So good my eastern European wife got homesick!"; this "beautiful and airy" (but sometimes "very noisy") former warehouse, in Borough, offers some "stylishly executed" (mainly) Polish fare; beware the vodkas though – "they've crushed many an after-work drinker". / SE1 8HA; www.balticrestaurant.co.uk; @BalticLondon; 11 pm, Sun 10.15 pm; closed Mon L; set pre theatre £35 (FP).

Bam-Bou W1 **£52** 335
1 Percy St 7323 9130 2–1C
With its "out-of-this-world" cocktails and "sexy" lighting, this "French colonial-style" Fitzrovia townhouse (rambling over numerous floors) is "a perfect destination for a date", serving French/Vietnamese cuisine of a "high standard". / W1T 1DB; www.bam-bou.co.uk; @CapriceHoldings; midnight; closed Sun D; booking: max 6; set weekday L £41 (FP).

The Banana Tree
Canteen **£35** 222
103 Wardour St, W1 7437 1351 3–2D
21-23 Westbourne Grove, W2 7221 4085 6–1C
166 Randolph Ave, W9 7286 3869 8–3A
75-79 Battersea Rise, SW11 7228 2828 10–2C
412-416 St John St, EC1 7278 7565 8–3D
As "a good standby for a quick bite", many would tip these Asian-fusion canteens for their "really well-flavoured" dishes at "cheap" prices; they can also seem "nothing special", though, and the branches can get "very noisy". / @bananatree247; 11 pm, Sun 10.30 pm; booking: min 6.

Bangkok SW7 **£40** 322
9 Bute St 7584 8529 5–2B
"Always busy", but "very unassuming" – this "westernised" South Kensington Thai hasn't changed that much in 40 years in business, and still offers "ever-enjoyable and tasty" fare at "reasonable prices". / SW7 3EY; www.thebankokrestaurant.co.uk; 10.45 pm; no Amex.

Bank Westminster
St James Court Hotel
SW1 **£61** 322
45 Buckingham Gate 7630 6644 2–4B
"Fine for a business lunch, but a bit unexciting for dinner" – one reporter neatly captures the spirit

of this large brasserie, near Buckingham Palace, which manages to be a rather colourless destination, despite its impressive conservatory at the rear. / SW1E 6BS; www.bankrestaurants.com; @bank_westmin; 11 pm; closed Sat L & Sun.

Banners N8 **£46** 345

21 Park Rd 8348 2930 1–1C

An institution for Crouch End folk, this "vibrant" 'world food' diner is still of note for its "amazing" breakfasts, plus other "reasonably priced" scoff, usually with a Caribbean slant; "the service has been good for 20 years now, which is impressive considering how busy they get!" / N8 8TE; www.bannersrestaurant.com; 11.30 pm, Fri & Sat midnight, Sun 11 pm; no Amex.

Baozi Inn WC2 **£18** 322

25 Newport Ct 7287 6877 4–3B

Small, crowded and noisy, this Chinatown café is short on creature comforts, but it does offer tasty, wallet-friendly Sichuanese staples – from noodle soups to BBQ pork buns ("so light and fluffy it's like eating a meaty cloud"). / WC2H 7JS; 10 pm, Fri & Sat 10.30 pm; no credit cards; no booking.

Bar Boulud Mandarin Oriental SW1 **£69** 334

66 Knightsbridge 7201 3899 5–1D

"The best burgers anywhere" head up the Franco-American menu at this NYC super-chef's "slick" and "surprisingly buzzy" brasserie, in the basement of a grand Knightsbridge hotel; "it's exactly the sort of place you'd expect to be mediocre, but it's very good indeed!" / SW1X 7LA; www.barboulud.com; 10.45 pm, Sun 9.45 pm; set always available £27 (FP).

Bar Esteban N8 NEW **£38** 533

29 Park Rd 8340 3090 1–1C

"Livening up Crouch End!" – this "cheerful and bustling" newcomer is "busy every night", thanks to its "large selection of tapas" that are "fantastic every time". / N8 8TE; www.baresteban.com; Mon-Sat 10.30 pm, Sun 9 pm; closed weekday L.

Bar Italia W1 **£28** 345

22 Frith St 7437 4520 4–2A

"The best espresso in London" is to be had at this "iconic" Soho spot, which – "although a little dented around the edges" – remains a veritable 24/7 "institution". / W1D 4RT; www.baritaliasoho.co.uk; @TheBaristas; open 24 hours, Sun 4 am; no Amex; no booking.

Barbecoa EC4 **£64** 223

20 New Change Pas 3005 8555 9–2B

"Phenomenal" views of St Paul's reward those who get the best seats at Jamie O's vast City venue; it's "very expensive", though, and while fans praise its "beautiful" steaks, others decry results as "dreadful". / EC4M 9AG; www.barbecoa.com; @barbecoa; Mon-Sat 10.30 pm, Sun 9.45 pm .

La Barca SE1 **£65** 222

80-81 Lower Marsh 7928 2226 9–4A

This "old-style" Italian veteran, by Waterloo, is certainly "good for business and the Old Vic"; more generally, it divides opinions – to critics it's simply "outdated", but fans argue it's "reliable if pricey". / SE1 7AB; www.labarca-ristorante.com; @labarca1976; 11.15 pm; closed Sat L & Sun.

Il Baretto W1 **£63** 222

43 Blandford St 7486 7340 2–1A

Fans say this "buzzy" Marylebone basement Italian is worth seeking out for its "tasty" food and "cheeky" staff; critics, though, find it a "noisy" place that's "too expensive for what it is", where the food is "mediocre" and service "erratic". / W1U 7HF; www.ilbaretto.co.uk; @IlBarettoLondon; 10.15 pm, Sun 9.45 pm.

Barnyard W1 NEW **£44** 332

18 Charlotte St 7580 3842 2–1C

Much-hyped wunderkind Ollie Dabbous has gone "democratic and accessible" for his first spin-off – a "cool" rustic-chic Fitzrovia diner, serving comfort food with a twist; critics, however, can see only a "painfully contrived" place, where the food "lacks oomph". / W1T 2LZ.

Barrafina **£42** 555

54 Frith St, W1 7813 8016 4–2A

10 Adelaide St, WC2 7440 1456 4–2D

"Our hands-down favourite, even with the nightmare queue!"; the Hart brothers' tiny Soho bar dazzles fans with its "unfailingly exciting" dishes ("especially the seafood and the tortilla"); the new Covent Garden sibling is likewise a wow, serving "the freshest food, with passion". / www.barrafina.co.uk; 11 pm, Sun 10 pm; no booking.

Barrica W1 **£40** 434

62 Goodge St 7436 9448 2–1B

Part of "the Goodge St Spanish cluster", this "cosy" venture dishes up "outstandingly delicious tapas", complemented by a wine list "full of things to discover", and all in a great "laid-back" atmosphere – "what's not to like?" / W1T 4NE; www.barrica.co.uk; 10.30 pm; closed Sun.

Bar Shu W1 **£52** 412

28 Frith St 7287 6688 4–3A

"You'll blow your socks off", when you sample the "rich and zingy" Sichuan cooking –

the "real McCoy" – on offer at this Soho café; "don't go for the ambience", though, or the "patchy" service. / W1D 5LF; www.barshurestaurant.co.uk; 10.30 pm, Fri & Sat 11 pm.

Basilico **£36** **4 4 1**
690 Fulham Rd, SW6 0800 028 3531 10–1B
26 Penton St, N1 0800 093 4224 8–3D
51 Park Rd, N8 8616 0290 1–1C
515 Finchley Rd, NW3 0800 316 2656 1–1B
175 Lavender Hill, SW11 0800 389 9770 10–2C
For take-away pizza, this small chain is, say fans, "the best in town", thanks to its "delicious" thin-crusts and "original" toppings; "dining-in potential is limited". / www.basilico.co.uk; @basilicopizzas; 11 pm; no booking.

Beach Blanket Babylon **£63** **1 2 3**
45 Ledbury Rd, W11 7229 2907 6–1B
19-23 Bethnal Green Rd, E1 7749 3540 12–1C
As "a great place to socialise", these striking and "atmospheric" Gaudi-esque hangouts, in Notting Hill and Shoreditch, make great party venues… if you can put up with the "appalling overpriced food". / www.beachblanket.co.uk; 10.30 pm; W11 booking advisable Fri-Sat.

Beast W1 NEW **£113** **3 2 3**
3 Chapel Pl 7495 1816 3–1B
"Surf 'n' turf on steroids"; this rather "pretentious" Goodman-group newcomer, just north of Oxford Street, may offer a menu focussed on "amazing steak and wonderful king crab", but it "hits your wallet hard". / W1G 0BG; @beastrestaurant; 10 pm; closed Mon & Sun.

The Begging Bowl SE15 **£39** **5 4 5**
168 Bellenden Rd 7635 2627 1–4D
"Best Thai food I've tasted outside Thailand!" – no wonder this "brisk" no-bookings local, in Peckham, is starting to make quite a name for itself. / SE15 4BW; www.thebeggingbowl.co.uk; Mon 9.45 pm, Tue-Sat 9.45 pm, Sun 3.15 pm; closed Sun D.

Beirut Express **£43** **4 2 2**
65 Old Brompton Rd, SW7 7591 0123 5–2B
112-114 Edgware Rd, W2 7724 2700 6–1D
"Despite the awful neon sign, the food is good!"; for a fast snack, these South Kensington and Bayswater Lebaneses are just the job – "in, shawarma, mezze, out". / www.maroush.com; W2 2 am; SW7 midnight.

Beiteddine SW1 **£54** **3 3 2**
8 Harriet St 7235 3969 5–1D
"Great food, reasonably priced… despite the area" – just a few yards from Sloane Street, this "friendly" and "reliable" Lebanese of long standing seems ever more like a survivor from another age. / SW1X 9JW; www.beiteddinerestaurant.com; midnight.

Belgo **£43** **2 4 3**
50 Earlham St, WC2 7813 2233 4–2C
67 Kingsway, WC2 7242 7469 2–2D
72 Chalk Farm Rd, NW1 7267 0718 8–2B
"Especially for groups", these "big", "down-to-earth" and "buzzy" moules and Belgian beer emporia make "good-value" standbys. / www.belgo-restaurants.co.uk; most branches 10.30 pm-11.30 pm; SW4 midnight, Thu 1 am, Fri & Sat 2 am, Sun 12.30 am.

Bellamy's W1 **£62** **3 4 4**
18-18a Bruton Pl 7491 2727 3–2B
"Genial" owner Gavin Rankin (who used to preside at Annabel's) is much in evidence at his "smart", "old-school" Gallic brasserie, "discreetly located" in a Mayfair mews; NB chaps – "most male customers wear suits". / W1J 6LY; www.bellamysrestaurant.co.uk; 10.30 pm; closed Sat L & Sun.

Bellevue Rendez-Vous SW17 **£48** **3 3 3**
218 Trinity Rd 8767 5810 10–2C
"Trinity Road is not known for its romantic qualities, but this small French restaurant near Wandsworth Common is an absolute gem" – it has recently come under new ownership, but happily the menu is so far "much the same". / SW17 7HP; www.bellevuerendezvous.com; 10.30 pm; closed Mon L; no Amex.

Belvedere W8 **£69** **2 2 4**
Holland Pk, off Abbotsbury Rd 7602 1238 7–1D
With its "tranquil and serene" setting in Holland Park, this "beautiful" and "old-fashioned" Art Deco feature is "a lovely restaurant for lunch on a sunny day", particularly on the terrace; you don't go for the service though ("slow" and "inattentive"), nor the food (often "unexciting"). / W8 6LU; www.belvedererestaurant.co.uk; 10.30 pm; closed Sun D; set weekday L & pre-theatre £41 (FP).

Benares W1 **£90** **3 3 3**
12a Berkeley Square Hs, Berkeley Sq 7629 8886 3–3B
"Atul Kochar is a master of spicing" and "continues to delight with the innovative interpretation of Indian cuisine", at his "slick and showy" Mayfair

operation; its ratings slipped a notch this year though – perhaps there's just more competition than once there was? / W1J 6BS; www.benaresrestaurant.co.uk; @benaresofficial; 10.30 pm; closed Sun; no trainers; set pre theatre £58 (FP).

Bengal Clipper SE1 £41 333
Shad Thames 7357 9001 9–4D
"Reliable" standards make this grand Indian veteran a handy South Bank standby; service is generally "so helpful" too, though it can be "slow". / SE1 2YR; www.bengalclipper.co.uk; 11.30 pm, Sun 11 pm.

Benito's Hat £26 342
12 Great Castle St, W1 7636 6560 3–1C
56 Goodge St, W1 7637 3732 2–1B
19 New Row, WC2 7240 5815 4–3C
King's Cross Station, N1 7812 1304 8–3C
12-14 St John St, EC1 7490 4727 9–1B
"Freshly filled burritos at keen prices" – these self-service Mexicans are great for "food on the run"; good cocktails and happy hour deals too. / www.benitos-hat.com; 10 pm, Thu-Sat 11 pm; Great Castle St closed Sun.

Bentley's W1 £82 333
11-15 Swallow St 7734 4756 3–3D
"Sit downstairs and be entertained by the team of charming oyster shuckers", if you visit this handy veteran fish restaurant, a couple of minutes from Piccadilly Circus; there's also a less interesting dining room upstairs. / W1B 4DG; www.bentleys.org; @bentleys_london; 10.30 pm; no jeans; booking: max 8; set pre theatre £54 (FP).

Bento Café NW1 £37 442
9 Parkway 7482 3990 8–3B
Well placed for Camden Town's Jazz Café, this Chinese/Japanese eatery "ought to be better regarded", thanks to its "vast" and "inexpensive" set menus… and the range of tofu on offer is "HUGE!" / NW1 7PG; bentocafe.co.uk; 10.15 pm, Fri & Sat 10.45 pm.

Benugo £36 234
Branches throughout London
"The spectacular ambience in the beautiful tea rooms of the V&A" and the BFI branch's "oasis" on the South Bank are highlights of this diverse fast-food chain; it still wins praise for "excellent coffee" and "interesting sandwiches", but it's "not as good as it used to be". / www.benugo.com; 4 pm-10 pm; W1 & EC1 branches closed Sat & Sun; W1 & EC1 branches, no credit cards.

The Berners Tavern London EDITION W1 £65 335
10 Berners St 7908 7979 3–1D
"One of the most impressive dining rooms in London" provides the "to-die-for" backdrop to a meal at this "glamorous" and "fun" Marylebone yearling – the food may be "skilfully executed", but it's "definitely not the main event". / W1T 3NP; 11.45 pm.

Best Mangal £36 443
619 Fulham Rd, SW6 7610 0009 5–4A
104 North End Rd, W14 7610 1050 7–2D
66 North End Rd, W14 7602 0212 7–2D
"The best kebabs" plus other "generous and fresh" dishes help make these "good and cheap" West London charcoal-grill outfits a "great standby". / www.bestmangal.com; midnight, Sat 1 am; no Amex.

Bevis Marks E1 £64 222
3 Middlesex St 7247 5474 9–2D
Kosher restaurants are a rarity, but it's still hard to get excited about this City spot, which moved from the eponymous synagogue a couple of years ago; "it means well", but critics say "prices are staggering for so-so food served in a soulless setting". / E1A 7AA; www.bevismarkstherestaurant.com; @BMTR_E1; 9 pm; closed Fri D, Sat & Sun.

Bianco43 £43 322
7 Northumberland Ave, WC2 7321 2915 2–3C
43 Greenwich Church St, SE10 8858 2668 1–3D
1-3 Lee Rd, SE3 8318 2700 1–4D
"Tucked away in touristy Greenwich", this three-year-old venture offers "proper Italian cooking", including some "excellent" pizzas; it's rather noisy and "cramped", though – why not "leave SE10 to the visitors and try the Blackheath Village branch"?

Bibendum SW3 £84 234
81 Fulham Rd 7581 5817 5–2C
An "amazing" airy dining room, "sophisticated" Gallic cooking, a "terrific" wine list and "very slick" service lend a great sense of "classic perfection" to this Brompton Cross landmark, say its fans; those who remember its glory days, though, may be particularly prone to thinking it "doesn't sparkle" nowadays. / SW3 6RD; www.bibendum.co.uk; 11 pm, Sun 10.30 pm; booking: max 12 at L, 10 at D; set weekday L £52 (FP), set dinner £55 (FP).

Bibendum Oyster Bar SW3 £60 243
81 Fulham Rd 7589 1480 5–2C
"For a pop-in lunch or light meal", this luxurious

seafood bar, on the way in to the Chelsea Conran Shop, can be ideal; after a recent revamp, the odd purist doesn't like the addition of hot dishes to the menu, but standards remain solid overall. / SW3 6RD; www.bibendum.co.uk; @bibendumrestaurant; 10 pm; no booking.

Bibimbap Soho W1 **£30** 333
11 Greek St 7287 3434 4–2A
"A gem" – this Soho Korean standby sets itself apart with the preparation of its namesake dish ("a hearty and tasty affair in a hot stone bowl"); "the decor is interesting too – lots of Polaroids of previous happy punters!" / W1D 4DJ; www.bibimbapsoho.com; @bibimbapsoho; 11 pm; closed Sun; no Amex.

Bibo SW15 NEW **£50** 433
146 Upper Richmond Rd 8780 0592 10–2B
From the Sonny's stable, a Putney newcomer on the site of Wallace & Co (RIP) that "shows real promise" – "OK, the area doesn't need another high-end Italian", but this place is "so well conceived and run that it's very welcome nonetheless". / SW15 2SW; www.biborestaurant.com; @biborestaurant; Mon-Fri 9.45 pm, Fri & Sat 10.45 pm, Sun 8.45 pm.

Big Apple Hot Dogs EC1 **£12** 44–
239 Old St 387441 12–1B
"The best hot dogs" continue to inspire all who report on this neat little cart, near Old Street. / EC1V 9EY; www.bigapplehotdogs.com; @BigAppleHotdogs.

Big Easy **£51** 222
12 Maiden Ln, WC2 3728 4888 4–3D
332-334 King's Rd, SW3 7352 4071 5–3C
Chelsea's long-established and "fun" US-style 'crab shack' now has a Covent Garden outpost; the new branch has its fans ("like I was back in New Orleans!"), but expansion seems to have strained standards overall – some "awful" meals have been recorded in both locations of late. / www.bigeasy.co.uk; @bigeasytweet; Mon-Thu 11 pm, Fri-Sat 11.30, Sun 10.30 pm.

Bilbao Berria SW1 NEW **£47** 343
2 Regent St 7930 8408 3–3D
Newly opened, a stylish tapas bar, with restaurant below; early reports are a little up-and-down, but – by the rather 'anonymous' standards of Theatreland – this struck us as a useful sort of operation, on our early-days visit. / SW1Y 4LR; Rated on Editors' visit.

Bill's **£39** 123
Branches throughout London
It's still praised for its "quirky" brunch options and "super kid-friendly" style, but this is a chain whose easy-going appeal risks being entirely lost in the dash for growth – increasingly, reporters find it "completely fake", and say the food is "very ordinary", or even plain "grim"! / most branches 11 pm; no booking.

The Bingham TW10 **£80** 334
61-63 Petersham Rd 8940 0902 1–4A
An "elegant" Richmond dining room, in a "sophisticated" boutique hotel, which offers "spectacular" Thames views, "top-class" cooking and a "wonderful" wine list; it's "not cheap", but the set lunch does offer "outstanding value". / TW10 6UT; www.thebingham.co.uk; 10 pm; closed Sun D; no trainers; set weekday L £49 (FP); SRA-1 star.

Bird E2 NEW **£34** 443
42-44 Kingsland Rd 7613 5168 12–1B
Not trying too hard to be hip, this new Shoreditch canteen offers some interesting twists on fried chicken, and – on our early-days visit – a warm welcome too. / E2 8DA; Rated on Editors' visit; www.birdrestaurants.com; @birdrestaurant; Thu-Sat 12.30 am, Sun-Wed 11.30 pm.

Bird in Hand W14 **£43** 344
Brook Green 7371 2721 7–1C
"Stick to the pizzas and you can't go wrong", at this "attractive and friendly" Italian, in a former Brook Green boozer. / W14 0LR; www.thebirdinhandlondon.com; @TBIHLondon; Mon-Sat 10 pm, Sun 9.15 pm.

Bird of Smithfield EC1 **£67** 223
26 Smithfield St 7559 5100 9–2B
The summer roof terrace is a major attraction at this ex-Ivy chef's solo debut – a sophisticated Smithfield brasserie; fans applaud its comfort food and laud it as an "expensive but impressive" experience, but not all reporters are wowed. / EC1A 9LB; www.birdofsmithfield.com; @BirdoSmithfield; 10 pm; closed Sun; 4+ need to give card details; SRA-1 star.

Bistro 1 **£23** 244
27 Frith St, W1 7734 6204 4–3A
75 Beak St, W1 7287 1840 3–2D
33 Southampton St, WC2 7379 7585 4–3D
"Good but not gastronomic food, served cheerfully and quickly" – that's the deal that makes these "terrifically well-located" West End bistros popular with all who comment on them. / www.bistro1.co.uk; @bistro1_london; midnight.

Bistro Aix N8 **£53** 433
54 Topsfield Pde, Tottenham Ln 8340 6346 8–1C
"A buzzy local bistro, like a bit of France in the middle of Crouch End" – "decent" cooking, and a "crowded but fun" interior. / N8 8PT; www.bistroaix.co.uk; @bistroaixlondon; 10 pm, Fri & Sat 11 pm; Mon-Thu D only, Fri-Sun open L & D; no Amex.

Bistro Union SW4 **£44** 223
40 Abbeville Rd 7042 6400 10–2D
This Clapham bistro "does simple things well", but don't be deceived by its connections to Adam Byatt (of nearby Trinity) – "nothing is earth-shattering". / SW4 9NG; www.bistrounion.co.uk; @BistroUnion; 10 pm, Sun 8 pm.

Bistrot Bruno Loubet The Zetter EC1 **£53** 333
St John's Sq, 86-88 Clerkenwell Rd 7324 4455 9–1A
Bruno Loubet's "impressive" bistro dishes – "with a French touch" plus some "modern flair" – still win plaudits for his relaxed Clerkenwell venture; even some fans feel "standards have slipped a little" of late, though, and critics now find the food "too rich" or "lacking excitement". / EC1M 5RJ; www.bistrotbrunoloubet.com; 10.30 pm, Sun 10 pm; SRA-3 stars.

Bistrotheque E2 **£56** 324
23-27 Wadeson St 8983 7900 1–2D
"It's certainly not located to encourage passing trade", but "it's worth the trip to Cambridge Heath" to hang out at this hip, happening and quite "elegant" warehouse-conversion; decent grub too. / E2 9DR; www.bistrotheque.com; @BISTROTHEQUE; 10.30 pm, Fri & Sat 11 pm; closed weekday L; set dinner £34 (FP).

Black & Blue **£53** 222
37 Berners St, W1 7436 0451 2–1B
90-92 Wigmore St, W1 7486 1912 3–1A
215-217 Kensington Church St, W8 7727 0004 6–2B
1 Mepham St, SE1 7928 9131 2–3D
1-2 Rochester Walk, SE1 7357 9922 9–4C
"Fantastic" burgers are, on many reports, the highlight of this quite "posh" chain (which offers some comfortable boothed seating); reactions to other aspects of the operations are more muted, but the steaks are generally "reliable" too. / www.blackandbluerestaurant.com; @BlackBlueGroup; most branches 11 pm, Fri & Sat 11.30 pm; W1 closed Sun; no booking.

Blackfoot EC1 NEW **£45** 332
46 Exmouth Mkt 7837 4384 9–1A
"Porktastic!"; "it feels like a greasy spoon, and you eat on fairly uncomfortable benches", but this Farringdon newcomer is already winning fans with its ribs and other barbecue treats. / EC1R 4QL; www.blackfootrestaurant.co.uk.

Blanchette W1 NEW **£35** 354
9 D'Arblay St 7439 8100 3–1D
Run by three Gallic brothers, this small Soho newcomer is having a "big impact", thanks to its "serious" and "exciting" French "take on tapas"; "very drinkable" wines too, and "service with a smile". / W1F 8DS; www.blanchettesoho.co.uk; @blanchettesoho; closed Sun D.

BLEEDING HEART EC1 **£62** 335
Bleeding Heart Yd, Greville St 7242 8238 9–2A
"Well hidden, but what a treasure!"; this age-old City-fringe warren – combining bistro, tavern and restaurant – wows romantics and business diners alike with its "olde-worlde" charm; the "outstanding" wine list, though, is of more note than the Gallic cuisine, which is merely "competent" nowadays. / EC1N 8SJ; www.bleedingheart.co.uk; @bleedingheartyd; 10.30 pm; closed Sun.

The Blind Pig Social Eating House W1 NEW **£36** 444
58 Poland St 7993 3251 3–2D
"A five-star experience" – the new cocktail bar at Jason Atherton's Social Eating House, in Soho is a "relaxed and welcoming" place, serving "fantastic bar snacks". / W1F 7NR; www.socialeatinghouse.com; @BLINDASAPIG; 10.30 pm.

Blue Elephant SW6 **£48** 323
The Boulevard 7751 3111 10–1B
Fans say the new location by Chelsea Harbour "works well" ("especially on a sunny day"), but this celebrated Thai (which moved from Fulham Broadway a couple of years ago) is still attracting mixed reports; as ever, the buffet-style Sunday brunch is the top attraction. / SW6 2UB; www.blueelephant.com; @BlueElephantLon; 11.30 pm, Sun 10.30 pm; closed Mon L.

Blue Legume **£41** 223
101 Stoke Newington Church St, N16 7923 1303 1–1C
177 Upper St, N1 7226 5858 8–2D
130 Crouch Hill, N8 8442 9282 8–1C
"For a big brunch and a decent coffee", these

"everyday" north London diners "do the simple things well"; "they're most definitely family-friendly" too, and "there are always kids and prams". / www.thebluelegume.co.uk; 10.30 pm; N8 closed L, N16 closed Sun D.

Bluebird SW3 **£64** 1 2 3
350 King's Rd 7559 1000 5–3C
Fans do praise the "lovely" menu and the "best cocktail list", at this "hangar-like" younger-scene Chelsea landmark; critics find it "overpriced", though, and think the food is "particularly poor". / SW3 5UU; www.bluebird-restaurant.co.uk; @bluebirdchelsea; 10.30 pm, Sun 9.30 pm; SRA-2 stars.

Blueprint Café Design Museum SE1 **£48** 3 2 5
28 Shad Thames, Butler's Wharf 7378 7031 9–4D
"Ask for a window table, to enjoy the great view of the Thames" (and Tower Bridge) – the main reason to seek out this first-floor South Bank restaurant; the food is "good, without being great", and service is on the "poor" side. / SE1 2YD; www.blueprintcafe.co.uk; @BlueprintCafe; 10.30 pm; closed Sun D; SRA-2 stars.

Bo Lang SW3 NEW **£67** 2 3 3
100 Draycott Ave 7823 7887 5–2C
We personally have enjoyed visits to this chic (and undoubtedly "expensive") new dim sum bar, near Brompton Cross, but the limited early-day survey feedback runs the whole gamut from "great" to "all style and no substance" – we can sort of understand both sides! / SW3 3AD; www.bolangrestaurant.co.uk.

Bob Bob Ricard W1 **£63** 3 4 5
1 Upper James St 3145 1000 3–2D
"Subdued light, romantic booths, and quirky touches like a button to summon champagne" – all conducive to creating a "brilliant" impression at this madly "luxurious" Soho diner; "you pay for all that gorgeousness", naturally, but the "high-end comfort food" is generally very "enjoyable". / W1F 9DF; www.bobbobricard.com; @BobBobRicard; Mon-Fri 11.15 pm, Sat midnight; closed Sat L & Sun; jacket.

Bobo Social W1 NEW
95 Charlotte St 7636 9310 2–1C
'Experimental' burgers and small plates come to Charlotte Street, as the high-end hamburger craze continues; we didn't have the chance to check 'em out before this guide went to press. / W1T 4PZ; www.bobosocial.com.

BOCCA DI LUPO W1 **£64** 5 4 4
12 Archer St 7734 2223 3–2D
"You'd be hard pressed to find better in Italy" – "refreshing" tapas-style dishes are "enthusiastically served" at this "exciting" backstreet spot, hidden away near Piccadilly Circus; it's "always jammed", and can get "too noisy" for some tastes. / W1D 7BB; www.boccadilupo.com; @boccadilupo; 11 pm, Sun 9.15 pm; booking: max 10.

Bocconcino W1 NEW
19 Berkeley St 7629 2000 3–3C
Mozzarella via Moscow – a new pizza opening set to consolidate the Russian grip on what we might as well call Mayfair's 'Novikov Quarter'. / W1J 8ED.

Al Boccon di'vino TW9 **£67** 4 3 5
14 Red Lion St 8940 9060 1–4A
"You get what they decide" ("more food than you can shake a stick at") plus wine (red or white?), at this "wacky, chaotic, and delightfully idiosyncratic" Richmond venue – a "brilliant" experience, "like a party in an Italian home", but "not cheap". / TW9 1RW; www.nonsolovinoltd.co.uk; 8 pm; closed Mon, Tue L & Wed L.

Bodean's **£45** 2 2 2
10 Poland St, W1 7287 7575 3–1D
4 Broadway Chambers, SW6 7610 0440 5–4A
169 Clapham High St, SW4 7622 4248 10–2D
16 Byward St, EC3 7488 3883 9–3D
"Nothing special, but it does what it says on the tin"; this US-inspired chain is hailed by fans as a "reliable" (if "unsubtle") choice, but some reports are ambivalent – "if you like your food trendily charred, and covered in BBQ sauce, this is the place for you". / www.bodeansbbq.com; 11 pm, Sun 10.30 pm; 8 or more.

La Bodega Negra W1 **£48** 2 3 4
13-17 Moor St 7758 4100 4–2B
A "dark" and "very sexy" Mexican that's just the job for "a fun night out"; the food's "OK" too, but even fans note that prices are "hefty". / W1D 5NH; www.labodeganegra.com; 1 am, Sun 11.30 pm.

Boisdale SW1 **£64** 3 3 4
13-15 Eccleston St 7730 6922 2–4B
With its "plush tartan decor", "meaty Scottish fare" and impressive list of whiskies and wines, this "convivial" Belgravia bastion "oozes a sense of 'male preserve'"; "smokers delight to find somewhere that positively encourages smoking… on the excellent roof terrace". / SW1W 9LX; www.boisdale.co.uk; @boisdaleCW; 11.30 pm; closed Sat L & Sun.

Boisdale of Canary Wharf E14 **£62** 343
Cabot Pl 7715 5818 11–1C
A "slightly bizarre" traditional find amongst the shiny towers of Canary Wharf, this "spacious" twin of the famous Belgravia Caledonian wins praise for its "surprisingly good" fare; regular jazz adds to the possibilities for business entertaining. / E14 4QT; www.boisdale.co.uk; 10.30 pm; closed Sun.

The Bolingbroke SW11 **£44** 323
174 Northcote Rd 7228 4040 10–2C
"A very good local" – a "buzzy" Battersea boozer, where the menus consist of "a good mix of upmarket pub grub and staples such as burgers". / SW11 6RE; www.renaissancepubs.co.uk; 10.30 pm, Sun 9 pm.

Bombay Brasserie SW7 **£59** 444
Courtfield Close, Gloucester Rd 7370 4040 5–2B
"They finally seem to have got it right!"; this South Kensington institution – London's "original" grand Indian of recent times – has at last fully recovered from its disastrous refurb, and is now once again an "exceptional" all-rounder; as ever, get a conservatory table if you can. / SW7 4QH; www.bombaybrasserielondon.com; @bbsw7; 11.30 pm, Sun 10.30 pm; closed Mon L.

Bombay Palace W2 **£59** 521
50 Connaught St 7723 8855 6–1D
"Sensational ingredients and spicing, even if the atmosphere is like an airport" – this grand Bayswater Indian may look "old hat" (and that's after a recent refurb!), and service is nothing to write home about, but for many reporters it's "still the best". / W2 2AA; www.bombay-palace.co.uk; 11.30 pm.

Bone Daddies W1 **£22** 344
30-31 Peter St 7287 8581 3–2D
"Addictive" noodles, "sticky and spicy ribs", "fried chicken to die for"... – that's the deal making a runaway hit of this "hip" Soho "ramen-erie", where "aged 40, you feel very old and square"; "the queues, OMG the queues..." / W1F 0AR; www.bonedaddiesramen.com; @bonedaddiesRbar.

Bonnie Gull W1 **£49** 544
21a Foley St 7436 0921 2–1B
"The sort of place you'd expect to find in a coastal town!"; this "cramped" Fitzrovia bistro serves "a genuine range" of "outstandingly fresh" fish and seafood, all with "personal" service and at competitive prices. / W1W 6DS; www.bonniegull.com; @BonnieGull; 9.45 pm.

Bonnie Gull Seafood Café EC1 NEW **£67** 433
55-57 Exmouth Mkt 3122 0047 9–1A
"Amazing" oysters – loyal customers can even win an Oyster Card, geddit? – head up a menu of "simply prepared and beautifully presented" fishy dishes at this "seaside-style" café. / EC1R 4QE; www.bonniegullseafoodcafe.com; @boniegull.

Boqueria SW2 **£34** 444
192 Acre Ln 7733 4408 10–2D
"Vibrant" tapas help win rave reviews for this "fun and laid-back" (if "noisy") spot, between Clapham and Brixton. / SW2 5UL; www.boqueriatapas.com; @BoqueriaTapas; 11 pm, Fri & Sat 12 am, Sun 10 pm; closed weekday L.

Il Bordello E1 **£51** 454
81 Wapping High St 7481 9950 11–1A
This "really buzzing" and "friendly" Wapping fixture is "a great favourite locally"; "it headlines as a pizzeria, but it's so much more" – whatever you choose, brace yourself for "large portions". / E1W 2YN; www.ilbordello.com; 11 pm, Sun 10.30 pm; closed Sat L.

La Bota N8 **£33** 343
31 Broadway Pde 8340 3082 1–1C
A "lovely" Crouch End tapas veteran, praised by the locals for its "consistently maintained standards of food and service", "generous portions" and "good prices". / N8 9DB; www.labota.co.uk; 11 pm, Fri-Sun 11.30 pm; closed Mon L; no Amex.

The Botanist SW1 **£64** 111
7 Sloane Sq 7730 0077 5–2D
If certainly offers "great people-watching" (especially for Made In Chelsea fans), and supporters of this ever-throbbing bar-restaurant "don't understand why it gets such a bad rap" – across the board, though, its survey ratings are dire. / SW1W 8EE; www.thebotanistonsloanesquare.com; @TheBotanistSW1; 10.45 pm; set Sun L £41 (FP).

La Bottega **£17** 344
20 Ryder St, SW1 7839 5789 3–4C
25 Eccleston St, SW1 7730 2730 2–4B
65 Lower Sloane St, SW1 7730 8844 5–2D
36 Monmouth St, WC2 7836 5255 4–2B NEW
97 Old Brompton Rd, SW7 7581 6622 5–2B
"Consistently good coffee", and "simple and fresh"

pasta too – all part of the ongoing success of these smart but "casual" and "friendly" café-delis. / *www.labottega65.com; Lower Sloane St 8 pm, Sat 6 pm, Sun 5 pm; Eccleston St 7 pm; Old Brompton Rd 8 pm; Ryder St closed Sat & Sun; no booking.*

La Bouchée SW7 **£48** 224
56 Old Brompton Rd 7589 1929 5–2B
"Very cosy" and "intimate" ("cramped"), this South Kensington spot may be a bit of a "throwback", but it's a charming one, offering "well-presented" Gallic bistro classics, "sometimes rather slowly". / *SW7 3DY; 11 pm, Sun 10.30 pm.*

Boudin Blanc W1 **£59** 223
5 Trebeck St 7499 3292 3–4B
"Prices seem to have increased dramatically over the years", at this Shepherd Market bistro – fans say it's still "worth it", but critics find food and service standards ever more "ordinary", although the al fresco tables are undoubtedly as charming as ever. / *W1J 7LT; www.boudinblanc.co.uk; 11 pm.*

Boulestin SW1 **£66** 222
5 St James's St 7930 2030 3–4D
Joel Kissin's relaunch (under a famous old name) of the "calmly atmospheric" former L'Oranger (RIP) premises in St James's has been rather a curate's egg; even fans may find its "classical French" formula "surprisingly expensive", and critics find the divide between the front café and rear dining area "strange and incoherent" too. / *SW1A 1EF; www.boulestin.co.uk; @BoulestinLondon; Mon-Wed 11 pm, Thu-Sat 11.30 pm; closed Sun; set pre theatre £48 (FP).*

Boulevard WC2 **£45** 233
40 Wellington St 7240 2992 4–3D
Despite its clichéd looks, this Covent Garden brasserie "does what it says on the tin" – "not bad food, reasonable prices, quick service and a buzzing atmosphere"; "try to sit on the first floor if you can". / *WC2E 7BD; www.boulevardbrasserie.co.uk; @BoulevardWC2; 11 pm, Fri & Sat 11.30 pm, Sun 10.30 pm; set pre theatre £32 (FP).*

The Boundary E2 **£65** 222
2-4 Boundary St 7729 1051 12–1B
It's the "magical" rooftop dining area which excites reporters on Sir Terence Conran's "cool-looking" Shoreditch venture (which also has a spacious basement restaurant); portions can be "small", though, and service is on the "sketchy" side. / *E2 7DD; www.theboundary.co.uk; 10.30 pm; D only, ex Sun L only.*

The Brackenbury W6 NEW **£50** 432
129-131 Brackenbury Rd 8741 4928 7–1C
"A welcome return from the dead" – this one-time Hammersmith gem (recently Port of Manila, RIP), relaunched by Ossie Gray (son of River Café founder Ruth), offers "imaginative" Mediterranean-influenced fare that's perhaps on the "pricey" side; the interior configuration, however, remains as "awkward" as ever. / *W6 0BQ; www.brackenburyrestaurant.co.uk; @BrackenburyRest.*

Bradley's NW3 **£57** 222
25 Winchester Rd 7722 3457 8–2A
"Very handy for the Hampstead Theatre", this Swiss Cottage spot perennially wins praise for its "careful cooking", "well-chosen wine" and "classy" decor; as ever, though, there are also critics who insist it's "gone off"! / *NW3 3NR; www.bradleysnw3.co.uk; 10 pm; closed Sun D; set weekday L & dinner £37 (FP).*

Brady's SW18 **£34** 333
Dolphin Hs, Smugglers Way 8877 9599 10–2B
Most reports on the Brady family's stalwart Battersea chippy say it's "even better" in its more "glitzy" new riverside home; it can also seem "less personable" here, though, and some long-term fans have found "delivery short of expectations" of late. / *SW18 1DG; www.bradysfish.co.uk; @Bradyfish; 10 pm, Sun 8.30 pm; closed Mon, Tue L, Wed L & Thu L; no Amex; no booking.*

La Brasserie SW3 **£57** 224
272 Brompton Rd 7581 3089 5–2C
"If you can't get to Paris this is the next best thing" – a "real, French-style brasserie with lots of action", on a prominent Chelsea site; the "very good and very large breakfast" – à l'anglaise – has always been a star weekend attraction. / *SW3 2AW; www.labrasserielondon.co.uk; @labrasserie; Mon-Sat 11.30 pm, Sun 11 pm; no booking, Sat L & Sun L.*

Brasserie Blanc **£53** 223
Branches throughout London
Looking for "reasonably priced food in a pleasant French brasserie-style environment"? – this "upmarket" chain is "worth a try", even if "it can be a bit hit-and-miss"; visitors should especially note the "superbly located" Covent Garden branch, with its first-floor terrace overlooking the Royal Opera House. / *www.brasserieblanc.com; most branches close between 10 pm & 11 pm; SE1 closed Sun D, most City branches closed Sat & Sun; SRA-2 stars.*

Brasserie Chavot W1 £66 333
41 Conduit St 7183 6425 3–2C
Fans of Eric Chavot's "elegant" Mayfair chamber do not stint in their praise for his "blisteringly good" brasserie fare; critics find the setting rather "lacking in warmth", though, and may even find the "rich and traditional" cuisine just a touch "passé" – no wonder Michelin approves! / W1S 2YQ; www.brasseriechavot.com; @brasseriechavot; 10.30 pm, Sun 9 pm.

Brasserie Max Covent Garden Hotel WC2 £72 343
10 Monmouth St 7806 1000 4–2B
On the intriguing Covent Garden junction which is Seven Dials, a "good-quality hotel restaurant", particularly noted for its "outstanding" breakfasts – choose from "the most extensive menu ever!" / WC2H 9HB; www.coventgardenhotel.co.uk; 11 pm; set always available £44 (FP).

Brasserie Toulouse-Lautrec SE11 £40 343
140 Newington Butts 7582 6800 1–3C
"A stalwart of Elephant & Castle", this "charming" and "unpretentious" Gallic restaurant offers a "short but sensible" menu at "good-value" prices; regular musical entertainment "adds zing". / SE11 4RN; www.btlrestaurant.co.uk; @btlrestaurant; 10.30 pm, Sat & Sun 11 pm.

BRASSERIE ZÉDEL W1 £39 245
20 Sherwood St 7734 4888 3–2D
Corbin & King's "extravagant" Art Deco-style basement, just seconds from Piccadilly Circus, offers "classic Gallic brasserie fodder" that's "workmanlike" at best – given the "magnificent" gilded decor, "first-class" service, and "unbelievably good prices", however, few reporters really seem to care! / W1F 7ED; www.brasseriezedel.com; @brasseriezedel; 11.45 pm; SRA-3 stars.

Bravas E1 NEW £42 434
St Katharine Docks 7481 1464 9–3D
"Overlooking the expensive boats moored in St Katharine Docks", this "lovely" newcomer is "a real find", and offers welcome relief from all the chains hereabouts; attractions include a "flavourful modern take on tapas", a "tasteful" interior and some good outside tables. / E1W 1AT; www.bravastapas.co.uk; @Bravas_Tapas.

Brawn E2 £49 534
49 Columbia Rd 7729 5692 12–1C
"Deep flavours and lovely textures" from a "quirky" menu, plus Caves de Pyrène's "glorious" biodynamic wines, decidedly make this "fascinating and characterful" East End bistro the group's star performer nowadays. / E2 7RG; www.brawn.co; @brawn49; 11 pm; closed Mon L & Sun D; no Amex.

Bread Street Kitchen EC4 £62 232
1 New Change 3030 4050 9–2B
This "cavernous" and "noisy" venture in a City shopping centre has its attractions for expense-accounters, not least for "power breakfasts"; it's a Gordon Ramsay production, though, and his involvement "has led to inflated prices for some pretty basic fare". / EC4M 9AF; www.breadstreetkitchen.com; @breadstreet; 11 pm, Sun 8 pm.

Briciole W1 £40 334
20 Homer St 7723 0040 6–1D
This "buzzy and busy" Italian-accented pub-conversion, in the backwoods of Marylebone, wins consistent praise for its "simple" tapas-sized dishes; some reporters prefer the quieter lunchtimes to "noisy peak times". / W1H 4NA; www.briciole.co.uk; @briciolelondon; 10.15 pm.

Brick Lane Beigel Bake E1 £7 531
159 Brick Ln 7729 0616 12–1C
"A London institution"; this "rough and ready" East End bakery offers "incomparable" salt beef beigels 24/7; "I spend more on the cab to get there than I do on the food!" / E1 6SB; open 24 hours; no credit cards; no booking.

Brigade The Fire Station SE1 £49 323
139 Tooley St 0844 346 1225 9–4D
In a former fire station near London Bridge, a "comfortable" bistro yearling that's particularly "great for everyday business meetings", even if "poor" service can sometimes be a let down. / SE1 2HZ; www.thebrigade.co.uk; @brigadeSE1; 10 pm.

The Bright Courtyard W1 £59 342
43-45 Baker St 7486 6998 2–1A
"Clean, modern, fresh Chinese food" – with dim sum the highlight – is winning ever more praise for this airy and coolly decorated Marylebone spot, whose parent establishment is in Shanghai. / W1U 8EW; www.lifefashiongroup.com; @BrightCourtyard; 10.45 pm, Thu-Sat 11.15 pm.

Brilliant UB2 £38 333
72-76 Western Rd 8574 1928 1–3A
A "legendary" Indian; it's "worth the trek" to seek out its "enjoyable" and "authentic" Punjabi food,

deep in the suburban heart of Southall. / UB2 5DZ; www.brilliantrestaurant.com; @BRILLIANTRST; 11 pm, Fri & Sat 11.30 pm; closed Mon, Sat L & Sun L.

Brinkley's SW10 **£53** 3 3 4
47 Hollywood Rd 7351 1683 5–3B
For the slightly older Chelsea set, a popular destination for a "good local dinner", and one which comes complete with an atmospheric garden; "good-value wine list" too. / SW10 9HX; www.brinkleys.com; 11.30 pm; closed weekday L.

The Brown Cow SW6 **£43** 4 4 4
676 Fulham Rd 7384 9559 10–1B
A heart-of-Fulham bistro that's really got into its stride in its first full year of operation; all reports praise its "interesting" menu of "well-cooked" gastropub-style fare. / SW6 5SA; www.thebrowncowpub.co.uk; @TheBrownCowPub; 10 pm.

The Brown Dog SW13 **£51** 3 3 3
28 Cross St 8392 2200 10–1A
"Barnes's secret pleasure" – a cutely "hidden-away" gastropub offering "a short menu of well-cooked favourites"; usually a "relaxed" spot, it gets "a bit more frenetic when the weekend comes". / SW13 0AP; www.thebrowndog.co.uk; @browndogbarnes; 10 pm, Sun 9 pm.

(Hix at Albemarle) Brown's Hotel W1 **£82** 2 3 3
Albemarle St 7518 4004 3–3C
With "plenty of space between tables for discreet conversation" (and "surprising original artworks" too), this woody Mayfair hotel dining room makes a "top business breakfast choice"; despite Mark Hix's involvement, though, other fare can be "decidedly average". / W1S 4BP; www.thealbemarlerestaurant.com; 11 pm, Sun 10.30 pm; set always available £60 (FP).

Browns **£47** 1 1 2
Branches throughout London
"Nice place, shame about the food" – a dreary chain whose only obvious asset is the sometimes grand and historic setting of its branches. / www.browns-restaurants.co.uk; most branches 10 pm-11 pm; EC2 closed Sat D & Sun; W1 closed Sun D.

Brula TW1 **£48** 4 4 4
43 Crown Rd 8892 0602 1–4A
"A little piece of France", in St Margarets; this "enduringly charming and consistent" restaurant dazzles its huge local fan club with its "intimate" style, "friendly" service and "classic" cuisine. / TW1 3EJ; www.brula.co.uk; @brula_tweet; 10.30 pm.

Brunswick House Café SW8 **£43** 2 2 5
30 Wandsworth Rd 7720 2926 10–1D
Set in a vast Georgian house, at Vauxhall Cross, now used as an architectural salvage showroom, this "quirky" restaurant certainly has a "fantastic" atmosphere; the seasonal food's not bad either, and there's a "very decent wine list". / SW8 2LG; www.brunswickhousecafe.co.uk; 10 pm; closed Sun D.

Bubba Gump Shrimp Company W1 NEW
13 Coventry St 3763 5288 4–4A
Now (finally!) open in the former Planet Hollywood premises near Piccadilly Circus, the first UK branch of an American chain loosely based on the characters in 'Forrest Gump'; if successful, more will follow – you have been warned! / W1D 7DH.

Bubbledogs W1 **£31** 2 3 4
70 Charlotte St 7637 7770 2–1C
"Hot dogs and champagne, what's not to love?", say fans of this "fun" and "trendy" Fitzrovia yearling; "a good hot dog is still pretty ordinary", sniff critics – "perhaps I should have drunk more fizz!" / W1T 4QG; www.bubbledogs.co.uk; @bubbledogsUK; 9 pm; closed Sun.

(Kitchen Table) Bubbledogs W1 **£94** 4 5 4
70 Charlotte St 7637 7770 2–1C
"A unique dining experience"; this "phenomenal" Fitzrovian – a horseshoe-shaped chef's table "secretively curtained" from the adjoining hot dog place – offers "passionate" service and course after course of "astonishingly clever food", "theatrically" prepared "before your very eyes". / W1T 4QG; www.kitchentablelondon.co.uk; @bubbledogsKT; 9.30 pm (6 pm & 7.30 pm seatings only); D only, closed Mon & Sun.

Buddha-Bar London SW1 NEW **£70** 1 2 3
145 Knightsbridge 3667 5222 5–1D
Re-located to Knightsbridge (from WC2), this Parisian-nightclub-style oriental has made remarkably few ripples; it can be "fun", but – given the hefty prices – "the food needs serious improvement". / SW1X 7PA; www.buddhabarlondon.com; @BuddhaBarLondon; 10 pm.

Buen Ayre E8 **£51** 4 2 2
50 Broadway Mkt 7275 9900 1–2D
A packed East End 'parrilla' offering what fans claim is "the best Argentinean steak in London"; only caveat? – "it's impossible to get a booking!" / E8 4QJ; www.buenayre.co.uk; 10.30 pm; no Amex; set weekday L £30 (FP).

Buenos Aires Cafe **£52** 3 3 3
86 Royal Hill, SE10 8488 6764 1–3D
17 Royal Pde, SE3 8318 5333 1–4D
"An independent oasis, standing out in the Blackheath mire"; "run by a retired Argentinian tango dancer" (who knew?), it's hailed for its "heavenly steaks" and "good veggie options too"; there is a more café-like offshoot in Greenwich. / www.buenosairesltd.com; SE3 10.30 pm; SE10 7 pm, Sat & Sun 6 pm; no Amex.

The Builders Arms SW3 **£46** 3 3 4
13 Britten St 7349 9040 5–2C
"As unpretentious as Chelsea can be, even if everyone still looks effortlessly loaded" – this lovely boozer, behind Waitrose, wins praise for "generous helpings" of "simple food done right". / SW3 3TY; www.geronimo-inns.co.uk; @BuildersChelsea; 10 pm, Thu-Sat 11 pm, Sun 9 pm; no booking; SRA-2 stars.

The Bull N6 **£46** 2 2 4
13 North Hill 8341 0510 1–1C
Fans of this "lovely" Highgate pub and micro-brewery hail it as a "superior" local and good all-rounder; it can seem "a bit up itself", though, and the excellent range of brews is a more reliable attraction than the sometimes disappointing food. / N6 4AB; thebullhighgate.co.uk; @Bull_Highgate; 10 pm.

Bull & Last NW5 **£60** 4 3 3
168 Highgate Rd 7267 3641 8–1B
"It's worth braving the crowds" to visit this Kentish Town marvel, which is "uncontested" as north London's top gastropub; "it just gets everything right", not least the "creative" comfort food and "fabulous selection of ales". / NW5 1QS; www.thebullandlast.co.uk; @thebullandlast; 10 pm, Sun 9 pm.

Bumpkin **£52** 3 2 2
119 Sydney St, SW3 3730 9344 5–2B
102 Old Brompton Rd, SW7 7341 0802 5–2B
209 Westbourne Park Rd, W11 7243 9818 6–1B
Westfield Stratford, E20 8221 9900 1–1D
A faux-rustic chain whose "truly British" and "seasonal" menu has "improved" of late; even fans can still find it "pricey" though, and it suffers from "hit-and-miss" service and an often-"loud" atmosphere. / www.bumpkinuk.com; 11 pm.

Bunnychow **£11**
74 Wardour St, W1 3697 7762 3–2D NEW
Unit 55 2-4 Bethnal Green Rd, E1 3697 7762 12–2B NEW
After the success of their food truck, and a pop-up at Shoreditch's Boxpark, these merchants of South African street food are now coming to Soho with a bricks and mortar operation. / www.bunnychow.com.

Buona Sera **£39** 2 3 3
289a King's Rd, SW3 7352 8827 5–3C
22 Northcote Rd, SW11 7228 9925 10–2C
A "useful" and "family-friendly" Battersea local, which remains a popular (if "very noisy") standby, thanks to its reliable and affordable pizza and pasta; the Chelsea offshoot benefits from curious ('70s) double-decker seating. / midnight; SW3 11.30 pm, Sun 10 pm; SW3 closed Mon L.

Burger & Lobster **£44** 3 2 3
Harvey Nichols, Knightsbridge, SW1 7235 5000 5–1D
29 Clarges St, W1 7409 1699 3–4B
36 Dean St, W1 7432 4800 4–2A
40 St John St, EC1 7490 9230 9–1B
Bow Bells Hs, 1 Bread St, EC4 7248 1789 9–2B
"A genius idea"; the name says it all about this "fun", "very loud" and "chaotic" concept, whose smash-hit status is signalled by "long queues at peak times"; as the chain grows, though, "quality is not what it was". / www.burgerandlobster.com; @Londonlobster; 10.30 pm; Clarges St closed Sun D, Bread St & St John St closed Sun.

Busaba Eathai **£39** 2 2 4
35 Panton St, SW1 7930 0088 4–4A
106-110 Wardour St, W1 7255 8686 3–2D
8-13 Bird St, W1 7518 8080 3–1A
44 Floral St, WC2 7759 0088 4–2D
313-319 Old St, EC1 7729 0808 12–1B
"Buzzy", "friendly" and unusually "stylish" for a chain, these "darkly-lit" communal Thai canteens are a "reliable" standby for a "quick" meal; perhaps the cooking is somewhat "Asian-by-numbers", but most reporters still find it "yummy" and "reasonably priced". / www.busaba.co.uk; 11 pm, Fri & Sat 11.30 pm, Sun 10 pm; W1 no booking; WC1 booking: min 10.

Bush Dining Hall W12 **£43** 1 2 3
304 Uxbridge Rd 8749 0731 7–1B
"A firm favourite with trendy SheBu locals" – this carefully distressed hangout (adjacent to a popular music venue) scores well for its "friendly buzz" and general "cool"; but what is "surprisingly good" food to fans is, to critics, "trying too hard, and failing". / W12 7LJ; www.bushhalldining.co.uk; @BushHallDining; 10.30 pm, Fri & Sat 10 pm; closed Sun D.

Butcher & Grill SW11 £43 223
39-41 Parkgate Rd 7924 3999 5–4C
For a "lovely brunch", this "attractive" Battersea local (with deli and butcher attached) is just the job; fans also applaud its "great steaks" at any time, but not everyone is convinced. / SW11 4NP; www.thebutcherandgrill.com; @ButcherGrill; 11 pm, Sun 4 pm; closed Sun D.

Butlers Wharf Chop House SE1 £60 222
36e Shad Thames 7403 3403 9–4D
Despite its impressive location near Tower Bridge, this large Thameside venue is only "mildly atmospheric"; the few reports it inspires suggest that its food (traditional British) and service are similarly middle of the road. / SE1 2YE; www.chophouse.co.uk; 10.45 pm, Sun 9.45 pm; SRA-2 stars.

La Buvette TW9 £44 334
6 Church Walk 8940 6264 1–4A
"A delightful location" – by a churchyard in central Richmond – and "cosy" interior bolster the appeal of this "charming" bistro, where "classic" ("often rich") dishes are matched with "interesting regional French wines". / TW9 1SN; www.labuvette.co.uk; @labuvettebistro; 10 pm; set weekday L £33 (FP).

Byron £36 233
Branches throughout London
"George Osborne likes them and so do we!"; the survey's second most commented-on multiple (after its former parent, PizzaExpress) cranks out "posh" burgers in "bright and buzzy" branches; despite the group's "relentless expansion", its ratings have held up quite well. / www.byronhamburgers.com; most branches 11 pm; SRA-2 stars.

C London W1 £100 112
25 Davies St 7399 0500 3–2B
"Eye-wateringly expensive" yet "sorely disappointing", this Mayfair Italian seems to survive mainly on its people-watching possibilities – "do they pay celebs to eat there, to get in the Daily Mail readers?" / W1K 3DE; www.crestaurant.co.uk; 11.45 pm.

C&R Cafe £30 422
3-4 Rupert Ct, W1 7434 1128 4–3A
52 Westbourne Grove, W2 7221 7979 6–1B
"Perfect for a casual Malaysian meal that's authentic and delicious" – these Chinatown and Bayswater cafés impress all who report on them with their "cheap and cheerful" charms. / www.cnrrestaurant.com; 11 pm.

The Cadogan Arms SW3 £49 331
298 King's Rd 7352 6500 5–3C
A Chelsea corner boozer, near the UGC cinema, offering "restaurant-quality food in a pub setting"; there are "especially good deals for large groups". / SW3 5UG; www.thecadoganarmschelsea.com; @TheCadoganArms; 10.15 pm, Sun 8.45 pm.

Café 209 SW6 £23 235
209 Munster Rd 7385 3625 10–1B
With "funny and charming" owner Joy very much in charge, a "brilliant" evening is pretty much guaranteed at this "cheap and cheerful" BYO caff in the depths of Fulham; the Thai fare veers from "pretty average" to "great". / SW6 6BX; 10.30 pm; D only, closed Sun, closed Dec; no Amex.

Le Café Anglais Whiteley's W2 £59 334
8 Porchester Gdns 7221 1415 6–1C
This "grand", "bright and airy" Deco-ish brasserie (with oyster bar) – oft-compared to a cruise liner dining room – makes an unlikely find, atop Whiteley's; it's never really seemed to fulfil its potential, and its future is uncertain at the time of writing, as chef-patron Rowley Leigh sold it back to the mall's owners in Sept 2014. / W2 4DB; www.lecafeanglais.co.uk; @LeCafeAnglais; 10.30 pm, Fri & Sat 11 pm, Sun 10 pm.

Café Bohème W1 £46 234
13 Old Compton St 7734 0623 4–2A
"For an authentic Parisian feel and superb coffee", this "cool" all-hours brasserie, in the very heart of Soho, "takes some beating"; arguably "you don't need to bother with the food", but it's at least "OK". / W1 5JQ; www.cafeboheme.co.uk; @CafeBoheme1; 2.45 am, Sun midnight; no reservations.

Café del Parc N19 £36 444
167 Junction Road 7281 5684 8–1C
"Spectacularly good" food makes this "tiny" spot a big hit up Tuffnell Park way; its "brilliant experimental Spanish fusion fare" comes tapas-style – there's no menu, as this is a "le-chef-propose sort of place". / N19 5PZ; www.delparc.com; 10.30 pm; open D only, Wed-Sun; no Amex.

Café des Amis WC2 £59 122
11-14 Hanover Pl 7379 3444 4–2D
"Frantic", "noisy", "squashed" – this bistro by the Royal Opera House doesn't want for custom; some reports, though, are vitriolic about its standards – "it seems to survive on special offers, pre-purchased vouchers and never-to-return

tourists", says one; the basement bar is better. / WC2E 9JP; www.cafedesamis.co.uk; @CafedAmis; 11.30 pm, Sun 7pm; set pre theatre £25 (FP).

Café du Marché EC1 £55 345
22 Charterhouse Sq 7608 1609 9–1B
"Discreetly located in an alley off Charterhouse Square," this City-fringe "classic" offers food that's "as authentically French as it gets"; it's the "wonderful", "rustic" atmosphere, though, which has long made it a hugely popular rendezvous for business, and – by night, when there's jazz – for romance. / EC1M 6DX; www.cafedumarche.co.uk; @lecafedumarche; 10 pm; closed Sat L & Sun.

Café East SE16 £22 422
100 Redriff Rd 7252 1212 11–2B
"Very authentic" and "delicious" too, the Vietnamese food on offer at this "very cheap" Bermondsey café pleases all who comment on it; "service can be brisk, but everything is amazing so it doesn't matter!" / SE16 7LH; www.cafeeast.foodkingdom.com; @cafeeastpho; 10.30 pm, Sun 10 pm; closed Tue.

Café in the Crypt St Martin's in the Fields WC2 £32 223
Duncannon St 7766 1158 2–2C
With its "handy" location on Trafalgar Square and its "atmospheric" setting in a huge crypt, this self-service refectory is "always busy"; no-one would make huge claims for its "nourishing and cheap" fare, but "at least the profits go to a good cause". / WC2N 4JJ; stmartin-in-the-fields.org/cafe-in-the-crypt; 8 pm, Thu-Sat 9 pm, Sun 6 pm; no Amex; no booking.

Café Murano SW1 NEW £52 444
33 St James's St 3371 5559 3–3C
"A new staple in St James's"; Angela Hartnett's "cheaper, more informal spin-off" is an "unpretentious and charming" venue, with "genial" service; it serves "proper" Italian dishes at prices that "don't shock". / SW1A 1HD.

Café Pistou EC1 NEW
8-10 Exmouth Mkt awaiting tel 9–1A
Backed by an ex-Gaucho head honcho, a brand new all-day Provençal café, in Farringdon's 'little trendy street'; one suspects more will follow. / EC1R 4QA; www.cafepistou.co.uk; @CafePistou.

Café Rouge £38 122
Branches throughout London
"Best avoided unless the children really won't wait" – these "fake French bistros" have their fans as a breakfast destination, but other meals are sometimes "so badly prepared and served" as to be simply "dire". / www.caferouge.co.uk; 11 pm, Sun 10.30 pm.

Café Spice Namaste E1 £56 443
16 Prescot St 7488 9242 11–1A
"A gem in a dreary City side street"; Cyrus Todiwala's "interesting Parsi take on Indian food" – with great game dishes, and "favouring spicing over heat" – maintains the long-standing acclaim for this "friendly" stalwart. / E1 8AZ; www.cafespice.co.uk; @cafespicenamast; 10.30 pm; closed Sat L & Sun; SRA-3 stars.

Caffè Caldesi W1 £56 342
118 Marylebone Ln 7487 0754 2–1A
In Marylebone, a "consistent", "reliable" and "friendly" neighbourhood Italian, with a particular name for its "delicious" homemade pasta. / W1U 2QF; www.caldesi.com; 10.30 pm, Sun 9.30 pm.

Caffè Nero £13 233
Branches throughout London
"The best mass-produced coffee"; with its "consistent" standards, this "friendly" multiple manages to seem "a bit less corporate" than the other major players; it serves "tasty paninis and soups" too. / most branches 7 pm; City branches earlier; most City branches closed all or part of weekend; some branches no credit cards; no booking.

Caffé Vergnano £32 333
Staple Inn, 337-338 High Holborn, WC1 7242 7119 9–2A
62 Charing Cross Rd, WC2 7240 3512 4–3B
Royal Festival Hall, SE1 7921 9339 2–3D
2 New Street Sq, EC4 7936 3404 9–2A
A small group of cafés of note for "simply fantastic coffee"; the SE1 branch, with its "good range of light Italian dishes", is probably the best place to eat by the RFH. / www.caffevergnano1882.co.uk; EC4 11 pm; SE1 midnight; WC2 8 pm, Fri & Sat midnight; EC4 Sat & Sun; no Amex.

La Cage Imaginaire NW3 £42 334
16 Flask Walk 7794 6674 8–1A
"In the foodie wasteland of Hampstead", this "cosy" little spot, on a super-cute lane, is a "reliable" place offering "traditional bistro food of good quality"; it's "none too expensive", either – "why isn't it packed?" / NW3 1HE; www.la-cage-imaginaire.co.uk; 11 pm.

Cah-Chi £37 432
394 Garratt Ln, SW18 8946 8811 10–2B
34 Durham Rd, SW20 8947 1081 10–2B
"Healthy and warming", "delicious" and "great value" – there's little not to like about the Korean scoff on offer at these "unassuming" but "busy"

Korean operations, in Earlsfield and Raynes Park; BYO. / www.cahchi.com; SW20 11 pm; SW18 11 pm, Sat & Sun 11.30 pm; SW20 closed Mon; cash only.

The Camberwell Arms SE5 NEW **£55** 444
65 Camberwell Church St 7358 4364 1–3C
"Another fab gastropub from the team behind the Canton Arms" – this excellent Camberwell newcomer offers some "delicious" food; "order from the blackboard, then hang out in the cocktail bar upstairs". / SE5 8TR; www.thecamberwellarms.co.uk; @camberwellarms; closed Mon L & Sun D.

Cambio de Tercio SW5 **£68** 434
161-163 Old Brompton Rd 7244 8970 5–2B
"Tirelessly energetic owner" Abel Lusa presides over this "special" Earl's Court venture – thanks to its "exciting and different" cuisine, "heavenly" wines and positively "Latin" atmosphere, it is often proclaimed "London's top Spanish restaurant". / SW5 0LJ; www.cambiodetercio.co.uk; @CambiodTercio; 11.15 pm, Sun 11 pm; set weekday L £46 (FP).

Camino N1 **£47** 233
3 Varnishers Yd, Regent Quarter 7841 7331 8–3C
"A great place to meet friends near King's Cross" – this handy hangout serves up tasty tapas washed down with "fabulous sangria". / N1 9FD; www.camino.uk.com; @CaminoLondon; Mon-Sat 10.30 pm, Sun 9.30 pm; set weekday L £26 (FP); SRA-3 stars.

Cannizaro House SW19 **£64** 234
West Side, Wimbledon Common 8879 1464 10–2A
A "beautiful" country house, by Wimbledon Common, with a "divine" terrace; the food is perhaps a secondary attraction, but no one disputes that – for a "romantic" setting – this is a hard place to beat; "good for business and functions" too. / SW19 4UE; www.cannizarohouse.com; 9.30 pm.

Canta Napoli **£38** 332
9 Devonshire Rd, W4 8994 5225 7–2A
136 High St, TW11 8977 3344 1–4A
"Lively and characterful", these "friendly" Chiswick and Teddington Italians offers an "excellent selection of basic dishes, including superb pizza and pasta". / 10.30 pm; no Amex.

Canteen **£42** 111
Royal Festival Hall, SE1 0845 686 1122 2–3D
Park Pavilion, 40 Canada Sq, E14 0845 686 1122 11–1C
Crispin Pl, Old Spitalf'ds Mkt, E1 0845 686 1122 12–2B
Such a shame this perennially promising English-canteen chain remains so "lacklustre"; it has some "useful" locations (on the South Bank especially), but too often suffers from "unmotivated" service and food that "fails to live up to the promise of the menu". / www.canteen.co.uk; 11 pm, E14 & W1 Sun 7 pm; no booking weekend L.

Cantina Laredo WC2 **£52** 443
10 Upper St Martin's Ln 7420 0630 4–3B
"I'm from Arizona, so I know an authentic Mexican!"; this grand-US-diner-style Covent Garden spot attracts consistent praise for "fresh-tasting" food that's "a cut above", and in "generous portions" too. / WC2H 9FB; www.cantinalaredo.co.uk; @CantinaLaredoUK; 11.30 pm, Sat midnight, Sun 10.30 pm.

Cantina Vinopolis Vinopolis SE1 **£54** 222
1 Bank End 7940 8333 9–3C
It doesn't fully live up to its cathedral-like setting under South Bank railway arches, but this café attached to a museum of wine served some "surprisingly good" meals this year – recommended pre-theatre, and for Sunday lunch. / SE1 9BU; www.cantinavinopolis.com; 10 pm; closed Sun D.

Canton Arms SW8 **£45** 334
177 South Lambeth Rd 7582 8710 10–1D
This "unpretentious" Stockwell gastropub isn't showing quite the staying power of its sibling, the Anchor & Hope; it can still dish up some "hearty and homely" dishes, but even some fans note the formula "doesn't always work". / SW8 1XP; www.cantonarms.com; 10 pm; closed Mon L & Sun D; no Amex; no booking.

Canvas SW1 NEW
1 Wilbraham Pl 7935 0858 5–2D
Michael Riemenschneider moved his 'design-your-own-menu" fine dining concept from Marylebone to Chelsea in mid-2014; we think a proper assessment will sadly have to wait until next year. / SW1X 9AE; www.canvaschelsea.com; @CanvasbyMR.

Capote Y Toros SW5 **£44** 434
157 Old Brompton Rd 7373 0567 5–2B
"Like being in Seville!"; part of the Cambio de Tercio group, this "buzzy" and "stylish" South Kensington spot offers "excellent tapas and a great selection of sherries". / SW5 0LJ; www.cambiodetercio.co.uk; @CambiodTercio; 11.15 pm; D only, closed Mon & Sun.

LE CAPRICE SW1 **£71** 344
Arlington Hs, Arlington St 7629 2239 3–4C
"Like Ol' Man River, just keeps rolling along!" – this "understated" '80s brasserie, behind The Ritz, "always make you feel like a million dollars"; its "robust" comfort food "won't let you down", but it's not as dazzling as it once was – the "people-watching" is the more reliable sparkler. / SW1A 1RJ; www.le-caprice.co.uk; @CapriceHoldings; 11.30 pm Mon-Sat, Sun 10.30 pm; set pre theatre £49 (FP).

Caraffini SW1 **£51** 253
61-63 Lower Sloane St 7259 0235 5–2D
"The menu hasn't changed in 15 years, nor have the staff!" – this "very Chelsea" favourite, just a couple of minutes from Sloane Square, still delights its devoted following with its "polished, old-school" charm, and "reliable" Italian fare. / SW1W 8DH; www.caraffini.co.uk; Mon-Fri 11.30 pm, Sat 11 pm; closed Sun.

Caravan **£46** 324
1 Granary Sq, N1 7101 7661 8–3C
11-13 Exmouth Mkt, EC1 7833 8115 9–1A
As "bustling brunch" hangouts go, it's hard to better these "fast and furious" operations – both the Exmouth Market original, and its "vast" and "vibey" offshoot by King's Cross – which serve an "imaginative" tapas-based menu, and coffee roasted in-house. / www.caravanonexmouth.co.uk; EC1 10.30 pm, Sun 4 pm; EC1 Sun D.

Carluccio's **£42** 112
Branches throughout London
"Pleasant" enough to look at, this faux-Italian chain also offers a "great range of breakfast items" and "makes a big fuss of kids" too – otherwise, the formula often seems "very stale" nowadays. / www.carluccios.com; most branches 11 pm, Sun 10.30 pm; no booking weekday L; SRA-3 stars.

Carob Tree NW5 **£33** 454
15 Highgate Rd 7267 9880 8–1B
"Always buzzing", this "terrific-value" Dartmouth Park Greek offers a menu on which "superb" fish is a particular highlight; great proprietor too – he "greets every diner like a long-lost cousin". / NW5 1QX; 10.30 pm, Sun 9 pm; closed Mon; no Amex.

The Carpenter's Arms W6 **£48** 334
91 Black Lion Ln 8741 8386 7–2B
In a tucked-away Hammersmith location, a cute neighbourhood pub with "consistently good" gastro fare; "lovely" garden too. / W6 9BG; www.carpentersarmssw6.co.uk; 10 pm, Sun 9 pm.

Casa Brindisa SW7 **£46** 222
7-9 Exhibition Rd 7590 0008 5–2C
A "reliable" tapas stop, handy for South Kensington tube, and with some nice al fresco tables; it's difficult, though, to disagree with the suggestion that it's "rather been left behind by a flurry of much better Spanish places that have subsequently opened". / SW7 2HE; www.casabrindisa.com; @TapasKitchens; 11 pm, Sun 10 pm.

Casa Malevo W2 **£58** 433
23 Connaught St 7402 1988 6–1D
"A little gem"; this Bayswater Argentinian serves up some "lovely" dishes (particularly for carnivores). / W2 2AY; www.casamalevo.com; @casamalevo; 10.30 pm; D only.

Casse-Croute SE1 **£37** 445
109 Bermondsey St 7407 2140 9–4D
"Just the sort of place you look for in Paris, and only rarely find" – this bijou Bermondsey yearling may only have a "limited" menu and "cramped" interior but it's "perhaps the best of the new-style old-style bistros!" / SE1 3XB; www.cassecroute.co.uk; @CasseCroute109.

Cattle Grid SW12 **£44** 323
1 Balham Station Rd 8673 9099 10–2C
Not much to say about this small outfit… but it does offer "perfectly acceptable burgers and chips, when you're out with the lads". / SW12 9SG; www.cattlegridrestaurant.com.

Cây Tre **£39** 333
42-43 Dean St, W1 7317 9118 4–2A
301 Old St, EC1 7729 8662 12–1B
"Lots of lovely fresh flavours" have won a wide following for this "buzzy" and "friendly" Vietnamese duo, in Soho and Shoreditch; at the latter, "arrive early or you may have to queue". / www.vietnamesekitchen.co.uk; 11 pm, Fri-Sat 11.30 pm, Sun 10.30 pm.

Cecconi's W1 **£75** 224
5a Burlington Gdns 7434 1500 3–3C
"For hedgies and beautiful people", this "sublimely well-heeled" and "buzzy" all-day Italian brasserie is a key Mayfair rendezvous (especially the "superb bar"); "breakfasts are the real deal", but otherwise "standards are average and prices steep" – "the atmosphere's the thing". / W1S 3EP; www.cecconis.co.uk; @SohoHouse; 11.30 pm, Sun 10.30 pm.

Cellar Gascon EC1 **£38** 333
59 West Smithfield Rd 7600 7561 9–2B
"Great snacks, such as mini-duck burgers, and good wines, all at reasonable prices" help make for

a superior light-bite experience, at this offshoot of Smithfield's famous Club Gascon, a few doors away. / EC1A 9DS; www.cellargascon.com; midnight; closed Sat & Sun; set weekday L £17 (FP), set always available £20 (FP).

Ceviche W1 **£46** 4 3 3
17 Frith St 7292 2040 4–2A
"Yummy ceviche as the name suggest" and other "tangy, tasty and well-executed" dishes – not to mention "excellent Pisco sours" – "help extend one's sense of what Peruvian food can be", at this "vibrant" and "distinctive" Soho rendezvous. / W1D 4RG; www.cevicheuk.com; @cevicheuk; 11.30 pm, Sun 10.15 pm; SRA-1 star.

Chabrot Bistrot d'Amis SW1 **£59** 3 4 3
9 Knightsbridge Grn 7225 2238 5–1D
"As French as they get, from the food to the decor" – a "splendid old-style bistro" (which in fact only opened a few years ago), just a short step from Harrods. / SW1X 7QL; www.chabrot.co.uk; 10.30 pm, Sun 9.30 pm; set always available £36 (FP).

Chakra W11 **£60** 2 1 1
157-159 Notting Hill Gate 7229 2115 6–2B
Some dishes are of "very good quality", so it's a shame this "haute cuisine" Kensington Indian isn't living up to its potential – it offers "small" portions at "high" prices, and service sometimes seems "very slow". / W11 3LF; www.chakralondon.com; @ChakraLondon; 11 pm, Sun 10.30 pm.

Chamberlain's EC3 **£70** 3 3 2
23-25 Leadenhall Mkt 7648 8690 9–2D
"A strong location" and some "very competent" (if "unadventurous") fish cooking underpin the attractions of this long-established fixture, atmospherically housed in Leadenhall Market; prices, though, can seem "forbidding". / EC3V 1LR; www.chamberlains.org; @chamberlainsldn; 9.15 pm; closed Sat & Sun.

Champor-Champor SE1 **£49** 3 2 3
62 Weston St 7403 4600 9–4C
"Surprisingly tasty" Thai/Malay dishes and "fabulous", if "bizarre", decor still draws fans to this hidden-away Borough spot; it's not nearly as commented-upon as once it was, however, and some former fans now find it "rather run-of-the-mill". / SE1 3QJ; www.champor-champor.com; @ChamporChampor; 10 pm; D only.

The Chancery EC4 **£53** 3 4 2
9 Cursitor St 7831 4000 9–2A
A rather "formal" business favourite, "discreetly located" near Chancery Lane; it "maintains its standards", with cooking that's often "first-class", and "helpful" service too. / EC4A 1LL; www.thechancery.co.uk; @chancerylondon; 10.30 pm; closed Sat L & Sun.

Chapters SE3 **£52** 2 3 2
43-45 Montpelier Vale 8333 2666 1–4D
This "dependable" Blackheath brasserie is, say fans, "a perfect neighbourhood spot", open all day and featuring a "good range of breakfasts"; sceptics, though, say "the food is nothing of note". / SE3 0TJ; www.chaptersrestaurants.com; @Chapters_ADD; 11 pm, Sun 9 pm; set weekday L £31 (FP), set dinner £35 (FP).

Charlotte's Bistro W4 **£51** 3 4 3
6 Turnham Green Ter 8742 3590 7–2A
"An amazing cocktail list in the tiny gin bar" adds to the appeal of this Chiswick spot as a "good, if slightly pricey, neighbourhood go-to"; it's "cramped" and "noisy", though, and the "brief but sensible menu" is no better than "reliable". / W4 1QP; www.charlottes.co.uk; @CharlottesW4; 10 pm, Fri & Sat 10.30 pm, Sun 9 pm; SRA-1 star.

Charlotte's Place W5 **£51** 3 4 3
16 St Matthew's Rd 8567 7541 1–3A
"Unexpectedly good for Ealing" – this "homely" bistro, on the Common, pleases all who comment on it with its "simple but flavoursome" food; service is notably "friendly and knowledgeable" too. / W5 3JT; www.charlottes.co.uk; @CharlottesW5; 10.30 pm, Fri & Sat 11 pm, Sun 9 pm; SRA-1 star.

Chelsea Bun Diner SW10 **£30** 3 2 3
9a Lamont Rd 7352 3635 5–3B
"Perfect, if cholesterol heavy" – a "workmen's caff, Chelsea-style", offering a range of "enormous" breakfasts which will "keep you going all day". / SW10 0HP; www.chelseabun.co.uk; 6 pm; L only; no Amex; no booking, Sat & Sun.

Chettinad W1 **£32** 3 4 3
16 Percy St 3556 1229 2–1C
"Good, authentic South Indian food" (mainly non-vegetarian) wins many plaudits for this "understated" café-style Fitzrovia two-year-old; "good-value lunchtime set menus". / W1T 1DT; www.chettinadrestaurant.com; @chettinadlondon; Mon-Sat 10.30 pm, Sun 9.30 pm; no Amex.

Cheyne Walk Brasserie SW3 £75 333

50 Cheyne Walk 7376 8787 5–3C

"Very Chelsea – limited and pricey, but satisfying in an unchallenging way"; this "intimate" Gallic brasserie in a nicely converted pub may be "unjustifiably expensive", but the cooking, largely from the central wood-grill, is "dependable". / SW3 5LR; www.cheynewalkbrasserie.com; 10.30 pm, Sun 9.30 pm; closed Mon L; set weekday L £43 (FP).

Chez Abir W14 NEW £33 432

34 Blythe Rd 7603 3241 7–1D

A new owner has taken over at this celebrated Lebanese café, behind Olympia (formerly called Chez Marcelle, but the lady has now retired); foodwise, even the few who feel "the magic is gone" say the cooking's still "perfectly good" and all agree "service is far better!" / W14 0HA.

CHEZ BRUCE SW17 £68 554

2 Bellevue Rd 8672 0114 10–2C

Bruce Poole's "quintessential neighbourhood restaurant", by Wandsworth Common, celebrates 10 years as the survey's No. 1 favourite; the secret? – "sublime" and "inspired" cuisine, "brilliant" wine, "welcoming but unobtrusive" staff… and a cheeseboard "to die for". / SW17 7EG; www.chezbruce.co.uk; @ChezBruce; 10 pm, Fri & Sat 10.30 pm, Sun 9 pm.

Chez Patrick W8 £47 354

7 Stratford Rd 7937 6388 5–2A

Host Patrick's "Gallic charm, japes and bonhomie" (and "expert" service) continue to delight, at this "deceptively slick" stalwart, which specialises in "fresh, beautifully cooked" fish; its quiet Kensington backwater location helps make for "a pleasurable escape from the hurly-burly". / W8 6RF; www.chez-patrick.co.uk; 10.30 pm; closed Sun D; set weekday L £26 (FP).

Chicken Shop £31 344

79 Highgate Rd, NW5 3310 2020 8–1B

141 Tooting High St, SW17 8767 5200 10–2B NEW

"Simple but amazing" and "great value too" – this "hip chicken" chain ("Nandos for grown-ups") "does exactly what it says on the tin"; the Kentish Town original, though, is much preferred to the "crowded" and "noisy" Tooting offshoot.

Chicken Shop & Dirty Burger E1 NEW £36

27 Mile End Rd 3310 2010 12–2D

Soho House married their two popular budget brands (see individual entries), at this Whitechapel newcomer in mid-2014; early-days reports give their blessing to the union. / E1 4TP; www.chickenshop.com; @chickenshop; closed weekday L.

Chilango £15 322

76 Chancery Ln, WC2 7430 1323 2–1D

27 Upper St, N1 7704 2123 8–3D

32 Brushfield St, E1 3246 0086 12–2B

64 London Wall, EC2 7628 7663 9–2C

142 Fleet St, EC4 7353 6761 9–2A

"Spot-on burritos every time" from "very fresh ingredients" inspires a consistent thumbs-up for this grab-and-go chain. / www.chilango.co.uk; @Chilango_uk; EC4, EC2, EC1 9 pm; N1 10 pm, Fri & Sat midnight; EC4, EC2, E1 closed Sat & Sun; no booking.

Chilli Cool WC1 £31 411

15 Leigh St 7383 3135 2–1D

"Scintillating" Sichuanese cooking ("I've never been served a dish with 30 whole red chillies sitting on it before!") is the draw to this "plain" Bloomsbury café – it certainly isn't the "poker-faced" and "abrupt" service. / WC1H 9EW; www.chillicool.com; 10.15 pm.

The Chiltern Firehouse W1 NEW £82 225

1 Chiltern St 7073 7676 2–1A

"So hard to get a table!" – poseurs and paparazzi abound at Nuno Mendes's hot Marylebone newcomer… but less starry-eyed reporters say the food is actually pretty "meh"; "superb fun," though, and the room itself is "amazing". / W1U 7PA; www.chilternfirehouse.com.

China Tang Dorchester Hotel W1 £72 223

53 Park Ln 7629 9988 3–3A

Fans of Sir David Tang's '30s-Shanghai Mayfair basement applaud the "wonderful" Art Deco ambience, and say the Peking duck in particular is "amazing"; critics, though, find the whole show monstrously "overrated". / W1K 1QA; www.chinatanglondon.co.uk; @ChinaTangLondon; 11.45 pm; max 14.

Chinese Cricket Club EC4 £55 421

19 New Bridge St 7438 8051 9–3A

Despite a setting which "feels like an airport departure lounge", this hotel dining room by Blackfriars Bridge wins plenty of plaudits for its "delightful" oriental fare – "best try the chef's tasting menu"! / EC4V 6DB; www.chinesecricketclub.com; @chineseclub; 10 pm; closed Sat & Sun L.

Chipotle **£17** 3 3 2
101-103 Baker St, W1 7935 9881 2–1A
181-185 Wardour St, W1 7494 4156 3–1D
114-116 Charing Cross Rd, WC2 7836 8491 4–1A
92-93 St Martin's Ln, WC2 7836 7838 4–4B
334 Upper St, N1 7354 3686 8–3D
"Quality meat and flavour-packed salsas" make these "stark" Mexican burrito-stops "a great option for a filling meal on the go"; but something's been lost in its trans-Atlantic translation – "in the US, I would go every time, but here they're not quite there". / www.chipotle.com; 10 pm - 11 pm.

Chisou **£51** 4 2 2
4 Princes St, W1 7629 3931 3–1C
31 Beauchamp Pl, SW3 3155 0005 5–2D
1-4 Barley Mow Pas, W4 8994 3636 7–2A
"Outstanding sushi" is the culinary standout at this "genuine" Japanese chain (where "a wide range of sakes" is also a feature), both at the "functional" Mayfair original and the "cute" Chiswick offshoot. / www.chisourestaurant.com; Mon-Sat 10.30 pm, Sun 9.30 pm.

Chiswell Street Dining Rooms EC1 **£62** 2 2 2
56 Chiswell St 7614 0177 12–2A
"Comfortable, smart and wood-panelled", this gastropub-style operation, near the Barbican, is neatly tailored to its local City business market; given the prices, though, standards aren't really much more than "tolerable" all-round. / EC1Y 4SA; www.chiswellstreetdining.com; @chiswelldining; 11 pm; closed Sat & Sun; set always available £36 (FP).

Chor Bizarre W1 **£63** 4 4 3
16 Albemarle St 7629 9802 3–3C
A madly antique-festooned Indian that's about as 'alternative' as Mayfair gets; the "honest" cooking is of "surprising quality" too – "not cheap, but not crazy either". / W1S 4HW; www.chorbizarre.com; @ChorBizarreUK; 11.30 pm, Sun 10.30 pm; set weekday L £40 (FP).

Chotto Matte W1 **£55** 4 2 4
11-13 Frith St 7042 7171 4–2A
"Is it a nightclub or a restaurant?" – either way, this "achingly trendy and noisy" newcomer, from the ping pong people, is a "welcome new entrant" to the Soho market, offering "fresh" and "zingy" fusion fare that's "more Japanese than Peruvian". / W1D 4RB; www.chotto-matte.com; @ChottoMatteSoho; Mon-Sat 1 am, Sun 11 pm.

Christopher's WC2 **£70** 3 2 3
18 Wellington St 7240 4222 4–3D
Predating London's current US craze, this "upmarket" surf 'n' turf venue occupies an "impressive" Covent Garden townhouse (complete with "buzzy" ground-floor bar); under new owners, it's "just like it was many years ago" – that's to say "top-quality" but "way overpriced", and with "patchy" service. / WC2E 7DD; www.christophersgrill.com; @christopherswc2; 11.30 pm, Sun 10.30 pm; booking: max 12; set weekday L & pre-theatre £39 (FP).

Churchill Arms W8 **£35** 3 3 5
119 Kensington Church St 7792 1246 6–2B
"Fast, furious and full of fun!"; you don't just get "delicious" Thai scoff at "silly-cheap" prices at this "quirky" pub, off Notting Hill Gate, but also a "fantastic" setting in a "cute and interesting" flower-filled conservatory. / W8 7LN; www.churchillarmskensington.co.uk; @ChurchilArmsW8; 10 pm, Sun 9.30 pm.

Chutney SW18 **£32** 4 4 2
11 Alma Rd 8870 4588 10–2B
"Traditional, yet very well done" – a well-established Wandsworth curry house, consistently rated a cut above the norm. / SW18 1AA; www.chutneyrestaurant.co.uk; 11.30 pm; D only.

Chutney Mary SW10 **£56** 4 5 4
535 King's Rd 7351 3113 5–4B
"If you're looking for an upmarket Indian meal", it's "hard to improve on" this "glamorous and romantic" stalwart on the border of Chelsea, with its "beautiful and subtle" dishes, and lovely and "very professional" service; look out for a change of venue in 2015. / SW10 0SZ; www.realindianfood.com; @RealindianFood; 11.45 pm, Sun 10.45 pm; closed weekday L; booking: max 8.

Chutneys NW1 **£31** 2 2 2
124 Drummond St 7388 0604 8–4C
"A stalwart of the 'Little India' South Asian culinary scene" – a "pleasant enough" café, known for its "astonishingly good-value lunchtime and Sunday evening buffet". / NW1 2PA; www.chutneyseuston.co.uk; 11 pm; no Amex; need 5+ to book.

Ciao Bella WC1 **£42** 2 4 3
86-90 Lamb's Conduit St 7242 4119 2–1D
"There are some real characters in the waiting team" of this "crazy, noisy and packed" '70s Italian, in Bloomsbury – a "good-humoured" place, offering cooking that's affordable but "fairly standard". / WC1N 3LZ; www.ciaobellarestaurant.co.uk; 11.30 pm, Sun 10.30 pm.

Cibo W14 **£51** 4 5 3
3 Russell Gdns 7371 6271 7–1D
"An old friend" on the Kensington/Olympia border; this "quiet, spacious and elegant" venue is often

Edwins
Ham Yard Restaurant
Hubbard & Bell
Pavillion

overlooked nowadays, but its "efficient and friendly" staff dish up "true Italian food" – "simply executed", but of "good quality". / W14 8EZ; www.ciborestaurant.net; 10.30 pm; closed Sat L & Sun D.

Cigala WC1 **£49** 332
54 Lamb's Conduit St 7405 1717 2–1D
In a "not terribly well-served part of town", Bloomsbury, this "busy, bustling and closely packed" Spanish restaurant serves "a really good selection of tapas"; the paella's not bad either. / WC1N 3LW; www.cigala.co.uk; 10.45 pm, Sun 9.45 pm.

Le Cigalon WC2 **£47** 333
115 Chancery Ln 7242 8373 2–2D
"An oasis of calm", near the Law Courts – this "beautiful and light" chamber (once auctioneers' premises) provides a "spacious" setting for this "slightly quirky" Provençal operation; "it's not as good as sibling, Club Gascon", though, and not especially atmospheric at night. / WC2A 1PP; www.cigalon.co.uk; @CIGALON_LONDON; 10 pm; closed Sat & Sun.

THE CINNAMON CLUB SW1 **£72** 334
Old Westminster Library, Great Smith St 7222 2555 2–4C
Westminster's "majestic" former library, near the Abbey, may make a "curious" setting for one of London's foremost Indians, but most reporters still acclaim its "thrilling take on contemporary subcontinental cuisine"; standards this year, though, were bit more up-and-down than usual. / SW1P 3BU; www.cinnamonclub.com; @CinnamonClub; 10.30 pm; closed Sun; no trainers; set weekday L & dinner £47 (FP); SRA-2 stars.

Cinnamon Kitchen EC2 **£55** 443
9 Devonshire Sq 7626 5000 9–2D
"Smart food with a kick" – from a "different" Indian-fusion menu – makes the Cinnamon Club's "elegant" City cousin a popular standby; some tables occupy an impressive atrium. / EC2M 4YL; www.cinnamon-kitchen.com; @cinnamonkitchen; 11 pm; closed Sat L & Sun; SRA-2 stars.

Cinnamon Soho W1 **£44** 432
5 Kingly St 7437 1664 3–2D
"Remarkable quality in a convenient location", just off Regent Street – the promise of this "cheaper member of the famous Cinnamon Club family", where the "fresh" dishes are "so light and tasty". / W1B 5PE; www.cinnamon-kitchen.com/soho-home; @cinnamonsoho; 11 pm, Sun 4.30 pm; closed Sun D.

City Barge W4 NEW **£43** 445
27 Strand-on-the-Green 8994 2148 1–3A
A "very good refurbishment" has at last breathed new life into this fine old pub, which has a "great location", by the river at Strand-on-the-Green; "outstanding fish" is – as you'd hope from an ex-Bentley's and ex-Scott's chef – a highlight. / W4 3PH; www.citybargechiswick.com; @citybargew4; 11 pm.

City Càphê EC2 **£14** 432
17 Ironmonger St no tel 9–2C
"The daily queue snaking down the street" attests to the charms of this Vietnamese canteen/take-away, near Bank – arrive before noon for "phenomenally good" pho, and "báhn mi that always hit the spot". / EC2V 8EY; www.citycaphe.com; 3 pm; L only, closed Sat & Sun.

City Miyama EC4 **£53** 331
17 Godliman St 7489 1937 9–3B
This City stalwart, in a "handy" location not far from St Paul's, draws the lunchtime Japanese crowd with its well-conceived cuisine, with sushi a highlight; well, it can't be the decor. / EC4B 5BD; www.miyama-restaurant.co.uk; 9.30 pm; closed Sat & Sun; set weekday L £34 (FP).

City Social EC2 NEW **£79** 454
Tower 42 25 Old Broad St 7877 7703 9–2C
"Views to die for", "fabulous" cooking and "incredibly attentive" service – Jason Atherton has served up "another hit" with this City newcomer, "breathing new life" into the 24th-floor premises which were formerly Rhodes 24 (RIP). / EC2N 1HQ; www.citysociallondon.com.

Clarke's W8 **£69** 332
124 Kensington Church St 7221 9225 6–2B
Sally Clarke's "simple yet adventurous" cuisine has long had many fans, but but it's impossible to avoid the feeling that her Kensington restaurant is "not as good as it used to be" – too many meals "lack inspiration and flair", and the recently refurbished interior can be "very noisy". / W8 4BH; www.sallyclarke.com; 10 pm; closed Sun; booking: max 14.

Claude's Kitchen Amuse Bouche SW6 **£48** 444
51 Parsons Green Ln 7371 8517 10–1B
"A gorgeous little spot, opposite Parson's Green tube", which is making ripples after a year in business, thanks to its "easygoing" style and "inventive" cuisine – "have a glass of bubbly in the downstairs bar, before you head up to the cosy candlelit dining room". / SW6 4JA; www.claudeskitchen.co.uk; @AmuseBoucheLDN; 10 pm; closed weekday L.

The Clink HMP Brixton SW2 NEW **£30** 2 3 5

Jebb Ave 7147 6724 10–2D

"Good luck to the whole project!"; you too can be a – temporary – guest of Her Majesty at Brixton nick, at this intriguing new rehabilitation project; "the food's nothing special, but the experience is quite something". / SW2 5XF; www.theclinkrestaurant.com; @theclinkcharity; 2 pm; L only; SRA-3 stars.

The Clissold Arms N2 £49 3 4 4

Fortis Grn 8444 4224 1–1C

"Good honest gastropub cooking" and "a great al fresco eating area" help win praise for this popular Muswell Hill boozer (famed for its links to The Kinks). / N2 9HR; www.clissoldarms.co.uk; @ClissoldArms; 10 pm, Sat 10.30 pm, Sun 9 pm.

CLOS MAGGIORE WC2 **£62** 4 5 5

33 King St 7379 9696 4–3C

"I don't know how a restaurant could be more romantic!"; the survey's No. 1 trysting spot is an unlikely "oasis" in the tourist hell that is Covent Garden; but it's not just the "twinkly conservatory" that sets pheromones pumping – there's a "phenomenal" wine list to back up "undoubtedly excellent" French cuisine. / WC2E 8JD; www.closmaggiore.com; @ClosMaggioreWC2; 11 pm, Sun 10 pm; max 7; set always available £43 (FP).

The Clove Club EC1 **£70** 4 4 4

Shoreditch Town Hall, 380 Old St 7729 6496 12–1B

"All the hype is worth it!", say fans of this "foodie hipster heaven" – a "highly professional" pop-up-turned-permanent, in Shoreditch's "beautiful" ("if noisy") old town hall; the "eclectic" menu "may look bizarre, but it works splendidly", though portions are rather "small". / EC1V 9LT; www.thecloveclub.com; @thecloveclub; 9.30 pm; closed Mon L & Sun; set weekday L £53 (FP).

Club Gascon EC1 **£74** 4 3 3

57 West Smithfield 7600 6144 9–2B

"Superbly constructed" SW French regional tapas with "sophistication and imagination" – plus wines "paired with panache" – are the long-running hallmarks of this City-fringe business favourite; prices are on the "astronomical" side, though, and service can sometimes be "very Gallic". / EC1A 9DS; www.clubgascon.com; @club_gascon; 10 pm, Fri & Sat 10.30 pm; closed Sat L & Sun; set weekday L £55 (FP).

Clutch E2 NEW **£30** 4 4 4

4 Ravenscroft St 7729 4402 12–1C

"Calling all fried chicken fans"; this "quirky" but "friendly" Hoxton newcomer serves a "simple but well-executed menu", and "good cocktails" too. / E2 7QG; www.clutchchicken.com.

Coco Di Mama EC4 **£10** 4 3 2

90 Fleet St 7583 9277 9–2A

"Superb" pasta "doused in tasty homemade sauce" plus "fantastic" coffee – this small City chain wins nothing but praise. / EC4Y 1DH; cocodimama.co.uk; 5 pm.

Colbert SW1 **£60** 1 2 3

51 Sloane Sq 7730 2804 5–2D

"Do they really run The Wolseley too?" – with its "surprisingly poor" food and too often "charmless" service, Corbin & King's year-old successor to Sloane Square's long-running Oriel brasserie is still "terribly disappointing"; come on chaps! / SW1W 8AX; www.colbertchelsea.com; @ColbertChelsea; Sun 10.30 pm, Mon-Thu 11 pm, Fri & Sat 11.30 pm; max 6; SRA-3 stars.

La Collina NW1 **£54** 4 3 2

17 Princess Rd 7483 0192 8–3B

"Unusual, high-quality Piedmontese cooking" adds to the "authentic" charm of this gourmet local, hidden away in Primrose Hill; "the small dining room at street level is austere, but the garden is a joy in summer". / NW1 8JR; www.lacollinarestaurant.co.uk; @LacollinaR; 10.15 pm, Sun 9.45 pm, Mon 9.30 pm; closed Mon L.

Le Colombier SW3 **£59** 3 4 4

145 Dovehouse St 7351 1155 5–2C

An extremely popular "classic French local", extolled for its "dependable" cooking, "attentive" service and "great backstreet location" (with charming terrace); prices do "reflect the 'old Chelsea' clientele" (though, paradoxically, top wines "offer real value"). / SW3 6LB; www.le-colombier-restaurant.co.uk; 10.30 pm, Sun 10 pm.

Colony Grill Room Beaumont Hotel W1 NEW

Brown Hart Gdns 7499 1001 3–2A

As this guide goes to print, London's most respected restaurateurs, Corbin & King of Wolseley fame, open their first hotel (and dining room) in a forgotten corner of Mayfair. / W1K 6TF; www.thebeaumont.com.

Como Lario SW1 **£48** 2 2 3

18-22 Holbein Pl 7730 2954 5–2D

"A proper neighbourhood Italian", just five minutes from Sloane Square; it's an "old favourite" for some reporters, even if the food is only "OK". / SW1W 8NL; www.comolario.co.uk; 11.30 pm, Sun 10 pm.

Compagnie des Vins Surnaturels WC2 NEW **£52** 4 2 2
8-10 Neals Yd 7344 7737 4–2C
"Interesting" wines and "delicious" small plates have helped this "cute" Covent Garden newcomer make waves; it's "hardly cheap", though, and early-days gripes include "tiny" tables and incidents of "poor" service. / WC2H 9DP; www.cvssevendials.com.

Comptoir Gascon EC1 **£44** 3 3 4
63 Charterhouse St 7608 0851 9–1A
"A good, cheap alternative to Club Gascon" – the "attractive" spin-off from the famous Smithfield tapas bar, nearby, "does a nice line in duck and other meaty treats", plus "excellent-value" wine. / EC1M 6HJ; www.comptoirgascon.com; @ComptoirGascon; 10 pm, Thu & Fri 10.30 pm; closed Mon & Sun.

Comptoir Libanais **£28** 2 2 2
59 Broadwick St, W1 7434 4335 3–2C
65 Wigmore St, W1 7935 1110 3–1A
1-5 Exhibition Rd, SW7 7225 5006 5–2C
Westfield, The Balcony, W12 8811 2222 7–1C
Westfield Stratford City, 2 Stratford Pl, E20 8555 6999 1–1D
"Reasonably priced mezze" and "very good juices" are among the attractions of this colourful and "friendly" Lebanese chain; critics, though, can find the food rather "variable". / www.lecomptoir.co.uk; W12 9 pm, Thu & Fri 10 pm, Sun 6 pm; W1 9.30 pm; W12 closed Sun D; no bookings.

Il Convivio SW1 **£58** 4 4 3
143 Ebury St 7730 4099 2–4A
"After all these years, Il Convivio still delights"; this "upmarket" Belgravia "gem" offers "first-rate" Italian cuisine in airy surroundings supporters find positively "beautiful" – it "deserves to be better known". / SW1W 9QN; www.etruscarerestaurants.com; 10.45 pm; closed Sun.

Coopers Restaurant & Bar WC2 **£50** 3 3 3
49a Lincolns Inn Fields 7831 6211 2–2D
Tucked away in Lincoln's Inn Fields (and with quite a grand dining room upstairs), a top haunt of local barristers and LSE academics – lunchtimes "can be noisy", but, by all accounts, "the food is worth it". / WC2A 3PF; www.coopers-restaurant.com; @coopers_bistro; 11 pm; closed Sat & Sun.

Copita W1 **£44** 3 2 4
27 D'Arblay St 7287 7797 3–1D
"Cramped, noisy and low-lit", this Soho spot is, say fans, a top example of "quintessential contemporary dining", whose "slightly left-field" tapas are "up there with Barrafina"; sceptics, however, feel "some dishes are more successful than others". / W1F 8EP; www.copita.co.uk; 10.30 pm; closed Sun.

Le Coq N1 **£44** 3 4 3
292-294 St Paul's Rd 7359 5055 8–2D
"Gorgeous chicken and roast potatoes to die for" – "all served with a smile" – dazzle fans of this year-old rôtisserie operation, near Highbury & Islington tube; refuseniks, though, find "the chicken too ordinary to be the star of the show!" / N1 2LH; www.le-coq.co.uk; @LeCOQrestaurant; 10.15 pm.

Coq d'Argent EC2 **£74** 2 2 3
1 Poultry 7395 5000 9–2C
An "impressive" favourite for "power-dining" – this popular City vantage-point owes its fame to its rooftop gardens and "wonderful views"; otherwise, it's a "sterile" sort of operation, and "massively overpriced" for what it is. / EC2R 8EJ; www.coqdargent.co.uk; 9.45 pm; closed Sun D; set always available & Sun L £49 (FP); SRA-2 stars.

Cork & Bottle WC2 **£48** 2 3 4
44-46 Cranbourn St 7734 7807 4–3B
"Thankfully Leicester Square is not totally lost to chain restaurants", and this "quirky" '70s basement "feels like a step back in time" (even after recent refurb); the food's not the main event, but "you're spoilt for choice for wines". / WC2H 7AN; www.thecorkandbottle.co.uk; @corkbottle1971; 11.30 pm, Sun 10.30 pm; no booking after 6.30 pm.

Cornish Tiger SW11 NEW **£48** 4 4 3
1 Battersea Rise 7223 7719 10–1C
On a Battersea strip where restaurants rarely have many culinary aspirations, this summer-2014 newcomer boast a chef who trained at the well-known Chapter One (Bromley) – early reports suggest it's a "great local". / SW11 1GH; www.cornishtiger.com; @cornishtiger; 9.45 pm; closed Mon; set dinner £32 (FP).

Corrigan's Mayfair W1 **£86** 2 2 2
28 Upper Grosvenor St 7499 9943 3–3A
For business dining with "gravitas", fans tip this "dark and staid" Mayfair dining room, and hail its "superbly presented classic dishes"; the more general view, though, is that the food is "nothing special", and "madly overpriced" too. / W1K 7EH; www.corrigansmayfair.com; 10.45 pm, Sun 9.30 pm; closed Sat L; booking: max 10.

Côte **£44** 2 2 2
Branches throughout London
How sad; though it's still a "default" choice for its army of fans, this brasserie chain is getting ever

more "formulaic" under its new (private equity) ownership; critics decry its "joyless" cuisine as "French-by-numbers" – "actually worse than Café Rouge!" / www.cote-restaurants.co.uk; 11 pm.

The Cow W2 **£56** 344
89 Westbourne Park Rd 7221 0021 6–1B
"Fresh-as-you-like seafood, among the west London glitterati" – Tom Conran's cramped but "friendly" Oirish boozer, on the Bayswater/Notting Hill border, "is a great pub in its own right", but its Guinness and oysters "make it a pearl!". / W2 5QH; www.thecowlondon.co.uk; 10.30 pm, Sun 10 pm; no Amex.

Coya W1 **£76** 423
118 Piccadilly 7042 7118 3–4B
"Ceviches raised to perfection" and other "surprising" flavours have instantly propelled this "vibrant" Mayfair Peruvian into the big league; service can sometimes be a touch "chaotic", though, and critics do fear the place has become "a bit too trendy for its own good". / W1J 7NW; www.coyarestaurant.com; @coyarestaurant; Sun-Wed 10.30 pm, Thu-Sat 11 pm; max party 12; set weekday L £50 (FP).

Crazy Bear W1 **£64** 224
26-28 Whitfield St 7631 0088 2–1C
"Seductive" decor makes for "a fun night out" at this "funky" Fitzrovia bar-restaurant; unfortunately, though, "'crazy' describes the prices too", and the pan-Asian cooking is "not what it was". / W1T 2RG; www.crazybeargroup.co.uk; @CrazyBearGroup; 10.30 pm; closed Mon L & Sun; no shorts.

Criterion W1 **£69** 225
224 Piccadilly 7930 0488 3–3D
"Possibly the most beautiful restaurant in London", this extraordinary neo-Byzantine room, right on Piccadilly Circus, is up there with The Ritz for beauty and romance – what a shame, then, about the "mediocre'" food and sometimes "stilted" service. / W1J 9HP; www.criterionrestaurant.com; 11.15 pm, Sun 10.30 pm.

The Crooked Well SE5 **£49** 344
16 Grove Ln 7252 7798 1–3C
In a "classy Camberwell enclave", this "amiable" gastropub is a real crowd-pleaser, thanks to its "accomplished" British grub (and some "fabulous" cocktails too). / SE5 8SY; www.thecrookedwell.com; @crookedwell; 10.30 pm; closed Mon L; no Amex.

Crussh **£17** 442
Branches throughout London
"Healthy food on the go" is the promise of this "friendly" small group, whose smoothies and juices are "a step up"; it also offers good salads and "filling and very tasty stews". / www.crussh.com; 4.30 pm-8 pm; many branches closed all or part of weekend; no credit cards in many branches.

Cumberland Arms W14 **£43** 443
29 North End Rd 7371 6806 7–2D
"Something of an oasis in the less than salubrious surroundings of the North End Road" – this handy gastropub, near Olympia, offers "a fabulous Mediterranean menu"; great music too. / W14 8SZ; www.thecumberlandarmspub.co.uk; @thecumberland; 10 pm, Sun 9.30 pm.

Cut 45 Park Lane W1 **£110** 222
45 Park Ln 7493 4545 3–4A
"The steaks are great", at US über-chef Wolfgang Puck's "corridor-like" Mayfair dining room; prices (especially wine) are "obscene", though, service can be "clueless", and the setting is "terrible". / W1K 1PN; www.45parklane.com; @the_cut_bar; 10.30 pm; set dinner £79 (FP).

Cyprus Mangal SW1 **£32** 431
45 Warwick Way 7828 5940 2–4B
An unremarkable-looking Pimlico fixture, often proclaimed for "the best kebab in town"; "there's always a line of taxis parked outside – what better recommendation?" / SW1V 1QS; cyprusmangal.co.uk/menu; 10.45 pm, Fri & Sat 11.45 pm.

Da Mario SW7 **£42** 233
15 Gloucester Rd 7584 9078 5–1B
An "always-welcoming" local "institution", near the Royal Albert Hall, offering a "down-to-earth" menu majoring in pizza; they "dote on kids". / SW7 4PP; www.damario.co.uk; 11.30 pm.

Da Mario WC2 **£46** 223
63 Endell St 7240 3632 4–1C
"A welcome change from all the Covent Garden chains" – an "idiosyncratic" spot, where the dishes from the "regularly changing blackboard menu" generally please. / WC2H 9AJ; www.da-mario.co.uk; 11.15 pm; closed Sun.

Dabbous W1 **£68** 432
39 Whitfield St 7323 1544 2–1C
Ollie Dabbous is struggling to preserve the wow factor at his concrete-walled Fitzrovia flagship – most reports still go nuts for his "game-changing" cuisine, but there was also quite a large minority this year which just "couldn't see what all the fuss is about". / W1T 2SF; www.dabbous.co.uk; @dabbous; 9.30 pm (bar open until 11.30 pm); closed Mon & Sun; set weekday L £46 (FP).

Daddy Donkey EC1 **£16** 432
100 Leather Ln 448448 9–2A
"A burrito big enough to serve a small family" is the pay-off for visitors to this Clerkenwell successor to a legendary van; "join the queue – it's worth the wait". / EC1N 7TE; www.daddydonkey.co.uk; @daddydonkey; Mon-Fri 4 pm; L only, closed Sat & Sun.

The Dairy SW4 **£40** 544
15 The Pavement 7622 4165 10–2D
"More interesting, more charming and less pretentious than many a fancy West End eatery" – this "daring" Clapham yearling may be a bit "cramped", but its "experimental" and "artistic" tapas-style cuisine really "sparkles". / SW4 0HY; www.the-dairy.co.uk; 9.45 pm; closed Mon, Tue L & Sun D.

Dalchini SW19 **£37** 342
147 Arthur Rd 8947 5966 10–2B
"Pleasing everyone with its mix of Indian and Chinese-influenced dishes" – this 'Hakka' restaurant, opposite Wimbledon Park tube, is rated "outstanding" by its fans; even the most sceptical report says it's "a decent local, and OK value overall". / SW19 8AB; www.dalchini.co.uk; 10.30 pm, Fri & Sat 11 pm, Sun 10 pm; no Amex.

Daphne's SW3 **£68**
112 Draycott Ave 7589 4257 5–2C
You're dating yourself if you remember the glory days of this Chelsea stalwart – once the favourite of Diana, Princess of Wales; after a fire, it reopened with a tightly packed new look in mid-2014, too late for survey feedback on the new incarnation. / SW3 3AE; www.daphnes-restaurant.co.uk; @CapriceHoldings; 11 pm, Sun 10 pm; set weekday L & pre-theatre £45 (FP).

Daquise SW7 **£49** 232
20 Thurloe St 7589 6117 5–2C
There's a "distinct Polish character" to this "shabby-chic" fixture (est 1947), by South Kensington tube, where the cooking mixes the "very traditional" (dumplings and so on) with more modern fare. / SW7 2LT; www.daquise.co.uk; @GesslerDaquise; 11 pm; no Amex.

The Dartmouth Arms SE23 **£38** 223
7 Dartmouth Rd 8488 3117 1–4D
"Lovely design" adds to the charms of this Forest Hill gastroboozer, acclaimed by fans for its "consistent posh pub grub". / SE23 3HN; www.thedartmoutharms.com; 10 pm, Sun 9 pm; no Amex.

The Dartmouth Castle W6 **£43** 343
26 Glenthorne Rd 8748 3614 7–2C
On the fringe of the "concrete jungle that Hammersmith has become", this "tucked away" Victorian pub serves "reliable gastropub fare" and "well-kept real ales". / W6 0LS; www.thedartmouthcastle.co.uk; @DartmouthCastle; 10 pm, Sun 9.30 pm; closed Sat L.

Daylesford Organic **£43** 224
44b Pimlico Rd, SW1 7881 8060 5–2D
Selfridges & Co, 400 Oxford St, W1 0800 123 400 3–1A
208-212 Westbourne Grove, W11 7313 8050 6–1B
Rather self-consciously stylish Pimlico and Notting Hill cafés to park your 4x4 outside; they're certainly "not cheap", but as "buzzy" brunch venues in particular, they have their fans. / www.daylesfordorganic.com; SW1 & W11 7 pm, Sun 4 pm; W1 9 pm, Sun 6.15 pm; W11 no booking L.

Dean Street Townhouse W1 **£56** 334
69-71 Dean St 7434 1775 4–2A
"Buzzy but relaxed, smart yet casual" – with its slick and clubby interior, this happening Soho House-group Soho brasserie totally looks the part; the "simple" menu is "uninspiring" or "well executed", to taste. / W1D 3SE; www.deanstreettownhouse.com; @deanstreettownhouse; 11.30 pm, Fri & Sat midnight, Sun 10.30 pm.

Defune W1 **£67** 321
34 George St 7935 8311 3–1A
An old-school, Marylebone sushi restaurant, where standards are still "excellent"; the pricing, though, "has gone completely bonkers", and the "decor doesn't make up for it either". / W1U 7DP; www.defune.com; 10.45 pm, Sun 10.30 pm.

Dehesa W1 **£49** 434
25 Ganton St 7494 4170 3–2C
The "enticing" tapas menu is "super-fresh and beautifully presented", at this Salt Yard spin-off, just off Carnaby Street (though the occasional reporter does feel portions are "getting smaller"); despite its "shoe-horned" conditions, it "manages to be both buzzy and intimate". / W1F 9BP; www.dehesa.co.uk; @SaltYardGroup; 10.45 pm; SRA-2 stars.

THE DELAUNAY WC2 **£57** 345
55 Aldwych 7499 8558 2–2D
"Wolesley-lite!"; Corbin & King's "classic, European grand café", on the edge of Covent Garden, is "more intimate" than its sibling, but otherwise

a chip off the old block – the "classy", "feel-good" ambience, and "reliable" (if "slightly ersatz") Austrian cuisine make it "a wow for business", especially at breakfast. / WC2B 4BB; www.thedelaunay.com; @TheDelaunayRest; midnight, Sun 11 pm; SRA-3 stars.

Delfino W1 **£51** 322
121A Mount St 7499 1256 3–3B
"Superb pizza" – with "lovely thin bases expertly cooked in a wood-burning oven" – is the draw to this "crowded" Mayfair spot, by the Connaught. / W1K 3NW; www.finos.co.uk; 10.45 pm; closed Sun.

Delhi Grill N1 **£34** 433
21 Chapel Mkt 7278 8100 8–3D
"Authentic homemade Indian food, like visiting your best auntie's" – reason to seek out this "innovative" curry shop, which occupies a "busy café setting", handy for Angel tube. / N1 9EZ; www.delhigrill.com; 10.30 pm; no credit cards.

La Delizia Limbara SW3 **£40** 443
63-65 Chelsea Manor St 7376 4111 5–3C
"A very simple, but in its own way rather perfect tiny Italian", in a quiet backstreet off the King's Road; the setting is "cramped" and minimalist, but it serves "lovely pizza, and a short list of pasta". / SW3 5RZ; www.ladelizia.org.uk; @ladelizia; 11 pm, Sun 10.30 pm; no Amex.

Department of Coffee EC1 **£15** 334
14-16 Leather Ln 7419 6906 9–2A
"How a coffee place should be" – "you may not be able to move for Macbooks and carefully cultivated goatees", but there's no denying that the coffee at this City spot is "fresh and strong". / EC1N 7SU; www.departmentofcoffee.co.uk; 6 pm, Sat & Sun 4 pm; L only.

The Depot SW14 **£42** 235
Tideway Yd, Mortlake High St 8878 9462 10–1A
"Lovely views of the Thames", especially from the new riverside seating area ("definitely a success"), are the main attraction at this "very popular" Barnes haunt; the food may not be the main point, but fans insist it's "getting better". / SW14 8SN; www.depotbrasserie.co.uk; @TheDepotBarnes; 10 pm, Sun 9.30 pm.

Les Deux Salons WC2 **£52** 122
40-42 William IV St 7420 2050 4–4C
Thanks not least to its "top location" (behind the Coliseum), Will Smith & Anthony Demetre's large faux-Parisian brasserie makes a great pre-theatre standby; it's "gone downhill since it opened", though, and too often seems plain "inept" nowadays. / WC2N 4DD; www.lesdeuxsalons.co.uk; @lesdeuxsalons; 10.45 pm, Sun 5.45 pm; closed Sun D.

Le Deuxième WC2 **£57** 221
65a Long Acre 7379 0033 4–2D
"A good place for a quick bite before curtain-up"; by the Royal Opera House, a restaurant that's "always reliable"... even if the menu "could use changing", and the decor "could do with livening up". / WC2E 9JH; www.ledeuxieme.com; @Le_Deuxieme; Mon-Thu 11 pm, Fri & Sat 11.30 pm, Sun 10 pm; set always available £30 (FP).

DF Mexico The Old Truman Brewery E1 NEW **£31** 334
Ely's Yd, 15 Hanbury St 3617 6639 12–2C
In Brick Lane's Old Truman Brewery, a casual new diner from the founders of Wahaca; the food has its moments, but the whole experience can be somewhat uneven. / E1 6QR; Rated on Editors' visit; www.dfmexico.co.uk.

dim T **£35** 223
56-62 Wilton Rd, SW1 7834 0507 2–4B
32 Charlotte St, W1 7637 1122 2–1C
1 Hampstead Ln, N6 8340 8800 8–1B
3 Heath St, NW3 7435 0024 8–2A
Tooley St, SE1 7403 7000 9–4D
For a "cheap 'n' cheerful" snack, fans recommend these "buzzy" canteens, and their "reliable", if rather "predictable", pan-Asian fare. / www.dimt.co.uk; @dim_t; most branches 11 pm, Sun 10.30 pm.

Diner **£34** 133
18 Ganton St, W1 7287 8962 3–2C
190 Shaftesbury Ave, WC2 3551 5225 4–1C
105 Gloucester Rd, SW7 7244 7666 5–2B
2 Jamestown Rd, NW1 7485 5223 8–3B
128 Curtain Rd, EC2 7729 4452 12–1B
These buzzy hangouts "pose as American diners", but "actually they are just bars with bad food", say critics; even fans may concede that it's "the atmosphere you go for". / www.goodlifediner.com; most branches 11 or 11.30 pm; booking: max 10.

Dinings W1 **£57** 541
22 Harcourt St 7723 0666 8–4A
"Only Tokyo offers fresher, better Japanese!" – Tomonari Chiba (ex-Nobu) crafts "mind-blowingly good" sushi at his "quirky" Marylebone den; no prizes for interior design though, and "don't look

at the prices whatever you do". / W1H 4HH; www.dinings.co.uk; @diningslondon; 10.30 pm; closed Sun.

DINNER MANDARIN ORIENTAL SW1 **£100** 333
66 Knightsbridge 7201 3833 5–1D
"The definition of occasion dining", say fans of Heston's Knightsbridge chamber, and its "extremely interesting" Olde English dishes; critics, though, complain of "dull" food and "silly" prices – the number of reporters who feel "the weird 15th-century presentation idea is a con" is on the rise. / SW1X 7LA; www.dinnerbyheston.com; 10.30 pm; set weekday L £68 (FP).

Dip & Flip SW11 NEW **£25** 432
87 Battersea Rise no tel 10–2C
"The dirtiest burger in London" is hailed by fans of this new dude-foodish Battersea café, where 'poutine' (cheesy Canadian fries) on the menu just adds to the "supreme nastiness"; "good value" too. / SW11 1HW; www.dipandflip.co.uk; @DipFlippo; Mon-Sat 10 pm, Sun 9 pm; no booking.

Dirty Bones W8 NEW **£39**
20 Kensington Church St 7920 6434 6–2B
This Kensington newcomer offers posh hot dogs by day, and by night a carnivorous menu offering many "simple big flavours", plus "friendly and relaxed" service and "good music" too; too few reports yet for a rating, however. / W8 4EP; www.dirty-bones.com; @DirtyBonesLDN; D only, closed Mon & Sun.

Dirty Burger **£14** 444
78 Highgate Rd, NW5 3310 2010 8–2B
Arch 54, 6 South Lambeth Rd, SW8 7074 1444 2–4D
"Dirty brilliance" – the award for "best burger-eating in a shack" goes to these Kentish Town and Vauxhall phenomena, whose "gorgeous, drippy burgers" and "fantastic crinkle-cut chips" are the stuff of urban legend. / www.eatdirtyburger.com; NW5, Mon-Thu midnight, Fri & Sat 1 am, Sun 11 pm – SW8 Mon-Thu 11 pm, Fri & Sat 2 am, Sun 8 pm.

Dishoom **£41** 434
12 Upper St Martins Ln, WC2 7420 9320 4–3B
Stable St, Granary Sq, N1 7420 9321 8–3C NEW
7 Boundary St, E2 7420 9324 12–1B
"A real buzz" distinguishes these "cool" and "different" – and very popular – Mumbai-style Parsi cafés, in Covent Garden and Shoreditch; the food is surprisingly "genuine", and "delicately spiced" too. / www.dishoom.com; @Dishoom; 11 pm, Sun 10 pm.

Diwana Bhel-Poori House NW1 **£31** 321
121-123 Drummond St 7387 5556 8–4C
"Been going since my distant student days… hasn't changed much!" – critics may say it's "time for a makeover" of the "pine-panelled '70s interior", but this "very cheap" Little India spot (near Euston) still has many fans for its "first-rate veggie curries, dosas and breads". / NW1 2HL; 11.45 pm, Sun 11 pm; no Amex; need 10+ to book.

The Dock Kitchen Portobello Dock W10 **£58** 345
344 Ladbroke Grove, Portobello Dock 8962 1610 1–2B
The "sublime post-industrial setting", next to a canal, is the high point of a visit to Stevie Parle's popular venture in deepest Notting Hill; as to the "eclectic" regular variation of cuisine? – fans love it, but sceptics find the results "pleasant, but not particularly interesting". / W10 5BU; www.dockkitchen.co.uk; @TheDockKitchen; 10 pm; closed Sun D; set weekday L £39 (FP).

The Don EC4 **£62** 343
20 St Swithin's Ln 7626 2606 9–3C
"Always a safe bet for business!" – this "slick" fixture near Bank (with "more atmospheric" basement bistro), remains one of the City's top lunching spots, thanks to its "surprisingly good" cooking and "interesting" wines (especially Kiwi and port). / EC4N 8AD; www.thedonrestaurant.com; @thedonlondon; 10 pm; closed Sat & Sun; no shorts.

don Fernando's TW9 **£44** 232
27f The Quadrant 8948 6447 1–4A
"If you're in Richmond and you need to refuel, look no further than don Fernando's" – a "happily unchanged place", by the station, serving "tasty tapas"; it's "a bit dated, but the staff make up for any shortcomings". / TW9 1DN; www.donfernando.co.uk; 11 pm, Sun 10 pm; no Amex; no booking.

Donna Margherita SW11 **£43** 433
183 Lavender Hill 7228 2660 10–2C
"Well worth quite a trip!" this "lovely" (and "seriously busy") Battersea Neapolitan inspires 'rave' reports on its "marvellous" pizza, and its "lively" spirit too. / SW11 5TE; www.donna-margherita.com; @DMargheritaUK; 10.30 pm, Fri & Sat 11 pm; Mon-Thu D only, Fri-Sun open L & D.

Donostia W1 **£45** 544
10 Seymour Pl 3620 1845 2–2A
"Take your taste buds to the very heart of San Sebastian", at this "authentic Basque tapas spot"

near Marble Arch, which offers "perfectly executed morsels" and "amicable" service in an "intimate" and "classy" setting. / W1H 7ND; www.donostia.co.uk; @DonostiaW1; 11 pm; closed Mon L.

Dorchester Grill Dorchester Hotel W1 £98 2 3 1
53 Park Ln 7629 8888 3–3A
Hardly anyone has a nice word to say about the "dreary" decor of this (inexplicably) "mock-Scottish" Mayfair grill room; it does makes a "good-value lunch destination" but, by night, the food can seem rather "expensive" for what it is. / W1K 1QA; www.thedorchester.com; @TheDorchester; 10.15 pm, Sat 10.45 pm, Sun 10.15 pm; no trainers.

Dose EC1 £13 4 4 2
70 Long Ln 7600 0382 9–1B
"Simply fantastic coffee" and a "really good selection of cakes and pastries" earn high praise for this "well-run" Antipodean coffee shop in Smithfield; main problem? – it "could do with bigger premises". / EC1A 9EJ; www.dose-espresso.com; L only, closed Sun; no Amex.

Dotori N4 £28 4 2 2
3 Stroud Green Rd 7263 3562 8–1D
"In an unlikely location near Finsbury Park station", a "crowded and very hard to book" South East Asian, offering "superb" (mainly Korean) food; "they should take over the shop next door and make a bit of elbow room!" / N4 2DQ; www.dotorirestaurant.wix.com/dotorirestaurant; 10.30 pm; closed Mon; no Amex.

Dragon Castle SE17 £38 3 1 1
100 Walworth Rd 7277 3388 1–3C
"The best dim sum south of the river" has made quite a name for this "keenly priced" fixture, near Elephant & Castle; declining service standards, though, have contributed to a rather "soulless" feel of late. / SE17 1JL; www.dragon-castle.com; @Dragoncastle100; Mon-Sat 11 pm, Sun 10 pm.

Drakes Tabanco W1 NEW £45 3 4 3
3 Windmill St 7637 9388 2–1C
"Not so much granny's tipple as a whole world of new flavours!" – this Andalusian-inspired Fitzrovia tavern leads on its offer of "interesting sherries direct from the barrel", which is supported by some very decent tapas; the ambience can vary from "quiet" to "shouty". / W1T 2HY; www.drakestabanco.com; 10 pm.

The Drapers Arms N1 £48 3 2 3
44 Barnsbury St 7619 0348 8–3D
This "very Farrow & Ball" gastropub is something of an Islington linchpin, with a "great atmosphere", and food that's of "a continually high standard and variety"; it can get "too busy and noisy" at peak times. / N1 1ER; www.thedrapersarms.com; @DrapersArms; 10.30 pm; no Amex.

Dub Jam WC2 NEW £24 4 4 3
20 Bedford St 7836 5876 4–3C
An "exciting" new Caribbean shack, serving up hot or smokey jerk BBQ, and rum cocktails; it may be in Covent Garden, but the "vibrant" decor is "straight off the beach!" / WC2E 9HP; www.dubjam.co.uk; @dubjambbq; 10 pm.

Duck & Waffle EC2 £68 2 2 5
110 Bishopsgate, Heron Tower 3640 7310 9–2D
"Views to die for" and "one of the most interesting breakfast menus in London" are twin-peak attractions of this 40th-floor City eyrie; it's open 24/7, but – especially given the "stratospheric" prices – the performance at other meals can seem "amateurish". / EC2N 4AY; www.duckandwaffle.com; @DuckandWaffle; open 24 hours.

Ducksoup W1 £53 2 2 3
41 Dean St 7287 4599 4–2A
"It can be a bit full of meedjah luvvies", but this "cosy" and bohemian Soho bistro is acclaimed for its "mix of small plates and quasi-tapas"; some dissenters, though, "just don't understand the hype". / W1D 4PY; www.ducksoupsoho.co.uk; @ducksoup; 10.30 pm; closed Sun D; Mon-Tue 6+ to book, Wed-Sat 3+ to book.

The Duke of Cambridge N1 £52 2 3 3
30 St Peter's St 7359 3066 1–2C
Cooking that's "far above usual pub grub" has helped win a big following for this Islington backstreet boozer; critics, though, do find it "overpriced" – "very unspecial, and all in the name of 'Organic'!" / N1 8JT; www.dukeorganic.co.uk; @dukeorganic; 10.30 pm, Sun 10 pm; no Amex.

Duke of Sussex W4 £46 3 2 4
75 South Pde 8742 8801 7–1A
"Delicious" food with a "Spanish slant" can come as something of a surprise at this fine Victorian tavern on the Chiswick/Acton borders, and it has a lovely garden too; "make sure you allow plenty of time, though, as the service can be hit-and-miss". / W4 5LF; www.metropolitanpubcompany.com; @thedukew4; 10.30 pm, Sun 9.30 pm.

Duke's Brew & Que N1 £44 3 2 3
33 Downham Rd 3006 0795 1–2D
"The ribs are the thing" ("other items can be hit-and-miss") at this US-style Dalson barbecue;

good beers too. / N1 5AA; www.dukesbrewandque.com; @DukesJoint; 10.30 pm, Sun 9.30 pm.

Durbar W2 **£33** 333
24 Hereford Rd 7727 1947 6–1B
Established in Bayswater in 1956, a "reliable and popular Indian", still hailed by loyal supporters as a "local gem". / W2 4AA; www.durbartandoori.co.uk; 11.30 pm; closed Fri L.

The Dysart Petersham TW10 **£68** 442
135 Petersham Rd 8940 8005 1–4A
In a large Arts & Crafts house overlooking Richmond Common, a year-old restaurant showcasing the skills of "genuinely talented" chef, Kenneth Culhane; atmosphere can be elusive though, and reports remain relatively few. / TW10 7AA; www.thedysartarms.co.uk; 9.30 pm; closed Sun D.

E&O W11 **£60** 323
14 Blenheim Cr 7229 5454 6–1A
"Still does pan-Asian better than anyone else", claim fans, but it's difficult to avoid the conclusion that this "vibrant" Notting Hill celeb-magnet has "gone downhill" of late – service is a touch "aloof", and the food "not quite as exciting". / W11 1NN; www.rickerrestaurants.com; 11 pm, Sun 10.30 pm; booking: max 6.

The Eagle EC1 **£33** 434
159 Farringdon Rd 7837 1353 9–1A
"The original gastropub and still one of the best"; this "fun" Farringdon watering hole has held true to its "unpretentious" formula over many years, and still offers "well-seasoned, honest, seasonal, posh-peasant food, plus very reasonable wine". / EC1R 3AL; www.theeaglefarringdon.co.uk; @eaglefarringdon; 10.30 pm; closed Sun D; no Amex; no booking.

Earl Spencer SW18 **£46** 323
260-262 Merton Rd 8870 9244 10–2B
Next to a trafficky stretch of highway, this Wandsworth gastropub makes a handy pit stop, with "consistently high standards". / SW18 5JL; www.theearlspencer.co.uk; @TheEarlSpencer; 11 pm; Mon-Thu D only, Fri-Sun open L & D; no booking Sun.

East Street W1 NEW **£36** 334
3-5 Rathbone Pl 7323 0860 3–1C
"Be transported to the food markets of SE Asia!" – that's the shtick at this colourful and "interesting" diner-style operation, just north of Oxford Street; it certainly makes "an interesting alternative to Wagamama!" / W1T 1HJ; www.eaststreetrestaurant.com; @EastStreetEats; 11 pm, Sun 10 pm.

Eat **£14** 222
Branches throughout London
"They don't seem as well organised as Pret but the food seems healthier!" – especially when it comes to "the best soups", some reporters prefer this sandwich-and-snack chain to its better-known competitor. / www.eat.co.uk; 4 pm-8 pm; most City branches closed all or part of weekend; no credit cards; no booking.

Eat 17 E17 NEW **£39** 345
28-30 Orford Rd 8521 5279 1–1D
"Delicious British food and value for money, in a great and buzzy, if slightly chaotic, atmosphere" – the formula that's proved a hit for this "casual" Walthamstow operation, which now has an offshoot in Hackney. / E17 9NJ; www.eat17.co.uk.

Eat Tokyo **£23** 422
50 Red Lion St, WC1 7242 3490 2–1D
15 Whitcomb St, WC2 7930 6117 4–4B
169 King St, W6 8741 7916 7–2B
18 Hillgate St, W8 7792 9313 6–2B
14 North End Rd, NW11 8209 0079 1–1B
"Spankingly fresh sushi" at "very reasonable prices" wins a major thumbs-up for these busy Japanese outfits; service is "prompt"… but "more focussed on getting the job done than wooing customers!"

Ebury Restaurant & Wine Bar SW1 **£53** 223
139 Ebury St 7730 5447 2–4A
"You wouldn't go here for gastronomic fireworks", but this "stress-free" Belgravia old-timer offers "decent value", and is "hard to beat for a relaxing evening". / SW1W 9QU; www.eburyrestaurant.co.uk; 10.15 pm.

Eco SW4 **£35** 334
162 Clapham High St 7978 1108 10–2D
"Excellent pizzas" (other dishes "can be a bit hit-and-miss") win many fans for this perennially trendy Clapham fixture. / SW4 7UG; www.ecorestaurants.com; @ecopizzaLDN; 11 pm, Fri & Sat 11.30 pm.

Ed's Easy Diner **£32** 123
12 Moor St, W1 7434 4439 4–2A
Trocadero, 19 Rupert St, W1 7287 1951 3–3D
Sedley Pl, 14 Woodstock St, W1 7493 9916 3–2B
Euston Station, NW1 7388 6967 8–3C

Southside Shopping Centre, SW18
8874 5634 10–2B
These Happy Days-style diners seem rather "formulaic" nowadays; they can still be "fun for all the family", but even some fans would concede that "the burgers can be bettered", and critics just say they're "ghastly". / www.edseasydiner.co.uk; Rupert St 10.30 pm, Fri & Sat 11.30 pm, Sun 10 pm; Moor St 11.30 pm, Thu-Sat midnight, Sun 10 pm, Sedley Place 9 pm, Thu-Sat 10 pm, NW1 Mon-Sat 10 pm, Sun 9 pm; Moor St no booking.

Edera W11 **£61** **343**
148 Holland Park Ave 7221 6090 6–2A
"Very fine" Sardinian cooking makes it well worth checking out this upscale and "reliable" Holland Park fixture; not too often, though – "please change the menu!" / W11 4UE; www.atoz.co.uk; 11 pm, Sun 10 pm.

Edwins SE1 NEW **£48** **334**
202-206 Borough High St 7403 9913 9–4B
A small and "romantic" new Borough Market bistro, from a chef who formerly worked at the trendy Riding House Café; on some accounts, it's an "inventive" and "classy" sort of joint, but early-days feedback is far from unanimous. / SE1 1JX; www.edwinsborough.co.uk; @edwinsborough; 9.30 pm; closed Sun D.

Eelbrook SW6 NEW
Eel Brook Common, New King's Rd
3417 0287 10–1B
A new spot, by Eel Brook Common, with Brett Barnes (previously of Ducksoup, Arbutus, and Hix) in the kitchen; it focuses on small plates with British, European and North African ingredients. / SW6 4SE; @EelbrookTweets.

8 Hoxton Square N1 NEW **£49** **332**
8-9 Hoxton Sq 7729 4232 12–1B
"A brilliant follow-up to 10 Greek St"; the "simple" new Hoxton sibling to the Soho spot has "the same winning formula" – "well-designed and well-executed food", complemented by "fantastic, regularly changing wines". / N1 6NU; www.8hoxtonsquare.com; @8HoxtonSquare.

Eight Over Eight SW3 **£57** **333**
392 King's Rd 7349 9934 5–3B
For "a fantastic evening with friends", Will Ricker's "buzzing and vibey" haunt, near World's End, remains a "fun" destination, offering "well-presented" Asian-fusion fare that's "always reliable". / SW3 5UZ; www.rickerrestaurants.com; 11 pm, Sun 10.30 pm.

Electric Diner W11 **£43** **244**
191 Portobello Rd 7908 9696 6–1A
If you're looking for "a classic, cool and vibey destination" that epitomises Notting Hill, you won't do much better than this well-established brasserie; top tip – a "cracking" brunch. / W11 2ED; www.electricdiner.com; @ElectricDiner; 11 pm, Sun 10 pm.

Elena's L'Etoile W1 **£53** **111**
30 Charlotte St 7636 7189 2–1C
In Fitzrovia, an "old-fashioned and very traditional French restaurant" (est 1896) serving "solid Gallic fare"; since Elena retired, "it's faded remarkably from its former glories" – "with a bit of effort, it could be so much better". / W1T 2NG; www.elenasletoile.co.uk; @elenasletoile; 10.30 pm; closed Sat L & Sun.

Elephant Royale Locke's Wharf E14 **£50** **222**
Westferry Rd 7987 7999 11–2C
Rather up-and-down reports of late on this riverside Thai (whose terrace offers stunning views of Greenwich); one thing is certain, though – "the fixed price lunch is much better value than the evening menu". / E14 3WA; www.elephantroyale.com; 10.30 pm, Fri & Sat 11 pm, Sun 10 pm; set weekday L £25 (FP), set Sun L £37 (FP).

Elliot's Café SE1 **£52** **433**
12 Stoney St 7403 7436 9–4C
"Quite ambitious cooking" and "funky natural wines" ("you might need advice") have helped make a hit of this convivial "bare-brick" café, which "truly takes on the atmosphere of Borough Market". / SE1 9AD; www.elliotscafe.com; @elliotscafe; 9.30 pm; closed Sun; 8 max.

Ember Yard W1 NEW **£51** **333**
60 Berwick St 7439 8057 3–1D
A Salt Yard spin-off which cooks over wood in an effort to differentiate itself from the tapas herd; results can be "interesting", but "edgy decor and friendly service don't make up for the feeling it's all been done better before… by the same people!" / W1F 8SU; www.emberyard.co.uk; @emberyard; SRA-2 stars.

Emile's SW15 **£44** **442**
96-98 Felsham Rd 8789 3323 10–2B
"Hidden away from passing trade", in a "quiet Putney backwater", this "cosy" stalwart has long survived by "pleasing the locals" – highlights include the signature Beef Wellington, and some "superb" wines. / SW15 1DQ; www.emilesrestaurant.co.uk; 11 pm; D only, closed Sun; no Amex.

The Empress E9 **£47** 343
130 Lauriston Rd 8533 5123 1–2D
"Ticking all the boxes for a great local" – a "friendly" gastroboozer, near Victoria Park , which continues to impress with its all-round quality. / E9 7LH; www.empresse9.co.uk; @elliottlidstone; 10 pm, Sun 9.30 pm; closed Mon L; no Amex.

The Engineer NW1 **£58** 223
65 Gloucester Ave 7483 1890 8–3B
With its "lovely" terrace, this Primrose Hill gastropub is still a "little gem"; feedback is limited nowadays though – given its glamorous past, it's hard not to find the current performance rather plodding. / NW1 8JH; www.theengineerprimrosehill.co.uk; @TheEngineerPub; 10 pm.

Enoteca Turi SW15 **£59** 443
28 Putney High St 8785 4449 10–2B
"Always a bit under the radar, owing to its less than perfect location", Giuseppe and Pamela Turi's "very accomplished" and "welcoming" Putney Bridge-side stalwart dependably offers "first-class Italian regional cooking" plus "a massive selection of carefully chosen Italian wines". / SW15 1SQ; www.enotecaturi.com; @enoteca_turi; 10.30 pm, Fri & Sat 11 pm; closed Sun.

The Enterprise SW3 **£58** 233
35 Walton St 7584 3148 5–2C
The food may be perfectly "wholesome and tasty", but it's the the "club"-like ambience which makes this "buzzing" corner bistro a true Chelsea "classic". / SW3 2HU; www.theenterprise.co.uk; 10 pm, Sat 10.30 pm; no booking, except weekday L.

Entrée SW11 **£58** 443
2 Battersea Rise 7223 5147 10–2C
With its "interesting but not pretentious" food, this Battersea venture is a "local favourite that never fails to please"; NB: "under-advertised BYO Tuesdays are a bonus". / SW11 1ED; www.entreebattersea.co.uk; @entreebattersea; 10.30 pm; closed Mon, Tue L, Wed L, Thu L, Fri L, Sat D & Sun D; set weekday L £35 (FP), set Sun L £39 (FP).

Er Mei WC2 NEW **£37** 443
6 Lisle St 7734 8128 4–3A
"A great find"; there's "no compromise" on the "challenging" and "wonderfully spicy" cooking at this "proper" Sichuanese newcomer, on the former Chinatown site of the Empress of Sichuan (RIP); service is "not what you'd expect" – it's "completely charming"! / WC2H 7BG.

Ergon W1 **£48** 443
16 Picton Pl 8899 6595 3–1A
"Finally, some good Greek food in the West End…"; this "interesting" newcomer, near Selfridges, serves "contemporary" cooking in a "cool and informal setting" – "my Greek friends were as impressed as I was!" / W1U 1BP; www.ergonproducts.co.uk; @ErgonLondon.

Eriki NW3 **£40** 432
4-6 Northways Pde, Finchley Rd 7722 0606 8–2A
"Very decent Indian food in a less than inspiring ambience" – the appeal of this Swiss Cottage spot changes little from year to year; "as a carnivore, I decided to go veggie here… and I was not disappointed". / NW3 5EN; www.eriki.co.uk; 10.45 pm; closed Sat L.

Esarn Kheaw W12 **£34** 431
314 Uxbridge Rd 8743 8930 7–1B
"The most authentic north eastern Thai cooking" – "bursting with strong hearty flavours" – is served by an "ebullient" long-time proprietor, at this Shepherd's Bush "gem"; "don't be put off by the slightly down-at-heel feel!" / W12 7LJ; www.esarnkheaw.co.uk; @esarn_kheaw; 11 pm; closed Sat L & Sun L; no Amex.

L'Escargot W1 **£60**
48 Greek St 7439 7474 4–2A
Under new ownership, this venerable Gallic classic, in the heart of Soho, has been transformed into a temple of theatricality (or, if you prefer, high camp); a full assessment will have to wait until next year's survey. / W1D 4EF; lescargotrestaurant.co.uk; @EscargotLondon; 11.15 pm; closed Sun D; set pre theatre £35 (FP).

Essenza W11 **£58** 333
210 Kensington Park Rd 7792 1066 6–1A
"Solid" and "friendly", this modest Notting Hill Italian never makes many waves; its small fan club, though, say it's "a winner every time". / W11 1NR; www.essenza.co.uk; 11.30 pm; set weekday L £37 (FP).

L'Etranger SW7 **£71** 342
36 Gloucester Rd 7584 1118 5–1B
"Huge and comprehensive", the wine list at this "slightly anodyne" South Kensington venture is "spectacular" (if "frankly overpriced")… perhaps to the extent of eclipsing the Asian/French cuisine, "imaginative" as it is. / SW7 4QT; www.etranger.co.uk; 11 pm, Sun 10.30 pm; set weekday L £46 (FP).

Everest Inn SE3 **£35** 444
41 Montpelier Vale 8852 7872 1–4D
"Nepalese food with flair", "sweet service" and "low prices" come together to create a winning

combination at this "cosy" fixture, which is "probably the best restaurant in Blackheath". / SE3 0TJ; www.everestinn.co.uk; midnight, Sun 11 pm.

Eyre Brothers EC2 **£57** 434
70 Leonard St 7613 5346 12–1B
An "elegant, modern, dark-wood sanctuary", near Silicon Roundabout, offering "clean and sophisticated" Hispanic cooking backed up by a "recherché list of Iberian wines"; its popularity with the business market long predates the 'emergence' of the area around it. / EC2A 4QX; www.eyrebrothers.co.uk; 10 pm; closed Sat L & Sun.

Faanoos **£27** 324
472 Chiswick High Rd, W4 8994 4217 7–2A
481 Richmond Road, SW14 8878 5738 1–4A
"Excellent flatbread cooked before your very eyes" is a highlight of the "great Persian fare" on offer at this duo of "reasonably-priced" local restaurants, in Chiswick. / SW14 11 pm; W4 11 pm; Fri & Sat midnight.

Fabrizio EC1 **£53** 442
30 Saint Cross St 7430 1503 9–1A
A handy little haunt, near Hatton Garden, where Fabrizio himself "is as charming as ever", and where the Sicilian dishes, using the "freshest produce", are "always exceptional". / EC1N 8UH; www.fabriziorestaurant.co.uk; 10 pm; closed Sat L & Sun.

Fabrizio N19 **£32** 342
34 Highgate Hill 7561 9073 8–1C
"A real gem on Highgate Hill"; this "wonderful neighbourhood trattoria" serves up "delicious pasta and pizza", and "with a smile" too; only downside? – it can prove "incredibly noisy". / N19 5NL; www.fabriziolondon.co.uk; 10 pm.

Fairuz W1 **£50** 433
3 Blandford St 7486 8108 2–1A
"People say it's a hidden gem and they are right" – it may be somewhat "cramped", but this Marylebone Lebanese is a "very reliable" destination, and "reasonably priced" too. / W1H 3DA; www.fairuz.uk.com; 11 pm, Sun 10.30 pm; set weekday L £30 (FP).

La Famiglia SW10 **£62** 222
7 Langton St 7351 0761 5–3B
This perennially fashionable '60s trattoria, at World's End, is a real "golden oldie", say fans – "just how an Italian ought to be"; those who look at the telescope from the other end, however, may perceive a "dinosaur" that's "subsiding into expensive mediocrity". / SW10 0JL; www.lafamiglia.co.uk; 11.45 pm.

Fat Boy's **£35** 233
10a-10b Edensor Rd, W4 8994 8089 10–1A
33 Haven Grn, W5 8998 5868 1–2A
201 Upper Richmond Rd, SW14 8876 0644 1–4A
431 Richmond Rd, TW1 8892 7657 1–4A
68 High St, TW8 8569 8481 1–3A
"Charming" staff serve "straightforward but fresh" Thai dishes at these "reliable" neighbourhood cafés; a "great-value set lunch" is a highlight. / www.fatboysthai.co.uk; 11 pm.

Faulkner's E8 **£30** 432
424-426 Kingsland Rd 7254 6152 1–1D
An old-school chippy that has remained impervious to Dalston's trendification; all reports agree, though, that it still knocks out "great" fish and chips. / E8 4AA; 10 pm, Fri-Sun 11 pm; no Amex; need 8+ to book.

The Fellow N1 **£46** 333
24 York Way 7833 4395 8–3C
"In an upcoming area handy for King's Cross and St Pancras", a gastropub that offers an "interesting and varied" menu (including "excellent skin-on chips"); the roof terrace is an unexpected boon in summer months. / N1 9AA; www.thefellow.co.uk; @24yorkway; 9.45 pm.

Fera at Claridge's Claridge's Hotel W1 NEW **£141** 455
55 Brook St 7107 8888 3–2B
"Hats off" to Simon Rogan, for the relaunch of this landmark Mayfair Art Deco chamber, where "gloriously attentive" service only adds to the enjoyment of the "phenomenal" meals – up to 17 courses that are "so different" (and, for those who so opt, come with some "exceptionally well-matched wines"). / W1K 4HR; www.claridges.co.uk/fera.

Fernandez & Wells **£34** 324
16a, St Anne's Ct, W1 7494 4242 3–1D
43 Lexington St, W1 7734 1546 3–2D
73 Beak St, W1 7287 8124 3–2D
Somerset Hs, Strand, WC2 7420 9408 2–2D
A "faintly chaotic" small chain, which offers "delicious bits and bobs", as well as "decent-value wines" and excellent coffee; the "magical" Somerset House location, with its high-ceilinged setting, is perhaps the one most actively worth seeking out. / www.fernandezandwells.com; Lexington St & St Anne's court 10 pm; Beak St 6 pm, Somerset House 11 pm; St Anne's Court closed Sun.

Fez Mangal W11 **£22** 5 4 3
104 Ladbroke Grove 7229 3010 6–1A
It may be "more of a take-away", but you can still have a "fantastic" time at this "very popular" Turkish grill in Notting Hill, where the menu – with "absolutely fresh grilled lamb" a highlight – offers "exceptional value"; BYO. / W11 1PY; www.fezmangal.co.uk; 11.30 pm; no Amex.

Ffiona's W8 **£54** 2 3 3
51 Kensington Church St 7937 4152 5–1A
"I went for brunch, and wanted to stay to dinner too!" – Ffiona's quirky dinner-party-style Kensington bistro seems especially popular for Sunday brunch nowadays, but her "home-cooking" can go down well at any time. / W8 4BA; www.ffionas.com; @ffionasnotes; 11 pm, Sun 10 pm; closed Mon; no Amex.

Fifteen N1 **£61** 1 1 1
15 Westland Pl 3375 1515 12–1A
"You pay for the celeb associations, rather than the calibre of the cooking", at this "seriously overpriced" and "ordinary" Hoxton trattoria – it "trades on Jamie Oliver's name alone". / N1 7LP; www.fifteen.net; @JamiesFifteen; 10 pm; booking: max 12.

The Fifth Floor Restaurant Harvey Nichols SW1 **£62** 3 3 3
109-125 Knightsbridge 7235 5250 5–1D
Still vanishingly few comments on the top-floor dining room at this famous Knightsbridge department store which, in its '90s heyday, was the talk of the town; no serious complaints though, and the occasional fan insists the cooking is "top-class". / SW1X 7RJ; www.harveynichols.com; 10.45 pm; closed Sun D; SRA-2 stars.

La Figa E14 **£41** 3 3 3
45 Narrow St 7790 0077 11–1B
"A lovely Limehouse Italian", serving up "enormous portions" – all part of what fans say is its "excellent value for money". / E14 8DN; www.lafigarestaurant.co.uk; 11 pm, Sun 10.30 pm.

Fino W1 **£53** 4 4 4
33 Charlotte St 7813 8010 2–1C
An "airy" basement provides a surprisingly "atmospheric" setting for the Hart brothers' Fitzrovia favourite; the appeal is very straightforward – "top-notch" tapas and a splendid selection of wines and sherries. / W1T 1RR; www.finorestaurant.com; 10.30 pm; closed Sat L & Sun; booking: max 12; SRA-1 star.

Fire & Stone **£42** 2 2 2
31-32 Maiden Ln, WC2 0844 371 2550 4–3D
Westfield, Ariel Way, W12 0844 371 2551 7–1C
"If you fancy a curry or roast on your pizza", this "smart" chain – with its "unique toppings" – is the place to start; rather too often, however, it's a case of "high expectations, but low delivery". / www.fireandstone.com; WC2 11 pm; W12 11.15 pm; E1 11pm, Sun 8 pm.

First Floor W11 **£47** 3 2 5
186 Portobello Rd 7243 0072 6–1A
A "beautiful" upper-floor high-ceilinged dining room makes this Portobello fixture a top spot for a special night out; the food "never fails to please", either (particularly the "very good-value fixed menu"). / W11 1LA; www.firstfloorportobello.co.uk; 10.30 pm; set Sun L £38 (FP).

Fischer's W1 NEW **£58** 2 3 3
50 Marylebone High St 7466 5501 2–1A
Corbin & King's debuts are often surprisingly shaky, and their new "Austrian-themed café", in Marylebone, is no exception; to fans, its "interesting" menu (and, of course, yummy Viennoiserie) helps make it "a joy"; for critics, though, the whole show is just too "fake". / W1U 5HN; www.fischers.co.uk; @fischers.

The Fish & Chip Shop N1 **£44** 4 4 4
189 Upper St 3227 0979 8–2D
"Thriving, and deservedly so", this "posh" but "jolly" chippy has been "a very welcome addition to Islington", though even fans can find it "expensive"; as this guide goes to press, we hear a new branch is to open in the City. / N1 1RQ; www.thefishandchipshop.uk.com; @TheFishChipShop; 11 pm, Sun 10 pm; SRA-1 star.

Fish Central EC1 **£30** 3 3 2
149-155 Central St 7253 4970 12–1A
"Unbelievably fresh fish at reasonable prices" keeps the customers happy at this "fab" and "buzzy" chippy, 'twixt Old Street and Islington; – "a great choice for those visiting the Barbican". / EC1V 8AP; www.fishcentral.co.uk; 10.30 pm, Fri & Sat 11 pm; closed Sun.

Fish Club **£39** 4 4 2
189 St John's Hill, SW11 7978 7115 10–2C
57 Clapham High St, SW4 7720 5853 10–2D
"Really exciting" dishes impress all who report on these "trusty" south London chippies – "it's all in the quality of the sourcing". / www.thefishclub.com; 10 pm; closed Mon L; no bookings.

Fish in a Tie SW11 **£37** 344
105 Falcon Rd 7924 1913 10–1C
"Mad crazy-busy on a Friday night" – this "fun" and "very friendly" bistro, behind Clapham Junction, offers inexpensive "Mediterranean-inspired" fare that's "consistently good", and which comes "at very reasonable prices". / SW11 2PF; www.fishinatie.co.uk; midnight, Sun 11 pm; no Amex.

Fish Market EC2 **£53** 343
16B New St 3503 0790 9–2D
"Very near, but seeming far from the bustle of Bishopsgate" – this "relaxed" operation, in an "interesting" converted warehouse, deserves to be better known for its "well-prepared fish dishes" and its "super staff". / EC2M 4TR; www.fishmarket-restaurant.co.uk; @FishMarketNS; 10.30 pm; closed Sun; SRA-3 stars.

fish! SE1 **£57** 222
Cathedral St 7407 3803 9–4C
On a good day, you find "plain" fish dishes of "good quality" in this "noisy" and "crowded" glazed shed, by Borough Market; some visitors, though, find standards "very average all-round", and at prices which can seem "ridiculous". / SE1 9AL; www.fishkitchen.com; @fishborough; 10.45 pm, Sun 10.30 pm.

Fishworks **£51** 322
7-9 Swallow St, W1 7734 5813 3–3D
89 Marylebone High St, W1 7935 9796 2–1A
"Fresh fish simply but expertly prepared" – that's really the whole story at these "predictable" bistros; neither service nor ambience, though, is anything to write home about. / www.fishworks.co.uk; 10.30 pm.

Fitou's Thai Restaurant W10 **£26** 432
1 Dalgarno Gdns 8968 0558 6–1A
"A great-value BYO Thai", by Little Wormwood Scrubs, offering food that's "good and fresh". / W10 5LL; www.fitourestaurant.co.uk; 10.30 pm; closed Sun L.

The Five Fields SW3 **£74** 554
8-9 Blacklands Ter 7838 1082 5–2D
"A gem in the heart of Chelsea"; this "brilliant" yearling is a formidable all-rounder, combining "sensational" and "clever" cooking with a "stunning and intimate" interior, plus service that "perfectly balances formality with being welcoming". / SW3 2SP; www.fivefieldsrestaurant.com; @The5Fields; 10 pm; D only, closed Mon & Sun.

Five Guys WC2 **£13** 322
1-3 Long Acre 0833 005 4–3C
"You need two hands, and three Hail Marys", say fans, to handle one of the "proper, sloppy burgers" at these "very American" joints, now in Islington as well as Covent Garden; overall, though, reporters aren't quite convinced that the transition over the Pond has been totally successful. / WC2E 9LH; www.fiveguys.co.uk.

500 N19 **£44** 342
782 Holloway Rd 7272 3406 8–1C
A "poky" but "personal" Archway Sicilian, where the cooking is "unusual", "generous" and "good value"; some customers, though, do find enjoyment limited by the "cramped and noisy" premises. / N19 3JH; www.500restaurant.co.uk; @500restaurant; 10.30 pm, Sun 9.30 pm; Mon-Thu D only, Fri-Sun open L & D.

Flat Iron **£22** 454
17 Beak St, W1 no tel 3–2D
9 Denmark St, WC2 no tel 4–1A NEW
"The best value-for-money steak and chips" make these trendy "no-frills" diners, in Soho and by Centrepoint "a perfect example of doing one simple thing well"; they're "cramped" mind, and there's "always a big queue, so get there early".

Flat White W1 **£11** 444
17 Berwick St 7734 0370 3–2D
"Great flat whites every time", plus a few choice snacks, keep 'em packing in to this "lovely little boutique coffee joint", in Soho. / W1F 0PT; www.flat-white.co.uk; L only; no credit cards; no booking.

Fleet River Bakery WC2 **£20** 323
71 Lincolns Inn Fields 7691 1457 2–1D
Tucked away in Holborn, a "very busy" café that offers "unusual breakfast choices", "delicious sandwiches" and excellent Monmouth Coffee… but where service can sometimes be "infuriatingly slow". / WC2A 3JF; www.fleetriverbakery.com; @Fleetriver; 5 pm, Sat 3 pm; L only, closed Sun.

Flesh and Buns WC2 **£50** 322
41 Earlham St 7632 9500 4–2C
"Plates of steamed buns with delicious fillings, and lots of little nibbles such as sushi" offer some "good Asian flavours" at this "industrial-style" Covent Garden basement yearling – a sibling to Bone Daddies; at the peak, though, the atmosphere can be "mad". / WC2H 9LX; www.fleshandbuns.com; @FleshandBuns; Mon-Tue 10.30 pm, Wed-Sat 9.30 pm, Sun 9.30 pm.

Food for Thought WC2 **£23** 442
31 Neal St 7836 0239 4–2C
"Cramped" but adored – this rambling Covent Garden basement has long offered "some of the best vegetarian food in town" at "good-value" prices;

BYO. / WC2H 9PR; www.foodforthought-london.co.uk; 8 pm, Sun 5 pm; closed Sun D; no credit cards; no booking.

Forman's E3 **£54** 4 3 3
Stour Rd, Fish Island 8525 2365 1–1D
It's not just the "lovely view of the Olympic Stadium" which make it worth a trip to this dining room inside the East End's famous producer of 'London-smoke' salmon – the food is relatively simple, but "top-notch". / E3 2NT; www.formans.co.uk/restaurant; @formanslondon; 9 pm; Closed Mon-Wed, Thu & Fri D only, Sat open L & D, closed Sun D.

(The Fountain)
Fortnum & Mason W1 **£61** 2 3 2
181 Piccadilly 7734 8040 3–3D
"Ideal for aunts, grannies or godchildren" – the buttery of HM's grocer remains "a nice spot for a traditional British experience"; highlights include "first-class" breakfasts, "excellent" afternoon teas and "legendary" knickerbocker glories. / W1A 1ER; www.fortnumandmason.com; @fortnumandmason; 7.45 pm; closed Sun D; Smart / formal dresswear.

(1707)
Fortnum & Mason W1 **£46** 3 4 3
181 Piccadilly 7734 8040 3–3D
"Take the wine flight", if you visit the famous grocer's basement wine bar, where you can "sample a huge variety of very good wines" – their whole list is available, plus £10 corkage; the tapas-style platters also make it a decent "snack lunch" option. / W1A 1ER; www.fortnumandmason.co.uk; @fortnumandmason; 8 pm, Sun 6 pm; closed Sun D.

(The Diamond Jubilee Tea Salon)
Fortnum & Mason W1 **£56** 3 5 5
181 Piccadilly 7734 8040 3–3D
"A totally extravagant experience, especially if you go for the champagne version" – afternoon tea at Fortnum's most recently-opened dining room is an "extremely restful" experience, "with a piano tinkling in the background", and one which usually satisfies all-round. / W1A 1ER; www.fortnumandmason.com; @fortnumandmason; 7 pm, Sun 6 pm; Deposit for 11+.

40 Maltby Street SE1 **£41** 4 4 4
40 Maltby St 7237 9247 9–4D
This "under-the-arches foodie destination" – in the 'new' Borough Market – offers a "most interesting selection of bio and small producer wines", complemented by "outstanding" small-plate dishes; "get there early as it's full by 8 pm". / SE1 3PA; www.40maltbystreet.com; @40maltbystreet; 9.30 pm; closed Mon, Tue, Wed L, Thu L, Sat D & Sun; no Amex; no bookings.

Four Regions TW9 **£44** 3 3 2
102-104 Kew Rd 8940 9044 1–4A
The definition of a "good local", this "friendly" and "efficient" Richmond Chinese "never disappoints", thanks not least to its "consistently good" cooking; lunch and pre-theatre menus come especially recommended. / TW9 2PQ; www.fourregions.co.uk; @fourregions; 11.30 pm, Sun 11 pm.

The Four Seasons **£32** 4 1 1
12 Gerrard St, W1 7494 0870 4–3A
23 Wardour St, W1 7287 9995 4–3A
84 Queensway, W2 7229 4320 6–2C
"Unbelievable" roast duck is the special attraction of these "down-at-heel" diners in Bayswater and Chinatown; "curt service and a complete lack of ambience" are all part of the package. / www.fs-restaurants.co.uk; Queensway 11 pm, Sun 10h45 pm; Gerrard St 1 am; Wardour St 1am, Fri-Sat 3.30 am.

Fox & Grapes SW19 **£55** 2 2 2
9 Camp Rd 8619 1300 10–2A
Most reporters like this "lovely fresh and vibrant local restaurant", in a large former boozer, right by Wimbledon Common; there are still quite a few doubters, though, for whom this is a "slightly oddball" place that's "expensive for what it is". / SW19 4UN; www.foxandgrapeswimbledon.co.uk; 9.30 pm, Sun 8.15 pm; no Amex.

The Fox & Hounds
SW11 **£47** 4 4 4
66 Latchmere Rd 7924 5483 10–1C
A Battersea gastroboozer "belonging to the team that operate the Atlas... and it shows!"; indeed, such is the quality of its "sympathetic interpretations of Mediterranean classics" that "it's getting harder and harder just to drop in and grab a table". / SW11 2JU; www.thefoxandhoundspub.co.uk; @thefoxbattersea; 10 pm; Mon-Thu D only, Fri-Sun open L & D.

The Fox and Anchor
EC1 **£49** 3 3 5
115 Charterhouse St 7250 1300 9–1B
"When you've had enough of east London trendiness", head for this "legendary" Clerkenwell pub, where "simple" British food is cooked with "lightness of touch" in perfect "olde worlde" splendour; breakfast with a pint is an institution. / EC1M 6AA; www.foxandanchor.com; @MeetMeAtTheFox; 11 pm.

Foxlow EC1 **£49** 3 3 3
St John St 7014 8070 9–2A
"Hawksmoor-lite"; this "democratic" Clerkenwell spin-off from the famous group is extolled by fans for its "really chilled" style and "impossibly tender"

meat; critics do say it "lacks a certain zing", though, and can find it "a bit expensive" too. / EC1M 4AN; www.foxlow.co.uk; @Foxlow(EC1); SRA-3 stars.

Foxtrot Oscar SW3 £55 222
79 Royal Hospital Rd 7352 4448 5–3D
Oddly divided views on Gordon Ramsay's tenure at this age-old Chelsea bolthole, a few doors from his flagship; fans say it's a "friendly" place serving "classy" fare – there are almost as many critics, though, for whom this is "just a poorly run local bistro, charging top prices". / SW3 4HN; www.gordonramsay.com/foxtrotoscar; @foxtrot_oscar; 10 pm, Sun 9 pm.

Franco Manca £22 433
144 Chiswick High Rd, W4 8747 4822 7–2A
76 Northcote Rd, SW11 7924 3110 10–2D
53 Bedford Hill, SW12 8772 0489 10–2C
NEW
Unit 4 Market Row, SW9 7738 3021 10–2D
Westfield Stratford, E20 8522 6669 1–1D
"Outstanding" sourdough crusts (an "ideal combo between chewy and crispy") and "keen" prices win many supporters for this mushrooming Neapolitan chain; in a quest for "unbelievably good" pizza, however, there's still no substitute for a visit to the the "carefree" Brixton original. / www.francomanca.co.uk; SW9 10.30, Mon 5 pm; W4 11 pm; E20 9 pm, Thu-Sat 10 pm, Sun 6 pm; SW9 no bookings.

Franco's SW1 £74 343
61 Jermyn St 7499 2211 3–3C
"Good enough, without being spectacular"; this "efficient" St James's Italian certainly has a handy location, especially for business, and it rarely positively disappoints; it can can seem rather "crowded", though, and prices are "high". / SW1Y 6LX; www.francoslondon.com; 10.30 pm; closed Sun; set pre-theatre £39 (FP), set weekday L £46 (FP).

Franklins SE22 £49 333
157 Lordship Ln 8299 9598 1–4D
"Assuredly good comfort cooking" continues to win plaudits for this "lovely East Dulwich local" – a converted pub, where there are "always new dishes on the notably seasonal menu". / SE22 8HX; www.franklinsrestaurant.com; @frankinsse22; 10.30 pm; no Amex.

Frantoio SW10 £56 223
397 King's Rd 7352 4146 5–3B
"A fun spot where the food is OK, but not the point" – that's the traditional view on this World's End Italian; it suffered from a couple of very 'down' reports though this year, and a feeling it's "lost its vim". / SW10 0LR; 11.15 pm, Sun 10.15 pm; set weekday L £36 (FP).

Frederick's N1 £62 234
106 Islington High St 7359 2888 8–3D
A surprisingly grand and spacious, and rather "pricey", Islington old-timer, which is a "lovely place to eat", especially if you nab a seat in the conservatory or garden; the rather "samey" cuisine, though, "has not really kept up with the times". / N1 8EG; www.fredericks.co.uk; 11 pm; closed Sun; set weekday L & dinner £36 (FP).

La Fromagerie Café W1 £39 324
2-6 Moxon St 7935 0341 3–1A
"Unusual, beautifully prepared, fresh and simple" dishes and "fabulous coffee" are to be had at this "relaxed" café, adjacent to Marylebone's famous cheese shop – a "great place for brunch", in particular. / W1U 4EW; www.lafromagerie.co.uk; @lafromagerieuk; 6.30 pm, Sat 6 pm, Sun 5 pm; L only; no booking.

The Frontline Club W2 £58 333
13 Norfolk Pl 7479 8960 6–1D
"Interesting photos" and "affordable, honest food" (plus, to be perfectly frank, a "lack of nearby competition") combine to make this comfy dining room – part of a war reporters' club – "the best restaurant near Paddington". / W2 1QJ; www.frontlineclub.com; 10.30 pm; closed Sat L & Sun.

Fujiyama SW9 £28 432
5-7 Vining St 7737 2369 10–2D
A "buzzy" Brixton canteen serving "excellent sushi (including selection/sharing plates) and decent Katsu and tempura"; "quick" service too. / SW9 8QA; www.newfujiyama.com; 11 pm.

Fulham Wine Rooms SW6 £52 234
871-873 Fulham Rd 7042 9440 10–1B
"The perfect place to entertain all wine buffs!" – a lively bar, offering a "very large assortment" of wines by the glass; the food is "probably of secondary interest". / SW6 5HP; www.greatwinesbytheglass.com; @winerooms; 11 pm; closed weekday L.

Fuzzy's Grub £14 322
6 Crown Pas, SW1 7925 2791 3–4D
15 Basinghall St, EC2 7726 6771 9–2C
58 Houdsditch, EC3 7929 1400 9–2D
10 Well Ct, EC4 7236 8400 9–2B
62 Fleet St, EC4 7583 6060 9–2A
"Roast in a bap – awesome!"; these British-themed diners are best known for their huge sarnies stuffed

with roast meats. / www.fuzzysgrub.co.uk; most branches between 3 pm and 5 pm; closed Sat & Sun; no Amex; no booking.

Gaby's WC2 **£35** 3 3 2
30 Charing Cross Rd 7836 4233 4–3B
"Still defying the developers" – this '60s "time warp", by Leicester Square tube, is a Theatreland "institution", thanks to its "super salt beef", "top falafel" and "amazing latkes", and "Gaby himself brightens up the dingy, claustrophobic space". / WC2H 0DE; midnight, Sun 10 pm; no Amex.

Gail's Bread **£27** 3 3 4
Branches throughout London
"For a pastry and to rest your feet", these "buzzy and friendly" cafés make an excellent standby. / www.gailsbread.co.uk; W11 & WC1 7 pm; NW3 & NW6 8 pm, W1 10 pm, SW7 9 pm, Sun 8 pm; no booking.

Gallery Mess
Saatchi Gallery SW3 **£52** 2 2 2
Duke of Yorks HQ, Kings Rd 7730 8135 5–2D
"For a break from shopping" ("or an agreeable venue to talk business)", this "stylish attachment" to the gallery near Sloane Square is a "buzzy" sort of place with very pretty views; sadly, though, neither food nor service rises to the location. / SW3 4RY; www.saatchigallery.com/gallerymess; @gallerymess; 9.30 pm, Sun 6 pm; closed Sun D; set dinner £34 (FP).

Gallipoli **£36** 3 4 3
102 Upper St, N1 7359 0630 8–3D
107 Upper St, N1 7226 5333 8–3D
120 Upper St, N1 7226 8099 8–3D
They may look "cramped" and slightly "clapped out", but these "retro" Turkish bistros, in Islington, offer "deliciously filling" mezze at "bargain" prices, in a "cheerful" and "friendly" setting. / www.cafegallipoli.com; 11 pm, Fri & Sat midnight.

Galvin at Windows
Park Lane London Hilton Hotel
W1 **£99** 2 3 5
22 Park Ln 7208 4021 3–4A
"Keen to impress foreign visitors" (or a date)? – head for this Mayfair chamber, where the panorama from the 28th floor includes "stunning" view over Buckingham Palace and its gardens; you need a "large wallet", though, and the food is much less memorable than the view. / W1K 1BE; www.galvinatwindows.com; @GalvinatWindows; 10 pm, Sat & Sun 10.30 pm; closed Sat L & Sun D; no shorts; set weekday L £56 (FP).

Galvin Bistrot de Luxe
W1 **£65** 3 4 4
66 Baker St 7935 4007 2–1A
With its "unpretentiously professional" service and "staunchly traditional" styling, the Galvin brothers' original Gallic bistro, in Marylebone, remains many reporters' favourite; the "classy" cuisine, though, has sometimes seemed to be "resting on its laurels" of late. / W1U 7DJ; www.galvinrestaurants.com; @galvin_brothers; Mon-Wed 10.30 pm, Thu-Sat 10.45 pm, Sun 9.30 pm; set weekday L £37 (FP), set dinner £39 (FP).

GALVIN LA CHAPELLE E1 **£74**
4 4 5
35 Spital Sq 7299 0400 12–2B
"A simply spectacular experience"; the Galvin brothers' "superlative" venture occupies a "stunning" cathedral-like Spitalfields hall; its "superb" Gallic dishes and "smooth" service make it a splendid choice for a business or romantic occasion. / E1 6DY; www.galvinrestaurants.com; 10.30 pm, Sun 9.30 pm; set weekday L, dinner & Sun L £48 (FP).

Ganapati SE15 **£43** 5 4 4
38 Holly Grove 7277 2928 1–4C
"Exquisite Keralan food" at "great-value" prices again inspires ecstatic reports on this "tiny and basic" neighbourhood "diamond" in "an unlikely corner of Peckham"; it's "rather cramped", but "always fun". / SE15 5DF; www.ganapatirestaurant.com; 10.30 pm, Sun 10 pm; closed Mon; no Amex.

Garnier SW5 **£56** 3 4 2
314 Earl's Court Rd 7370 4536 5–2A
The Garnier brothers' "classic" Gallic yearling, in Earl's Court, offers bourgeois cooking "of a generally high standard", and "fairly priced" wines too; the decor is "very boring", though, and "being on a busy road doesn't boost the ambience". / SW5 9BQ; www.garnierestaurant.com; Mon-Sat 10.30 pm, Sun 10 pm; set weekday L £43 (FP).

Le Garrick WC2 **£42** 2 2 3
10-12 Garrick St 7240 7649 4–3C
A veteran Covent Garden wine bar, offering "authentic" French staples at "quite sensible prices", which fans proclaim a "fabulous oasis"… but "it's the atmosphere downstairs, especially when there is live music, that sets the place apart". / WC2E 9BH; www.frenchrestaurantlondon.co.uk; @le_garrick; 10.30 pm; closed Sun.

Garrison SE1 **£48** 3 3 3
99-101 Bermondsey St 7089 9355 9–4D
A "charming" Bermondsey corner boozer that's "a bit cramped, but has a buzz about it" –

for anything "from a great breakfast to an evening meal", it rarely fails to hit the spot. / SE1 3XB; www.thegarrison.co.uk; @TheGarrisonSE1; 10 pm, Fri & Sat 10.30 pm, Sun 9.30 pm.

Gastro SW4 **£43** 2 1 5
67 Venn St 7627 0222 10–2D
"Toujours français!" – it may offer a rather "limited" menu, but this notably "pleasant" bistro, by the Clapham Picture House, is "a great choice for a quick bite" (or breakfast); nice al fresco tables too. / SW4 0BD; midnight; no Amex.

The Gate **£44** 3 2 2
51 Queen Caroline St, W6 8748 6932 7–2C
370 St John St, EC1 7278 5483 8–3D
"Serious, thoughtful and imaginative" veggie cooking has carved out a big name for this Hammersmith fixture, and its newer sibling near Sadler's Wells; they've lost their mojo a bit in recent years, though, and W6 seems more "densely packed" and "café-like" since its recent refurbishment. / www.thegaterestaurants.com; @gaterestaurant; EC1 10.30 pm, W6 10.30, Sat 11 pm.

Gaucho **£72** 2 1 1
25 Swallow St, W1 7734 4040 3–3D
60a, Charlotte St, W1 7580 6252 2–1C
89 Sloane Ave, SW3 7584 9901 5–2C
Tooley St, SE1 7407 5222 9–4D
93a Charterhouse St, EC1 7490 1676 9–1B
"Did they fly the meat in from Argentina on a private jet?" – this "opulent" and business-friendly chain offers "beautiful" steaks and a "fabulously diverse Argentinian wine list", but its "exploitative" prices are becoming a major turn-off for some reporters. / www.gauchorestaurants.co.uk; 11 pm, Fri & Sat 11.30 pm, SE10, Piccadilly midnight, Sun 11 pm; EC3 & EC1 closed Sat & Sun; WC2 & EC2 closed Sat L & Sun.

Gauthier Soho W1 **£63** 5 5 4
21 Romilly St 7494 3111 4–3A
Ring the bell for entry to Alexis Gauthier's "wonderfully quirky" Soho townhouse – a perfect venue "for a luxurious date"; the "dreamy" Gallic cuisine (with much emphasis on vegetables) and "impeccable" service are far from secondary attractions, however, and the "superb" wine list includes "some real curiosities". / W1D 5AF; www.gauthiersoho.co.uk; 10.30 pm; closed Mon L & Sun; set weekday L £46 (FP).

LE GAVROCHE W1 **£136** 5 5 5
43 Upper Brook St 7408 0881 3–2A
"Steeped in classic Gallic tradition", this "formal" Mayfair basement is "immune from trends and fashion", and – with Michel Roux Jr often very much in evidence – "unsurpassed" for those looking for a "majestic" old-school meal; "the bill makes you cry", though, so "book months ahead for the fantastic lunch deal". / W1K 7QR; www.le-gavroche.co.uk; @legavroche_; 10 pm; closed Sat L & Sun; jacket required; set weekday L £86 (FP).

Gay Hussar W1 **£48** 2 3 4
2 Greek St 7437 0973 4–2A
This Soho "stalwart" (famed for its socialist-intelligentsia associations) is an "unchanging" and "comforting" favourite for fans of its "hearty" middle European cooking; some reporters, though, are less starry-eyed – "it may be an icon, but it's mediocre and cramped". / W1D 4NB; www.gayhussar.co.uk; 10.45 pm; closed Sun; set pre theatre £33 (FP).

Gaylord W1 **£56** 3 3 2
79-81 Mortimer St 7580 3615 2–1B
"Delicious" food ("if a little pricey and rather creamy") still wins a following for this "bizarrely old-fashioned" grand subcontinental, just north of Oxford Street; critics, though, find it "unmemorable, given the prices". / W1W 7SJ; www.gaylordlondon.com; 10.45 pm, Sun 10.30 pm.

Gazette **£39** 2 2 4
79 Sherwood Ct, Chatfield Rd, SW11 7223 0999 10–1C
100 Balham High St, SW12 8772 1232 10–2C
147 Upper Richmond Rd, SW15 8789 6996 10–2B NEW
Despite sometimes "pedestrian" cooking and service "infused with Gallic indifference", this small chain generally wins praise for its "classic bistro style" and affordable prices; they must be doing something right, as a new branch has just opened, in Putney. / www.gazettebrasserie.co.uk; 11 pm.

GB Pizza EC1 **£29** 4 4 3
50 Exmouth Mkt 7278 6252 9–1A
"Delicious thin and crispy pizza in a pared-down setting and at very good-value prices" – this new Farringdon pizzeria (which has an acclaimed Margate sibling) gets an instant thumbs-up from reporters. / EC1R 4QD; www.greatbritishpizzacompany.wordpress.com.

Geales **£48** 2 1 2
1 Cale St, SW3 7965 0555 5–2C
2 Farmer St, W8 7727 7528 6–2B
Of this duo of posh chippys, it's the Notting Hill original which is more often praised for "properly cooked" (if "not cheap") fresh fish than the Chelsea offshoot; service impresses at neither branch. / www.geales.com; @geales1; 10.30 pm, Sun 9.30 pm; Mon L.

Gelupo W1 **£10** 5 2 3
7 Archer St 7287 5555 3–2D
"The best ice cream outside Italy", "magnificent" granitas, and superb coffee are all reasons to seek out this tiny Soho café, opposite Bocca di Lupo (same owners); "skip dessert wherever you are dining, and go here!" / W1D 7AU; www.gelupo.com; 11 pm, Fri & Sat 12.30 am; no Amex; no booking.

Gem N1 **£31** 3 4 4
265 Upper St 7359 0405 8–2D
A "buzzy old Islington favourite" – a "friendly" sort of place which always "gets the staples right"; these include "great-value Turkish mezze". / N1 2UQ; www.gemrestaurant.org.uk; @Gum_restaurant; 11 pm, Fri & Sat midnight, Sun 10.30 pm; no Amex.

La Genova W1 **£60** 2 2 2
32 North Audley St 7629 5916 3–2A
If you regard "old-style" as a compliment, this veteran Mayfair Italian may suit you – "good for a business lunch", and "expensive, but so reliable". / W1K 6ZG; www.lagenovarestaurant.com; 11 pm; closed Sun.

George & Vulture EC3 **£49** 2 3 5
3 Castle Ct 7626 9710 9–3C
These "unique" dining rooms – frequently visited by Dickens – can make "a wonderful place for an indulgent old-fashioned City lunch"; perhaps more for chaps, though – "you don't find many women". / EC3V 9DL; 2.15 pm; L only, closed Sat & Sun.

Gifto's Lahore Karahi UB1 **£18** 3 2 2
162-164 The Broadway 8813 8669 1–3A
This Formica-topped canteen may be "brisk and brusque", but it remains a Southall linchpin with its "authentic" spicing and its "great value" food ("especially the grills"). / UB1 1NN; www.gifto.com; 11.30 pm, Sat-Sun midnight.

Gilak N19 **£36** 3 3 2
663 Holloway Rd 7272 1692 8–1C
At the "unprepossessing end of Holloway Road", this "friendly" Archway Iranian is a staple for local students, thanks to its "lovely food and flavours" – think stews, kebabs, salads… / N19 5SE; www.gilakrestaurant.co.uk; @Gilakrestaurant; 11 pm; no Amex.

Gilbert Scott St Pancras Renaissance NW1 **£61** 2 2 4
Euston Rd 7278 3888 8–3C
"A very bad first impression for visitors off the Eurostar!"; the "beautifully restored" Neo-Gothic interior of Marcus Wareing's St Pancras dining room may be "extraordinary"… but everything else about it is decidedly run-of-the-mill. / NW1 2AR; www.thegilbertscott.co.uk; @Thegilbertscott; 10.45 pm.

Gilgamesh NW1 **£71** 2 2 3
The Stables, Camden Mkt, Chalk Farm Rd 7428 4922 8–3B
"For a special occasion", this huge pan-Asian venue in Camden Lock, with its barmily lavish wood carving, makes a "stunning" impression on first-timers; the style can ultimately seem rather "tacky", though, and critics find the whole performance rather "tired". / NW1 8AH; www.gilgameshbar.com; 11 pm, Fri & Sat 11.30 pm; set weekday L £33 (FP).

Gin Joint EC2 NEW **£51** 2 3 3
Barbican Centre, Silk St 7588 3008 12–2A
Searcy's relaunched (and renamed) brasserie within the Barbican Centre has all the hallmarks of the predecessors on this site – a "useful" and "pleasant" standby, where the food is sometimes "surprisingly good". / EC2Y 8DS; www.searcys.co.uk/venues/gin-joint; @ginjoint_london.

Ginger & White **£17** 3 3 4
2 England's Ln, NW3 7722 9944 8–2A
4a-5a, Perrins Ct, NW3 7431 9098 8–2A
These chic Hampstead and Belsize Park cafés have quite a name, not just for "brilliant" coffee, but for "great food" too – brunch a speciality. / www.gingerandwhite.com; 5.30 pm, W1 6 pm; W1 closed Sun.

Giraffe **£42** 1 2 1
Branches throughout London
"Don't go without kids… but with them it's perfect!" – this "buzzy" Tesco-owned 'world food' chain is generally "unspectacular" foodwise, but its "varied brunch menu" is a big draw and the "free balloons, plastic giraffes and so on" ensure "children love it". / www.giraffe.net; 10.45 pm, Sun 10.30 pm; no booking, Sat & Sun 9 am-5 pm.

The Glasshouse TW9 **£65** 5 5 3
14 Station Pde 8940 6777 1–3A
"A good runner-up to Chez Bruce"; this "first-class" Kew sibling to London's favourite restaurant is a "very good-value" destination, where the food is "always fabulous and seasonal" and staff "always go the extra mile"; if there's a weakness, it's the light but "noisy" interior. / TW9 3PZ; www.glasshouserestaurant.co.uk; @The_Glasshouse; 10.15 pm, Sun 9.45 pm; set weekday L £47 (FP).

Gold Mine W2 **£34** 3 2 1
102 Queensway 7792 8331 6–2C
"The best Cantonese roast duck in London" is the star attraction at this "crowded" Bayswater spot; "just don't expect 5 service!" / W2 3RR; 11 pm.*

Golden Dragon W1 **£34** 322

28-29 Gerrard St 7734 1073 4–3A

Some of "the best dim sum in Chinatown", say fans, is to be had at this prominent establishment – a top 'plain vanilla' choice in these parts, complete with traditionally "indifferent" service. / W1 6JW; Mon-Thu 11.15 pm, Fri & Sat 11.30 pm, Sun 11 pm Sun.

Golden Hind W1 **£26** 342

73 Marylebone Ln 7486 3644 2–1A

"Premier League fish and chips" served by "friendly and efficient staff" have won a big fan club for this "exemplary", if "functional", Marylebone institution; BYO. / W1U 2PN; 10 pm; closed Sat L & Sun.

Good Earth **£57** 332

233 Brompton Rd, SW3 7584 3658 5–2C
143-145 The Broadway, NW7 8959 7011 1–1B
11 Bellevue Rd, SW17 8682 9230 10–2C

"Consistency" and "very good quality" have long made it "worth paying the money" for these comfortable Chinese stalwarts, in Knightsbridge and Mill Hill; but the sentiment that it "doesn't quite hit the high notes it did" was more in evidence this year. / www.goodearthgroup.co.uk; 11 pm, Sun 10.30 pm.

Goodman **£65** 333

24-26 Maddox St, W1 7499 3776 3–2C
3 South Quay, E14 7531 0300 11–1C
11 Old Jewry, EC2 7600 8220 9–2C

"Testosterone-fuelled" and often "noisy", these "stylish" Mayfair, City and Canary Wharf steakhouses are natural "power-lunching" spots par excellence; "go hungry" – "the choice of cuts is almost overwhelming" and the quality of the meat is, for a chain, "stunning" (and – "a nudge ahead of Hawksmoor"). / www.goodmanrestaurants.com; 10.30 pm; W1 & E14 closed Sun; EC2 closed Sat & Sun.

Gordon Ramsay SW3 **£127** 343

68-69 Royal Hospital Rd 7352 4441 5–3D

Critics of GR's Chelsea flagship still decry it as "lacking innovation or interest", and even fans warn of "hysterical laughter at the prices"; its ratings recovered somewhat this year, though, supported by more praise for a "class act", and in particular Clare Smyth's cuisine that's "amazing from start to finish". / SW3 4HP; www.gordonramsay.com; @GordonRamsey; 10.15 pm; closed Sat & Sun; no jeans or trainers; booking: max 8; set weekday L £58 (FP).

Gordon's Wine Bar WC2 **£33** 235

47 Villiers St 7930 1408 4–4D

"Get a seat in the cave – it's about as interesting a place to get drunk as there is!"; by Embankment tube, this cellar wine bar, which also boasts a huge terrace, is a "fun" spot, with an "excellent and varied" wine list; "you don't really go for the food". / WC2N 6NE; www.gordonswinebar.com; 11 pm; no booking.

The Goring Hotel SW1 **£82** 355

15 Beeston Pl 7396 9000 2–4B

"Class personified"; this "very grown-up" dining room, in a "luxurious" family-run hotel near Victoria, is perhaps the last redoubt of "classically English" virtues – its "superb" staff dish up such "safe" staples as "perfect" breakfasts, "unbeatable" beef Wellington and, obviously, the "best ever afternoon tea". / SW1W 0JW; www.thegoring.com; 10 pm; closed Sat L; no jeans or trainers; table of 8 max.

Gourmet Burger Kitchen **£30** 222

Branches throughout London

For an "honest, proper burger and trimmings", many fans still tip these "no-nonsense" cafés; this year, however, ratings slipped noticeably behind younger rival Byron, and a growing band of critics perceive a "former favourite" that's now "nothing special". / www.gbkinfo.com; most branches close 10.30 pm; no booking.

Gourmet Pizza Company Gabriels Wharf SE1 **£31** 223

56 Upper Ground 7928 3188 9–3A

"Very busy and buzzy", this PizzaExpress in disguise boasts a great South Bank location (with terrace and City views); "at weekends, be prepared to wait if you haven't booked". / SE1 9PP; www.gourmetpizzacompany.co.uk; 11.30 pm.

Gourmet San E2 **£25** 421

261 Bethnal Green Rd 7729 8388 12–1D

It's not much to look at, but that's nothing to do with the real appeal of this Bethnal Green Sichuanese – "outstanding and varied food at great prices". / E2 6AH; www.oldplace.co.uk; 11 pm; D only.

Les Gourmets des Ternes W9 NEW **£58**

18 Formosa St 7286 3742 8–4A

A pocket-sized new Maida Vale outpost of a bistro in Paris's 8ème; one initial report suggests it's "not nearly as good as the original", but it's too early for a verdict – more reports please… / W9 1EE; www.lesgourmetslondon.com; closed Mon & Sun D.

The Gowlett SE15 **£32** 4 3 4
62 Gowlett Rd 7635 7048 1–4C
"Superb crispy pizzas" are the speciality at this "friendly local", in Peckham Rye, which also boasts a handsome wood-panelled interior and an ever-changing range of draft beers. / SE15 4HY; www.thegowlett.com; @theGowlettArms; 10.30 pm, Sun 9 pm; no credit cards.

Goya SW1 **£46** 2 3 2
34 Lupus St 7976 5309 2–4C
A useful destination in thinly-provided Pimlico; even some fans of this "solid local" may concede its tapas are "not the best in town", but the "buzzy" ground-floor bar is a "friendly" sort of standby. / SW1V 3EB; www.goyarestaurant.co.uk; 11.30 pm, Sun 11 pm.

Grain Store N1 **£53** 3 2 3
1-3 Stable St, Granary Sq 7324 4466 8–3C
Bruno Loubet's "industrial chic" yearling divides opinions; fans hail "a real boon to the rejuvenation of King's Cross", and praise the "must-try" meat-lite cooking and "fun" vibe – critics sense a degree of "hype", though, about an "echoey" place with "tame" food, "high" prices and "misdirected" service. / N1C 4AB; www.grainstore.com; @GrainStoreKX; 10.30 pm; closed Sun D; booking: max 14; SRA-3 stars.

The Grand Imperial Guoman Grosvenor Hotel SW1 **£60** 3 2 2
101 Buckingham Palace Rd 7821 8898 2–4B
Excellent lunchtime dim sum is the top reason to seek out this cavernous dining room, adjacent to Victoria Station; at other times it can seem "a touch pricey for what it is.". / SW1W 0SJ; www.grandimperiallondon.com; 10.30 pm.

Granger & Co **£49** 2 3 4
175 Westbourne Grove, W11 7229 9111 6–1B
Buckley Building, 49 Clerkenwell Grn, EC1 7251 9032 9–1A
"For an easy meal with a stylish crowd in a fun setting", these "chilled" Antipodean diners, in Notting Hill and Clerkenwell, fit the bill, especially for brunch; fans say the "uncomplicated" Asian-influenced food is "appealing" too, but critics say it's "inconsistent" and "overpriced".

The Grapes E14 **£43** 1 2 5
76 Narrow St 7987 4396 11–1B
A Limehouse relic majoring in fish 'n' chips and Sunday roast – no culinary haunt this, but fans insist that's "not an issue for a 500-year-old pub in a famous street, on the bank of the Thames". / E14 8BP; www.thegrapes.co.uk; @TheGrapesLondon; 9.30 pm; closed Sat L & Sun D; no Amex.

Grazing Goat W1 **£57** 3 2 3
6 New Quebec St 7724 7243 2–2A
Quietly located near Marble Arch, a gastropub which can make a "surprisingly good" central standby; the food is "well presented and tasty", if perhaps "a bit pricey" for what it is. / W1H 7RQ; www.thegrazinggoat.co.uk; @TheGrazingGoat; 10 pm, Sun 9.30 pm; ; SRA-3 stars.

Great Nepalese NW1 **£34** 3 4 2
48 Eversholt St 7388 6737 8–3C
"The location in a scruffy Euston side street doesn't promise much", but the menu at this Nepalese stalwart "delivers in spades", offering "interesting" national dishes, as well as the usual north Indian suspects. / NW1 1DA; www.great-nepalese.co.uk; 11.30 pm, Sun 10 pm.

Great Queen Street WC2 **£45** 3 3 3
32 Great Queen St 7242 0622 4–1D
"Hearty" and "well-cooked" British seasonal fare from an ever-changing menu has made a big name for this "casual", "cramped" and "very noisy" Covent Garden fixture; some former fans, though, do fear it's slipping. / WC2B 5AA; www.greatqueenstreetrestaurant.co.uk; @greatqueenstreet; 10.30 pm; closed Sun D; no Amex.

The Greedy Buddha SW6 **£33** 3 2 2
144 Wandsworth Bridge Rd 7751 3311 10–1B
A Fulham Indian where some "brilliant" meals are recorded; service, though, can be rather "amateur". / SW6 2UH; www.thegreedybuddha.com; @thegreedybudha; 10.30 pm, Fri & Sat 11.30 pm; no Amex.

Green Cottage NW3 **£41** 3 1 1
9 New College Pde 7722 5305 8–2A
Still "much loved by the regulars", a generally "reliable" Swiss Cottage Cantonese; the setting "is not inspiring", though, and the service can seem "weary". / NW3 5EP; 10.30 pm, Sun 9.30 pm; no Amex.

Green Man & French Horn WC2 **£45** 3 4 4
54 St Martin's Ln 7836 2645 4–4C
An "idiosyncratic" bistro menu complements "a brilliant selection of Loire wines" (favouring biodynamic vintages) at this "squashed" but "lively" ex-pub, in the heart of Theatreland – it's now better

rated than its nearby parent, Terroirs. / WC2N 4EA; www.greenmanfrenchhorn.co; @gm_fh.

Green's SW1 **£75** 3|4|4
36 Duke St 7930 4566 3–3D
Simon Parker Bowles's "clubby" bastion of the St James's Establishment "remains absolutely as it always has been", and its loyal clientele – who enjoy its unhurried meals of "unadventurous" English fare – would't have it any other way; a move, possibly to Mayfair, is on the cards for late-2015. / SW1Y 6DF; www.greens.org.uk; 10.30 pm; closed Sun; no jeans or trainers.

Greenberry Café NW1 NEW **£40** 3|3|3
101 Regent's Park Rd 7483 3765 8–2B
"Everything a neighbourhood café should be"; this "light and airy" glass-fronted spot, in Primrose Hill, is "a great improvement on its predecessor Troika" (RIP), offering good coffee, cakes, brunches and light meals, and "sweet" service too. / NW1 8UR; greenberrycafe.co.uk; 10 pm; closed Sun D; no Amex; set always available £25 (FP).

The Greenhouse W1 **£128** 4|4|4
27a Hays Mews 7499 3331 3–3B
"An oasis of peace", "tucked away" in a Mayfair mews with "discreet" service, where Arnaud Bignon's "inventive but un-gimmicky" cuisine is the counterpoint to an "enormous", "connoisseur's" wine list; apart from the fact it's "cripplingly expensive", what's not to like? / W1J 5NY; www.greenhouserestaurant.co.uk; 10.15 pm; closed Sat L & Sun; booking: max 8; set weekday L £65 (FP).

Grumbles SW1 **£43** 2|3|3
35 Churton St 7834 0149 2–4B
"Not glamorous" but still a "great local eatery" – this prehistoric Pimlico bistro may offer "very simple" cuisine, but it's "good value, especially at lunch". / SW1V 2LT; www.grumblesrestaurant.co.uk; 10.45 pm.

Guglee **£33** 3|4|4
7 New College Pde, NW3 7317 8555 8–2A
279 West End Ln, NW6 7317 8555 1–1B
With their "deliciously light, but not insubstantial" dishes and "fresh, modern ambience", these West Hampstead and Swiss Cottage Indians are "a cut above your average local curry house". / www.guglee.co.uk; 11 pm.

The Guinea Grill W1 **£67** 3|3|3
30 Bruton Pl 7499 1210 3–3B
Tucked away in a mews, attached to a quaint pub, this "old-school" dining room serves "solid" steak and pies in quaint (slightly "tired") comfort; this is Mayfair, though, and prices are "hardly pub prices!" / W1J 6NL; www.theguinea.co.uk; @guineagrill; 10.30 pm; closed Sat L & Sun; booking: max 8.

The Gun E14 **£59** 3|3|5
27 Coldharbour 7515 5222 11–1C
"A refuge from the sterility of Canary Wharf" – this "atmospheric and tastefully refurbished" tavern "could not have a better riverside location", with stunning views over to the O2; the food "doesn't disappoint" either, if at prices which reflect the local market. / E14 9NS; www.thegundocklands.com; @thegundocklands; 10.30 pm, Sun 9.30 pm.

Gung-Ho NW6 **£40** 3|4|2
328-332 West End Ln 7794 1444 1–1B
"Situated in the 'burbs, but the food is anything but 'local'", say fans of this West Hampstead stalwart, whose reputation for "always helpful" service and "delicious" cooking is recovering after last year's change of ownership. / NW6 1LN; www.stir-fry.co.uk; 11.30 pm; no Amex.

Gustoso Ristorante & Enoteca SW1 **£43** 3|5|3
33 Willow Pl 7834 5778 2–4B
"Tucked away in a quiet Westminster backstreet, but known by those in the know", this Sardinian yearling is becoming "a firm favourite" – it's run by "very welcoming" people, and its "simple" food is "authentic" and "affordable". / SW1P 1JH; ristorantegustoso.co.uk; @GustosoRist; 10.30 pm, Fri & Sat 11 pm, Sun 9.30 pm.

GYMKHANA W1 **£63** 5|4|4
42 Albemarle St 3011 5900 3–3C
Straight into the super-league of London's nouvelle Indians, this "unstuffy" yearling, near The Ritz, offers a "sensationally subtle" cuisine, including some "wonderfully original game and other dishes" – it's "worth the hassle to get a table". / W1S 4JH; www.gymkhanalondon.com; @GymkhanaLondon; 10.30 pm; closed Sun.

Haché **£37** 3|3|4
329-331 Fulham Rd, SW10 7823 3515 5–3B
24 Inverness St, NW1 7485 9100 8–3B
153 Clapham High St, SW4 7738 8760 10–2D
147-149 Curtain Rd, EC2 7739 8396 12–1B
"The place to go if you're after a juicy patty!" – this "small and friendly" group "continues to set the standards for high-grade burgers"; survey ratings support those who say it "definitely outperforms the bigger operators". / www.hacheburgers.com; 10.30 pm, Fri-Sat 11 pm, Sun 10 pm.

Hakkasan **£89** 4 2 4
17 Bruton St, W1 7907 1888 3–2C
8 Hanway Pl, W1 7927 7000 4–1A
These "dark and brooding" nightclub-style haunts "elevate westernised Chinese food to a new level" – despite their crowds, noise, "snotty" service and "out-of-this-world" prices, they are the bedrock for what's now a growing global brand; "to avoid a second mortgage, check out the extraordinary dim sum at lunchtime". / www.hakkasan.com; midnight, Sun 11 pm.

Halepi W2 **£44** 3 4 2
18 Leinster Ter 7262 1070 6–2C
Just north of Hyde Park, an "old-fashioned" taverna still worth seeking out for its "well-cooked" Greek dishes; even supporters, though, can find it "expensive, for what's on offer". / W2 3ET; www.halepi.co.uk; midnight.

Ham Yard Restaurant Ham Yard Hotel W1 NEW **£51** 2 2 2
1 Ham Yd 3642 2000 3–2D
All credit to Firmdale Hotels for developing this unbelievably central site, whose courtyard feels a million miles from Soho; shame there's still so much to do, though – our early-days visit found a menu seemingly extracted from a late-'90s time-capsule, and reporters found the atmosphere remarkably "lacklustre". / W1D 7DT; Rated on Editors' visit; www.hamyardhotel.com; @ham_yard.

The Hampshire Hog W6 **£50** 2 2 3
227 King St 8748 3391 7–2B
"Bright and cheerful", this pub near Hammersmith Town Hall benefits not only from a "lovely" interior, but also from a "large and very attractive garden"; foodwise it had great early-days promise, but some more "ordinary" meals were reported this year. / W6 9JT; www.thehampshirehog.com; @TheHampshireHog; 11 pm; closed Sun D; SRA-2 stars.

Harbour City W1 **£40** 2 1 1
46 Gerrard St 7439 7859 4–3B
"Incredibly cheap, impeccable dim sum" – the main reason to visit this Gerrard Street stalwart, which is "otherwise very undistinguished". / W1D 5QH; www.harbourcity.com.hk; 11.30 pm, Fri & Sat midnight, Sun 10.30 pm.

Hard Rock Café W1 **£49** 3 2 4
150 Old Park Ln 7629 0382 3–4B
"Still rocking!"; the world's first Hard Rock is "still buzzing after 40 years", and you do get "a good burger"; brace yourself, though, for the noise. / W1K 1QZ; www.hardrock.com/london; @HardRockLondon; midnight; need 20+ to book.

Hardy's Brasserie W1 **£49** 2 2 4
53 Dorset St 7935 5929 2–1A
"Largely unchanged over the years", this "pleasant" Marylebone haunt is a "great place to spend a quiet evening"; the fact that it's "now open for weekend breakfasts" is a "real bonus" too. / W1U 7NH; www.hardysbrasserie.com; @hardys_W1; 10 pm; closed Sat & Sun.

Hare & Tortoise **£30** 3 2 3
11-13 The Brunswick, WC1 7278 9799 2–1D
373 Kensington High St, W14 7603 8887 7–1D
38 Haven Grn, W5 8810 7066 1–2A
296-298 Upper Richmond Rd, SW15 8394 7666 10–2B
90 New Bridge St, EC4 7651 0266 9–2A
"A great place to grab a meal" – this "fuss-free" pan-Asian chain "knocks Wagamama into a cocked hat", offering great sushi, noodles and "tasty Asian dishes" at "impressively low prices". / www.hareandtortoise-restaurants.co.uk; 10.45 pm, Fri & Sat 11.15 pm; EC4 10 pm; EC4 closed Sun; W14 no bookings.

Harry Morgan's NW8 **£40** 2 2 2
31 St John's Wood High St 7722 1869 8–3A
"Not beautiful, or gourmet, but dependable"; this classic Jewish deli, in St John's Wood, is arguably a bit "pricey" and "tired", but it still inspires a high degree of loyalty, especially for the "really good salt beef" which is its trademark. / NW8 7NH; www.harryms.co.uk; 10.30 pm.

Harwood Arms SW6 **£59** 4 3 3
Walham Grove 7386 1847 5–3A
"Don't be fooled, this ain't pub grub!" – "top-quality" dishes (especially game) are cooked "with flair" at this esteemed boozer in the backwoods of Fulham; from a very high starting point, though, standards have "slipped" a bit in recent times. / SW6 1QP; www.harwoodarms.com; 9.15 pm, Sun 9 pm; closed Mon L.

Hashi SW20 **£36** 4 4 3
54 Durham Rd 8944 1888 10–2A
A "charming and intimate" local, "tucked away in Raynes Park"; its "beautiful" sushi and sashimi, say fans, are "as good as at any Japanese you'd find in Mayfair". / SW20 0TW; www.hashicooking.co.uk; 10.30 pm; closed Mon; no Amex.

The Havelock Tavern W14 **£44** 3 2 3
57 Masbro Rd 7603 5374 7–1C
"This archetypal Olympia gastropub has mellowed

in recent years" – the sullen service of old has mercifully been ditched, but so has the former promise of excitement, though the food is still "of good quality". / W14 0LS; www.havelocktavern.com; @HavelockTavern; 10 pm, Sun 9.30 pm; no booking.

The Haven N20 **£50** 222
1363 High Rd 8445 7419 1–1B
"West End quality on the edge of London" – the optimistic view on this popular (and sometimes "very noisy") local; not everyone's convinced, though, and sceptics say "standards have dropped" in recent times. / N20 9LN; www.haven-bistro.co.uk; 11 pm.

Hawksmoor **£64** 443
5a, Air St, W1 7406 3980 3–3D
11 Langley St, WC2 7420 9390 4–2C
3 Yeoman's Row, SW3 7590 9290 5–2C NEW
157 Commercial St, E1 7426 4850 12–2B
10-12 Basinghall St, EC2 7397 8120 9–2C
"Absurdly juicy" steaks and "first-class cocktails" underpin huge acclaim for Huw Gott & Will Beckett's "casual and laid-back" temples to meat; even fans admit prices are "eye-watering", though, and ratings are beginning to fall some way behind those of its main rival, Goodman. / www.thehawksmoor.com; all branches between 10 pm & 11 pm; EC2 closed Sat-Sun.

Haz **£37** 233
9 Cutler St, E1 7929 7923 9–2D
34 Foster Ln, EC2 7600 4172 9–2B
112 Houndsditch, EC3 7623 8180 9–2D
6 Mincing Ln, EC3 7929 3173 9–3D
For a "relatively cheap and cheerful" bite in the City, these "very buzzy and busy" Turkish outlets make a "slightly different" choice, and the fare is generally pretty "decent". / www.hazrestaurant.co.uk; 11.30 pm; EC3 closed Sun.

Hazuki WC2 **£41** 222
43 Chandos Pl 7240 2530 4–4C
This really handily located Japanese, by the Coliseum, seems to risk losing its way; the set lunch menus may still be worth seeking out, but a worrying number of reports have found the whole performance rather "tired" of late. / WC2M 4HS; www.hazukilondon.co.uk; 10.30 pm, Sun 9.30 pm.

Heddon Street Kitchen W1 NEW
3-9 Heddon St 7592 1212 3–2C
Gordon Ramsay makes his first leap into the heart of the West End with this new restaurant just off Regent Street, modelled on his City venture Bread Street Kitchen. / W1B 4BE; www.gordonramsay.com/heddon-street.

Hedone W4 **£80** 543
301-303 Chiswick High Rd 8747 0377 7–2A
"Truly staggering!"; after three years in operation, Mikael Jonsson's "unsung" open-kitchen venture, in outer Chiswick, has finally got properly into its stride – his "incredibly clever" modern Scandi dishes deliver "small bites of perfection and amazement". / W4 4HH; www.hedonerestaurant.com; 9.30 pm; closed Mon, Tue L, Wed L & Sun; set weekday L £74 (FP).

Hélène Darroze The Connaught Hotel W1 **£125** 234
Carlos Pl 3147 7200 3–3B
"Beautiful, decadent and extravagant", this Mayfair dining room certainly looks the part to host some "stunning" fine dining experiences, and fans do indeed say it offers "perfection"; there are, though, too many reports of "very average" experiences too… and all at "ferocious" prices! / W1K 2AL; www.the-connaught.co.uk; @TheConnaught; 9.30 pm; closed Mon & Sun; jacket & tie; set weekday L £65 (FP).

The Henry Root SW10 **£56** 223
9 Park Walk 7352 7040 5–3B
"A very flexible format", accommodating anything from a bar snack to a slap-up meal, helps make this "warm and now well-established" Chelsea hangout "a good neighbourhood all-rounder" – "not fine food, but reliable". / SW10 0AJ; www.thehenryroot.com; @thehenryroot; 10.45 pm, Sun 8.45 pm.

Hereford Road W2 **£49** 332
3 Hereford Rd 7727 1144 6–1B
"For nose-to-tail eating without the price tag", Tom Pemberton's "noisy" Bayswater fixture wins praise for his "well-cooked", notably "seasonal" dishes (with "less offal and more fish and veg of late"); however, it does not achieve ratings quite as stellar as its foodie renown would imply. / W2 4AB; www.herefordroad.org; @3HerefordRoad; 10.30 pm, Sun 10 pm; set weekday L £32 (FP).

Hibiscus W1 **£122** 332
29 Maddox St 7629 2999 3–2C
As usual, Claude Bosi's low-key foodie temple, in Mayfair, polarises reporters – fans extol an "outstanding" venture serving "truly memorable" dishes, but a large minority of critics complain of "overwrought" dishes at "extortionate" prices. / W1S 2PA; www.hibiscusrestaurant.co.uk; @HibiscusLondon; 11 pm; closed Mon & Sun; set weekday L £56 (FP).

High Road Brasserie W4 £54 223
162-166 Chiswick High Rd 8742 7474 7–2A
As a venue for an "excellent breakfast" or "family brunch", this prominently sited Soho House group brasserie offers a handy perch for the Chiswick Set to see and be seen – al fresco tables are particularly prized. / W4 1PR; www.brasserie.highroadhouse.co.uk; @sohohouse; 10.45 pm, Fri & Sat 11.45 pm, Sun 10 pm.

High Timber EC4 £56 344
8 High Timber 7248 1777 9–3B
"A hidden gem, only 100m from the Millennium Bridge", and offering "stunning" views from the outside tables; its culinary appeal is "straight down the line" – "excellent steak" plus "amazing South African wines", so "be sure to walk through the temperature-controlled cellars". / EC4V 3PA; www.hightimber.com; @HTimber; 10 pm; closed Sat & Sun; set weekday L £39 (FP).

Hill & Szrok E8 NEW £40
60 Broadway Mkt 7833 1933 1–2D
"Affordable treats for carnivores" – that's the key attraction of Broadway Market's new "butcher by day, restaurant by night"; early-days survey feedback, though, was too limited to justify a rating. / E8 4QJ; www.hillandszrok.co.uk.

Hilliard EC4 £28 422
26a Tudor St 7353 8150 9–3A
"Queues of affluent lawyers" attest to the quality of the "first-class" sandwiches – and a "good selection of hot dishes" too – at this cramped all-day operation, by the Temple. / EC4Y 0AY; www.hilliardfood.co.uk; 6 pm; L only, closed Sat & Sun; no booking.

Hix W1 £65 222
66-70 Brewer St 7292 3518 3–2D
Fans hail Mark Hix's discreet Soho dining room as a "very cool" urban haunt, where "top ingredients" are "flawlessly prepared"; even fans can find it "overpriced", though, and harsher critics say it's "heavy weather" all-round – "best bet is to remain in the excellent basement bar!" / W1F 9UP; www.hixsoho.co.uk; @HixRestaurants; 11.30 pm, Sun 10.30 pm; set weekday L & pre-theatre £43 (FP).

Hix Oyster & Chop House EC1 £58 322
36-37 Greenhill Rents, Cowcross St 7017 1930 9–1A
Mark Hix's "busy" but decidedly "basic" Smithfield dining room offers a "great range of surf 'n' turf", generally quite well realised; it's pricey though, and the "friendly" service can be "slow". / EC1M 6BN; www.restaurantsetcltd.com; @HixRestaurants; 11 pm, Sun 10 pm; closed Sat L.

Hixter EC2 NEW £81 333
9a Devonshire Sq 7220 9498 9–2D
"Great meat" features in reports on Mark Hix's trendy (son of Tramshed) steak 'n' chicken joints, near Liverpool Street – "cramped and noisy, but always fun"; now open on the South Bank too. / EC2M 4AE; www.hixter.co.uk; @hixtercity; closed Sat & Sun.

HKK EC2 £70 553
Broadgate Quarter, 88 Worship St 3535 1888 12–2B
"An amazing realm of taste sensations" rewards those who explore the "superb, bite-sized Cantonese banquet menu" on offer at this "reliably incredible" City-fringe yearling; the contemporary interior, though, is rather "austere". / EC2A 2BE; www.hkklondon.com; @HKKlondon; 10 pm; closed Sun.

Hoi Polloi Ace Hotel E1 £57 233
100 Shoreditch High St 8880 6100 12–1B
"A fun addition to Shoreditch" – this "large dining space" scores well for its "hip" style and "in-crowd buzz", even if the cooking can be "a touch underwhelming". / E1 6JQ; hoi-polloi.co.uk; @wearehoipolloi; Sun-Wed midnight, Thu-Sat 1 am; up to 6, 7-12 alacarte credit card details cancellation within 48 hours set menu 13-20.

Holborn Dining Room Rosewood London WC1 NEW £58 223
252 High Holborn 3747 8633 2–1D
"A vast barn of a room" – sheer size often seems to be the main impression of this impressive new Midtown space; food and service are rated "merely average", but this certainly makes a "good business lunch option" nonetheless. / WC1V 7EN; www.holborndiningroom.com; @HolbornDining; 11.15pm, Sun 10.30 pm.

Hole in the Wall W4 £41 233
12 Sutton Lane North 8742 7185 7–2A
For Chiswick folk, an "excellent local gastropub", of particular note for a "grassy back garden, big enough for kids to roam in"; the food's quite 'gastro' too. / W4 4LD; www.holeinthewallchiswickco.uk; @HoleInTheWallW4; 9.45 pm, Sun 9.15 pm; closed Mon L & Tue L.

Holy Cow SW11 £25 433
166 Battersea Pk Rd 7498 2000 10–1C
A "really top Indian take-away", offering "cheap and very authentic" curries (which is why, exceptionally, we list it here); of its numerous branches, the Battersea operation listed is "definitely a cut above". / SW11 4ND; www.holycowfineindianfood.com; 11 pm, Sun 10.30 pm; D only.

Homage Waldorf Hilton WC2 **£75** 1 1 2
22 Aldwych 7836 2400 2–2D
A "lovely" former ballroom, with "an excellent location" on the fringe of Covent Garden; sadly, though, the experience of dining here is too often characterised as "shambolic" – what a waste! / WC2B 4DD; www.waldorfhilton.co.uk/dining-bars/homage-grand-s; Mon-Wed 10 pm, Thu-Sat 10.30 pm, Sun 9.30 pm; D only; set pre theatre £48 (FP).

Homeslice WC2 NEW **£23** 5 3 2
13 Neal's Yd 7836 4604 4–2C
"They know how to make pizza exciting again", at this "rammed" Covent Garden yearling, where servings are "ENORMOUS" – "you'll think you can't finish, but you'll find a way!"; "staff are cheerful in the face of the queue, but it's too noisy a place to linger". / WC2H 9DP; www.homeslicepizza.co.uk; @homesliceLDN; Mon-Sat 10 pm, Sun 7.15 pm.

Honest Burgers **£38** 4 4 4
4 Meard St, W1 3609 9524 4–2A
159 Portobello Rd, W11 awaiting tel 6–1B
54-56 Camden Lock Pl, NW1 8617 3949 8–2B
72 Tooting High St, SW17 3601 5700 10–2B NEW
Brixton Village, Coldharbour Ln, SW9 7733 7963 10–2D
"A leading light in London's burger explosion!"; "for quick and tasty food, you'll be hard pressed to better" this "brilliant" chain, with its Ginger Pig-sourced meat and "lusciously addictive" chips; "plan ahead to beat the queues" though – at weekends, they're "dreadful". / www.honestburgers.co.uk; @honestburgers; 10 pm - 11 pm; SW9 closed Mon D.

Honey & Co W1 **£32** 4 4 3
25a, Warren St 7388 6175 2–1B
"You have to squeeze in, go with the flow, and not stand on ceremony", but the pay-off at this "tiny" but "committed" café, near Warren Street tube, is "superb" and "zesty" modern Israeli food prepared "with real flair". / W1T 5JZ; www.honeyandco.co.uk; @Honeyandco; closed Sun.

The Horseshoe NW3 **£48** 3 2 3
28 Heath St 7431 7206 8–2A
Two things make this Hampstead pub "very popular" – an "ever-changing" menu, and "sensational beer from Camden Brewery" (which was formerly produced on-site); oh, and the dearth of local competition probably helps too! / NW3 6TE; www.thehorseshoehampstead.com; @getluckyatthehorseshoe; 10 pm, Fri & Sat 11 pm.

Hot Stuff SW8 **£20** 3 3 2
23 Wilcox Rd 7720 1480 10–1D
"Tasty, deeply flavoured curries, with lots of interesting specials" – reason to seek out this "unassuming" Indian BYO, deep in Vauxhall. / SW8 2XA; www.eathotstuff.com; 9.30 pm; closed Mon; no Amex.

House of Ho W1 NEW **£59** 4 3 2
57-59 Old Compton St 7287 0770 4–3A
"Creative" and "tasty" fare has helped this Vietnamese newcomer make quite a splash; located on Soho's main drag, it's aiming to be a "cool venue for a young crowd", but can suffer from "a lack of atmosphere". / W1D 6HP; www.houseofho.co.uk; @houseofho; Mon-Fri 10.30 pm, Thu-Sun 11.30 pm.

The Hoxton Grill EC2 **£52** 2 2 4
81 Great Eastern St 7739 9111 12–1B
The "NYC warehouse-y" style makes for a "funky" vibe, at this "buzzing" Shoreditch venue, tipped by fans for its diner-style fare – the odd "really bad" experience was reported this year, but breakfasts and burgers are usually praised. / EC2A 3HU; www.hoxtongrill.co.uk; @hoxtongrill; 11.45 pm; set weekday L £34 (FP).

Hubbard & Bell Hoxton Hotel WC1 NEW
199-206 High Holborn 7661 3030 2–1D
From Soho House, a new 'Brooklyn-style' all-day restaurant in London's newest Midtown hotel. / WC1V 7BD; www.hubbardandbell.com.

Hudsons SW15 **£42** 2 2 3
113 Lower Richmond Rd 8785 4522 10–1A
"They have everything covered when it comes to breakfast", at this "cheap and cheerful" Putney bistro – a perennially popular hang out for local thirty-somethings. / SW15 1EX; www.hudsonsrestaurant.co.uk; @hudsonsw15; 10 pm, Sun 9.30 pm; closed Tue L.

Hummus Bros **£17** 3 3 2
88 Wardour St, W1 7734 1311 3–2D
37-63 Southampton Row, WC1 7404 7079 2–1D
62 Exmouth Mkt, EC1 7812 1177 9–1A
128 Cheapside, EC2 7726 8011 9–2B
"Upbeat and friendly", these "quick-snack" spots "do exactly what you'd expect, quickly, freshly, efficiently and at a good price"; "you leave feeling healthy too". / www.hbros.co.uk; W1 10 pm, Thu-Sat 11 pm; WC1 9 pm, EC1 10 pm, Thu-Sat 11 pm, Sun 4 pm; WC1, EC2 closed Sat & Sun; no booking.

Hunan SW1 **£65** 5 3 1
51 Pimlico Rd 7730 5712 5–2D
"The best Chinese in town" – Michael Peng "continues the traditions set by his father", at this "delightfully odd" and "cramped" Pimlico stalwart; there's no menu – "tell them what you like, and mouthwatering little plates from heaven just keep on coming". / SW1W 8NE; www.hunanlondon.com; 9.30 pm; closed Sun; set weekday L £48 (FP).

Huong-Viet An Viet House N1 **£35** 3 2 2
12-14 Englefield Rd 7249 0877 1–1C
"After two decades, I'm still a fan"; this Vietnamese fixture, in a community centre – built as De Beauvoir's public baths – remains pretty much as it ever was; BYO. / N1 4LS; 11 pm; closed Sun; no Amex.

Hush **£58** 2 2 3
8 Lancashire Ct, W1 7659 1500 3–2B
95-97 High Holborn, WC1 7242 4580 2–1D
"One of the best outdoor terraces in central London" helps make the tucked-away Mayfair branch of this small group a "lovely place to meet"; the "comfort food" is "all a bit bland", with the EC4 and WC1 branches more likely to be judged "underwhelming". / www.hush.co.uk; @Hush_Restaurant; W1 10.45 pm; WC1 10.30 pm, Sun 9.30 pm; WC1 closed Sun.

Hutong The Shard SE1 **£77** 2 2 4
31 St Thomas St 3011 1257 9–4C
"A view to die for" rewards those who ascend to this "exciting" Chinese dining room on the 33rd floor of London's great new landmark – "you certainly pay for it", though, and reporters are split between those who think this is an "expensive but impressive" destination, and those who just find standards "very average". / SE1 9RY; www.hutong.co.uk; @HutongShard; 11 pm.

Ibérica **£46** 3 2 3
195 Great Portland St, W1 7636 8650 2–1B
12 Cabot Sq, E14 7636 8650 11–1C
89 Turnmill St, EC1 7636 8650 9–1A NEW
Fans are "very impressed" by these modern tapas joints – the "airy" Gt Portland St original is the best, and the E14 branch is "one of the Wharf's better restaurants"; drifting survey ratings, however, suggest the food is not what it once was. / 11 pm; W1 closed Sun D.

Imli Street W1 **£38** 3 4 4
167-169 Wardour St 7287 4243 3–1D
A "very busy" Soho operation, where "flavoursome and interesting" Indian street food comes in "small dishes", encouraging "lots of sampling", and at prices which "won't break the bank". / W1F 8WR; www.imlistreet.com; 11 pm, Sun 10 pm.

Inaho W2 **£40** 4 3 2
4 Hereford Rd 7221 8495 6–1B
"Top-quality Japanese in a charming chalet!" – imagine having "lovely sushi in someone's front room", and you have a pretty good picture of this tiny Bayswater shack. / W2 4AA; 10.30 pm; closed Sat L & Sun; no Amex or Maestro.

Inamo **£45** 2 2 2
4-12 Regent St, SW1 7484 0500 3–3D
134-136 Wardour St, W1 7851 7051 3–1D
"A gimmick, yes, but fun to go once" – using your table as a touchscreen to order your oriental lunch or dinner is, obviously, something "kids love", but most adults seem to enjoy it too; everything else is a bit incidental. / www.inamo-restaurant.com; @InamoRestaurant; 11 pm, SW1 12 am.

India Club Strand Continental Hotel WC2 **£25** 3 2 1
143 Strand 7836 0650 2–2D
"Hopefully, it will never change!"; with its "decent" subcontinental food and "oddly compelling" ambience, this "down-at-heel" canteen, near the Indian High Commission, retains a devoted fan club; BYO. / WC2R 1JA; www.strand-continental.co.uk; 10.50 pm; no credit cards; booking: max 6.

Indian Moment SW11 **£35** 3 4 3
44 Northcote Rd 7223 6575 10–2C
"A slightly healthier curry option" – this Battersea spot wins praise for its non-traditional food preparation, and "attractive" modern design too. / SW11 1NZ; www.indianmoment.co.uk; @indianmoment; 11.30 pm, Fri & Sat midnight; no Amex.

Indian Ocean SW17 **£30** 4 4 3
214 Trinity Rd 8672 7740 10–2C
"A local indian that never disappoints"; with its "fresh and well-cooked dishes" and its "very good" service, this Wandsworth institution continues to achieve "surprisingly good" standards. / SW17 7HP; www.indianoceanrestaurant.com; 11.30 pm.

Indian Rasoi N2 **£38** 4 4 3
7 Denmark Ter 8883 9093 1–1B
"Really unusual Indian fare" with "clear flavours, subtle spicing, and little resort to creamy sauces" wins acclaim for this "tiny" but "brilliant" Muswell Hill spot; it's "always full". / N2 9HG; www.indian-rasoi.co.uk; 10.30 pm; no Amex.

Indian Zilla SW13 **£44** 5 5 3
2-3 Rocks Ln 8878 3989 10–1A
Manoj Vasaikar's "subtly spiced and creative" dishes attract rave reviews for this "posh" Barnes curry house (an offshoot of Indian Zing) – "factor in the price, and it's one of the best Indians in town". / SW13 0DB; www.indianzilla.co.uk; 11 pm, Sun 10.30 pm; closed weekday L.

Indian Zing W6 **£48** 5 4 3
236 King St 8748 5959 7–2B
"Bursts of gorgeous flavours" characterise Manoj Vasaikar's "lovely and light" modern Indian cooking, which has won a gigantic fan club for this "always-busy" little place, near Ravenscourt Park; "closely-packed tables" are the only real gripe. / W6 0RS; www.indianzing.co.uk; @IndianZing; 11 pm, Sun 10 pm; set always available £30 (FP).

Indigo One Aldwych WC2 **£65** 2 3 3
1 Aldwych 7300 0400 2–2D
"A good view of the bar from the balcony" adds to the buzz at this Theatreland mezzanine dining room; its affordable set deals make it an "excellent pre-theatre venue", and handy for business too. / WC2B 4BZ; www.onealdwych.com; 10.15 pm.

Inn the Park SW1 **£50** 2 2 4
St James's Pk 7451 9999 2–3C
"A beautiful location in the heart of St James's Park, but the food is average" – that's always been the trade-off at this striking all-day café, which celebrated its 10th year with a refurb in 2014. / SW1A 2BJ; www.peytonandbyrne.co.uk; @PeytonandByrne; 8.30 pm; closed Sun D; no Amex.

Inside SE10 **£43** 4 4 1
19 Greenwich South St 8265 5060 1–3D
"Well worth putting up with the disappointing ambience for the sake of the delicious food" – Guy Awford is a "chef-patron who cares", and the cooking at his "cramped" and "unpretentious" side street restaurant is "still the best in Greenwich". / SE10 8NW; www.insiderestaurant.co.uk; @insideandgreenwich; 10.30 pm, Fri & Sat 11 pm; closed Mon & Sun D.

Ippudo London WC2 NEW
Central St Giles Piazza 7240 4469 4–1B
This globally popular ramen bar opens its first European outpost in Central St Giles. / WC2H 8AG; ippudo.co.uk; @IppudoLondon.

Isarn N1 **£46** 4 3 2
119 Upper St 7424 5153 8–3D
An "understated" Islington spot where the "unstereotypical" Thai cuisine is "a cut above" the norm. / N1 1QP; www.isarn.co.uk; 11 pm, Sun 10.30 pm.

Ishtar W1 **£45** 3 4 3
10-12 Crawford St 7224 2446 2–1A
"A great little Turkish restaurant in Marylebone", and world-famous thereabouts for "the best-value set lunch in town". / W1U 6AZ; www.ishtarrestaurant.com; 11 pm, Sun 10.30 pm.

Itsu **£33** 2 3 2
Branches throughout London
"Guilt-free" fast food – "healthy and fresh" soups, sushi and other Asian-inspired snacks – win praise for this "exploding" cafeteria chain. / www.itsu.co.uk; 11 pm; E14 10 pm; some are closed Sat & Sun; no booking.

The Ivy WC2 **£72** 2 3 3
1-5 West St 7836 4751 4–3B
This former Theatreland idol still wows fans with its "slick and polished" style and "predictable" nursery fare; those who remember the glory days when this was London's favourite restaurant, though, may find its current performance "embarrassing" – time, they say, "for a complete overhaul". / WC2H 9NQ; www.the-ivy.co.uk; @CapriceHoldings; 11 pm, Sun 10 pm; no shorts; booking: max 6; set weekday L & dinner £50 (FP).

Izgara N3 **£34** 3 2 1
11 Hendon Lane 8371 8282 1–1B
"Great mezze" and a "sensible choice of charcoal- or oven-cooked meats" – the attractions which ensure this Turkish venture, in North Finchley, is always "busy and cramped". / N3 1RT; www.izgararestaurant.net; 11.30 pm; no Amex.

Jackson & Rye W1 **£40** 1 1 2
56 Wardour St 7437 8338 3–2D
A "NYC-wannabe", this smartly turned out new Soho diner does have a "nice bar" and it can turn out a decent brunch too; service, though, can be "truly awful", and the cooking is "by numbers". / W1D 4JG; www.jacksonrye.com; @jacksonrye.

Jai Krishna N4 **£19** 4 3 2
161 Stroud Green Rd 7272 1680 8–1D
"Nearly 30 years on, still excellent value for money"; this "very welcoming" South Indian veggie, in Stroud Green, "always delivers exceptional food"... "and it's BYO too". / N4 3PZ; 10.30 pm; closed Sun; no credit cards.

Jamaica Patty Co. WC2 NEW **£10** 3 2 2
26 New Row 7836 3334 4–3C
"Great Jamaican patties... in central London!" – not much to add about this brightly lit Covent

Garden pit stop, where the fuel is "cheap" and "tasty". / WC2N 4LA; www.jamaicapatty.co.uk.

Jamie's Diner W1 NEW **£50** 2 1 2
32a, Shaftsbury Ave 3697 4117 3–3D
Jamie Oliver's "family-friendly" new Soho diner is "billed as a 'pop-up', but has all the hallmarks of a chain roll-out to come"; fans say its classic US diner dishes are "done well", but true to past form, critics just see "style over substance". / W1D 7EF; www.jamieoliversdiner.com; @jamiesdiner; Mon-Fri 11pm, Sat & Sun 10.30 pm; set weekday L & dinner £30 (FP).

Jamie's Italian **£44** 1 1 2
Branches throughout London
"How does he get away with it?"; although these cult-of-Jamie diners do have have their fans (especially 'en famille'), few chains incite as much harsh criticism as this one, with many reporters finding them "completely overrated", "lamentable", "the most disappointing ever"… / www.jamiesitalian.com; @JamiesItalianUK; 11.30 pm, Sun 10.30 pm; over 6.

Jin Kichi NW3 **£42** 5 4 3
73 Heath St 7794 6158 8–1A
"I come all the way from Surrey to my favourite restaurant!"; how does this "tiny" and "cramped" Hampstead old-timer justify such a trek? – "expert" Japanese cooking, with "fantastic" teriyaki a highlight. / NW3 6UG; www.jinkichi.com; 11 pm, Sun 10 pm; closed Mon L.

Joanna's SE19 **£44** 3 4 4
56 Westow Hill 8670 4052 1–4D
Still a "longstanding favourite"; thanks to its "very pleasant" food and "good house cocktails", this "old-school" Crystal Palace brasserie continues to elicit very positive reports from locals. / SE19 1RX; www.joannas.uk.com; @JoannasRest; 10.45 pm, Sun 10.15 pm.

Joe Allen WC2 **£53** 1 2 4
13 Exeter St 7836 0651 4–3D
Fortunately, the "buzzy" atmosphere has long been the "whole point" of this late-night Theatreland basement (est NYC '65, London '77), where the best bet foodwise is the "authentic" (and famously off-menu) burger; despite new owners in recent times though, its performance generally remains "tired". / WC2E 7DT; www.joeallen.co.uk; Sun-Thu 11.45 pm, Fri & Sat 12.45 am; set weekday L & dinner £34 (FP).

Joe's Brasserie SW6 **£43** 2 4 3
130 Wandsworth Bridge Rd 7731 7835 10–1B
"Average food is strongly supported by a very reasonable wine list", at John Brinkley's ever-"popular", deepest Fulham stalwart; "good terrace" too. / SW6 2UL; www.brinkleys.com; 11 pm.

José SE1 **£41** 5 4 5
104 Bermondsey St 7403 4902 9–4D
There's no let-up in the superlatives for José Pizarro's "tiny", "intimate" and "packed" Bermondsey corner bar; waiting for a table "can be a bore", but it's well worth it for tapas that are "light years ahead" of most rivals, plus "fantastic" wines. / SE1 3UB; www.josepizarro.com; @Jose_Pizarro; 10.30 pm, Sun 5.30; closed Fri D, Sat D & Sun D.

Joy King Lau WC2 **£35** 3 2 2
3 Leicester St 7437 1132 4–3A
"Tremendous" old-school Cantonese food makes this three-floor venture, off Leicester Square, "a very much better-than-average Chinatown destination"; its "not the best ambience or service, but it's the food and prices you go for". / WC2H 7BL; www.joykinglau.com; 11.30 pm, Sun 10.30 pm.

The Jugged Hare EC1 **£64** 3 3 3
49 Chiswell St 7614 0134 12–2A
"Great hearty British food" – majoring in "meat, meat and more meat, plus a little fish" – makes this "fantastic and buzzy" gastroboozer a very popular City standby, even if at times it's "so noisy it's impossible to chat". / EC1Y 4SA; www.juggedhare.com; @juggedhare; 11 pm, Sun 10 pm; set pre theatre £44 (FP).

Julie's W11 **£66** 1 1 5
135 Portland Rd 7229 8331 6–2A
"Very special" and "unfailingly romantic", this deeply '70s Holland Park labyrinth undoubtedly is… but when will someone put a rocket under the kitchen – "it's bad enough that the cooking is so poor, but at these prices?" / W11 4LW; www.juliesrestaurant.com; 11 pm.

The Junction Tavern NW5 **£45** 3 4 4
101 Fortess Rd 7485 9400 8–2B
"Just what you want from a local gastropub" – this Kentish Town spot continues to generate impressively consistent ratings. / NW5 1AG; www.junctiontavern.co.uk; @Junction Tavern; 10.15 pm, Sun 9.15 pm; Mon-Thu D only, Fri-Sun open L & D; no Amex.

Juniper Dining N5 £46 332
100 Highbury Pk 7288 8716 8–1D
A "very good local", in Highbury, offering simple yet "excellent" seasonal British dishes (many gluten-free); early-evening set price menus offer "extremely good value for money". / N5 2XE; www.juniperdining.co.uk; @Juniperdining; 9.30 pm; closed Mon & Sun D.

JW Steakhouse Grosvenor House Hotel W1 £77 222
86 Park Ln 7399 8460 3–3A
The steaks at the vast, characterless and pricey Mayfair dining room "can disappoint", but the puds are "awesome" – the cheesecake, in particular, is "superb, and big enough for two!" / W1K 7TN; www.jwsteakhouse.co.uk; 10.30 pm, Fri & Sat 11 pm.

K10 £37 432
20 Copthall Ave, EC2 7562 8510 9–2C
3 Appold St, EC2 7539 9209 12–2B
"Well above average for a fastish food experience", these City operations do a good line in "reasonably-priced" sushi, plus some non-Japanese fare (including hot dishes), which you grab from the passing conveyor; thumbs up for the lively new Appold/Sun St branch. / www.k10.com; Appold 9 pm, Wed-Fri 9.30 pm; both branches Sat & Sun, Copthall closed Mon-Fri D.

Kadiri's NW10 £23 432
26 High Rd 8459 0936 1–1A
"A true taste of India!"; this '70s spot, in Willesden, is "cramped, but well worth it" – the food's "fabulous" and the menu "much more varied than usual". / NW10 2QD; www.kadiris.com.

Kaffeine W1 £12 345
66 Great Titchfield St 7580 6755 3–1C
"Outstanding coffee made with care and consideration", "amazingly inventive sandwiches and salads" plus "cakes to die for" – no wonder this "great independent" has a following out of step with its modest size. / W1W 7QJ; www.kaffeine.co.uk; @kaffeinelondon; L only; no Amex; no bookings.

Kai Mayfair W1 £97 442
65 South Audley St 7493 8988 3–3A
Some "exemplary and exquisite" meals won stellar ratings this year for this Mayfair Chinese "classic"; the interior can "lack atmosphere", though, and prices are "off the scale". / W1K 2QU; www.kaimayfair.co.uk; @kaimayfair; 10.45 pm, Sun 10.15 pm.

Kaifeng NW4 £62 322
51 Church Rd 8203 7888 1–1B
A Hendon stalwart that's still, say fans, "the best Chinese-kosher restaurant in town" (and coeliac- and allergy-friendly too); it's the kind of place where "standards never drop… but then again nor do the prices!" / NW4 4DU; www.kaifeng.co.uk; 10 pm; closed Fri & Sat; set Sun L £44 (FP).

Kaosarn £26 434
110 St Johns Hill, SW11 7223 7888 10–2C
Brixton Village, Coldharbour Ln, SW9 7095 8922 10–2D
"Delicious", "spicy"' and "fragrant" – the Thai food at these BYO cafés, in Brixton Village and Battersea, is an "amazing bargain"; no wonder they're "always hopping"! / SW9 10 pm, Sun 9 pm; sw11 closed Mon L.

Karma W14 £40 442
44 Blythe Rd 7602 9333 7–1D
"Tucked away in a place you wouldn't expect to find much life", this Olympia backwoods Indian is of note for its "unusually authentic" curries; "atmosphere can be lacking", though – "perhaps why the delivery service is so popular!" / W14 0HA; www.k-a-r-m-a.co.uk; @KarmaKensington; 11 pm; no Amex.

Karpo NW1 £49 321
23 Euston Rd 7843 2221 8–3C
With its "interesting" and "tasty" fare, this dining room opposite St Pancras can sometimes seem quite a "find"; the setting is "stark", though, and service can come "with attitude". / NW1 2SD; www.karpo.co.uk; @karporestaurants; 10.30 pm.

Kaspar's Seafood and Grill The Savoy Hotel WC2 £74 333
100 The Strand 7836 4343 4–3D
Critics may say it "lacks imagination", but the Savoy's former River Restaurant wins a solid thumbs-up from reporters for its "very acceptable" fish and fruits de mer, and "lovely" setting (especially if you get one of the few window tables); "excellent" breakfast too. / WC2R 0EU; www.kaspars.co.uk; 11 pm; set always available £42 (FP); SRA-3 stars.

Kateh W9 £43 543
5 Warwick Pl 7289 3393 8–4A
A "treasure near Little Venice", offering "top-drawer" dishes which "reflect the diversity and depth of Persian food"; "it may be cramped", but otherwise it's "hard to fault". / W9 2PX; www.katehrestaurant.co.uk; 11 pm, Sun 9.30 pm; closed weekday L.

Kazan **£46** 3 3 3
77 Wilton Rd, SW1 7233 8298 2–4B
93-94 Wilton Rd, SW1 7233 7100 2–4B
"We went as it was handy, but I'd go back as the food was a cut above!"; this Pimlico spot – which has a spin-off café on the other side of the road – serves "fine and subtle" mezze and grills. / www.kazan-restaurant.com; 10 pm.

The Keeper's House Royal Academy W1 **£60** 3 2 3
Royal Academy Of Arts, Piccadilly 7300 5881 3–3D
"Tucked away" in the basement of the Royal Academy, an "interesting" year-old restaurant (restricted to 'Friends' at lunchtime) – fans find it "lovely" all-round, but critics decry "style over substance". / W1J 0BD; www.keepershouse.org.uk; 8.30 pm; D only, closed Sun.

Ken Lo's Memories SW1 **£60** 3 4 3
65-69 Ebury St 7730 7734 2–4B
A grand Belgravia Chinese veteran, sometimes accused of "resting on its old reputation"; what's almost more striking, though, is the ongoing enthusiasm of the fans, for whom it's still "top-notch" and "always reliable". / SW1W 0NZ; www.memoriesofchina.co.uk; 10.45 pm, Sun 10 pm.

Kennington Tandoori SE11 **£48** 4 4 3
313 Kennington Rd 7735 9247 1–3C
"Wonderful Indian food" with "superb flavours" wins nothing but praise for this "busy" local fixture, whose "very varied clientele" includes a good number of politicos. / SE11 4QE; www.kenningtontandoori.com; @TheKTL; 11.30 pm; no Amex.

Kensington Place W8 **£54** 4 5 3
201-209 Kensington Church St 7727 3184 6–2B
"They seem to have found their feet again at last!" – this "incredibly noisy" '90s 'goldfish bowl', just off Notting Hill Gate, has notably "friendly" service, and offers "comforting, classy and nourishing" dishes, majoring in "fish from their own fish shop" next door. / W8 7LX; www.kensingtonplace-restaurant.co.uk; @kprestaurantW8; 10.30 pm; closed Mon L & Sun D; SRA-2 stars.

Kensington Square Kitchen W8 **£33** 3 4 4
9 Kensington Sq 7938 2598 5–1A
A "refreshingly one-off café", on a scenic square off bustling Kensington High Street, which is particularly attractive as a breakfast option, cramped as it is. / W8 5EP; www.kensingtonsquarekitchen.co.uk; @KSKRestaurant; 3.30 pm; L only; no Amex.

The Kensington Wine Rooms W8 **£50** 2 2 3
127-129 Kensington Church St 7727 8142 6–2B
A "huge range of wines by the glass" garners plenty of praise for this pub-conversion near Notting Hill Gate – the food is rather incidental. / W8 7LP; www.greatwinesbytheglass.com; @wine_rooms; 10.45 pm; set weekday L £30 (FP).

Kentish Canteen NW5 **£44** 2 4 3
300 Kentish Town Rd 7485 7331 8–2C
"Every area should have one", say fans of this "pleasant" and "friendly" Kentish Town spot, praising its "small but well judged menu"; sceptics though say that the cooking "strives to be a cut above, and doesn't quite make it". / NW5 2TG; www.kentishcanteen.co.uk; @kentishcanteen; 10.30 pm.

(Brew House) Kenwood House NW3 **£33** 2 2 5
Hampstead Heath 8341 5384 8–1A
"A delicious breakfast, with fresh ingredients, on the edge of Hampstead Heath" is one of the headline attractions – along with afternoon tea – at Kenwood House's relaunched café, whose garden tables, in particular, are "perfect on a sunny day". / NW3 7JR; www.companyofcooks.com; @EHKenwood; 6 pm (summer), 4 pm (winter); L only.

Kerbisher & Malt **£19** 3 3 2
53 New Broadway, W5 8840 4418 1–2A
164 Shepherd's Bush Rd, W6 3556 0228 7–1C
170 Upper Richmond Rd West, SW14 8876 3404 1–4A NEW
50 Abbeville Rd, SW4 3417 4350 10–2D NEW
"Exceptionally fresh fish, lightly prepared" wins praise for this modern-day reinvention of the chippy; there's some feeling it "promises more than it delivers", though, and critics find the cooking no more than "OK". / www.kerbisher.co.uk; 10 pm - 10.30pm, Sun 9 pm - 9.30 pm; W6 Closed Mon; no booking.

Kettners W1 **£60** 2 2 3
29 Romilly St 7734 6112 4–2A
With its "very traditionally-styled dining room", and a champagne bar for pre-prandials, this Soho "old favourite" (originally established 1867) still has its fans, especially pre-theatre; critics are pretty

strident, though – "this is the most overpriced rubbish I've ever had!" / W1D 5HP; www.kettners.com; 11 pm, Fri & Sat 11.30 pm, Sun 9.30 pm.

Khan's W2 £23 422
13-15 Westbourne Grove 7727 5420 6–1C
"Still a standard-bearer for Indian food"; this authentic (no-booze) Bayswater veteran has a style and ambience sometimes compared, not always favourably, to a subcontinental railway station. / W2 4UA; www.khansrestaurant.com; 11.30 pm, Sat-Sun midnight.

Kiku W1 £55 542
17 Half Moon St 7499 4208 3–4B
With its "delicious" and "authentic" cuisine, it's perhaps no wonder this Mayfair fixture is "full of Japanese from the consulate"; only quibble – the "cold" ambience of the room. / W1J 7BE; www.kikurestaurant.co.uk; 10.15 pm, Sun 9.45 pm; closed Sun L.

Kikuchi W1 £52 521
14 Hanway St 7637 7720 4–1A
"Just for the sushi – nothing else"; this hard-to-find spot, off Tottenham Court Road, serves "excellent" food, but the surroundings are "basic", and service – though some find it "endearing" – can be "below par". / W1T 1UD; 10.30 pm; closed Sun.

Kimchee WC1 £39 423
71 High Holborn 7430 0956 2–1D
This "very busy" Midtown Korean "Wagamama lookalike" offers "a great intro to Asian food", and is "a useful, quick place" for "a fun and affordable lunch"; service though can be amateur. / WC1V 6EA; www.kimchee.uk.com; @kimcheerest; 10.30 pm.

Kings Road Steakhouse & Grill Marco Pierre White SW3 £56 211
386 King's Rd 7351 9997 5–3B
This Chelsea steakhouse does have its fans who praise its "consistently excellent steak and other dishes"; equally passionate are its foes – "I've eaten in countless places in the 12 years I've lived in London, and none has felt as overpriced and cynical as this". / SW3 5UZ; www.londonsteakhousecompanies.com; 10.30 pm, Sun 10 pm.

Kipferl N1 £43 333
20 Camden Pas 77041 555 8–3D
"Something a bit different!" – "unfussy yet sophisticated", this Islington deli-restaurant offers such Austrian delights as "hearty" soups and "outstanding" strudel. / N1 8ED; www.kipferl.co.uk; @KipferlCafe; 9.30 pm; closed Mon.

Kiraku W5 £35 532
8 Station Pde 8992 2848 1–3A
"It's easy to find a more expensive Japanese, but harder to find a better one", say fans of this "canteen-like" outfit, near Ealing Common tube; "everything tastes so very fresh" – "for value, it can't be beaten". / W5 3LD; www.kiraku.co.uk; @kirakulondon; 10 pm; closed Mon; no Amex.

Kitchen W8 W8 £65 543
11-13 Abingdon Road 7937 0120 5–1A
Offering "very complex" dishes at "amazing value-for-money" prices, and "courteous" service too, this "grown-up" Kensington spot, part-owned by Phil (The Square) Howard, has a large and devoted following. / W8 6AH; www.kitchenw8.com; @KitchenW8; 10.15 pm, Sun 9.15 pm; set weekday L £43 (FP), set Sun L £53 (FP).

Koba W1 £44 323
11 Rathbone St 7580 8825 2–1C
"One of the best Korean restaurants in town"; this Fitzrovia spot generally hits the spot, although the occasional critic can find the cuisine "somewhat muted"... "but the Soju and the table cooking make up for it!" / W1T 1NA; 10.30 pm; closed Sun L.

Koffmann's The Berkeley SW1 £82 553
The Berkeley, Wilton Pl 7107 8844 5–1D
"Masterful chef" Pierre Koffmann – the man who made La Tante Claire London's best restaurant of the '90s – is truly back with a vengeance at this Knightsbridge venue, though nowadays his "faultless" Gallic gastronomy seems more "gutsy" than of old; the deep-basement setting, though, will never truly sparkle. / SW1X 7RL; www.the-berkeley.co.uk/top_restaurants.aspx; 10.30 pm; set pre theatre £52 (FP).

Kolossi Grill EC1 £33 344
56-60 Rosebery Ave 7278 5758 9–1A
A Farringdon veteran that its devotees have enjoyed for more than three decades; they say that, for value, its bargain-basement Greek Cypriot meze just "can't be beaten". / EC1R 4RR; www.kolossigrill.com; 11 pm; closed Sat L & Sun.

Konditor & Cook £27 342
Curzon Soho, 99 Shaftesbury Ave, W1 0844 854 9367 4–3A
46 Gray's Inn Rd, WC1 0844 854 9365 9–1A
10 Stoney St, SE1 0844 854 9363 9–4C
22 Cornwall Road, SE1 0844 854 9361 9–4A
30 St Mary Axe, EC3 0844 854 9369 9–2D
"Dark, dense, fudgey, squishy, incredible"... and that's just the Boston Brownies – there's a "vast selection" of "fatally tempting" cakes

on offer at this "enthusiastic" small group; "great coffee" and "tasty hot food" too. / www.konditorandcook.com; 6 pm; W1 11 pm; WC1 & EC3 closed Sat & Sun; SE1 closed Sun; no booking.

Kopapa WC2 **£58** 2 2 2
32-34 Monmouth St 7240 6076 4–2B
Peter Gordon is a chef with pedigree (Sugar Club, Providores), and his "excellent and interesting" Pacific-fusion dishes please many visitors to this "crowded" Theatreland café; reports are very up-and-down, though, and doubters "just can't see what the excitement is about". / WC2H 9HA; www.kopapa.co.uk; @Kopapacafe; 10.45 pm, Sun 9.45 pm.

Koya W1 **£35** 4 4 3
49 Frith St 7434 4463 4–2A
"No faff, just incredible food"; this "tiny" and "simple" Soho Japanese is ferociously popular, especially for its udon noodles. / W1D 4SG; www.koya.co.uk; @KoyaUdon; 10.30 pm; no booking.

Koya-Bar W1 **£34** 4 4 4
50 Frith St 7434 4463 4–2A
A "better space than the original Koya" (next door), this "pleasingly functional noodle bar" feels "more like Tokyo than any of the other recent similar openings"; good breakfasts too. / W1D 4SQ; www.koyabar.co.uk; Mon-Wed 10 pm, Thu-Sat 10.30 pm, Sun 9.30 pm.

Kulu Kulu **£32** 3 1 1
76 Brewer St, W1 7734 7316 3–2D
51-53 Shelton St, WC2 7240 5687 4–2C
39 Thurloe Pl, SW7 7589 2225 5–2C
"Don't go if you want posh surroundings" but, "for a cheap sushi-fix", these "run down and scruffy" conveyor-cafés do the job; their "generous" portions are "freshly made", and "prices are good". / 10 pm; SW7 10.30 pm; closed Sun; no Amex; no booking.

Kurobuta W2 NEW **£55** 4 2 3
17-20 Kendal St 3475 4158 6–1D
After his King's Road pop-up, Nobu's former head chef opened this "welcome addition to London's rock 'n' roll Asian dining scene" – a "very casual" and "buzzy" izakaya-style spot, in Bayswater, serving "all sorts of funky Japanese dishes" which deliver "incredible and unusual" flavours. / W2 2AW; www.kurobuta-london.com; @KurobutaLondon; 10.30 pm; groups of 6+ cancelling less than 48hrs in advance are charged £25pp.

The Ladbroke Arms W11 **£50** 3 1 4
54 Ladbroke Rd 7727 6648 6–2B
A "smart" gastropub, with "idyllic" outside tables, whose "dependable" cooking has helped make this quite a Notting Hill stalwart; of late, however, some reporters have formed the view that the service "stinks" – what a shame! / W11 3NW; www.capitalpubcompany.com; @ladbrokearms; 9.30 pm; no booking after 8 pm.

Ladurée **£62** 2 2 2
Harrods, 87-135 Brompton Rd, SW1 3155 0111 5–1D
71-72 Burlington Arc, Piccadilly, W1 7491 9155 3–3C
1 Covent Garden Mkt, WC2 7240 0706 4–3D
14 Cornhill, EC3 7283 5727 9–2C
"Exquisite macaroons and other mouthwateringly delicious pastries" win fans for these bijoux and pricey outposts of the Parisian pâtisserie; larger branches also offer a more extensive grand-café menu. / www.laduree.com; SW1 8.45 pm, Sun 5.45 pm; W1 6.30 pm, Sun 5 pm, EC3 8 pm; EC3 closed Sat-Sun; W1 no booking, SW1 no booking 3 pm-6 pm.

The Lady Ottoline WC1 **£50** 2 2 3
11a, Northington St 7831 0008 2–1D
"In an area where the choice is limited" (Bloomsbury), this beautifully restored Victorian pub makes a "happy" sort of destination; middling survey ratings though, suggest it's not quite living up to its potential. / WC1N 2JF; www.theladyottoline.com; @theladyottoline; 10 pm, Sun 8 pm.

Lahore Karahi SW17 **£23** 4 2 2
1 Tooting High Street, London 8767 2477 10–2C
"Great-value, no-nonsense food" is the winning formula behind this bustling, canteen-style Tooting Pakistani; don't forget to BYO. / SW17 0SN; www.lahorekarahi.co.uk; midnight; no Amex.

Lahore Kebab House **£26** 5 2 2
668 Streatham High Rd, SW16 8765 0771 10–2D
2-10 Umberston St, E1 7488 2551 11–1A
"Still the gold standard, despite its expansion", this "noisy" and "vibrant" Pakistani canteen in Whitechapel (with spin-offs) has a massive fan club for its "divine" lamb chops, and "great curries" too – who cares if the "Formica-tabled" ambience is "not the nicest"?; BYO. / midnight.

Lamberts SW12 **£47** 554
2 Station Pde 8675 2233 10–2C
"Excels in every way"; this "enterprising" and "pleasant" favourite, near Balham station, is a "wonderful" and "sensibly priced" operation – "more relaxed than Chez Bruce, but snapping at its heels in terms of quality". / SW12 9AZ; www.lambertsrestaurant.com; @lamberts_balham; 10 pm, Sun 5 pm; closed Mon & Sun D; no Amex; SRA-3 stars.

(Winter Garden)
The Landmark NW1 **£82** 234
222 Marylebone Rd 7631 8000 8–4A
"Free-flowing champagne and an extensive array of wonderful dishes" make for an "excellent Sunday brunch" in the "beautiful" atrium of this Marylebone hotel; its afternoon teas and so on also have their fans. / NW1 6JQ; www.landmarklondon.co.uk; @landmarklondon; 10.30 pm; no trainers; booking: max 12; set weekday L £49 (FP).

Langan's Brasserie W1 **£64** 224
Stratton St 7491 8822 3–3C
For its (older) fan club, this famous brasserie veteran near the Ritz "fits like an old slipper" – it's "always fun", and still "always buzzing"; the uninitiated, however, may merely find standards "no better than average". / W1J 8LB; www.langansrestaurants.co.uk; @langanslondon; 11 pm, Fri & Sat 11.30 pm, Sun 10 pm.

Lantana Cafe **£35** 334
13-14 Charlotte Pl, W1 7323 6601 2–1C
Unit 2, 1 Oliver's Yd, 55 City Rd, EC1 7253 5273 12–1A
"Tucked away down a Fitzrovia side street", this Oz café is "THE chilled place for coffee and brunch with friends"; we receive little feedback on its spin-offs in Shoreditch and Camden Town.

Lardo E8 **£39** 324
Richmond Rd 8533 8229 1–2D
It helps to be "25, skinny and wearing a checked shirt", but all are welcome to enjoy this "buzzy" Hackney two-year-old, where the "well-sourced" Italian small plates "hit all the right notes". / E8 3NJ; www.lardo.co.uk; @lardolondon; 10.30 pm, Sun 9.30 pm.

Latium W1 **£54** 453
21 Berners St 7323 9123 3–1D
Maurizio Morelli's "subtle" venture remains "one of the best Italians in central London"; it stars "terrific" Roman cooking ("magnificent ravioli"), "courteous and respectful" service, and a wine list "that's an attraction in itself". / W1T 3LP; www.latiumrestaurant.com; @LatiumLondon; 10.30 pm, Sat 11 pm; closed Sat L & Sun L.

Launceston Place W8 **£75** 344
1a Launceston Pl 7937 6912 5–1B
"Tucked away in the backstreets of Kensington", this "calm, comfortable and intimate" townhouse is picture book-perfect for a "discreet, romantic dinner"; fans applaud its "elegant" cuisine too (although it can sometimes seem rather "safe"). / W8 5RL; www.launcestonplace-restaurant.co.uk; 10 pm; closed Mon & Tue L; SRA-2 stars.

The Lawn Bistro
SW19 **£61** 222
67 High St 8947 8278 10–2B
A "French-themed" bistro of two years' standing that's been "very welcome in Wimbledon Village"; indeed, "on a good day, it's the best place in the area", but results can 'miss', and even fans can feel that "portions are too small and prices too high"! / SW19 5EE; www.thelawnbistro.co.uk; @thelawnbistro; 9.30 pm, Sat 10 pm; closed Mon & Sun D.

THE LEDBURY W11 **£135** 554
127 Ledbury Rd 7792 9090 6–1B
"Superb meals seem natural", at Brett Graham's "flawless" Notting Hill stand-out: yet again London's No. 1 restaurant; there's "no pomp" – staff are "so naturally courteous and efficient" – and his "inspired" cuisine is "as close to perfect as you can get". / W11 2AQ; www.theledbury.com; @theledbury; 10.15 pm; closed Mon L & Tue L; set weekday L £62 (FP).

Lemonia NW1 **£45** 234
89 Regent's Park Rd 7586 7454 8–3B
"Always packed, even on Mondays", this "unchanging" Primrose Hill mega-taverna is a north London "phenomenon"; doubtless its straightforward old-favourite dishes "could be improved", but staff are "unflappable" and the atmosphere is "always cheerful". / NW1 8UY; www.lemonia.co.uk; @Lemonia_Greek; 11 pm; closed Sun D; no Amex.

Leon **£26** 333
Branches throughout London
"I just wish there were more branches!" – this "superbly innovative" chain went "from strength to strength" this year, consistently applauded for "very wholesome" dishes that are "healthy, tasty and fresh" and, "very attractively presented" too. / www.leonrestaurants.co.uk; 10 pm; W1 8.45 pm; E14 8 pm; EC4 closed Sun; W1 closed Sat & Sun; no booking L.

Leong's Legends W1 **£37** 323
3 Macclesfield St 7287 0288 4–3A
"A lovely, atmospheric tucked-away location" ("like a private club") adds to the charms of this budget Chinatown diner, which specialises in soup

dumplings (Xiao Long Baou); the cooking has been rather "up and down" of late, "but the best is very good". / W1D 6AX; www.leongslegend.com; 11 pm, Sat 11.30 pm; no booking.

Levant W1 **£54** 2 2 3
Jason Ct, 76 Wigmore St 7224 1111 3–1A
Some fans still find this "expensive" party-Lebanese, near Selfridges, a "fun" destination (especially "in a group"); the food rarely excites, though, and the music can seem "painfully loud". / W1U 2SJ; www.levant.co.uk; 9.45pm, Fri & Sat midnight.

The Lido Café Brockwell Lido SE24 **£45** 2 2 3
Dulwich Rd 7737 8183 10–2D
"It's great to sit overlooking the swimming pool" – the special attraction of eating at this "lovely" south London lido, which is a "fun destination for all ages"; the food's generally "not bad" either. / SE24 0PA; www.thelidocafe.co.uk; @thelidocafe; 9.30 pm; closed Sun D; no Amex.

The Light House SW19 **£56** 2 3 3
75-77 Ridgway 8944 6338 10–2B
Something of a "flagship for Wimbledon dining", this "airy" and "accommodating" local favourite dishes up food that "certainly does not want for creativity" – the realisation, however, "doesn't always nail it". / SW19 4ST; www.lighthousewimbledon.com; 10.30 pm; closed Sun D; set weekday L £34 (FP), set always available £38 (FP).

Lima W1 **£56** 4 2 2
31 Rathbone Pl 3002 2640 2–1C
"Taste bud-reviving" Peruvian dishes (with "outstanding ceviches" and "delicious" pisco sours) win ongoing acclaim for this Fitzrovia yearling (which recently added a Covent Garden offshoot); service can be "inefficient", though, and the interior is "cramped and noisy". / W1T 1JH; www.limalondon.com; @lima_london; 10.30 pm; closed Sun; set weekday L & pre-theatre £40 (FP); SRA-1 star.

Lima Floral WC2 NEW **£57**
14 Garrick St 7240 5778 4–3C
Newly established in re-emerging Covent Garden, an offshoot of Fitzrovia's Lima; too few reports yet for a rating, but they tend to suggest it's a satisfactory destination for Peruvian fare, rather than an earth-shattering one. / WC2E 9BJ; www.limafloral.com; @Lima_london; 11.30 pm; closed Sun D.

Linnea TW9 **£48** 5 4 3
Kew Green 8940 5696 1–3A
"Would be 3x the price in Knightsbridge or Soho"; Jonas Karlsson's newcomer on the Green may be "a bit clinical" ambience-wise, but some locals are already tipping his cooking ("a Scandi take on modern European") as "better even than the nearby Glasshouse". / TW9 3BH; www.linneakew.co.uk; 10.30 pm; closed Mon & Sun.

Lisboa Pâtisserie W10 **£8** 4 4 2
57 Golborne Rd 8968 5242 6–1A
"Great coffee, and perhaps the best pastries in London!" win ongoing acclaim for this "stalwart" Portuguese café in North Kensington; it's "always busy". / W10 5NR; 7 pm; L & early evening only; no booking.

Little Bay **£32** 2 3 4
228 Belsize Rd, NW6 7372 4699 1–2B
228 York Rd, SW11 7223 4080 10–2B
171 Farringdon Rd, EC1 7278 1234 9–1A
"How do they offer such good value?" – that's always the question at these "eccentric and outlandishly themed" budget bistros, where the "food is uninspiring, but hard to fault at the price". / www.little-bay.co.uk; @TheLittleBay; 11.30 pm, Sun 11 pm; no Amex, NW6 no credit cards.

Little Georgia Café **£39** 3 2 3
14 Barnsbury Rd, N1 7278 6100 8–3D
87 Goldsmiths Row, E2 7739 8154 1–2D
They weren't joking about the "little", when they named this reasonably priced Hackney café (which now has an offshoot in Islington); "interesting and tasty brunch dishes" are a highlight. / www.littlegeorgia.co.uk.

Little Social W1 **£74** 3 3 3
5 Pollen St 7870 3730 3–2C
"Small", "cosy" and "comforting" – this Mayfair mews bistro can seem "a nicer and less pretentious place that its famous sibling, Pollen Street Social, just across the road"; since last year, however, survey satisfaction has notably headed south – has it been overlooked as the Atherton empire explodes? / W1S 1NE; www.littlesocial.co.uk; @_littlesocial; 10.30 pm; closed Sun; set weekday L £42 (FP).

LMNT E8 **£37** 2 3 5
316 Queensbridge Rd 7249 6727 1–2D
"You just have to go with the whole weird experience!", at this bonkers, pharaoh-kitsch Dalston pub-conversion; not everyone loves the food, but it's mostly rated well. / E8 3NH; www.lmnt.co.uk; 10.30 pm; Mon-Thu D only, Fri-Sun open L & D; no Amex.

The Lobster House SW18 NEW **£55** 2 2 3
94 Point Pleasant 8871 1226 10–2B
This "chilled" new 'pontoon bar' has a "lovely location", on the river by Wandsworth Park; foodwise the clue is in the name, and though not all reporters are wowed, fans say its surf 'n' turf offering is "awesome". / SW18 1PP; www.thelobster-house.co.uk.

Lobster Pot SE11 **£62** 4 3 2
3 Kennington Ln 7582 5556 1–3C
"Real" Breton seafood "of the highest quality" is a surprise find at this "tiny" family-run stalwart; that's not just because of its lost-in-Kennington location, but also in view of the surreal nautical decor – listen out for the seagulls! / SE11 4RG; www.lobsterpotrestaurant.co.uk; 10.30 pm; closed Mon & Sun; booking: max 8.

Locanda Locatelli Hyatt Regency W1 **£77** 3 3 4
8 Seymour St 7935 9088 2–2A
A "perennial favourite" for most reporters, Giorgio Locatelli's "great-looking" (and "calm") Marylebone Italian offers "very accomplished" cuisine and "amazing" wines; service can be "snooty", though, and a few refuseniks say the food's "not really up to the hype and prices". / W1H 7JZ; www.locandalocatelli.com; 11 pm, Thu-Sat 11.30 pm, Sun 10.15 pm; booking: max 8.

Locanda Ottomezzo W8 **£66** 3 4 3
2-4 Thackeray St 7937 2200 5–1B
"An always-appealing menu of beautifully cooked Italian food served with charm and passion" has won this Kensington venture a strong neighbourhood following; "for easy eats and good coffee", visit the café. / W8 5ET; www.locandaottoemezzo.co.uk; 10.30 pm, Fri & Sat 10.45 pm; closed Mon L, Sat L & Sun.

Loch Fyne **£45** 2 2 2
2-4 Catherine St, WC2 7240 4999 2–2D
77-78 Gracechurch St, EC3 7929 8380 9–3C
"Never a wow, but fairly reliable" – one reporter nicely captures the slight ambivalence that envelopes many reports on this national fish-and-seafood chain; it undoubtedly has its fans, though, and some "good locations" too. / www.lochfyne-restaurants.com; 10 pm; WC2 10.30 pm.

The Lockhart W1 **£54** 2 2 2
24 Seymour Pl 3011 5400 2–2A
Critics of this southern-USA yearling attack its "alarmingly uneven standards" and "surprisingly unatmospheric" interior; fans, though, love its "down-home, sinfully delicious and calorific" treats, which include "the best fried chicken" and "amazing cornbread". / W1H 7NL; www.lockhartlondon.com; @LockhartLondon; 10.30 pm; closed Mon.

Lola Rojo SW11 **£43** 3 2 3
78 Northcote Rd 7350 2262 10–2C
"Dependable and inventive Spanish food" that's "priced so that you don't feel guilty about going regularly" wins praise for this modern Hispanic venue, in Battersea. / SW11 6QL; www.lolarojo.net; 10.30 pm, Sat & Sun 11 pm; no Amex.

London House SW11 NEW **£57** 4 5 4
7-9 Battersea Sq 7592 8545 10–1C
"Ramsay does it right!" – his "slick" Battersea newcomer debuts as one of the highest-rated in the GR empire, winning praise for accomplished cooking and often-"excellent" value; good wine list too. / SW11 3RA; www.gordonramsay.com/london-house; @londonhouse; Mon-Fri 10 pm; closed Mon, Tue L, Wed L & Thu L.

Look Mum No Hands! EC1 **£30** 3 3 4
49 Old St 7253 1025 9–1B
"Worth pulling on the Lycra for" – this bike-themed Clerkenwell café (part of a cycle shop) offers "wholesome, if slightly cranky, fare" and "the best filter coffee in town"; "they show all the major cycling races too". / EC1V 9HX; www.lookmumnohands.co.uk; @lookmumnohands; 10 pm.

The Lord Northbrook SE12 **£36** 3 4 4
116 Burnt Ash Rd 8318 1127 1–4D
"A great pub, in an area lacking great pubs!" – this "large" and "handsome" Lea Green hostelry serves "very enjoyable" and "varied" cooking alongside "an ever-changing roster of interesting real ales". / SE12 8PU; www.thelordnorthbrook.co.uk; 9 pm, Fri & Sat 10 pm.

Lorenzo SE19 **£42** 3 4 3
73 Westow Hill 8761 7485 1–4D
Thanks to its "authentic Italian food", this Upper Norwood fixture is always "very busy"; "book on the ground floor", though – the "basement can be slightly overpowering and cramped". / SE19 1TX; www.lorenzo.uk.com; 10.30 pm.

Lotus Chinese Floating Restaurant E14 **£43** 3 2 2
9 Oakland Quay 7515 6445 11–2C
"The prices seem to keep going up, but the quality of the dim sum is still very good", at this boat

permanently moored near Canary Wharf; it's particularly "popular and bustling" at lunch – "be sure to arrive early". / E14 9EA; www.lotusfloating.co.uk; 10.30 pm; closed Mon.

Lucio SW3 **£63** 222
257 Fulham Rd 7823 3007 5–3B
Many locals still love this Chelsea Italian, hailing its "professionalism" and "superb home-cooking"; even fans note it's "expensive", though, and critics sense it's become "arrogant" to boot. / SW3 6HY; www.luciorestaurant.com; 10.45 pm.

Lucky Seven W2 **£40** 333
127 Westbourne Park Rd 7727 6771 6–1B
"Back to the USA in the '50s" – Tom Conran's authentic-looking diner, on the fringe of Notting Hill, is a top spot for burger and shakes; "you really do feel like you're back in America". / W2 5QL; www.lucky7london.co.uk; 10.15 pm, Sun 10 pm; no Amex; no booking.

Lupita WC2 **£39** 323
13-15 Villiers St 7930 5355 4–4D
A "really tasty Mexican", by Charing Cross – it makes "a handy no-reservations option when you need a tasty bite on a budget". / WC2N 6ND; www.lupita.co.uk; @LupitaUK; 11 pm, Fri & Sat 11.30 pm, Sun 10 pm.

Lutyens EC4 **£74** 222
85 Fleet St 7583 8385 9–2A
Sir Terence Conran's deadly-dull but "convenient" City-fringe brasserie offers a "bland" (but "pricey") menu that's "easy for business" – "the food comes and goes without notice, so you can get on with work!" / EC4Y 1AE; www.lutyens-restaurant.com; 9.45 pm; closed Sat & Sun; set dinner £49 (FP).

Lyle's E1 NEW **£66** 442
The Tea Building, 56 Shoreditch High St 3011 5911 12–1B
"Sparse" the decor may be, but this Shoreditch newcomer surprises with its "very intelligent and interesting dishes, with a real light touch" (in the school of St John), and "excellent" service too. / E1 6JJ; www.lyleslondon.com; @lyleslondon; 10 pm; closed Sat L & Sun.

M EC2 NEW
2-3 Threadneedle Walk 3327 7770 9–2C
From former Gaucho head honcho, Martin Williams, comes this big City opening; boasting two restaurants in one – M Grill and M Raw – the menu maxes out on beef. / EC2 8HP; www.mrestaurants.co.uk; @mrestaurants_.

Ma Cuisine TW9 **£42** 343
9 Station Approach 8332 1923 1–3A
"A petite venue with lots of charm", near Kew Gardens station; its traditional bistro fare is "very reliable", and "cheap" too, "if you stick to the set menus". / TW9 3QB; www.macuisinekew.co.uk; 10 pm, Fri & Sat 10.30 pm; no Amex.

Ma Goa SW15 **£40** 442
242-244 Upper Richmond Rd 8780 1767 10–2B
"Never disappointing!"; this family-run Putney "old favourite" has won local adulation with its "interesting" Goan home-cooking and "smiley" service; oh, and great value too. / SW15 6TG; www.ma-goa.com; @magoarestaurant; 10.30 pm, Fri & Sat 11 pm.

Made In Camden Roundhouse NW1 **£39** 333
Chalk Farm Rd 7424 8495 8–2B
An attractive bar-dining room that manages not to play total second fiddle to Camden Town's hip Roundhouse, which it's part of; the "excellent selection of small plate-style light dishes" are "perfect for lunch". / NW1 8EH; www.madeincamden.com; 10.15 pm.

Made in Italy **£42** 334
14a, Old Compton St, W1 0011 1214 4–2B
50 James St, W1 7224 0182 3–1A
249 King's Rd, SW3 7352 1880 5–3C
"Excellent pizza" served by-the-metre retains a loyal fan club for the buzzy Chelsea original; the other offshoots inspire little feedback. / www.madeinitalygroup.co.uk; 11 pm, Sun 10 pm; SW3 closed Mon L.

Madhu's UB1 **£35** 433
39 South Rd 8574 1897 1–3A
With its "superb" cuisine, and smart interior, this celebrated Indian, is "probably marginally the best in Southall"; they also do the subcontinental catering for some top West End hotels. / UB1 1SW; www.madhus.co.uk; 11.30 pm; closed Tue, Sat L & Sun L.

The Magazine Restaurant Serpentine Gallery W2 **£50** 235
Kensington Gdns 7298 7552 6–2D
Zaha Hadid's "seductive" architecture lends a "lively cosmopolitan" vibe to this "beautiful" new structure, in Hyde Park; there's "nothing much wrong with the food", and "the walk to and fro is good for the digestion". / W2 3XA; www.magazine-restaurant.co.uk; @TheMagazineLDN; Tue & Sun 6 pm, Wed-Sat 10.45 pm; closed Mon, Tue D & Sun D.

Magdalen SE1 **£55** 443
152 Tooley St 7403 1342 9–4D
"Lots of offal" and unusual "carnivorous" dishes appear on the "creative" seasonal menu of this "hidden gem" in the still-thin environs of City Hall – a very "honest" and "pleasingly low-key" venture that's ideal for "a discreet business lunch". / SE1 2TU; www.magdalenrestaurant.co.uk; @Magdalense1; 10 pm; closed Sat L & Sun; set weekday L £35 (FP).

Maggie Jones's W8 **£55** 235
6 Old Court Pl 7937 6462 5–1A
"It was better in the '70s" – apparently – but this rustic (if "very cramped") stalwart, near Kensington Palace, retains a "special", romantic allure, and remains "very popular" for its solid Anglo-French fare. / W8 4PL; www.maggie-jones.co.uk; 11 pm, Sun 10.30 pm; set Sun L £42 (FP).

Maguro W9 **£38** 443
5 Lanark Pl 7289 4353 8–4A
This very small Maida Vale Japanese was once a local secret… but "has now become so popular it can sometimes be difficult to get a table"; it serves "really good" food, but "without the stellar prices". / W9 1BT; www.maguro-restaurant.com; 10.30 pm; no Amex.

Maison Bertaux W1 **£16** 423
28 Greek St 7437 6007 4–2A
"Shabby", "cramped", "chaotic"… "please don't change!" – this most "quirky" of Soho cafés (est 1871) continues to delights fans with its "epic" croissants and "delicious" cakes. / W1D 5DQ; www.maisonbertaux.com; @Maison_Bertaux; 10.15 pm, Sun 8 pm.

Malabar W8 **£44** 442
27 Uxbridge St 7727 8800 6–2B
"It just keeps going!"; "always-reliable", this elegantly understated Notting Hill Indian veteran "has maintained high standards over many years". / W8 7TQ; www.malabar-restaurant.co.uk; 11 pm, Sun 10.30 pm; set Sun L £25 (FP).

Malabar Junction WC1 **£41** 323
107 Gt Russell St 7580 5230 2–1C
A spacious and "charming" Keralan venue, near the British Museum; it can be quiet… "which is surprising as it's really good and reasonably priced". / WC1B 3NA; www.malabarjunction.com; 11 pm.

The Mall Tavern W8 **£46** 223
71-73 Palace Gardens Ter 7229 3374 6–2B
Near Notting Hill Gate, an attractive gastropub which has made quite a name for its "impressive menu and wine list"; some "fantastic" meals are recorded, but reports have become much less consistent than they once were. / W8 4RU; www.themalltavern.com; @themalltavern; 10 pm; no Amex.

The Malt House SW6 **£58** 443
17 Vanston Pl 7084 6888 5–3A
Even those "apprehensive about its Made in Chelsea connections" applaud this Fulham gastroboozer for its "interesting" food; "very good service" too. / SW6 1AY; www.malthousefulham.co.uk; @MalthouseFulham; 10 pm, Sun 9 pm.

Mandalay W2 **£27** 331
444 Edgware Rd 7258 3696 8–4A
It may be "very basic" and "at the run-down end of the Edgware Road", but this "friendly" family-run operation offers "different" Burmese dishes that are "cheap" and "tasty"; "always book to avoid disappointment – even on a Monday night!" / W2 1EG; www.mandalayway.com; 10.30 pm; closed Sun.

Mandarin Kitchen W2 **£41** 411
14-16 Queensway 7727 9012 6–2C
"Still the place for lobster noodles" (and "so many other interesting dishes" too), this "densely packed" Bayswater Chinese may be a bit of a "dump", but it remains as "reliable" a destination as you'll find. / W2 3RX; 11.15 pm.

Mangal 1 E8 **£31** 532
10 Arcola St 7275 8981 1–1C
"The best Turkish grill in London" is to be found at this "sparsely decorated" and "brilliant-value" BYO café; "there are quite a few similarly named establishments in Dalston – accept no imitations!" / E8 2DJ; www.mangal1.com; @Mangalone; midnight, Sat & Sun 1 am; no credit cards.

Mangal II N16 **£37** 332
4 Stoke Newington Rd 7254 7888 1–1C
Famously Gilbert & George's nightly supper haunt – a "cheap and cheerful" Ockabasi offering some of the "best grilled meats in Dalston". / N16 8BH; www.mangal2.com; 1 am.

Mango Food of India SE1 **£46** 322
5-6 Cromwell Buildings, Redcross Way 7407 0333 9–4C
Mainly of interest to Borough Market visitors who

find themselves craving an Indian meal – a "cramped" operation offering "some innovative takes on your standard offerings". / SE1 9HR; www.lovemango.co.uk; 11 pm.

Mango Room NW1 **£45** 332
10-12 Kentish Town Rd 7482 5065 8–3B
"One of the best in Camden Town!" – a popular and laid-back haunt which "after all these years, is still serving interesting and very good Caribbean food". / NW1 8NH; www.mangoroom.co.uk; 11 pm.

Mango Tree SW1 **£54** 112
46 Grosvenor Pl 7823 1888 2–4B
This Belgravia outpost of an international Thai operation inspires deeply mixed reports, too many of them very disappointing; they're "always rammed though, thanks to the coupon-dining crowd". / SW1X 7EQ; www.mangotree.org.uk; 11 pm, Thu-Sat 11.30 pm, Sun 10.30 pm.

Manicomio **£61** 323
85 Duke of York Sq, SW3 7730 3366 5–2D
6 Gutter Ln, EC2 7726 5010 9–2B
"Glorious al fresco seating" adds lustre to both of these Chelsea and City Italians – "efficient", if somewhat "perfunctory", operations serving food that's "competent, if a little overpriced". / www.manicomio.co.uk; SW3 10.30 pm, Sun 10 pm; EC2 10 pm; EC2 closed Sat & Sun.

Manna NW3 **£57** 232
4 Erskine Rd 7722 8028 8–3B
The UK's longest-established veggie, in Primrose Hill, is mainly of interest as an historical footnote nowadays – it's not without (local) fans, but pricey and perennially inconsistent. / NW3 3AJ; www.mannav.com; @mannacuisine; 10 pm; closed Mon.

Marani W1 NEW **£68** 332
54-55 Curzon St 7495 1260 3–3B
Implausibly located in a charming townhouse in the heart of Mayfair (on the former site of Tempo, RIP), an "interesting" family-run Georgian newcomer – "charming, albeit a little amateur at times". / W1J 8PG; www.maranilondon.co.uk; 11 pm.

MARCUS THE BERKELEY SW1 **£116** 333
Wilton Pl 7235 1200 5–1D
"Marcus Wareing seems to have taken his eye off the ball"; an allegedly informalising refurbishment (plus snappier name) has somehow succeeded in making his Knightsbridge dining room even stuffier than before, and its "good, not amazing" cuisine is struggling to justify prices some reporters find "ridiculous". / SW1X 7RL; www.marcuswareing.com; @marcuswareing; 10.45 pm; closed Sun; no jeans or trainers; booking: max 8.

Margaux SW5 NEW **£64** 333
152 Old Brompton Rd 7373 5753 5–2B
A "local bistro", newly opened in Earl's Court, where "good-rather-than-amazing" Gallic fare vies for attention with the thoughtful wine selection. / SW5 0BE; www.barmargaux.co.uk.

Marianne W2 **£91** 443
104 Chepstow Rd 3675 7750 6–1B
"A joyous experience"; Marianne Lumb' serves "astonishing, delicate and wonderful" dishes in the "small and most delightful" dining room of this "intimate" Bayswater yearling – a "very romantic" location, where "the focus is on your food and your partner". / W2 5QS; www.mariannerestaurant.com; @Marianne_W2; 9.15 pm; closed Mon; set weekday L £65 (FP).

Market NW1 **£50** 432
43 Parkway 7267 9700 8–3B
A Camden Town "treasure" that's "worth seeking out" – a "welcoming" bare-bricked bistro offering a menu of updated "classic" dishes that are "well-cooked and well-served". / NW1 7PN; www.marketrestaurant.co.uk; @MarketCamden; 10.30 pm, Sun 3 pm; closed Sun D; set weekday L £32 (FP).

Maroush **£48** 422
I) 21 Edgware Rd, W2 7723 0773 6–1D
II) 38 Beauchamp Pl, SW3 7581 5434 5–1C
V) 3-4 Vere St, W1 7493 5050 3–1B
VI) 68 Edgware Rd, W2 7224 9339 6–1D
'Garden') 1 Connaught St, W2 7262 0222 6–1D
The "fresh bright flavours" of the Lebanese cuisine leap off the plates of this long-established chain; a "top shawarma" in the bustling café/take-aways (I and II) offers a budget-friendly alternative to the grander adjoining dining rooms. / www.maroush.com; most branches close between 12.30 am-5 am.

Masala Zone **£33** 343
9 Marshall St, W1 7287 9966 3–2D
48 Floral St, WC2 7379 0101 4–2D
147 Earl's Court Rd, SW5 7373 0220 5–2A
75 Bishop's Bridge Rd, W2 7221 0055 6–1C
80 Upper St, N1 7359 3399 8–3D
"Surprised at how good this chain was!" – these "cheerful and lively" Indian pit stops deliver

a "highly professional" package of "fresh and distinctive street food" at "reasonable prices", and in "very convenient locations" too.
/ www.realindianfood.com; 11 pm, Sun 10.30 pm; no Amex; booking: min 10.

MASH Steakhouse W1 **£83** 332
77 Brewer St 7734 2608 3–2D
"Not cheap, but it's a great space with great steaks", says one fan of this "beautiful" subterranean Art Deco chamber, hidden away near Piccadilly Circus; critics find prices high, though, and complain of a "lack of any real atmosphere".
/ W1F 9ZN; www.mashsteak.dk/restaurants/london; 11.30 pm, Sun 11 pm; closed Sun L; set pre theatre £46 (FP).

Massimo Corinthia Hotel SW1 **£76** 244
10 Northumberland Ave 7998 0555 2–3D
The "opulent" setting may be "amazing", but this Italian dining room, near Trafalgar Square, has put in a mixed performance since its launch a few years ago; of late, however, it has begun to garner more praise, especially for the "excellent-value" set lunch, and "charming" service too. / SW1A 2BD; www.massimo-restaurant.co.uk; @massimorest; 10.45 pm; closed Sun; set weekday L & pre-theatre £38 (FP).

Masters Super Fish SE1 **£30** 411
191 Waterloo Rd 7928 6924 9–4A
"Very popular with cabbies" – this, "basic no-frills chippy" is "just as advertised, which is to say, pretty super"; sadly, though, "it's being discovered by tourists – damn those TripAdvisor reviews!"
/ SE1 8UX; 10.30 pm; closed Sun, Mon L; no Amex; no booking Fri D.

Matsuba TW9 **£44** 432
10 Red Lion St 8605 3513 1–4A
"Outstanding quality for Richmond" – this very "competent" Japanese café serves "beautifully cooked and presented dishes" (including some Korean options); sushi is of a "high standard".
/ TW9 1RW; www.matsuba-restaurant.com; @matsuba; 10.30 pm; closed Sun.

Matsuri SW1 **£86** 331
15 Bury St 7839 1101 3–3D
For "authentic teppan-yaki exquisitely done", this long-established St James's basement is just the job, even if the "ambience could be better"; "the sushi bar is a secret gem". / SW1Y 6AL; www.matsuri-restaurant.com; 10.30 pm, Sun 10 pm.

Maxela SW7 **£46** 433
84 Old Brompton Rd 7589 5834 5–2B
"The butcher cuts the meat in front of you", at this "known-only-to-the-cognoscenti" South Kensington yearling, whose "wonderful cuts of Italian beef" are "the most flavoursome ever". / SW7 3LQ; www.maxela.co.uk; @MaxelaUk; 11 pm.

maze W1 **£80** 222
10-13 Grosvenor Sq 7107 0000 3–2A
The food is "first-rate", say fans of this Gordon Ramsay production in Mayfair, where dishes are served tapas-style; critics, though, just find the whole operation "haphazard" and "confused" – at the prices, it "just doesn't make sense". / W1K 6JP; www.gordonramsay.com/maze; 10.30 pm.

maze Grill W1 **£76** 111
10-13 Grosvenor Sq 7495 2211 3–2A
Gordon Ramsay's "utterly forgettable" Mayfair grill restaurant is often just "a total embarrassment" nowadays – "like an upmarket McDonalds" but "with prices off the Richter scale"; "the bill stunned my wife into silence, a feat I've failed to achieve for some years…" / W1K 6JP; www.gordonramsay.com; 11 pm; no shorts.

Mazi W8 **£59** 322
12-14 Hillgate St 7229 3794 6–2B
"Innovative modern Greek cuisine" wins plenty of plaudits for this "busy" yearling, off Notting Hill Gate; the dining room, though, is undoubtedly rather "cramped". / W8 7SR; www.mazi.co.uk; @mazinottinghill; 10.30 pm; closed Mon L & Tue L; set weekday L £33 (FP).

Meat Mission N1 **£33** 433
14-15 Hoxton Mkt 7739 8212 12–1B
"Burger to die for, lethal cocktails, fantastic decor… what more could you want?" – this "buzzy" ("extremely noisy") Hoxton Square outlet of the 'Meat' franchise is, say fans, "incredibly cheap for the quality". / N1 6HG; www.meatmission.com; @MEATmission; midnight, Sun 10 pm.

MEATLiquor W1 **£36** 323
74 Welbeck St 7224 4239 3–1B
"Dingy" and deafening, this dive off Oxford Street has quite a name for its "dirty, luscious burgers"; ratings are slipping though – "the rock 'n' roll grunge act doesn't seem quite as new any more".
/ W1G 0BA; www.meatliquor.com; @MEATliquor; 11 pm, Fri & Sat 1 am, Sun 9.30 pm; closed Sun; no booking.

MEATmarket WC2 **£31** 4 2 2
Jubilee Market Hall, 1 Tavistock Ct 7836 2139 4–3D
"If you like greasy burgers with just the right slip-factor", this "über-trendy" burger joint – overlooking Covent Garden's Jubilee Market, and with its "grouchy, too-cool-for-school" service – may be just the ticket. / WC2E 8BD; www.themeatmarket.co.uk; 11 pm, Sun 10 pm; no Amex.

Mediterraneo W11 **£59** 3 3 3
37 Kensington Park Rd 7792 3131 6–1A
It "feels like the real deal", sitting at a table in this "good simple Italian, by Portobello Market" – quite a local favourite, and still, say fans, serving the "best tiramisù" in town. / W11 2EU; www.mediterraneo-restaurant.co.uk; 11.30 pm, Sun 10.30 pm; booking: max 10.

MEDLAR SW10 **£67** 5 4 3
438 King's Rd 7349 1900 5–3B
"Ambitious", "meticulously executed" cuisine and "an interesting and varied wine list" (presided over by an award-winning sommelier) make this Chelsea spot "more than just a neighbourhood gem"; fans say the ambience is "lovely" too, though critics find it "unremarkable". / SW10 0LJ; @medlarchelsea; 10.30 pm; set weekday L £49 (FP).

Mele e Pere W1 **£50** 2 2 2
46 Brewer St 7096 2096 3–2D
"It deserves more recognition", say fans of this "buzzy" Italian basement, in Soho, who laud its "well priced small plates and interesting wines"; it can be "extremely noisy", though, and sceptics feel it "promises more than it delivers". / W1F 9TF; www.meleepere.co.uk; @meleEpere; 11 pm.

Menier Chocolate Factory SE1 **£52** 1 2 3
51-53 Southwark St 7234 9610 9–4B
"A wonderful idiosyncratic South Bank building which also houses a small theatre"; "if you're on the meal 'n' ticket deal it's a no-brainer, but otherwise look elsewhere, as the food is rather plain and ordinary". / SE1 1RU; www.menierchocolatefactory.com; @MenChocFactory; 10.45 pm; closed Mon & Sun D; set dinner £33 (FP).

The Mercer EC2 **£60** 3 2 2
34 Threadneedle St 7628 0001 9–2C
As "a City business restaurant" this former banking hall – with its "unspectacular but well-cooked" cuisine – can come as a "pleasant surprise"; it has enlarged in recent times, so must be doing something right! / EC2R 8AY; www.themercer.co.uk; 9.30 pm; closed Sat & Sun.

Merchants Tavern EC2 NEW **£58** 4 4 4
35-42 Charlotte Rd awaiting tel 12–1B
"A fantastic addition to the East End's finer dining scene" – this "exciting" newcomer, complete with "vast open kitchen", delivers "simple but inspiring" cooking, with "great attention to detail", and in a "gorgeous" setting too. / EC2A 3PD; www.merchantstavern.co.uk; @merchantstavern; 11 pm, Sun 9 pm; closed Mon; set weekday L £39 (FP).

Le Mercury N1 **£30** 2 3 4
140a Upper St 7354 4088 8–2D
A "useful" and "fun" Islington bistro veteran, long known for "quick", "simple" and "tasty" Gallic fare, at "bargain" prices. / N1 1QY; www.lemercury.co.uk; 12.30 am, Sun 11 pm.

Meson don Felipe SE1 **£40** 2 2 4
53 The Cut 7928 3237 9–4A
"So Spanish" – even critics of this rammed veteran tapas bar, near the Old Vic, applaud its "great, bustling atmosphere"; everyone likes the large list of wines and sherries, but the food divides opinion. / SE1 8LF; www.mesondonfelipe.com; 11 pm; closed Sun; no Amex; no booking after 8 pm.

Carom at Meza W1 **£33** 4 4 3
100 Wardour St 7314 4002 3–2D
"Is it a disco or a restaurant?"; this huge and "lively" Soho Indian may have decor "like a singles' cocktail lounge", but the food is "surprisingly good", and it's an ideal choice for a "night out in a big group"! / W1F 0TN; www.meza-soho.co.uk; 11 pm; closed Sat L & Sun; SRA-3 stars.

Meza SW17 NEW **£15** 4 4 3
34 Trinity Rd 0772 211 1299 10–2C
"The secret's out!"; with its "fresh and super-tasty Lebanese cuisine at enticingly low prices", this "tiny", "crowded" and "jolly" Tooting spot has made quite a name for itself. / SW17 7RE; 10 pm; closed Mon L.

Michael Nadra **£54** 5 3 1
6-8 Elliott Rd, W4 8742 0766 7–2A
42 Gloucester Ave, NW1 7722 2800 8–2B
Michael Nadra's "memorably delicious" cuisine offers "tremendous value for money", at both his Chiswick base and his year-old Camden Town offshoot; both sites are "difficult" however, although the "cramped" W4 site is higher rated than the "cave-like" one in NW1. / www.restaurant-michaelnadra.co.uk; @michaelnadra; W4 10 pm, Fri-Sat 10.30 pm, NW1 10.30 pm, Sun 9 pm; W4 closed Sun D.

Mien Tay **£31** 4 2 2
180 Lavender Hill, SW11 7350 0721 10–1C
122 Kingsland Rd, E2 7729 3074 12–1B
"Highly authentic" Vietnamese scoff impresses all who comment on these "mad-chaotic" Battersea and Shoreditch greasy spoons; no-one cares that the decor is a little "down-at-heel", or that service is "fast and furious". / 11 pm, Fri & Sat 11.30 pm, Sun 10.30 pm; cash only.

Mildreds W1 **£41** 4 3 4
45 Lexington St 7494 1634 3–2D
"A London institution" – this "perfect little Soho nook" continues to dish up "excellent" veggie food "that converts even die-hard carnivores". / W1F 9AN; www.mildreds.co.uk; 10.45 pm; closed Sun; no Amex; no booking.

Mill Lane Bistro NW6 **£47** 3 3 2
77 Mill Ln 7794 5577 1–1B
"There is an enormously large selection of brunch places in West Hampstead, but none comes close to this" – a "reliable local", where the "superb French take on a cooked breakfast" is particularly worth checking out. / NW6 1NB; www.milllanebistro.com; @millanebistro; closed Mon & Sun D; no Amex; set weekday L £28 (FP).

Min Jiang
The Royal Garden Hotel
W8 **£75** 5 3 5
2-24 Kensington High St 7361 1988 5–1A
"The best Peking duck ever, plus breathtaking views over Kensington Gardens" – the potent recipe for success at this "exciting" 8th-floor dining room – one of London's foremost Chinese restaurants, and all the more remarkable for "breaking the rule that rooms with views are always dire!" / W8 4PT; www.minjiang.co.uk; 10 pm.

Mint Leaf **£55** 3 2 3
Suffolk Pl, Haymarket, SW1 7930 9020 2–2C
Angel Ct, Lothbury, EC2 7600 0992 9–2C
These slick and ambitious designer Indians – in a basement near Trafalgar Square, and in the City – are certainly a "step up from most curry houses"; the level of survey feedback they inspire, however, is now very modest compared to their glory days. / www.mintleafrestaurant.com; SW1 11 pm, Sun 10.30 pm; EC2 10.30 pm; SW1 closed Sat & Sun L; EC2 closed Sat & Sun.

Miran Masala W14 **£23** 5 4 2
3 Hammersmith Rd 7602 4555 7–1D
"The fantastic flavours of real Pakistani cooking" are to be found at this basic BYO café, bang opposite Olympia. / W14 8XJ; www.miranmasala.com; 10.45 pm.

Mirch Masala **£24** 3 1 1
171-173 The Broadway, UB1 8867 9222 1–3A
1416 London Rd, SW16 8679 1828 10–2C
213 Upper Tooting Rd, SW17 8767 8638 10–2D
111-113 Commercial Rd, E1 7377 0155 12–2D
For "addictive" Pakistani curries, these "buzzy" south London BYO-canteens are well-established "cheap and cheerful" champions; ratings were hit, though, by the occasional 'off' report this year. / www.mirchmasalarestaurant.co.uk; midnight.

Mishkin's WC2 **£43** 1 2 3
25 Catherine St 7240 2078 4–3D
"The least successful of Russell Norman's creations", this "chilled" Covent Garden diner offers "NY-Yiddish-inspired comfort food" realised to a decidedly "mediocre" standard – "save your money, and head for the Big Apple!" / WC2B 5JS; www.mishkins.co.uk; @MishkinsWC2; 11.15 pm, Sun 10.15 pm.

The Modern Pantry
EC1 **£56** 3 3 3
47-48 St Johns Sq 7553 9210 9–1A
"A fun and quirky" choice – Anna Hansen's "bright" and "airy" Clerkenwell dining room provides "genuinely different" flavour combinations that "can hit real highs", even on its popular brunch menu; critics, however, just dismiss the food as "weird". / EC1V 4JJ; www.themodernpantry.co.uk; @themodernpantry; 10.30 pm, Sun 10 pm; SRA-3 stars.

Momo W1 **£70** 2 2 5
25 Heddon St 7434 4040 3–2C
"It can be too noisy", but the ultra-"buzzy" and glam souk-style vibe seduces many visitors to this fashion-crowd party-Moroccan, on the fringe of Mayfair; the (pricey) food is relatively uneventful. / W1B 4BH; www.momoresto.com; @momoresto; 11.30 pm, Sun 11 pm.

Mon Plaisir WC2 **£59** 2 3 4
19-21 Monmouth St 7836 7243 4–2B
"Nothing really changed since our first visit in the '60s!" – Covent Garden's "stalwart" Gallic bistro (in fact, much expanded over the years) is a "romantic" old favourite, with top-value menus at lunch and pre-theatre; the food? – "never surprising, always reliable". / WC2H 9DD; www.monplaisir.co.uk; 11 pm; closed Sun; set pre-theatre £31 (FP), set weekday L £35 (FP).

Mona Lisa SW10 **£28** 3 3 3
417 King's Rd 7376 5447 5–3B
A veteran World's End greasy spoon, known for its simple but "always-tasty" Italian dishes, and for the

diversity of its 'dukes-to-dustmen' clientèle. / SW10 0LR; 11 pm, Sun 5.30 pm; closed Sun D; no Amex.

Monmouth Coffee Company £12 554
27 Monmouth St, WC2 7379 3516 4–2B
Arches Northside, Dockley Rd, SE16 7232 3010 9–4D
2 Park St, SE1 7940 9960 9–4C
The coffee is "sublime" and the "perfectly trained staff" help create a "harmonious" ambience at these cult cafés; in Borough Market, "the rustic, communal wooden tables are laden with moreish bread, butter and a selection of preserves – get stuck in!" / www.monmouthcoffee.co.uk; 6 pm-6.30 pm; SE16 12 pm; closed Sun; SE16 open Sat only; no Amex; no booking.

The Morgan Arms E3 £47 434
43 Morgan St 8980 6389 1–2D
A "very popular gastropub in Mile End's backstreets", serving up "lovely" food that's complemented by a "good selection of ales". / E3 5AA; www.morganarmsbo.com; @TheMorganArms; 10 pm, Sun 9 pm.

Morito EC1 £36 444
32 Exmouth Mkt 7278 7007 9–1A
Moro's "cramped" little sister is a "bustling" and "basic" sort of Farringdon destination, serving "epic" tapas with "speed and style"; "no booking is a pain, but I guess otherwise you'd never get in!" / EC1R 4QE; www.morito.co.uk; @moritotapas; 11 pm, Sun 4 pm; closed Sun D; no Amex; no booking for D.

Moro EC1 £60 544
34-36 Exmouth Mkt 7833 8336 9–1A
"Year-after-year, true to its mission!"; this "consistently superb" Exmouth Market favourite has incredibly staying power, maintaining its "outstandingly flavourful" Moorish/Hispanic food, "excellent Iberian wines" and "buzzy scene"; as ever, it's "too noisy". / EC1R 4QE; www.moro.co.uk; 10.30 pm; closed Sun D.

Motcombs SW1 £62 233
26 Motcomb St 7235 6382 5–1D
"Old-fashioned in the best way", say (generally older) fans of this "welcoming" dining room, below a Belgravia wine bar; even they may concede that the food is "not the best", but it is "reliable". / SW1X 8JU; www.motcombs.co.uk; 11 pm; closed Sun D.

Moti Mahal WC2 £61 443
45 Gt Queen St 7240 9329 4–2D
With its "unusual and exciting" cooking, and "charming" and "attentive" service too, this somewhat overlooked Covent Garden outpost of a Delhi-based group is well worth seeking out. / WC2B 5AA; www.motimahal-uk.com; @motimahal59; 10.45 pm; closed Sat L & Sun; set pre theatre £29 (FP).

Moxon's Fish Bar SW12 £27 543
7 Westbury Pde 8675 2468 10–2C
"Oceans of praise" lap around fishmonger Robin Moxon's new addition to the Clapham scene – a "tiny but perfectly run upmarket chippy", offering "outstanding traditional fish 'n' chips" and "interesting specials" too. / SW12 9DZ; www.moxonsfishbar.com; @moxonsfish; 10 pm; closed Mon, Tue L, Wed L, Thu L, Sat L & Sun; no Amex.

Mr Chow SW1 £85 332
151 Knightsbridge 7589 7347 5–1D
"Resting on its laurels" or "still consistently delivering"? – opinions may differ on this once-glamorous but "overcrowded" Knightsbridge Chinese; there's some agreement, though, that "the prices reflect the location". / SW1X 7PA; www.mrchow.com; 11.45 pm; closed Mon L.

Mr Kong WC2 £32 333
21 Lisle St 7437 7341 4–3A
"One of Chinatown's better restaurants", with "smiling" service and "reliable" cooking from a menu which features "many interesting and unusual dishes". / WC2H 7BA; www.mrkongrestaurant.com; 2.45 am, Sun 1.45 am.

Murano W1 £99 444
20-22 Queen St 7495 1127 3–3B
Angela Hartnett's "inspiring" Italian cooking (often "with a twist") is currently on a high, at this "delightful" and "well-spaced" Mayfair spot – an exceptional "all-rounder" that's "ideal for that special occasion", be it for business or pleasure. / W1J 5PP; www.muranolondon.com; @muranolondon; 11 pm; closed Sun; set weekday L £50 (FP).

Nando's £31 222
Branches throughout London
This peri-peri chicken chain "does what you expect" – "well-cooked chicken, delivered quickly and without fuss"; "it somehow feels less wrong than taking the little ones for a cheap burger!" / www.nandos.co.uk; 11.30 pm, Sun 10.30 pm; no Amex; no booking.

Napulé SW6 **£40** 443
585 Fulham Rd 7381 1122 5–4A
This Fulham Broadway outpost of the Made in Italy chain is "really good for a casual supper" – there's "a good vibe" and the pizza, in particular, is "superb". / SW6 5UA; www.madeinitalygroup.co.uk; 11.30 pm, Sun 10.30 pm; closed weekday L; no Amex.

The Narrow E14 **£53** 112
44 Narrow St 7592 7950 11–1B
"They shouldn't trade on the Ramsay name"; his Limehouse pub is not just "poor", but "well overpriced" too – "the only saving grace is the spectacular location, right on the banks of the Thames". / E14 8DP; www.gordonramsay.com; @thenarrow; 10.30 pm, Sun 10 pm.

The National Dining Rooms National Gallery WC2 **£53** 112
Sainsbury Wing, Trafalgar Sq 7747 2525 2–2C
"A wasted opportunity" – such a shame about the "deplorable" service and lacklustre cooking at this spacious central dining room; "great views of Trafalgar Square from the window tables" are the only undoubted plus. / WC2N 5DN; www.thenationaldiningrooms.co.uk; 7 pm; Sat-Thu closed D, Fri open L & D; no Amex.

National Gallery Café National Gallery WC2 **£46** 312
East Wing, Trafalgar Sq 7747 5942 4–4B
For a "convenient" central location, an older fan base tip the "comfortable banquettes" of this tranquil haunt, right on Trafalgar Square; "disengaged" service, though, leaves some reporters decidedly disenchanted. / WC2N 5DN; www.thenationaldiningrooms.co.uk; 11 pm, Sun 6 pm; closed Sun D; no Amex.

Natural Kitchen **£37** 323
55 Baker St, W1 7935 0987 2–1A
77-78 Marylebone High St, W1 3012 2123 2–1A
7 Pepys St, EC3 7702 4038 9–3D
15-17 New Street Sq, Fetter Ln, EC4 7353 5787 9–2A
These "airy" deli-diners offer "a pleasant snacking experience", despite service that's prone to be "amateur" and "slow". / EC4 9 pm; EC3 4 pm; W1 8 pm, Sat & Sun 7 pm; EC4 & EC3 closed Sat & Sun.

Nautilus NW6 **£43** 441
27-29 Fortune Green Rd 7435 2532 1–1B
Ignore the "basic" decor ("no-fuss, no-frills Formica special"), and there are "unbeatable fish and chips" to be had at this West Hampstead veteran; "the lovely waitresses have been there as long as I have been going – 40 years!" / NW6 1DU; 10 pm; closed Sun; no Amex.

Navarro's W1 **£43** 224
67 Charlotte St 7637 7713 2–1C
A "delightful" tiled interior is the special feature of this veteran Fitzrovia bar, which serves "good solid tapas at an affordable price". / W1T 4PH; www.navarros.co.uk; @SpanishEchelon; 10 pm; closed Sun.

Nazmins SW18 **£38** 344
396-398 Garratt Ln 8944 1463 10–2B
A "superb neighbourhood place"; this Earlsfield spot is your "quintessential" Indian, offering "a good selection of curries and brilliant breads". / SW18 4HP; www.nazmins.com; @nazmins; 11.30 pm.

Needoo E1 **£26** 432
87 New Rd 7247 0648 12–2D
Just round the corner from the legendary Tayyabs, this East End Pakistani BYO is "altogether less stressful" than its famous rival, and offers "brilliant" scoff too. / E1 1HH; www.needoogrill.co.uk; 11.30 pm.

The New Angel W2 NEW **£82** 443
39 Chepstow Pl 7221 7620 6–1B
TV chef John Burton-Race's Bayswater newcomer pleases early-days reporters, as it did us, with its "elegant" decor – in a bourgeois style you don't often see in London nowadays – and its "surprisingly generous" modern European cooking. / W2 4TS; www.thenewangel-nh.co.uk; @newangel_london.

New Mayflower W1 **£40** 432
68-70 Shaftesbury Ave 7734 9207 4–3A
"It's always reassuring to see so many Chinese customers"; "excellent into the small hours", this Chinatown stalwart serves up "consistently good" Cantonese fare; "service used to be a bit rough and gruff but is nowadays of a good standard". / W1D 6LY; www.newmayflowerlondon.com; 4 am; D only; no Amex.

New Street Grill EC2 **£57** 234
16a New St 3503 0785 9–2D
For business, this "well-spaced" warehouse conversion decked out "with lots of dark wood and leather" makes "a very good option in the wasteland round Liverpool Street"; "great steaks", but sceptics complain of "unexceptional" food at "relatively high" prices. / EC2M 4TR; www.newstreetgrill.co.uk; @newstreetgrill; 10.45 pm; closed Sat L & Sun D; SRA-3 stars.

New Tom's W11 NEW **£54**
226 Westbourne Grove 7243 3341 6–1B
Long mainly of note as a "lazy" weekend brunch destination, this Notting Hill deli-bistro was relaunched in 2014; it still has the same proprietor, though, as when it was just called 'Tom's' – Tom Conran, that is. / W11 2RH; www.newtoms.co.uk.

New World W1 **£37** [3][2][3]
1 Gerrard Pl 7434 2508 4–3A
"The fun factor, with the circulating trolleys, is arguably better than the food itself" – perhaps why this gigantic Chinatown classic remains a particular hit with reporters for dim sum. / W1D 5PA; www.newworldlondon.com; 11.30 pm, Sun 11 pm.

Newman Street Tavern W1 **£41** [3][2][3]
48 Newman St 3667 1445 3–1D
"Nice to find a good central gastropub"; this very popular Marylebone spot certainly fits the bill with its "thoughtful" but "uncomplicated" cooking, and its "laid-back" style. / W1T 1QQ; www.newmanstreettavern.co.uk; @NewmanStTavern; 10.30 pm; closed Sun D; SRA-2 stars.

1901
Andaz Hotel EC2 **£65** [1][1][3]
40 Liverpool St 7618 7000 12–2B
"A preferred business breakfast choice, but at other times of day the cooking isn't strong enough to make a visit worthwhile" – this "airy" and undeniably impressive-looking chamber, by Liverpool Street, falls far below its potential. / EC2M 7QN; www.andazdining.com; 10 pm; closed Sat L & Sun; booking: max 20.

Nizuni W1 **£47** [4][4][2]
22 Charlotte St 7580 7447 2–1C
"The freshest sushi, plus decent hot dishes" from a mixed Korean/Japanese menu – most reporters are "very impressed" with this café-style Fitzrovia spot. / W1T 2NB; www.nizuni.com; @nizuni; 10.45 pm; closed Sun L.

Nobu
Metropolitan Hotel W1 **£90** [4][2][2]
19 Old Park Ln 7447 4747 3–4A
"It's certainly no longer London's hottest place", service remains "moody", and "the bill is always more than you expect"… but this once-path-breaking Mayfair dining room still offers "brilliant" Japanese fusion fare, and "great people-watching" too. / W1K 1LB; www.noburestaurants.com; @NobuOldParkLane; 10.15 pm, Fri & Sat 11 pm, Sun 10 pm.

Nobu Berkeley W1 **£90** [3][2][2]
15 Berkeley St 7290 9222 3–3C
"Lovely sushi" and other "superb" Japanese-fusion dishes still win praise for this "busy" Mayfair rendezvous, despite its "rushed" service and "horrible" prices; really, though, this is a place you go "to see and be seen". / W1J 8DY; www.noburestaurants.com; 11 pm, Sun 9.45 pm; closed Sat L & Sun L.

The Noodle House WC2 NEW **£39**
117 Shaftsbury Ave 3725 5777 4–2B
"Slightly off the beaten track" (well, as much as you can be in Covent Garden), this new offshoot of a pan-Asian chain is praised in early reports (few), as an "enjoyable café" serving "great-tasting food". / WC2H 8AD; www.tnhlondon.com; @noodlehouseLDN; Mon-Tue 9.45 pm, Wed-Sat 10.45 pm, Sun 8.45 pm.

Noor Jahan **£39** [4][4][4]
2a, Bina Gdns, SW5 7373 6522 5–2B
26 Sussex Pl, W2 7402 2332 6–1D
"It never changes… thankfully"; this "excellent neighbourhood curry house", in Earl's Court, is a "basic but classic" affair that's "always reliable, and always packed"; W2 is good too – "not sophisticated, but you couldn't ask for a better local cuzza!" / 11.30 pm, Sun 10 pm.

Nopi W1 **£56** [5][4][4]
21-22 Warwick St 7494 9584 3–2D
"Wow-factor flavours" – "pungent and dramatic!" – make "every mouthful amazing" at Yottam Ottolenghi's contemporary Middle Eastern spot, just off Regent Street; it offers "small-plate dining at its best", in an "informal", "cosy" and "beautiful" setting. / W1B 5NE; www.nopi-restaurant.com; @ottolenghi; 10.15 pm, Sun 4 pm; closed Sun D.

Nordic Bakery **£15** [3][3][3]
14a, Golden Sq, W1 3230 1077 3–2D
37b, New Cavendish St, W1 7935 3590 2–1A
48 Dorset St, W1 7487 5877 2–1A
Cinnamon buns which "never disappoint", and "fabulous" coffee too – particular attractions which keep many reporters coming back to these "restrained" ("austere") and "refreshingly different" cafés. / Golden Square 8 pm, Sat 7 pm, Sun 7 pm; Cavendish Street & Dorset Street 6 pm.

The Norfolk Arms WC1 **£46** [4][3][2]
28 Leigh St 7388 3937 8–4C
"Looks like any old pub, except for the legs of jamón hanging in the window" – this "Spanish-inspired" gastropub-cum-tapas bar, near King's Cross, is something of a "hidden gem". / WC1H 9EP; www.norfolkarms.co.uk; 10.15 pm.

North China W3 **£41** 4|4|3

305 Uxbridge Rd 8992 9183 7–1A

"A great family-run restaurant in Acton, which surpasses most places in Chinatown"; the setting may be a touch "gloomy" for some tastes, but the food is "lovely". / W3 9QU; www.northchina.co.uk; 11 pm, Fri & Sat 11.30 pm.

The North London Tavern NW6 **£46** 3|3|3

375 Kilburn High Rd 7625 6634 1–2B

A "homely" boozer, handily located near Kilburn's Tricycle Theatre, where the food is "definitely better than pub standard"; prices, though, "are moving up". / NW6 7QB; www.northlondontavern.co.uk; @NorthLondonTav; 10.30 pm, Sun 9.30 pm.

North Sea Fish WC1 **£38** 3|3|2

7-8 Leigh St 7387 5892 8–4C

"The fish is as fresh as the decor is tired", at this "old-fashioned-plush" Bloomsbury chippy; who cares if it sometimes feels "like an OAP daycare centre"? / WC1H 9EW; www.northseafishrestaurant.co.uk; Mon-Sat 10 pm, Sun 5.30 pm; closed Sun; no Amex.

The Northall Corinthia Hotel SW1 **£64** 3|4|3

10a, Northumberland Ave 7321 3100 2–3C

The "smart" and "spacious" dining room of this new(ish) grand hotel, off Trafalgar Square, deserves to be more widely known – it's "a little pricey", but "on a good day, provides top ingredients, simply cooked!" / SW1A 2BD; www.thenorthall.co.uk; @CorinthiaLondon; 10.45 pm.

Northbank EC4 **£54** 3|3|3

1 Paul's Walk 7329 9299 9–3B

"A great location by the Millennium Bridge" is the particular attraction of this bar-restaurant facing Tate Modern; with its leather booths and "British comfort food in generous portions", it makes a good option for a business lunch. / EC4V 3QH; www.northbankrestaurant.co.uk; @NorthbankLondon; 10 pm; closed Sun.

Notes **£18** 2|4|4

31 St Martin's Ln, WC2 7240 0424 4–4C
36 Wellington St, WC2 7240 7899 4–3D
6a, Tileyard Studios, N7 7700 0710 8–2C
1 Ropemaker St, EC2 7628 5178 12–2A NEW

As "a welcome haven from the Trafalgar Square hubbub", the best-known branch of these atmospheric cafés (by the Coliseum) is well-worth seeking out; the "excellent" coffee, though, does outshine the "straightforward" snacks. / Wellington St Mon-Wed 10 pm, Thu-Fri 11 pm, Sun 6 pm; St Martin's Ln Mon-Wed 9 pm, Thu-Sat 10 pm, Sun 6 pm; N7 closed Sat-Sun.

Notting Hill Kitchen W11 **£31** 2|3|2

92 Kensington Park Rd 7313 9526 6–2B

Remarkably little feedback on this quite grand, year-old, Portuguese-run restaurant and tapas bar; fans vaunt its "interesting" menu and "attentive" service, but even they may note that it's "not cheap" for what it is. / W11 2PN; Rated on Editors' visit; www.nottinghillkitchen.co.uk; @NottingHillKTN; 10 pm; closed Mon L, Tue L, Wed L & Sun.

Noura **£57** 2|2|2

16 Hobart Pl, SW1 7235 9444 2–4B
17 Hobart Pl, SW1 7235 9696 2–4B
2 William St, SW1 7235 5900 5–1D
16 Curzon St, W1 7495 1050 3–4B

These swankily located Lebanese joints have their fans, but they inspire little survey feedback... which tends to support those who say they offer only "standard" food, and that service is "in need of improvement". / www.noura.co.uk; 11.30 pm, Sun 10 pm; 16 Hobart Place closed Sun.

Novikov (Asian restaurant) W1 **£102** 1|2|3

50A Berkeley St 7399 4330 3–3C

"Eye-popping prices and arrogance" are coming to characterise the once-promising pan-Asian section of this blingy Mayfair spot; "if someone else is paying", though, it can still be fun for people-watching – "minigarchs, massage therapists, shiny people, expense-accounters..." / W1J 8HD; www.novikovrestaurant.co.uk; 11.15 pm.

Novikov (Italian restaurant) W1 **£101** 1|1|1

50A Berkeley St 7399 4330 3–3C

A "tasteless bling-fest" where the food is "surprisingly OK", but prices are "insane" – the "noisy" Italian section of the eponymous Moscow restaurateur's Eurotrash magnet, in the heart of Mayfair. / W1J 8HD; www.novikovrestaurant.co.uk; 11.30 pm.

Numero Uno SW11 **£53** 3|4|4

139 Northcote Rd 7978 5837 10–2C

"A trusted friend for many years" – this "buzzy" neighbourhood stalwart for "the between-the-Commons crowd" is "often packed", thanks to its "hearty" and "consistent" Italian fare, and its "charming and helpful" service. / SW11 6PX; 11.30 pm; no Amex.

Nuovi Sapori SW6 **£44** 3|4|3

295 New King's Rd 7736 3363 10–1B

A "good local Italian", down Fulham way; expect "basic but well-prepared" cuisine and "very friendly service". / SW6 4RE; 11 pm; closed Sun.

Nusa Kitchen **£12** 442

9 Old St, EC1 7253 3135 9–1B
2 Adam's Ct, EC2 7628 1149 9–2C
88 Cannon St, EC4 7621 9496 9–3C

"Soup is dull unless it comes from Nusa!" – "Asian flavours are used brilliantly", in the "strong-tasting" dishes on offer at these City and Farringdon pit stops. / www.nusakitchen.co.uk; 4 pm; Sat & Sun; no booking.

Oak **£51** 444

243 Goldhawk Rd, W12 8741 7700 7–1B
137 Westbourne Park Rd, W2 7221 3355 6–1B

"Incredible thin and crispy pizza" – especially at the "really buzzing" Bayswater original – helps make these "airy" and "fun" west London pub-conversions perennially popular hangouts; in W2, there's a "vibey" bar upstairs too.

Obika **£47** 221

11 Charlotte St, W1 7637 7153 2–1C
19-20 Poland St, W1 3327 7070 3–1D
96 Draycott Ave, SW3 7581 5208 5–2C
35 Bank St, E14 7719 1532 11–1C

Our mystification at the ongoing success of these 'Mozzarella bars' continues, as they inspire very little survey feedback, and such as there is divides equally between those who say they're "a bit of a hidden gem", and those who say: "don't bother". / www.obika.co.uk; 10 pm - 11 pm; E14 Closed Sun.

Oblix
The Shard SE1 **£85** 225

31 St Thomas St 7268 6700 9–4C

The views are "to die for", and many reporters are "pleasantly surprised" to find that food and service can match up, at this 32nd-floor South Bank eyrie; critics, though, find the food "mediocre", and service "disinterested". / SE1 9RY; www.oblixrestaurant.com; @OblixRestaurant; 11 pm.

Odette's NW1 **£58** 334

130 Regent's Park Rd 7586 8569 8–3B

Bryn Williams's famously "romantic" Primrose Hill "classic" has been "on fine form" of late, attracting improved survey ratings for his accomplished cuisine, and the "not too formal, but classy" ambience; the "excellent" weekday lunch is a particular hit. / NW1 8XL; www.odettesprimrosehill.com; @Odettes_rest; Sun-Thu 10 pm, Fri & Sat 10.30 pm; no Amex; set weekday L £31 (FP), set always available £37 (FP).

Ognisko Restaurant SW7 **£52** 234

55 Prince's Gate, Exhibition Rd 7589 0101 5–1C

Recently "rejuvenated", a "lovely, grand and spacious" dining room, complete with a "wonderful terrace", near the Science Museum; it offers "Polish cuisine, well executed" (and some "excellent cocktails" too). / SW7 2PN; www.ogniskorestaurant.co.uk; 11 pm; closed Mon L; no trainers.

The Old Brewery SE10 **£49** 234

The Pepys Building, Old Royal Naval College 3327 1280 1–3D

A "big, breezy and bustling" Greenwich venue in the "lovely" environs of the Naval College, with a large sun-trap garden; its impressive artisanal beers are complemented by "simple but filling" dishes. / SE10 9LW; www.oldbrewerygreenwich.com; @OldBrewery; 10 pm, Fri & Sat 10.30 pm; D only; no Amex.

The Old Bull & Bush NW3 **£42** 323

North End Rd 8905 5456 8–1A

"A real gem" of an old inn, opposite Golders Hill Park... as long as you don't mind the fact that your meal may take "an eternity" to arrive. / NW3 7HE; www.thebullandbush.co.uk; 9.30 pm, Sat 10 pm, Sun 9 pm.

Oliveto
Olivo Restaurants SW1 **£66** 422

49 Elizabeth St 7730 0074 2–4A

"Phenomenal" thin-crust pizza and other "utterly delightful" Sardinian dishes make this "kid-friendly" Belgravian a real crowd-pleaser (and it gets jammed at weekends); given the locale, no surprise that prices can seem "pretty steep". / SW1W 9PP; www.olivorestaurants.com; 11 pm, Sun 10.30 pm; booking: max 7 at D.

Olivo SW1 **£57** 442

21 Eccleston St 7730 2505 2–4B

"Expensive but excellent" Belgravia's 'original' Olivo looks pretty "tired" nowadays, and it gets pretty "noisy" too; "after all these years", though, the Sardinian cuisine remains "fresh" and "authentic". / SW1 9LX; www.olivorestaurants.com; 10.30 pm; closed Sat L & Sun L.

Olivocarne SW1 **£54** 442

61 Elizabeth St 7730 7997 2–4A

Fans of this Italian meat-specialist in the heart of Belgravia say it is the "undiscovered gem of the Olivo group" – this may be something to do with the bizarre and decidedly "unatmospheric" decor. / SW1W 9PP; www.olivorestaurants.com; Mon-Sat 11 pm, Sun 10.30 pm .

Olivomare SW1 **£61** 5 3 2
10 Lower Belgrave St 7730 9022 2–4B
"Brilliant-quality fish" and "first-class" seafood win top marks for this Sardinian venture in Belgravia; fans say the "spartan" '60s sci-fi decor is "crazy" and "cool", but it can equally well be seen as "weird" and "noisy". / SW1W 0LJ; www.olivorestaurants.com; 11 pm, Sun 10.30 pm; booking: max 10.

Olley's SE24 **£40** 4 3 2
65-69 Norwood Rd 8671 8259 10–2D
A Brockwell Park institution, still celebrated for "excellent" fish 'n' chips; "managing to sustain its quality over the years is a great achievement – long may it stay the course!" / SE24 9AA; www.olleys.info; 10 pm, Sun 9.30 pm; no Amex; set weekday L £23 (FP); SRA-3 stars.

Olympic Olympic Studios SW13 NEW **£47** 2 2 3
117-123 Church Rd 8912 5161 10–1A
"A popular addition to Barnes", this "casual" neighbourhood joint (plus "fantastic" cinema) is a great use of an Edwardian building where many of legendary '70s rock tracks were recorded; to fans, its "buzzy" new guise makes it the perfect local, but critics say it's too "loud", with "hit-and-miss" service. / SW13 9HL; www.olympiccinema.co.uk; @Olympic_Cinema; 10 pm.

Olympus Fish N3 **£34** 4 4 1
140-144 Ballards Ln 8371 8666 1–1B
"Take-away is particularly good value" – and "you can opt for grilled as well as battered" – at this "no-frills" but "friendly" Finchley chippy, which "does exactly what it says on the tin". / N3 2PA; 11 pm.

On The Bab EC1 NEW **£36** 4 3 4
305 Old St 7683 0361 12–1B
"Serving innovative and delicious Korean street food, and good cocktails too" ensures this "cheap and cheerful" Shoreditch newcomer is usually pretty "lively". / EC1V 9LA; www.onthebab.com; @onthebab; 10.30 pm, Sun 10 pm; no bookings.

One Canada Square E14 **£61** 2 3 1
1 Canada Sq 7559 5199 11–1C
Carved out from a corner of the marbled lobby of one of Canary Wharf's great towers, this brasserie yearling certainly has a handy location; perhaps inevitably, it can feel "like an airport lounge", and critics find the cuisine "fussy", and "pricey" too. / E14 5AB; www.onecanadasquarerestaurant.com; @OneCanadaSquare; 10.45 pm; closed Sun.

101 Thai Kitchen W6 **£33** 4 2 1
352 King St 8746 6888 7–2B
"Tastes like Thailand"; "fiery" dishes – including some "real novelties" on the specials board – make this obscure café near Stamford Brook worth seeking out; "don't go for the decor!" / W6 0RX; www.101thaikitchen.com; 10.30 pm, Fri & Sat 11 pm.

One Kensington W8 NEW **£71** 2 3 1
1 Kensington High St 7795 6533 5–1A
Staff try hard ("almost too hard"), but this potentially "classy" Kensington newcomer needs work – the food can seem "overcomplicated", and the airy interior "still feels like the bank it originally was"; "bring back Zaika!" / W8 5NP; www.one-kensington.com; 10.30 pm; closed Mon L.

1 Lombard Street EC3 **£71** 2 1 2
1 Lombard St 7929 6611 9–3C
This heart-of-the-City "stalwart", in a former banking hall, is still often hailed as "a good place to impress clients" (or for breakfast); too often of late, however, it has struck reporters as "bland" or "soulless" – "you probably wouldn't go if you weren't on expenses!" / EC3V 9AA; www.1lombardstreet.com; 10 pm; closed Sat & Sun; 6 max in main restaurant; set dinner £49 (FP).

One-O-One Sheraton Park Tower SW1 **£94** 5 3 1
101 Knightsbridge 7290 7101 5–1D
"Still London's finest fish restaurant by a mile!"; this Knightsbridge hotel dining room may have "all the ambience of Davy Jones's locker", but Pascal Proyart's Breton-based cuisine is without peer. / SW1X 7RN; www.oneoonerestaurant.com; @oneoone; 10 pm; booking: max 6; set weekday L £54 (FP), set dinner £63 (FP).

The Only Running Footman W1 **£60** 2 2 2
5 Charles St 7499 2988 3–3B
"Solid", "useful", "consistent" – the sort of epithets reporters apply to the "traditional" dining possibilities at this "busy" boozer, near Claridge's. / W1J 5DF; www.therunningfootmanmayfair.com; @theorfootman; 10 pm.

Opera Tavern WC2 **£41** 4 4 4
23 Catherine St 7836 3680 4–3D
"Divine small plates of Iberico, pata negra ham and must-try mini-burgers" – all among the "stylish" treats on offer at this "jammed", "good-natured" and "fun" sibling to Salt Yard, in a handily central Covent Garden pub-conversion. / WC2B 5JS; www.operatavern.co.uk; @saltyardgroup; 11.15 pm; closed Sun D; SRA-2 stars.

The Orange SW1 **£57** 334
37 Pimlico Rd 7881 9844 5–2D
"Delicious thin-based pizzas" headline an "enticing" menu, at this "bright", "airy" and "relaxing" gastropub, in the heart of Pimlico. / SW1W 8NE; www.theorange.co.uk; @TheOrangeSW1; 10 pm, Sun 9.30 pm; SRA-3 stars.

Orange Pekoe SW13 **£26** 344
3 White Hart Ln 8876 6070 10–1A
"A favourite of Barnes ladies who lunch" – "everything an independent tearoom-cum-coffee shop should be", it offers an "excellent range of teas", plus "fabulous" coffee, cake and salads. / SW13 0PX; www.orangepekoeteas.com; 5 pm; L only.

The Orange Tree N20 **£44** 123
7 Totteridge Ln 8343 7031 1–1B
"It's a beautiful pub in a great location, and wonderful on a sunny afternoon", but this popular Totteridge boozer "should be so much better" on the food front; problem? – "there is no competition". / N20 8NX; www.theorangetreetotteridge.co.uk; @orangetreepub; 9.45 pm, Fri & Sat 10.30 pm, Sun 9 pm.

Orchard WC1 **£42** 333
11 Sicilian Ave 7831 2715 2–1D
This snug Bloomsbury café – Vanilla Black's more informal sibling – is located in a pretty Italianate arcade with some exceptional al fresco table; "delicious" sarnies and cakes, plus "lovely" veggie fare. / WC1A 2QH; Mon-Fri 7.30 pm, Sat 6.45 pm; closed Sun.

Orpheus EC3 **£42** 431
26 Savage Gdns 7481 1931 9–3D
A "brilliant seafood place hidden away near Tower Hill" – this '70s "time warp" in a railway arch is a place where you should "ignore the decor", and focus on the "excellent choice of fresh fish". / EC3N 2AR; www.orpheusrestaurant.co.uk; L only, closed Sat & Sun.

Orrery W1 **£75** 344
55 Marylebone High St 7616 8000 2–1A
"Staff are impeccable, and so is the food", say fans of this "calm and considered" first-floor dining room, overlooking a Marylebone churchyard – a "really lovely space with lots of natural light"; even fans, though, can find it "expensive for what it is". / W1U 5RB; www.orreryrestaurant.co.uk; @orrery; 10.30 pm, Fri & Sat 11 pm; set Sun L £52 (FP); SRA-2 stars.

Orso WC2 **£56** 332
27 Wellington St 7240 5269 4–3D
"Unpretentious, and reasonably-priced for Covent Garden" – this "reliable" basement Italian restaurant may give little hint nowadays of its fashionable past, but it's a "friendly" sort of place, and still with a fan club among reporters, especially pre- or post-Royal Opera House. / WC2E 7DB; www.orsorestaurant.co.uk; @Orso_Restaurant; 11.30 pm; set weekday L £34 (FP), set always available £37 (FP), set pre-theatre £39 (FP).

Oslo Court NW8 **£63** 454
Charlbert St, off Prince Albert Rd 7722 8795 8–3A
"Back to the '70s"; this "faultless" Regent's Park spot may be a "throwback", but it's an "incredibly good" one, where "nearly every table has a birthday to celebrate"; pièce de résistance? – "the famed dessert trolley", the arrival of which is "the best entertainment in town". / NW8 7EN; 11 pm; closed Sun; no jeans or trainers.

Osteria Antica Bologna SW11 **£41** 333
23 Northcote Rd 7978 4771 10–2C
This "great local Italian", near Clapham Junction, has been serving up "genuine" Bolognese cuisine for over two decades, and is a handy "cheap and cheerful" destination. / SW11 1NG; www.osteria.co.uk; @OsteriaAntica; 10.30 pm, Sun 10 pm.

Osteria Basilico W11 **£55** 334
29 Kensington Park Rd 7727 9957 6–1A
"A classy neighbourhood Italian" that's long been an "easy-going" and "always-fun" linchpin of Notting Hill – "authentic and of consistently high quality"; arrive early if you want a table on the ground floor. / W11 2EU; www.osteriabasilico.co.uk; 11.30 pm, Sun 10.15 pm; no booking, Sat L.

Osteria Dell'Angolo SW1 **£57** 342
47 Marsham St 3268 1077 2–4C
A "very polished" Westminster corner Italian, whose "sharp" service and "very reliable" cooking naturally equip it for business; shame the atmosphere is so "subdued". / SW1P 3DR; www.osteriadellangolo.co.uk; @Osteria_Angolo; 10.30 pm; closed Sat L & Sun.

Ostuni NW6 **£43** 233
43-45 Lonsdale Rd 7624 8035 1–2B
In a former Victorian workshop, in Queen's Park, a Puglian yearling praised for its "lovely ambience" and its "non-typical" cuisine; the menu is "limited", though, with results ranging from "delicious" to "not yet quite right". / NW6 6RA; www.ostuniristorante.co.uk; 10 pm.

Barnyard

Big Easy

Marcus

Q-Grill

Otto's WC1 **£52** 454
182 Grays Inn Rd 7713 0107 2–1D
"Otto is quite a character", contributing much to the "pleasingly eccentric" ambience of his "determinedly old-fashioned" Bloomsbury two-year-old; the food is "the sort of French cuisine you thought had died a death", so don't forget to order your canard à la presse in advance – pure "theatre". / WC1X 8EW; www.ottos-restaurant.com; 10 pm; closed Sat L & Sun.

Ottolenghi **£48** 533
13 Motcomb St, SW1 7823 2707 5–1D
63 Ledbury Rd, W11 7727 1121 6–1B
1 Holland St, W8 7937 0003 5–1A
287 Upper St, N1 7288 1454 8–2D
Yotam Ottolenghi's "visually stunning" Middle Eastern-inspired creations – "unbelievable salads in such a variety" and "the most delicious cakes imaginable" – make his "innovative" cafés just the ticket for a life-enhancing brunch; shame, though, about "the queues and the crowding". / www.ottolenghi.co.uk; N1 10.15 pm; W8 & W11 8 pm, Sat 7 pm, Sun 6 pm; N1 closed Sun D; Holland St takeaway only; W11 & SW1 no booking, N1 booking for D only.

Outlaw's Seafood and Grill The Capital Hotel SW3 **£67** 442
22-24 Basil St 7589 5171 5–1D
Nathan Outlaw's "perfectly executed seafood" and "discreet" service win many accolades for this accomplished small dining room by Harrods, especially for the "very good-value set lunch" (or the "BYO deal on Thursdays"); shame the ambience of this oddly-shaped chamber is "a bit flat and formal". / SW3 1AT; www.capitalhotel.co.uk; @hotelcapital; 10 pm; closed Sun; set weekday L £35 (FP).

(Brasserie) Oxo Tower SE1 **£71** 122
Barge House St 7803 3888 9–3A
"Is it worth paying significantly more than West End prices, just for the brilliant view?" – as ever, the brasserie of this South Bank riverside landmark is too often "unimpressive on all levels". / SE1 9PH; www.harveynichols.com/restaurants/oxo-tower-london; 11 pm, Sun 10 pm; set pre theatre £51 (FP).

(Restaurant) Oxo Tower SE1 **£86** 112
Barge House St 7803 3888 9–3A
"Ugh!"; this "lazy" tourist trap at the top of the eponymous South Bank fixture remains "as awful as ever" – "take away the spectacular view, and everything else is rubbish". / SE1 9PH; www.harveynichols.com/restaurants; @OxoTowerWharf; 11 pm, Sun 10 pm.

Ozer WC2 **£48** 232
36 Tavistock St 7240 3773 3–1C
"Good-value tasty fare, pre- or post-theatre", and not bad for lunch either – the Sofra chain's flagship is a handy standby, especially for those who work at neighbouring Broadcasting House, serving a wide-ranging Turkish/Middle Eastern menu. / WC2E 7PB; www.sofra.co.uk; 11 pm.

Le P'tit Normand SW18 **£42** 343
185 Merton Rd 8871 0233 10–2B
Although it is as "long-lasting" and "traditional" a Gallic bistro as you could hope to find, this Southfields fixture "has been gradually improving" in recent years; it offers "classic" dishes and "carefully chosen" wines, all at "good-value" prices. / SW18 5EF; www.leptitnormand.co.uk; 10 pm, Sun 3 pm; closed Mon, Tue L, Wed L, Thu L & Sun D; set weekday L £30 (FP).

Pachamama W1 NEW
18 Thayer St 7935 9393 2–1A
Another addition to London's growing Peruvian dining scene – this time in Marylebone – combining dishes and cocktails native to Peru with British fare. / W1U 3JY; www.pachamamalondon.com; @pachamama_ldn.

The Paddyfield SW12 **£28** 332
4 Bedford Hill 8772 1145 10–2C
"Fresh spring rolls, salads and really good noodles" impress most, if not quite all, reporters on this Balham Thai/Vietnamese; the BYO policy helps make it quite a "cheap" night out too. / SW12 9RG; www.thepaddyfield.co.uk; 11 pm; D only; no credit cards.

Il Pagliaccio SW6 **£39** 233
182-184 Wandsworth Bridge Rd 7371 5253 10–1B
An "excellent neighbourhood pizza joint", in Sands End, that's both family- and wallet-friendly; the odd culinary miss is "more than forgiven, as the place is so much fun and full of life". / SW6 2UF; www.paggs.co.uk; @pagliaccipizza; midnight; no Amex.

Le Pain Quotidien **£38** 223
Branches throughout London
"Not cheap, but pleasant" – this "welcoming", "rustic"-style international café-bakery chain is ideal for a "great healthy brunch" or an "imaginative salad". / www.painquotidien.com; most branches close between 7 pm-10 pm; no booking at some branches, especially at weekends.

The Painted Heron SW10 **£58** 5 3 2
112 Cheyne Walk 7351 5232 5–3B
A recent change of management has done nothing to diminish the "intricate but unfussy" charms of this "fabulous modern Indian", tucked-away off the Chelsea Embankment; "why does it never get the plaudits it deserves?" / SW10 0DJ; www.thepaintedheron.com; Mon-Sat 10.30 pm, Sun 10 pm; no Amex.

The Palmerston SE22 **£52** 3 3 2
91 Lordship Ln 8693 1629 1–4D
"Precision and taste are evident in every dish", at this "jovial" East Dulwich "haven" – "a massive notch above standard gastropub fare". / SE22 8EP; www.thepalmerston.co.uk; @thepalmerston; 10 pm, Sun 9.30 pm; no Amex; set weekday L £27 (FP).

Palmyra TW9 **£42** 4 3 2
277 Sandycombe Rd 8948 7019 1–3A
A small Kew Lebanese, offering "delicious" and "authentic" dishes – from "tasty and succulent" meats ("and in generous portions") to mezzes with "an original twist". / TW9 3LU; www.palmyrarestaurant.co.uk; 11 pm; no Amex.

The Palomar W1 NEW **£40** 4 5 4
34 Rupert St 7439 8777 4–3A
"Genuinely new and different", this "brilliant" modern Israeli opening is "off to a flying start" with its "interesting fusion-style menu", "buzzing" atmosphere and "infectiously enthusiastic" staff; handy location too, three minutes' walk from Piccadilly Circus. / W1D 6DN; www.thepalomar.co.uk.

The Pantechnicon SW1 **£57** 3 3 4
10 Motcomb St 7730 6074 5–1D
More a "bar-bistro" than a boozer, this "buzzing" Belgravian may be no bargain, but it offers "a nice blend of 'quality' attributes" and attracts "a good mix of customers"; for more grandeur and comfort, head upstairs. / SW1X 8LA; www.thepantechnicon.com; @ThePantechnicon; Weekdays 10 pm, Sun 9.30 pm; SRA-3 stars.

Pappa Ciccia **£40** 4 3 3
105 Munster Rd, SW6 7384 1884 10–1B
41 Fulham High St, SW6 7736 0900 10–1B
"Simply delicious and authentic pizza" (in "huge portions") and "friendly service" too makes these BYO Fulham spots "lovely" places to live near – "I've moved, but I still wish this was on my doorstep!" / www.pappaciccia.com; 11 pm, Sat & Sun 11.30 pm; Munster Rd no credit cards.

Paradise by Way of Kensal Green W10 **£47** 3 4 5
19 Kilburn Ln 8969 0098 1–2B
The decor at this "charming" Kensal Green fixture is "an object lesson in shabby-chic glamour", and its "super-helpful and glamorous staff" serve up lovely food of "gastropub+" aspiration; nowhere is perfect though – "parking is tricky". / W10 4AE; www.theparadise.co.uk; @weloveparadise; 10.30 pm, Fri & Sat 11 pm, Sun 9 pm; closed weekday L; no Amex.

Paradise Hampstead NW3 **£31** 4 5 4
49 South End Rd 7794 6314 8–2A
"The staff remember you, and make the effort", at this "old-fashioned" curry "stalwart", in South End Green – world-famous locally for its "excellent, if standard, array of dishes" and "terrific value". / NW3 2QB; www.paradisehampstead.co.uk; 10.45 pm.

El Parador NW1 **£36** 4 4 4
245 Eversholt St 7387 2789 8–3C
"Why go elsewhere?", say fans of this "cosy" Camden Town gem – "it's the loveliest family-run tapas place you could wish for", and the dishes are "always fresh and interesting". / NW1 1BA; www.elparadorlondon.com; 11 pm, Fri & Sat 11.30 pm, Sun 9.30 pm; closed Sat L & Sun L; no Amex.

Paramount Centre Point WC1 **£75** 2 2 4
101-103 New Oxford St 7420 2900 4–1A
"Incredible views" and the ultra-central location should inspire adulation for Centre Point's 32nd-floor dining room; the verdict, though? – with its "substandard" food and slack service, it's only "almost worth it"; maybe just grab a cocktail? / WC1A 1DD; www.paramount.uk.net; @ParamountSoho; 11 pm, Sun 10 pm.

Parlour NW10 NEW **£46** 4 4 3
5 Regent St 8969 2184 1–2B
"A great find, in the backwaters of Kensal Rise" (by the better-known Paradise); Jesse Dunford Wood's "fun" and casual hangout serves "insanely great" retro scoff at "everyday prices". / NW10 5LG; www.parlourkensal.com; @ParlourUK; 11 pm.

Patara **£55** 3 3 3
15 Greek St, W1 7437 1071 4–2A
7 Maddox St, W1 7499 6008 3–2C
181 Fulham Rd, SW3 7351 5692 5–2C
9 Beauchamp Pl, SW3 7581 8820 5–1C
"Charming" service, "beautiful" decor and a wide choice of "refined" dishes win enduring popularity for this "old-favourite" Thai chain; "after so many

years, there's nothing new on the menu" however, and sceptics find standards "nothing special" nowadays. / www.pataralondon.com; 10.30 pm; Greek St closed Sun L.

Paternoster Chop House EC4 **£55** 333
Warwick Ct, Paternoster Sq 7029 9400 9–2B
An "airy" (but "noisy") steakhouse, whose al fresco tables enjoy "great views of St Paul's"; it's attracted more praise of late for its "fast and efficient" service of "simple" but "expensive" dishes – just the ticket for City types. / EC4M 7DX; www.paternosterchophouse.co.uk; @paternoster1; 10.30 pm; closed Sat & Sun D; SRA-3 stars.

Patio W12 **£36** 355
5 Goldhawk Rd 8743 5194 7–1C
"A great find"; this "eccentric" Polish operation offers "extraordinary value"; the fare is "home-cooked", and comes in "huge portions", but it's the "cute" '50s decor and superb service from the owner – not to mention "loads of flavoured vodkas" – that really set it apart. / W12 8QQ; www.patiolondon.com; 11 pm, Sat & Sun 11.30 pm; closed Sat L & Sun L.

Pâtisserie Valerie **£27** 122
Branches throughout London
Those who remember the "former glories" of this once-tiny chain see its current venture capital-backed growth as a "travesty"; others still find it an OK pit stop, though, for a coffee and croissant, or a teatime bun. / www.patisserie-valerie.co.uk; most branches close between 5 pm-8 pm; no booking except Old Compton St Sun-Thu.

Patogh W1 **£24** 322
8 Crawford Pl 7262 4015 6–1D
"A little corner of Iran"; this "dingy" grill, just off the Edgware Road, serves "tender and tasty" lamb kebabs plus "other varieties of singed flesh"; BYO. / W1H 5NE; 11 pm; no credit cards.

Patty and Bun **£21** 423
54 James St, W1 7487 3188 3–1A
22-23 Liverpool St, EC2 7621 1331 9–2D
NEW
"If they laced dishes with crack, they wouldn't be more addictive", say fans of the "ultimate dirty burgers" (and "superb" wings too) served by these "funky" pit stops, near Selfridges and now in the City; they're "seriously cramped" though, and the queues can be "unreal". / www.pattyandbun.co.uk.

Paul **£27** 322
Branches throughout London
"The only place to get an authentic baguette sandwich" – France's biggest café-pâtisserie chain impresses with its "excellent-quality sweets and savouries", mostly to take away (but Covent Garden has its own dining room); service can be "tragically slow, and so French…". / www.paul-uk.com; most branches close between 7 pm-8.30 pm; no booking.

Pavilion W8 NEW **£62** 343
96 Kensington High St 7262 0905 5–1A
Jon Hunt's (of Foxton's fame) "unusual" and ultra-plush marbled hall – attached to a swish Kensington business centre – has been quite a hit, and early reports applaud Adam Simmonds's "excellent" cuisine; on our visit, though, it seemed almost as much of a bar as a restaurant, perhaps most suited to a drink or brunch? / W8 4SG; www.kensingtonpavilion.com; closed Mon, Tue, Wed, Thu, Fri, Sat & Sun.

Pearl Liang W2 **£47** 322
8 Sheldon Sq 7289 7000 6–1C
This "popular" Paddington Basin basement – with modern, opium den styling – has carved quite a name for its "unusual" dim sum, and other "high-quality" dishes; ratings are not what they were, though, and critics say it's "no longer worth the trip". / W2 6EZ; www.pearlliang.co.uk; 11 pm; set weekday L £26 (FP).

The Peasant EC1 **£47** 334
240 St John St 7336 7726 8–3D
"A very good and old-established gastropub" (early-'90s), in Clerkenwell, which still wins plaudits for the "upmarket bistro" fare served in its upstairs dining room; the atmosphere is "convivial" ("noisy") too. / EC1V 4PH; www.thepeasant.co.uk; @ThePeasant; 10.45 pm, Sun 9.30 pm.

Peckham Bazaar SE15 NEW **£45** 333
119 Consort Rd 0787 510 7471 1–4D
"Interesting" Balkan cuisine (and some "interesting and fairly priced" wines too) help make this converted house a popular south London destination; menu highlight – "perfect BBQ". / SE15 3RU; www.peckhambazaar.com.

Peckham Refreshment Rooms SE15 NEW **£36** 333
12-16 Blenheim Grove 7639 1106 1–4D
A "jammed" yearling, serving an "interesting", "tapas-like" British menu from a regularly changing menu; "you teeter on uncomfortable high stools" though, so it's "not a place to linger". / SE15 4QL; www.peckhamrefreshment.com.

Pellicano SW3 **£60** 353
35 Ixworth Pl 7589 3718 5–2C
This "perennial favourite" Chelsea backstreet Italian

has now shifted to a new "warm and welcoming" home, part of a small hotel, on the same street as always; remarkably, regulars say the food is "better than ever"! / SW3 3QX; www.pellicanorestaurant.co.uk; 11 pm, Sun 10.30 pm; set always available £38 (FP).

E Pellicci E2 **£21** 2 4 5
332 Bethnal Green Rd 7739 4873 12–1D
An "old-school east London caff", known for its "beautiful" (listed) Art Deco interior, and "warm welcome"; it does a "great breakfast", and "really cheap too". / E2 0AG; 4.15 pm; L only, closed Sun; no credit cards.

Penkul & Banks EC2 NEW **£45** 4 4 2
77 Curtain Rd 7729 2966 12–1B
On the former site of Beard to Tail, this new café-bar-restaurant promises 'eclectic modern European cuisine with an Asian twist' (read: tapas and sharing plates). / EC2A 3BS; Rated on Editors' visit.

Pentolina W14 **£44** 4 5 4
71 Blythe Rd 3010 0091 7–1D
"It popped up from nowhere, and is still going strong!" – this "cosy and romantic" backstreet Italian is "becoming a stalwart of the Brook Green/Hammersmith scene", thanks to its "classic Italian home-cooking", and "delightful" service too. / W14 0HP; www.pentolinarestaurant.co.uk; 10 pm; closed Mon & Sun; no Amex.

The Pepper Tree SW4 **£27** 4 4 3
19 Clapham Common S'side 7622 1758 10–2D
"A great cheap and cheerful eatery", near Clapham Common tube, where communal canteen-style tables "add to the atmosphere" – its "very good" Thai cuisine is "ideal for a quick bite when out and about". / SW4 7AB; www.thepeppertree.co.uk; 10.45 pm, Sun & Mon 10.15 pm; no Amex; no booking.

Pescatori **£56** 3 2 2
11 Dover St, W1 7493 2652 3–3C
57 Charlotte St, W1 7580 3289 2–1C
"Fish is done well", at these simple and low-key West End Italians; they may be "dull" but – viewed as a standby choice – they "could be worse". / www.pescatori.co.uk; 11 pm; closed Sat L & Sun.

Petersham Hotel TW10 **£65** 3 5 5
Nightingale Ln 8940 7471 1–4A
An "old-fashioned" and "genteel" Richmond dining room ("diners all look like UKIP supporters!"), which benefits from "superb Thames views" ("if you can get a window table") and "fantastic" service too; the food is good, if "rather unimaginative" – "ideal for entertaining elderly relations!" / TW10 6UZ; www.petershamhotel.co.uk; @ThePetersham; 9.45 pm, Sun 8.45 pm; set Sun L £57 (FP).

Petersham Nurseries TW10 **£72** 2 1 4
Church Ln, Off Petersham Rd 8940 5230 1–4A
"An earth-floored greenhouse with distressed antiques, and lush foliage" creates the "special and romantic" atmosphere at this quirky venue, near Richmond; it's never really recovered since Skye Gyngell left, though, and – with its "inept" service – can feel "like an overpriced garden centre café" nowadays. / TW10 7AG; www.petershamnurseries.com; L only, closed Mon.

La Petite Maison W1 **£86** 4 3 4
54 Brook's Mews 7495 4774 3–2B
"Bubbly and genuinely French in feel", but "flashy and expensive" too, this mews spot brings the authentic charms of the Côte d'Azur to the backwoods of Mayfair – these include "perfect sunny-days food", "snooty" service and Russian oligarchs aplenty. / W1K 4EG; www.lpmlondon.co.uk; @lpmlondon; 10.30 pm, Sun 9 pm.

Pétrus SW1 **£92** 4 4 4
1 Kinnerton St 7592 1609 5–1D
"An outstanding all-rounder" – Gordon Ramsay's Belgravia dining room may be a bit "corporate" in feel, but no one's complaining about its "wonderful culinary creativity", "legendary wine list" or "tip-top" service. / SW1X 8EA; www.gordonramsay.com/petrus; @petrus; 10.15 pm; closed Sun; no trainers; set weekday L £59 (FP).

Peyote W1 NEW **£62** 3 3 2
13 Cork St 7409 1300 3–3C
"London needed Peyote", say fans of this "upscale" new Mayfair Mexican, lauding its "exciting" and "absolutely delicious" cuisine; tables are "cramped", though, and critics find the food "not really that much better than Wahaca". / W1S 3NS; www.peyoteresaurant.com.

Pham Sushi EC1 **£38** 5 4 1
159 Whitecross St 7251 6336 12–2A
"Awesome" sushi and sashimi is the "main asset" of this small and basic restaurant near the Barbican; all at "incredible-value" prices too. / EC1Y 8JL; www.phamsushi.co.uk; @phamsushi; 9.45 pm; closed Sat L & Sun.

The Phene SW3 **£42** 1 2 3
9 Phene St 7352 9898 5–3C
It's "fun", it's "happening", and "in the garden,

the sun always seem to shine", but this "charming" Chelsea pub can suffer from "stressed out" service and "very poor" food. / SW3 5NY; www.thephene.com; @ThePheneSW3; 10 pm.

Pho **£37** 3 3 3
163-165 Wardour St, W1 7434 3938 3–1D
3 Great Titchfield St, W1 7436 0111 3–1C
Westfield, Ariel Way, W12 07824 662320 7–1C
48 Brushfield St, E1 7377 6436 12–2B
86 St John St, EC1 7253 7624 9–1A
As Vietnamese street food-inspired chains go, these "honest" outlets are surprisingly "convivial"; as the chain grows apace, however, the food is becoming more middle-of-the-road – "no fireworks, but tasty" is a pretty typical verdict nowadays. / www.phocafe.co.uk; EC1 10 pm, Fri & Sat 10.30 pm; W1 10.30 pm; W12 9 pm, Sat 7 pm, Sun 6 pm; EC1 closed Sat L & Sun; W1 closed Sun; no Amex; no booking.

Phoenix Palace NW1 **£55** 3 2 2
5-9 Glentworth St 7486 3515 2–1A
This "bustling" and "un-anglicised" fixture, near Baker Street, serves a "wide-ranging menu, and the best dishes are the most unusual ones" – "go with Chinese friends to get the dishes not on the menu"; its "a favourite for dim sum" too – "arrive by noon, or be prepared to queue". / NW1 5PG; www.phoenixpalace.co.uk; 11.15 pm, Sun 10.15 pm.

Piccolino **£52** 2 2 2
21 Heddon St, W1 7287 4029 3–2C
11 Exchange Sq, EC2 7375 2568 12–2B
A low-profile but "always reliable" Italian chain, whose decent value and kid-friendliness wins it somewhat better ratings than many better-known competitors. / www.piccolinorestaurants.co.uk; 11 pm, Sun 10 pm; EC2 closed Sat & Sun.

Picture W1 **£33** 3 5 2
110 Great Portland St 7637 7892 2–1B
Run by an ex-Arbutus/Wild Honey team, this "enthusiastic" yearling, a short walk from Broadcasting House, dishes up "thoroughly tempting" – but "surprisingly inexpensive" – small plates, "with a smile"; the setting is "relaxed", or a touch "uncomfortable", to taste. / W1W 6PQ; Rated on Editors' visit; www.picturerestaurant.co.uk; 10 pm; closed Sun.

PIED À TERRE W1 **£99** 5 5 3
34 Charlotte St 7636 1178 2–1C
Marcus Eaves's "fabulous food, beautifully presented" maintains David Moore's "plush" Fitzrovia fixture as one of the capital's foremost foodie temples; the ambience can seem "stuffy" though (going on "dull", if you sit at the front). / W1T 2NH; www.pied-a-terre.co.uk; @davidpied; 10.45 pm; closed Sat L & Sun; booking: max 7; set weekday L £52 (FP).

Pig & Butcher N1 **£49** 4 3 3
80 Liverpool Rd 7226 8304 8–3D
"Modern but hearty" cuisine, with the meaty emphasis the name suggests, has helped make this Islington gastroboozer quite a hit; "fabulous Sunday lunches" a highlight. / N1 0QD; www.thepigandbutcher.co.uk; @pigandbutcher; 10.30 pm; Mon-Thu D only, Fri-Sun open L & D.

The Pig's Ear SW3 **£54** 2 2 3
35 Old Church St 7352 2908 5–3C
An Art Nouveau-themed Chelsea boozer, where you can eat "in the quiet upstairs dining room, or downstairs with a bit of buzz"; fans say it's "what a gastropub should be", but it can be "totally let down" by "limp and tasteless" cooking. / SW3 5BS; www.thepigsear.info; 10 pm, Sun 9 pm.

Pilpel **£9** 4 4 2
38 Brushfield Street, London, E1 7247 0146 12–2B
Old Spitalfields Mkt, E1 7375 2282 12–2B
146 Fleet St, EC4 7583 2030 9–2A
Paternoster Sq, EC4 7248 9281 9–2B
"Amazing falafel that tastes like it does in Jerusalem" – the "authentic" attraction of this "reliable" small chain. / www.pilpel.co.uk.

ping pong **£33** 2 2 3
29a James St, W1 7034 3100 3–1A
45 Gt Marlborough St, W1 7851 6969 3–2C
74-76 Westbourne Grove, W2 7313 9832 6–1B
Southbank Centre, SE1 7960 4160 2–3D
Bow Bells Hs, 1 Bread St, EC4 7651 0880 9–2B
As a "fun" standby, these stylish budget hangouts do have their fans; however, the "exotic cocktails" and "interesting tea selection" are a safer bet than the dim sum itself ("nothing special"), and service is sometimes "awful". / www.pingpongdimsum.com; @pingpongdimsum; 10 pm-11.30 pm; EC2 & EC4 closed Sat & Sun; booking: min 8.

El Pirata W1 **£39** 2 3 5
5-6 Down St 7491 3810 3–4B
This "super-bustling tapas bar" is a "fun" little dive that's well worth knowing about – the food may only be "satisfactory" but, by Mayfair standards, it's very affordable. / W1J 7AQ; www.elpirata.co.uk; @elpirataw1; 11.30 pm; closed Sat L & Sun; set weekday L £19 (FP).

El Pirata de Tapas W2 £42 332
115 Westbourne Grove 7727 5000 6–1B
A Bayswater bar where the "dark and romantic" decor is "ideal for a date"; it offers "delicious" and "very economical" modern tapas, as well as some "lovely" Spanish wines. / W2 4UP; www.elpiratadetapas.co.uk; @Pirate_de_Tapas; 11 pm, Sun 10 pm; Mon-Thu D only, Fri-Sun open L & D.

Pitt Cue Co W1 £25 544
1 Newburgh St 7287 5578 3–2D
"The best BBQ ever… and I grew up in the southern States"! – reporters "drool at the mere thought" of a visit to this "awesome little place", off Carnaby Street, with its its "genius" pulled pork, burnt tips, pickles and other carnivorous treats; no wonder the queue is "everlasting". / W1F 7RB; www.pittcue.co.uk; @PittCueCo; SRA-1 star.

Pizarro SE1 £48 344
194 Bermondsey St 7407 7339 9–4D
"Why travel to Spain?"; at this Bermondsey favourite, José P dishes up "daringly simple" tapas which pack "a real punch"; it's "an unpretentious dining room full of the buzz of happy diners", but this year's survey ratings weren't quite as ecstatic as last year's. / SE1 3TQ; www.josepizarro.com/restaurants/pizarro; @Jose_Pizarro; 11 pm, Sun 10 pm.

Pizza East £48 434
310 Portobello Rd, W10 8969 4500 6–1A
79 Highgate Rd, NW5 3310 2000 8–1B
56 Shoreditch High St, E1 7729 1888 12–1B
Permanent long queues attest to the success of this "happening" chain, where the "unusual" dishes offer "a great twist on pizza"; beware, though – "it's like there's a sign on the door, saying 'No Entry without beard, check shirt and Converses'". / www.pizzaeast.com; @PizzaEast; E1 Sun-Wed 11 pm, Thu 12 am, Fri-Sat 1am; W10 Mon-Thu 11.30 pm, Fri-Sat 12 am, Sun 10.30 pm.

Pizza Metro SW11 £45 443
64 Battersea Rise 7228 3812 10–2C
"Good fun", "excellent pizza" and "amazing pasta" – not much to fault at these local pioneers of pizza-by-the-metre, both at the Battersea original, and the newer one in Notting Hill. / SW11 1EQ; www.pizzametropizza.com; @pizzametropizza; 11 pm; no Amex.

Pizza Pilgrims £23 444
102 Berwick St, W1 0778 066 7258 3–2D
11-12 Dean St, W1 0778 066 7258 3–1D
Kingly Ct, Carnaby St, W1 7287 8964 3–2C
"The van was great", and now the Elliot brothers have translated their pop-up into a duo of "funky" Soho outfits – the "fantastic" thin crusts and "minimal but extremely authentic" selection of toppings have mercifully survived the transition, so "the hordes pile in" – "expect to queue".

PizzaExpress £39 223
Branches throughout London
"Still the best pizza on the high street"; turning 50 this year, this "old faithful" remains the yardstick by which other multiples are judged; "frequent updating" keeps the formula fresh, but there is one constant – "they really get kids!". / www.pizzaexpress.co.uk; 11.30 pm-midnight; most City branches closed all or part of weekend; no booking at most branches.

Pizzeria Oregano N1 £41 443
18-19 St Albans Pl 7288 1123 8–3D
On account of its "great pizza, and fabulous pasta too", this unpretentious spot, just off Upper Street, remains quite the "neighbourhood favourite". / N1 0NX; www.pizzaoregano.co.uk; @PizzeriaOregano; 11 pm, Fri 11.30 pm, Sun 10.30 pm; closed weekday L.

Pizzeria Pappagone N4 £38 334
131 Stroud Green Rd 7263 2114 8–1D
"Multiple birthday parties nightly" help ensure this "buzzing" Stroud Green Italian is "always packed"; "delicious pizzas, and a great range of pastas and specials ensure you never get bored". / N4 3PX; www.pizzeriapappagone.co.uk; midnight.

Pizzeria Rustica TW9 £39 443
32 The Quadrant 8332 6262 1–4A
"A great little find", and handy for Richmond station too – this "lively" family-run spot wins high praise for its "tasty" stone-baked pizza. / TW9 1DN; www.pizzeriarustica.co.uk; 11 pm, Fri & Sat 11.30 pm, Sun 10.30 pm.

PJ's Bar and Grill SW3 £51 234
52 Fulham Rd 7581 0025 5–2C
The "quintessential classic brunch place" for the Chelsea set; the food may be nothing to write home about, but as a "fun and buzzy place to be" it's "still very passable and enjoyable". / SW3 6HH; www.pjsbarandgrill.co.uk; @PJsBARANDGRILL; 10.30 pm, Sun 10 pm.

Plateau E14 £62 133
Canada Pl 7715 7100 11–1C
"A dependable business lunch location", made distinctive by its impressive elevated views over Canary Wharf; it's very much in the "bland and boring" style which was has traditionally been the D&D Group's hallmark, so let's hope the evolution

sometimes apparent elsewhere begins to manifest itself here! / E14 5ER; www.plateau-restaurant.co.uk; @plateaulondon; 10.15 pm; closed Sat L & Sun; set dinner £38 (FP); SRA-2 stars.

Plum + Spilt Milk Great Northern Hotel N1 **£46** 2 3 3
King's Cross 3388 0800 8–3C
By railway station hotel standards, this "glamorous" and "moodily lit" King's Cross dining space is certainly "a good option" and fans say the setting is nothing short of "magical"; the food, though, is "fairly routine". / N1C 4TB; www.gnhlondon.com; @PlumSpiltMilk; 11 pm, Sun 10 pm.

Plum Valley W1 **£46** 4 2 3
20 Gerrard St 7494 4366 4–3A
"A quality restaurant amidst many mediocre choices", and one that's "pretty swanky and fun" by Chinatown standards too; innovative dim sum is a highlight. / W1D 6JQ; www.plumvalleylondon.com; 11.30 pm.

Pod **£14** 3 3 2
Branches throughout London
"Tasty" breakfasts, and "great, healthy and delicious" lunches – the sort of fare which makes these City and West End pit stops a hit with all who comment on them. / www.podfood.co.uk; 3 pm-4 pm, WC2 7 pm, Sat 8 pm, Sun 5 pm; branches closed Sat & Sun, St Martin's & City Rd closed Sun.

Poissonnerie de l'Avenue SW3 **£69** 4 3 2
82 Sloane Ave 7589 2457 5–2C
"Old-fashioned, but still superb"; this tightly packed Brompton Cross "classic" has a loyal older following for its "high-quality fish, reverently served". / SW3 3DZ; www.poissonneriedelavenue.co.uk; 11.30 pm, Sun 10,30 pm; set weekday L £52 (FP).

La Polenteria W1 NEW **£37** 3 4 3
64 Old Compton St 7434 3617 4–3A
This basic new Soho bistro does indeed just serve polenta, albeit in various styles – "an eclectic idea which deserves to get more traction!" / W1D 4UQ; www.lapolenteria.com; @La_Polenteria; 11 pm.

POLLEN STREET SOCIAL W1 **£84** 4 4 3
8-10 Pollen St 7290 7600 3–2C
A "very slick" Mayfair hangout, where Jason Atherton's "flavour-popping" menu includes many "stunning" dishes; its "light and bright" interior and "vibrant" style, however, ensures that it's "not the place for a romantic supper!" / W1S 1NQ; www.pollenstreetsocial.com; @PollenStSocial; 10.45 pm; closed Sun; set weekday L £53 (FP).

Polpo **£37** 2 3 5
41 Beak St, W1 7734 4479 3–2D
6 Maiden Ln, WC2 7836 8448 4–3D
126-128 Notting Hill Gate, W11 7229 3283 6–2B NEW
2-3 Cowcross St, EC1 7250 0034 9–1A
Service that's "too cool for school" (but still "so friendly") helps set the "urbane" tone at Russell Norman's "warm and cosy" NYC-style Venetian tapas bars; the wait for a table can be "tedious", though, especially as the food is "rather hit-and-miss" nowadays. / www.polpo.co.uk; W1 & EC1 11 pm; WC2 11 pm, Sun 10.30 pm; W1 & EC1 closed D Sun.

Pond N16 NEW
Stamford Works, 3 Gillett St 3772 6727 1–1C
Dalston says "aloha" to this restaurant that promises New Hawaiian cuisine; the initial press was encouraging. / N16 8JH; pond-dalston.com.

Le Pont de la Tour SE1 **£72** 2 2 3
36d Shad Thames 7403 8403 9–4D
It's hard to beat the "sensational" Tower Bridge views from the D&D Group's grand South Bank "icon"; for a date, or as a "smart and efficient business venue" it still has many fans, but foodwise it's "lost its passion", and is "far too expensive" nowadays. / SE1 2YE; www.lepontdelatour.co.uk; @lepontdelatour; 10.30 pm, Sun 9.30 pm; no trainers; set weekday L & dinner £42 (FP); SRA-1 star.

Popeseye **£52** 3 4 2
108 Blythe Rd, W14 7610 4578 7–1C
277 Upper Richmond Rd, SW15 8788 7733 10–2A
"So the room is tired and I ended up smelling of the frying fat", but even so reporters (generally) applaud these "good-value" west London bistros, where "superlative steak and chips" is the only menu option. / www.popeseye.com; 10.30 pm; D only, closed Sun; no credit cards.

La Porchetta Pizzeria **£34** 3 3 3
33 Boswell St, WC1 7242 2434 2–1D
141-142 Upper St, N1 7288 2488 8–2D
147 Stroud Green Rd, N4 7281 2892 8–1D
74-77 Chalk Farm Rd, NW1 7267 6822 8–2B
84-86 Rosebery Ave, EC1 7837 6060 9–1A
"Amazing pizza" plus a wide variety of other Italian dishes, all in very "good portions", are to be had at these "vibrant" north London fixtures – "a perfect standby for a quick, cheap and cheerful

meal", and "very welcoming to kids" too. / www.laporchetta.net; last orders varies by branch; WC1 closed Sat L & Sun; N1,EC1 & NW1 closed Mon-Fri L; N4 closed weekday L; no Amex.

Portal EC1 **£59** 344
88 St John St 7253 6950 9–1B
"A fantastic ambassador" for Portuguese food ("which is generally underrated"), this Clerkenwell fixture also benefits from a "refined and beautiful" interior – "particularly the super-sized conservatory" – and an "eclectic and distinctive" list of wines and ports. / EC1M 4EH; www.portalrestaurant.com; @portalrestaurant; 10.15 pm; closed Sat L & Sun; SRA-3 stars.

La Porte des Indes W1 **£63** 334
32 Bryanston St 7224 0055 2–2A
A deceptively large and unexpectedly lavishly-themed basement ("like being in the Tropics"), near Marble Arch; "it's a bit expensive", but serves "interesting" French-colonial Indian food that's "just a little bit different from the norm". / W1H 7EG; www.laportedesindes.com; @LaPorteDesIndes; 11.30 pm, Sun 10.30 pm.

Il Portico W8 **£50** 253
277 Kensington High St 7602 6262 7–1D
A "nice old-fashioned trattoria" that's "always packed"; opinions differ on the "home-cooking" – averaging out somewhere round "more than adequate" – but it's the "family who run it with love and care" who really make this a Kensington institution. / W8 6NA; www.ilportico.co.uk; 10.45 pm; closed Sun.

Portobello Ristorante W11 **£48** 344
7 Ladbroke Rd 7221 1373 6–2B
Just off Notting Hill Gate, a "very cheerful" independent, neighbourhood spot, with a lovely summer terrace; no-one minds the "slightly haphazard" service, given "great pizza" (sold 'al metro') and "other consistently good dishes". / W11 3PA; www.portobellolondon.co.uk; 10.30 pm, Sun 10.15 pm.

The Portrait National Portrait Gallery WC2 **£53** 224
St Martin's Pl 7312 2490 4–4B
"Who can resist a date with Nelson?" – the "stunning view" from this top-floor dining room in the heart of the West End is its particular attraction; fans are "pleasantly surprised" by the cooking too, though the less starry-eyed can find it "uninspiring". / WC2H 0HE; http://www.npg.org.uk/visit/shop-eat-drink.php; Thu-Fri 8.30 pm; Sun-Wed closed D.

Potli W6 **£38** 434
319-321 King St 8741 4328 7–2B
"Brilliant and always-buzzy", this "top-notch" Hammersmith Indian offers many "spicy" and "delicious" dishes; of late, however, delivery has perhaps been a touch more "uneven" than it was. / W6 9NH; www.potli.co.uk; @Potlirestaurant; 10.30 pm, Fri & Sat 11.30 pm.

La Poule au Pot SW1 **£63** 335
231 Ebury St 7730 7763 5–2D
A date "can't fail", at this "so French" and "gorgeous" farmhouse-style half-centenarian, whose "low light and dark corners" (and top al fresco tables on sunny days) have long made it a classic romantic choice; the "rustic" cooking is "good… for '70s-style fare" and "if you parler français, service is very good". / SW1W 8UT; www.pouleaupot.co.uk; 11 pm, Sun 10 pm; set weekday L £42 (FP).

Prawn On The Lawn N1 **£27** 453
220 St Paul's Rd 3302 8668 8–2D
"The name may sound like the debris left behind after a picnic", but this "cute" new restaurant and wine bar attracts rave reports for its "amazingly fresh" seafood and its "crisp wines by the glass" too. / N1 2LY; prawnonthelawn.com; @PrawnOnTheLawn; Tue-Wed 9 pm, Thu-Sat 10 pm; closed Mon & Sun; no Amex.

Pret A Manger **£15** 242
Branches throughout London
"I went to one in Boston recently, and it was just as good as always!" – as London-based success-stories go, this gold-standard sandwiches-and-more chain has become "a legend"; it must help that it has "the friendliest staff by a mile". / www.pret.com; generally 4 pm-6 pm; closed Sun (except some West End branches); City branches closed Sat & Sun; no Amex; no booking.

Primeur N5 NEW **£46**
116 Petherton Rd no tel 1–1C
A summer opening just too late to gather any survey feedback, this Clissold Park spot is backed by a team whose experience includes Brunswick House, Rita's and Wright Brothers – sounds as if should be a handy addition to the area. / N5 2RT; www.primeurN5.co.uk; @Primeurs1; no booking.

Princess Garden W1 **£59** 433
8-10 North Audley St 7493 3223 3–2A
"Amazingly good-value" dim sum is the highlight at this "elegant" and "upmarket", if perhaps slightly "soulless", Mayfair Chinese; at other times, it's a "totally reliable" option for "classic" Cantonese cooking. / W1K 6ZD; www.princessgardenofmayfair.com; 11 pm.

Princess of Shoreditch EC2 **£47** 343

76 Paul St 7729 9270 12–1B

"A slightly cramped room above what was a traditional corner boozer" – the main dining option at this trendy and "still reliable" Shoreditch stalwart. / EC2A 4NE; www.theprincessofshoreditch.com; @princessofs; 10 pm, Sun 8 pm; no Amex.

Princess Victoria W12 **£46** 344

217 Uxbridge Rd 8749 5886 7–1B

"Large, light and airy", this huge tavern, in deepest Shepherd's Bush, "has the real feel of a Victorian gin palace to it"; the food is of consistent good quality, and there's an "excellent wine list" too. / W12 9DH; www.princessvictoria.co.uk; @pvwestlondon; 10.30 pm, Sun 9.30 pm; no Amex.

Princi W1 **£34** 324

135 Wardour St 7478 8888 3–2D

"Love it, love it, love it!" – this "crazy and buzzy" ("packed to the rafters") Milanese-inspired deli-coffee shop-pâtisserie is "perfect for a quick bite in Soho"; "fantastic" pizza a highlight. / W1F 0UT; www.princi.com; midnight, Sun 10 pm; no booking.

Prix Fixe W1 **£38** 344

39 Dean St 7734 5976 4–2A

It may be "slap bang in the middle of Soho", but this "little French bistro" is well off the hipster trail; it's a "useful" and impressively "consistent" operation however, and "keenly priced" too. / W1D 4PU; www.prixfixe.net; @prixfixelondon; 11.30 pm.

Provender E11 **£39** 432

17 High St 8530 3050 1–1D

"A rose among the thorns of Wanstead High Street"; Max Renzland has a long west London pedigree, but he's now behind this "welcoming" Gallic bistro out East, where the set menus, in particular, are hailed for their "very good value". / E11 2AA; www.provenderlondon.co.uk; @ProvenderBistro; Sun 9 pm, Mon-Fri 10 pm.

The Providores W1 **£68** 422

109 Marylebone High St 7935 6175 2–1A

"Pacific Rim cooking at its best", and "an NZ wine list that reaches the bits other Kiwis can't reach" still inspires positive reports on Peter Gordon's tightly-packed first-floor Marylebone dining room… even if it is "beginning to get a bit long in the tooth". / W1U 4RX; www.theprovidores.co.uk; 10.30 pm; SRA-2 stars.

(Tapa Room) The Providores W1 **£54** 323

109 Marylebone High St 7935 6175 2–1A

Peter Gordon's "really interesting" Pacific-fusion tapas have helped this "bustling" Marylebone bar-diner make quite a name, especially for a "diverse and innovative brunch"; its "cramped" premises "rapidly gets too busy", though, and the food no longer seem as special as once it did. / W1U 4RX; www.theprovidores.co.uk; @theprovidores; 10.30 pm, Sun 10 pm.

Prufrock Coffee EC1 **£13** 433

23-25 Leather Ln 0785 224 3470 9–2A

"Coffee, made by people who really care about coffee" inspires high praise for this "quirky" Holborn spot; the sandwiches and snacks are "surprisingly good as well". / EC1N 7TE; www.prufrockcoffee.com; @PrufrockCoffee; L only; no Amex.

Punjab WC2 **£27** 333

80 Neal St 7836 9787 4–2C

In Covent Garden, the "UK's oldest North Indian restaurant" (they claim) maintains quite a fan club, who say the food is "terrific"; not everyone is quite convinced, though, and on a bad day service can seem "rushed" and "pushy". / WC2H 9PA; www.punjab.co.uk; 11 pm, Sun 10.30 pm.

Q Grill NW1 NEW **£55** 332

29-33 Chalk Farm Rd 7267 2678 8–2B

"Be transported to the US", at this grand new barbecue restaurant, near Camden Lock; curiously, for a place evidently striving so hard to be "über-trendy", though, it's the ambience which reporters find the weakest link. / NW1 8AJ; www.q-grill.co.uk; @QGrillLondon; Sat 11 pm, Sun 9.30 pm.

Quaglino's SW1 **£65**

16 Bury St 7930 6767 3–3D

For years, this guide pointed out that this once-glamorous St James's brasserie was in ever more desperate need of refurbishment… and its owners, the D&D Group, finally got round to completing precisely that that in mid-2014; let's hope for major improvement – there was certainly plenty of scope! / SW1Y 6AJ; www.quaglinos.co.uk; @quaglinos; 10.30 pm, Fri & Sat 11 pm; closed Sun; no trainers; set weekday L £38 (FP), set pre-theatre £43 (FP); SRA-2 stars.

The Quality Chop House EC1 **£41** 454

94 Farringdon Rd 7278 1452 9–1A

"Meat and two veg to perfection" ("you can buy the meat from their butcher next door") wins praise for Farringdon's revived 'working class caterer', despite its "authentically narrow" bum-numbing benches;

"completely charming" service and "excellent" wines too. / EC1R 3EA; www.thequalitychophouse.com; @QualityChop; 10.30 pm; closed Sun; SRA-2 stars.

Quantus W4 **£38** 3 5 4

38 Devonshire Rd 8994 0488 7–2A

"Tucked away in the same street as the much better known La Trompette", this Chiswick spot is "a local gem" that's worth seeking out; service, led by "very welcoming" owner Leo, has "real flair", and the food, with a South American bent, "can be excellent". / W4 2HD; www.quantus-london.com; 10 pm; closed Mon L, Tue L & Sun; set weekday L £35 (FP).

Quattro Passi W1 NEW **£154** 2 2 2

34 Dover St 3096 1444 3–3C

"Outstanding food… I felt I was eating at their sister restaurant on the Amalfi Coast", says an early-days fan of this Mayfair newcomer; prices, though – especially of wines – are "at nosebleed level", and doubters just cannot persuade themselves they're justified. / W1S 4NG; www.quattropassi.co.uk; @quattropassiuk; 10.30 pm; closed Sun D; set weekday L £98 (FP).

Queen's Head W6 **£39** 2 2 4

13 Brook Grn 7603 3174 7–1C

It's the vast green space at the rear and cute, ancient interior which makes it quite an "event" to visit this Brook Green tavern; the food – "not really very good" – is beside the point. / W6 7BL; www.queensheadhammersmith.co.uk; 10 pm, Sun 9 pm.

The Queens Arms SW1 **£43** 4 4 4

11 Warwick Way 7834 3313 2–4B

A "lively" Pimlico gastroboozer where the food "seems to have improved" of late – for more calm to enjoy it, head for the "airy and light" dining room upstairs. / SW1V 1QT; www.thequeensarmspimlico.co.uk; @thequeensarms; 11 pm, Sun 10.30 pm.

Le Querce SE23 **£40** 4 4 2

66-68 Brockley Rise 8690 3761 1–4D

"Divine homemade pasta" and "esoteric" ice creams and sorbets top the bill at this "delightful and genuine" family-run Sardinian, in Brockley Park; this year, though, did see the occasional "can't-see-what-the-fuss-is-about" report. / SE23 1LN; www.lequerce.co.uk; 10 pm, Sun 8.30 pm; closed Mon & Tue L.

Quilon SW1 **£69** 4 3 2

41 Buckingham Gate 7821 1899 2–4B

"Marvellous" Keralan cooking that's prepared "with a light touch" puts this "sleek and sophisticated" dining room, near Buckingham Palace, firmly on London's culinary map; the ambience, however, remains determinedly "low-key". / SW1E 6AF; www.quilon.co.uk; @TheQuilon; 10.45 pm, Sun 10.15 pm; set weekday L £47 (FP); SRA-2 stars.

Quirinale SW1 **£59** 4 4 2

North Ct, 1 Gt Peter St 7222 7080 2–4C

A "quiet" subterranean spot, hidden away in a Westminster backstreet, dishing up "classy and consistent" Italian cuisine; thanks to popularity with "MPs, civil servants and the quangocracy", it is busiest at lunchtimes. / SW1P 3LL; www.quirinale.co.uk; @quirinaleresto; 10.30 pm; closed Sat & Sun.

Quo Vadis W1 **£56** 3 4 4

26-29 Dean St 7437 9585 4–2A

The "hospitable" air of the Hart brothers' "charming" Soho old-timer makes it a haven for those in search of a "good-value set lunch" or a civilised pre-theatre meal; Jeremy Lee's "distinctive" British cuisine has its fans too, but it can be "variable", or too "quirky" for some tastes. / W1D 3LL; www.quovadissoho.co.uk; 10.45 pm; closed Sun.

Rabbit SW3 NEW

172 King's Rd 3750 0172 5–3C

On the former site of Choys (RIP), the people behind The Shed in Notting Hill bring this new nose-to-tail restaurant to the environs of Chelsea Old Town Hall. / SW3 4UP; www.rabbit-restaurant.com.

Rabot 1745 SE1 NEW **£71** 2 3 3

2-4 Bedale St 7378 8226 9–4C

"It is NOT a gimmick!", say advocates of the "high standard of cooking" at this "intriguing" newcomer, backed by the Hotel Chocolat people, which features cocoa in most dishes (and which is also of note for an atmospheric covered terrace overlooking Borough Market); critics, though, just find the cooking rather "mundane". / SE1 9AL; www.rabot1745.com; @rabot1745; closed Mon.

Racine SW3 **£66** 2 2 2

239 Brompton Rd 7584 4477 5–2C

"You feel like you're in Paris", say devotees of this Knightsbridge fixture, who applaud its "seriously good bourgeois cooking" and "old-school" style; sagging survey ratings, however, support those who feel it's "going downhill" – "fairly average" nowadays, and "pricey" too. / SW3 2EP; www.racine-restaurant.com; @racine_kitchen; 10.30 pm, Sun 10 pm; set weekday L & dinner £36 (FP).

Ragam W1 £27 541
57 Cleveland St 7636 9098 2–1B
"Whenever I go, I'm amazed I don't go more often!"; in 24 years, the survey view of this "very small" and "tired"-looking outfit, in the shadow of the Telecom Tower, has never really wavered – it's a total "winner", serving "wondrous" South Indian dishes at "unbeatable" prices. / W1T 4JN; www.ragam.co.uk; 10.45 pm; essential Fri & Sat.

Randall & Aubin W1 £55 445
16 Brewer St 7287 4447 3–2D
"Just right for Soho"; this "high energy" champagne and seafood bar is a "fun" place in a very handy location; it's "always full". / W1F 0SG; www.randallandaubin.com; @edbaineschef; 11 pm, Sat midnight, Sun 10 pm; booking for L only; SRA-1 star.

Rani N3 £27 322
7 Long Ln 8349 4386 1–1B
A "long-established vegetarian" (and vegan) in Finchley, which offers "great Gujarati home-cooking"; you don't really need to know what to order, as the main attraction is the huge buffet. / N3 2PR; www.raniuk.com; 10 pm; no Amex.

Ranoush £47 432
338 King's Rd, SW3 7352 0044 5–3C
43 Edgware Rd, W2 7723 5929 6–1D
86 Kensington High St, W8 7938 2234 5–1A
"Great Lebanese at good-value prices" – these budget offshoots of the swanky Maroush chain make excellent pit stops; highlights include juices, shawarma and mezze. / www.maroush.com; most branches close between 1 am-3 am.

Raoul's Café £46 223
105-107 Talbot Rd, W11 7229 2400 6–1B
113-115 Hammersmith Grove, W6 8741 3692 7–1C
13 Clifton Rd, W9 7289 7313 8–4A
"Spectacular" eggs top the bill at these laid-back west London cafés, which are almost invariably tipped as "a safe bet for breakfast or brunch", which they carry off "with panache"; other meals inspire practically no feedback. / www.raoulsgourmet.com; 10.15 pm, W11 6.15 pm; booking after 5 pm only.

Rasa £38 443
6 Dering St, W1 7637 0222 3–2B
Holiday Inn Hotel, 1 Kings Cross, WC1 7833 9787 8–3D
55 Stoke Newington Church St, N16 7249 0344 1–1C
56 Stoke Newington Church St, N16 7249 1340 1–1C
"Aromatic, spicy and delicious South Indian food at brilliant prices" has won renown for this "consistently fabulous" and "charming" small chain; fans still say "you've got to head to Stoke Newington for the full effect", but W1 is actually higher rated these days. / www.rasarestaurants.com; 10.45 pm; WC1 & W1 closed Sun.

Rasoi SW3 £104 544
10 Lincoln St 7225 1881 5–2D
"The best Indian in London by a country mile"; Vineet Bhattia's "elegant" Chelsea townhouse offers many "mind-blowing" dishes – "outstanding, even amongst the elite places" – in a set of "intimate and unstuffy" dining rooms; you spend a bomb of course, but it's "worth it". / SW3 2TS; www.rasoirestaurant.co.uk; @GujaratiRasoi; 10.30 pm, Sun 10 pm; closed Mon & Sat L.

Ravi Shankar NW1 £33 432
132-135 Drummond St 7388 6458 8–4C
A veteran of the 'Little India' cluster, by Euston station; "it's certainly cheap 'n' cheerful, but what it lacks in decor and style it makes up for in dosas and thalis" – "there's so much choice, even carnivores don't miss the meat!" / NW1 2HL; 10.30 pm; no Amex or Maestro.

Raw Duck E8 NEW
197 Richmond Rd 8986 6534 1–2D
Rising like a phoenix from the ashes after the original location was demolished, this sibling to Soho restaurant Ducksoup has now reopened; a review of this effectively new operation will have to wait till next year. / E8 3NJ.

The Real Greek £40 222
56 Paddington St, W1 7486 0466 2–1A
60-62 Long Acre, WC2 7240 2292 4–2D
Westfield, Ariel Way, W12 8743 9168 7–1C
1-2 Riverside Hs, Southwark Br Rd, SE1 7620 0162 9–3B
6 Horner Sq, E1 7375 1364 12–2B
Could it be that this Greek chain is finally sorting itself out? – it won more praise this year for the "predictable reliability" of its "tasty" mezze. / www.therealgreek.com; 10.45 pm; WC2 10.30 pm, E1 Sun 7 pm; EC1 closed Sun, N1 closed Sun-Mon; WC2 no booking.

Red Dog £41 323
37 Hoxton Sq, N1 3551 8014 12–1B
27-31 Bedford Rd, SW4 3714 2747 10–2D NEW
'Authentic Kansas City Bar-B-Q' is the promise at this Hoxton hangout, whose hickory-smoked meatilicious treats generally win the thumbs-up from reporters; a new Clapham branch opened shortly after the survey closed.

Red Fort W1 **£65** 332
77 Dean St 7437 2525 4–2A
"It's set the standard for Indian food for years", say fans of this Soho stalwart (which underwent a "faintly impersonal" modern revamp a few years ago); others are more cautious – "it was good on an 'offer', but would have seemed overpriced at full tariff". / W1D 3SH; www.redfort.co.uk; 11.15 pm, Sun 10.15 pm; closed Sat L & Sun L; set weekday L & pre-theatre £38 (FP).

The Red Pepper W9 **£45** 422
8 Formosa St 7266 2708 8–4A
"Still a great local favourite" – seating may be "cramped", and service "amateur", but this Maida Vale fixture still attracts a big following for its "excellent" pizzas. / W9 1EE; Sat 11 pm, Sun 10.30 pm; closed weekday L; no Amex.

Le Relais de Venise L'Entrecôte **£43** 323
120 Marylebone Ln, W1 7486 0878 2–1A
18-20 Mackenzie Walk, E14 3475 3331 11–1C
5 Throgmorton St, EC2 7638 6325 9–2C
"A fantastic concept!"; "you can have anything you like, so long as it's steak" – which comes "slathered in secret sauce", with salad and "awesome" fries – at these "crammed" and "efficient" Gallic bistros; "go early or late to avoid the queues". / www.relaisdevenise.com; W1 11 pm, Sun 10.30 pm; EC2 10 pm; EC2 closed Sat & Sun; no booking.

Reubens W1 **£55** 322
79 Baker St 7486 0035 2–1A
Scant feedback of late on this long-serving kosher deli-restaurant in Marylebone; fans insist it still serves "excellent salt beef", and "great chicken schnitzel" too. / W1U 6RG; www.reubensrestaurant.co.uk; 10 pm; closed Fri D & Sat; no Amex.

Rextail W1 NEW **£80** 122
13 Albermarle St 3301 1122 3–3C
"Not worth the money" – Arkady Novikov's new Mayfair basement brasserie-steakhouse takes huge flak from reporters for its "joyless" food and "silly" prices; the lunchtime prix-fixe, though, has its uses. / W1S 4HJ; www.rextail.co.uk; @Rextail_London.

The Rib Man N1 **£12** 534
KERB, King's Cross no tel 8–3C
"Wow… just wow!" – eloquent feedback on the "ribs to die for", "greatest pulled pork" and "mean range of hot sauces and rubs" at Mark Gevaux's food stall at KERB, behind King's Cross. / N1; www.theribman.co.uk; @theribman.

Rib Room Jumeirah Carlton Tower Hotel SW1 **£103** 332
Cadogan Pl 7858 7250 5–1D
If only all hotel makeovers were as successful as the rejuvenation of this "spacious" Belgravia dining room – "a high quality traditional experience", now offering what fans say is "the best roast beef in London", albeit at "huge" cost. / SW1X 9PY; www.jumeirah.com; @RibRoomSW1; 10.45 pm, Sun 10.15 pm; set weekday L £66 (FP).

Riccardo's SW3 **£43** 222
126 Fulham Rd 7370 6656 5–3B
Critics of this Chelsea Italian small-plates veteran have "no idea why it's so popular", citing "complacent" service and "bland and underwhelming" realisation of its "simple" cuisine; supporters, however, sense the beginnings of a return to old form. / SW3 6HU; www.riccardos.it; @ricardoslondon; 11.30 pm.

Riding House Café W1 **£55** 224
43-51 Great Titchfield St 7927 0840 3–1C
Breakfast and brunch "NYC-style" – "hearty, delicious and creative" – have helped generate a big buzz around this "vibey" Fitzrovia brasserie; lunches and dinners, though, can underwhelm. / W1W 7PQ; www.ridinghousecafe.co.uk; 11 pm, Sun 10.30 pm.

Rising Sun NW7 **£44** 343
137 Marsh Ln, Highwood Hill 8959 1357 1–1B
"The best Italian food for miles around" – a surprise find at this "lovely", if sometimes "chaotic", family-run gastropub, in Mill Hill. / NW7 4EY; www.therisingsunmillhill.co.uk; @therisingsunpub; 9.30 pm, Sun 8.30 pm; closed Mon L.

(Palm Court) The Ritz W1 **£44** 345
150 Piccadilly 7493 8181 3–4C
Sure it's "overpriced", but the "institution" which is afternoon tea at the Ritz wins impressively consistent survey approval – book well ahead for an "amazing" experience! / W1C 9BR; www.theritzlondon.com; 9.30 pm; jacket & tie.

The Ritz Restaurant The Ritz W1 **£122** 345
150 Piccadilly 7493 8181 3–4C
"Totally overwhelming" in its "magical" Louis XVI style, this chamber overlooking Green Park is often acclaimed as "the most elegant dining room in England"; "it doesn't always get the best food crits" but many "marvellous" meals were reported

this year… as you'd hope, given the "daunting" prices. / W1J 9BR; www.theritzlondon.com; @theritzlondon; 10 pm; jacket & tie; set dinner & pre-theatre £80 (FP).

Riva SW13 **£60** 342

169 Church Rd 8748 0434 10–1A

"Either you love it, or hate it"; to foodies ("Heston and AA Gill were on the next table!"), Andreas Riva's Barnes Italian is a "smooth" classic with "wonderful" cooking… but to sceptics it's a "tired"-looking, "expensive" place where "regulars are favoured, and it shows". / SW13 9HR; 10.30 pm, Sun 9 pm; closed Sat L.

Rivea Bulgari Hotel SW7 NEW **£68** 242

171 Knightsbridge 7151 1025 5–1C

"Light and interesting food… just it feels like eating in a hotel lounge"; this Ducasse-branded newcomer, in a glitzy Knightsbridge basement, impresses most reporters with its French-Italian small-plate cuisine, but feedback is far from consistent – "promised much, delivered little", says one of the unconvinced. / SW7 1DW; www.bulgarihotels.com; 10.15 pm.

THE RIVER CAFÉ W6 **£90** 323

Thames Wharf, Rainville Rd 7386 4200 7–2C

It's "still the benchmark", say its many fans, but even some devotees discern a "drop in standards" of late at this world-famous Hammersmith Italian, and to its growing legions of critics it's an "overcrowded" and "impersonal" place, where "uneventful" dishes come at "merciless" prices. / W6 9HA; www.rivercafe.co.uk; @RiverCafeLondon; 9 pm, Sat 9.15 pm; closed Sun D.

Rivington Grill **£50** 223

178 Greenwich High Rd, SE10 8293 9270 1–3D

28-30 Rivington St, EC2 7729 7053 12–1B

"Always busy and buzzy", these Shoreditch and Greenwich brasseries can be handy "for a lazy breakfast" or a burger; but could one not expect more of a Caprice group production? – "they're never terrible, but never as good as hoped either". / www.rivingtongrill.co.uk; 11 pm, Sun 10 pm; SE10 closed Mon, Tue L & Wed L.

Roast SE1 **£69** 222

Stoney St 0845 034 7300 9–4C

In its "fabulous" location, looking down on Borough Market, this "light and airy" British restaurant dishes up "hands down, the best breakfast"; thereafter, however, it "seems to be aimed at tourists and businessmen", and can seem "really overpriced for what it is". / SE1 1TL; www.roast-restaurant.com; 10.45 pm; closed Sun D; set weekday L & dinner £50 (FP); SRA-3 stars.

Rocca Di Papa **£43** 223

73 Old Brompton Rd, SW7 7225 3413 5–2B

75-79 Dulwich Village, SE21 8299 6333 1–4D

"No fuss, just straightforward Italian food" – the reason to seek out these "busy, busy, busy" South Kensington and Dulwich Village spots, which major in "delicious thin-crust pizzas". / SW7 11.30 pm; SE21 11 pm.

Rochelle Canteen E2 **£41** 444

Arnold Circus 7729 5677 12–1C

"Worth the effort!"; Melanie Arnold & Margot Henderson's "quirky" and "incredibly hard-to-find" daytime venture, hidden away behind the wall of a Victorian school in Shoreditch, attracts a dedicated following with a "daily-changing" menu which makes much use of "super-fresh produce". / E2 7ES; www.arnoldandhenderson.com; L only, closed Sat & Sun; no Amex.

Rocket **£46** 333

36-38 Kingsway, WC2 7242 8070 2–1D NEW

2 Churchill Pl, E14 3200 2022 11–1C

201 Bishopsgate, EC2 7377 8863 12–2B

6 Adams Ct, EC2 7628 0808 9–2C

For "great pizza" and other "decent staples", these "bustling" diners are worth knowing about as "reasonable-value" destinations in pricey areas – tucked away in an alleyway off Bond Street, hidden in a courtyard by Bank, and in Canary Wharf (with great views). / 10.30 pm, Sun 9.30 pm; W1 closed Sun; EC2 closed Sat & Sun; SW15 Mon-Wed D only, Bishopsgate closed Sun D, E14.

Roka **£80** 534

30 North Audley St, W1 7305 5644 3–2A NEW

37 Charlotte St, W1 7580 6464 2–1C

71-91 Aldwych, WC2 7580 6464 2–2D NEW

Unit 4, Park Pavilion, 40 Canada Sq, E14 7636 5228 11–1C

"Forget Nobu – this is much better!"; "Zuma's little sisters" offer "light-hearted and creative" Japanese-fusion dishes that "explode on the palate", and "terrific" cocktails too; the Charlotte Street original is the best, with the new Mayfair branch "not as convincing"; late-2014 sees a large new Aldwych branch. / www.rokarestaurant.com; 11.15 pm, Sun 10.30 pm; booking: max 8.

The Rooftop Café
The Exchange SE1 NEW **£44** 3|4|5
28 London Bridge St 3102 3770 9–4C
"A lovely hidden gem in the shadow of The Shard"; "it takes a bit of finding", but this "bright" and "airy" café, on top of an office block, rewards diners with great views and an "ever-changing, concise and well-executed menu". / SE1 9SG; www.theexchange.so/rooftop; @ExchangeLDN; closed Mon D, Tue D & Sun.

Roots at N1 N1 **£49** 5|5|3
115 Hemingford Rd 7697 4488 8–3D
A candlelit ex-pub, in Islington, which now functions as "an excellent upmarket Indian", and one with "considerable charm" too; it serves an "attractive", if "minimalist", menu of "brilliant" dishes – "much better value than the big names". / N1 1BZ; www.rootsatn1.com; @rootsatn1; 10 pm, Sun 9 pm; closed Mon, Tue–Sat D only, Sun open L & D.

Rossopomodoro **£39** 2|2|2
50-52 Monmouth St, WC2 7240 9095 4–3B
214 Fulham Rd, SW10 7352 7677 5–3B
1 Rufus St, N1 7739 1899 12–1B
10 Jamestown Rd, NW1 7424 9900 8–3B
46 Garrett Ln, SW18 079319 20377 10–2B
The "aggressive branch buildout" has done nothing for reporters' esteem for this Neapolitan-based pizza chain; fans still praise its "authentic" style, but overall it's difficult to escape the verdict of the reporter who says it's now "like PizzaExpress without the excitement". / www.rossopomodoro.co.uk; 11.30 pm; WC2 Sun 11.30 pm.

Roti Chai W1 **£46** 4|4|3
3 Portman Mews South 7408 0101 3–1A
"Inspired by Indian street food", an excellent two-year-old, near Selfridges, which serves up dishes that are "precisely spiced", "authentic" and "very good value"; both the café and more "formal" basement come recommended. / W1H 6HS; www.rotichai.com; @rotichai; 10.30 pm.

Rotorino E8 NEW **£48** 2|2|3
432-434 Kingsland Rd 7249 9081 1–1D
This "chic" new easterly counterpoint to Stevie Parle's Dock Kitchen has instantly been hailed as a "buzzy addition to Dalston"; reports on the food, however, range all the way from "amazing" to "embarrassing" – "microscopic" portions can give rise to particular complaint. / E8 4AA; www.rotorino.com; @Rotorino.

Rotunda Bar & Restaurant
Kings Place N1 **£53** 2|1|3
90 York Way 7014 2840 8–3C
The "great" canalside area is the crown jewel feature of this attractive arts centre brasserie, near King's Cross; the steak, in particular, can be "excellent" too, but "patchy" service has led to some decidedly up-and-down reports this year. / N1 9AG; www.rotundabarandrestaurant.co.uk; @rotundalondon; 10.30 pm, Sun 6.30 pm.

Roux at Parliament Square
RICS SW1 **£78** 3|4|2
12 Great George St 7334 3737 2–3C
"Mainly of interest to the parliamentary and business crowd", the Rouxs' high-ceilinged dining room offers "elegant" cuisine of a "high grade", with "charming and efficient" staff helping to offset the somewhat "library-like" atmosphere. / SW1P 3AD; www.rouxatparliamentsquare.co.uk; 10 pm; closed Sat & Sun.

Roux at the Landau
The Langham W1 **£97** 3|3|3
1c Portland Pl 7965 0165 2–1B
The Roux brothers' "quiet and dignified" outpost, opposite Broadcasting House, offers "outstanding food and service in a really beautiful space", say its fans (and "superb value" too, if you go for the set lunch); this year, however, there were also quite a few critics, who found meals "below expectations". / W1B 1JA; www.thelandau.com; @Langham_Hotel; 10 pm; closed Sat L & Sun; no trainers.

Rowley's SW1 **£69** 2|2|3
113 Jermyn St 7930 2707 3–3D
Original features – dating from the premises' days as the first Wall's butchers shop – "add to the charm" of a visit to this St James's "staple"; it's "possibly overpriced", but has won more praise of late for its "good chateaubriand and unlimited fries" ("brought around regularly, hot from the pan"). / SW1Y 6HJ; www.rowleys.co.uk; @rowleys_steak; 10.30 pm.

Royal Academy W1 **£53** 1|2|2
Burlington Hs, Piccadilly 7300 5608 3–3D
"It's a shame the advantage of its location is not built on" – this potentially "delightful" heart-of-the-West-End café could be a brilliant standby, but, despite a recent refurbishment, it remains "below par". / W1J 0BD; www.royalacademy.org.uk; 9 pm; L only, ex Fri open L & D; no booking at L.

Royal China **£47** 4|2|2
24-26 Baker St, W1 7487 4688 2–1A
805 Fulham Rd, SW6 7731 0081 10–1B
13 Queensway, W2 7221 2535 6–2C
30 Westferry Circus, E14 7719 0888 11–1B
"Fantastic, Hong Kong-quality dim sum" – many reporters would say "the best in town" – makes this "unwelcoming" Cantonese chain a London benchmark; the "garish" decor "may not

be what you'd have at home, but fits the occasion brilliantly". / www.royalchinagroup.co.uk; 10.45 pm, Fri & Sat 11.15 pm, Sun 9.45 pm; no booking Sat & Sun L.

Royal China Club W1 £62 443
40-42 Baker St 7486 3898 2–1A
"Hong Kong comes to London", at the Royal China group's "top-class" Marylebone flagship; "superb dim sum" is a highlight of the sometimes "amazing" Cantonese cuisine. / W1U 7AJ; www.royalchinagroup.co.uk; 11 pm, Fri & Sat 11.30 pm, Sun 10.30 pm.

The Royal Exchange Grand Café The Royal Exchange EC3 £55 224
The Royal Exchange Bank 7618 2480 9–2C
An "excellent location", in a huge and gracious covered courtyard, surrounded by luxury shops, helps make this heart-of-the-City seafood bar "perfect for business" – "the food is not really good enough to be any sort of distraction". / EC3V 3LR; www.royalexchange-grandcafe.co.uk; @rexlondon; 9.30 pm; closed Sat & Sun; SRA-1 star.

RSJ SE1 £48 342
33 Coin St 7928 4554 9–4A
"The best Loire wine list in the world" has long been the special appeal of this remarkably consistent stalwart, near the National Theatre; it would win few prizes for interior design, but service is "efficient", and the food is "dependable" and "reasonably-priced". / SE1 9NR; www.rsj.uk.com; @RSJWaterloo; 11 pm; closed Sat L & Sun.

Rugoletta N2 NEW £38 442
59 Church Ln 8815 1743 1–1B
"Beautiful Italian home-cooking" (with "outstanding" pizzas a highlight) – at "very reasonable" prices – has made quite a hit of this East Finchley spot; its new Barnet offshoot is "less cramped but just as good" (but not, unlike the original, BYO). / N2 8DR; www.larugoletta.com; 10.30 pm; closed Sun.

Rules WC2 £72 345
35 Maiden Ln 7836 5314 4–3D
"For tourists, but not touristy"; with its "beautiful" antique interior, London's oldest restaurant (Covent Garden, 1798) may be perennially packed with visitors but – with its "true" English fare and "seamless" service – it mercifully transcends its tourist-trap potential; game a speciality. / WC2E 7LB; www.rules.co.uk; 11.30 pm, Sun 10.30 pm; no shorts; set weekday L £49 (FP).

Le Sacré-Coeur N1 £36 234
18 Theberton St 7354 2618 8–3D
A venerable bistro in Islington which, say fans, "goes from strength to strength"; not all reporters are quite so enamoured, but even they usually concede it's at least a "decent neighbourhood restaurant". / N1 0QX; www.lesacrecoeur.co.uk; 11 pm, Sat 11.30 pm, Sun 10.30 pm; set weekday L £23 (FP).

Sacro Cuore NW10 £32 434
45 Chamberlayne Rd 8960 8558 1–2B
"Faultless dough" and "well-sourced ingredients from Italy" add to the "authenticity" of this diminutive two-year-old pizzeria, in Kensal Rise; on the downside, it can be "too noisy". / NW10 3NB; www.sacrocuore.co.uk/menu.html; @SacroCuorePizza; 10.30 pm; closed weekday L; no Amex; need 4+ to book, Fri & Sat no bookings.

Sagar £38 322
17a Percy St, W1 7631 3319 3–2B
31 Catherine St, WC2 7836 6377 4–3D
157 King St, W6 8741 8563 7–2C
"If you're looking for Indian street snacks" or "yummy dosas", the branches of this unpretentious chain are generally "a delight", "even for non-veggies"; "you don't go for the ambience". / www.sagarveg.co.uk; Sun-Thu 10.45 pm, Fri & Sat 11.30 pm.

Sager & Wilde E2 £22 344
193 Hackney Rd 8127 7330 12–1C
A Hoxton "oasis" – a "personal" operation, where an interesting wine list, including some "beautiful" finds, is backed up by "a good small selection of food". / E2 8JP; www.sagerandwilde.com; closed weekday L.

Saigon Saigon W6 £41 343
313-317 King St 8748 6887 7–2B
It may look "tired", but all reporters recommend this "pretty authentic" Vietnamese on Hammersmith's main drag – "reasonable value and great fun". / W6 9NH; www.saigon-saigon.co.uk; @saigonsaigonuk; 11.30 pm, Sun & Mon 10 pm.

St John EC1 £65 442
26 St John St 7251 0848 9–1B
It's "not everyone's cup of tea", but Fergus Henderson's famous advertisement for 'nose-to-tail' (offal-heavy) British eating still inspires adulation; some fans also adore the spartan aesthetic of his Smithfield ex-smokehouse, which others just find "uncomfortable". / EC1M 4AY; www.stjohngroup.uk.com; @SJRestaurant; 11 pm; closed Sat L & Sun D.

St John Bread & Wine E1 £55 534
94-96 Commercial St 7251 0848 12–2C
"A new and fantastic experience every time";

with its menu of "quirky" small-plate dishes (usually meaty) and "cheapish and unusual wines", this "noisy" Shoreditch canteen is "always a joy"; indeed, the survey rates it more highly than its fabled Smithfield parent. / E1 6LZ; www.stjohngroup.uk.com/spitalfields; @StJBW; 10.30 pm, Sun 9.30 pm.

St Johns N19 **£48** 335
91 Junction Rd 7272 1587 8–1C
A "lovely" setting, in a huge former ballroom – plus the constant "buzz of a full house" – helps make this Archway "neighbourhood favourite" a very charming destination; the cooking is often "first rate" too, although some reporters discern "a little more variability" of late. / N19 5QU; www.stjohnstavern.com; @stjohnstavern; 11 pm, Sun 9.30 pm; Mon-Thu D only, Fri-Sun open L & D; no Amex; booking: max 12.

St Pancras Grand St Pancras Int'l Station NW1 **£53** 222
The Concourse 7870 9900 8–3C
"It's a railway café on a grand scale", but that's about the only plus of this "beautiful" but "very patchy" brasserie… even if apologists insist it's "much better than anything on offer at the Gare du Nord!" / NW1 2QP; www.searcys.co.uk; @SearcysBars; 10.30 pm.

Sakana-tei W1 **£35** 442
11 Maddox St 7629 3000 3–2C
"Just like Tokyo, the food is everything, the service takes an interest, and the place is falling apart" – that's the deal at this Mayfair basement. / W1S 2QF; 10 pm; closed Sun.

Sake No Hana SW1 **£69** 212
23 St James's St 7925 8988 3–4C
This landmark building in St James's may have a "very cool" dining room, but this "pretentious" Japanese, with its sometimes "intrusive" and "uppity" service, inspires little affection among reporters; "it only survives thanks to its location". / SW1A 1HA; www.sakenohana.com; @sakenonhana; 11 pm, Fri & Sat 11.30 pm; closed Sun.

Sakura W1 **£33** 222
23 Conduit St 7629 2961 3–2C
"A good range of well prepared classic dishes" and a "very convenient" location draw fans to this "reasonably-priced" Mayfair spot. / W1S 2XS; www.sakuramayfair.com; 10 pm.

Salaam Namaste WC1 **£35** 332
68 Millman St 7405 3697 2–1D
"A real find for Bloomsbury!" – this "brightly decorated" Indian puts "a slightly modern twist on the usual offerings", and offers "fresh and spicy" fare that's "better than average". / WC1N 3EF; www.salaam-namaste.co.uk; @SalaamNamasteUK; 11.30 pm, Sun 11 pm.

Sale e Pepe SW1 **£65** 223
9-15 Pavilion Rd 7235 0098 5–1D
"Not changed in 40 years" – this "noisy" trattoria, near Harrods may be "expensive for ordinary Italian food", but "it still has that buzz, and the staff are fun!" / SW1X 0HD; www.saleepepe.co.uk; 11.30 pm; no shorts.

Salloos SW1 **£61** 442
62-64 Kinnerton St 7235 4444 5–1D
It may look "drab", but this age-old Pakistani, in a Belgravia mews, is a perennial "undiscovered gem", serving "melting lamb chops" and other "wonderful" tandoori dishes; "it doesn't come cheap" – what does, round here? – but "it's worth it, now and then". / SW1X 8ER; www.salloos.co.uk; 11 pm; closed Sun; need 5+ to book.

The Salt House NW8 **£46** 212
63 Abbey Rd 7328 6626 8–3A
Erratic reports of late from this large and "buzzy" St John's Wood gastropub; for a sunny day, though, it does have some "delightful" al fresco seating. / NW8 0AE; www.salthouseabbeyroad.com; @thesalthousenw8; 11 pm, Fri & Sat midnight.

Salt Yard W1 **£47** 343
54 Goodge St 7637 0657 2–1B
"Unusual and excellent" Italian/Spanish tapas and "an original wine list" have made a big name for this "buzzy" Fitzrovia fixture; the site can seem a touch "claustrophobic", though, and the occasional critic senses "a decrease in standards since the heady early days". / W1T 4NA; www.saltyard.co.uk; @SaltYardGroup; 10.45 pm; closed Sun; SRA-2 stars.

Salvation In Noodles N1 NEW **£33** 443
122 Balls Pond Rd 7254 4534 1–1C
"Wow, I haven't had such great pho since I was in Vietnam!" – early reports on this "infuriatingly hip" Dalston spot agree the food is "authentic", and service is "friendly" too. / N1 4AE; www.salvationinnoodles.co.uk; @SINDalston; 10.30 pm; closed weekday L.

Sam's Brasserie W4 **£49** 344
11 Barley Mow Pas 8987 0555 7–2A
"Tucked away down an alleyway", off Chiswick's main drag, this versatile and atmospheric hangout is a "consistently good neighbourhood brasserie", ideal for a "heavenly" family brunch, but also useful for a business lunch or any sort of general get-

together. / W4 4PH; www.samsbrasserie.co.uk; @samsbrasserie; 10.30 pm, Sun 10 pm; set weekday L £32 (FP); SRA-3 stars.

San Carlo Cicchetti W1 £47 333
215 Piccadilly 7494 9435 3–3D
Handily sited a few paces from Piccadilly Circus, a "bustling" Italian tapas bar, offering "a good food selection and friendly service"; on the downside its serried ranks of tables are "rather cramped". / W1J 9HN; www.sancarlo.co.uk; @SanCarlo_Group; midnight.

San Daniele del Friuli N5 £43 343
72 Highbury Park 7226 1609 8–1D
"An excellent long-established local", in Highbury Park, that's "very friendly and feels like being in Italy"; the cooking is never less than "sound". / N5 2XE; www.sandanielehighbury.co.uk; 10.30 pm; closed Mon L, Tue L, Wed L & Sun; no Amex.

San Lorenzo Fuoriporta SW19 £67 222
38 Wimbledon Hill Rd 8946 8463 10–2B
Mixed views on this stalwart '70s Italian; for fans, this is "Wimbledon's top destination", but for doubters the cooking's "solid, not inspirational", and it "trades on the loyalty of regulars". / SW19 7PA; www.sanlorenzosw19.squarespace.com; @fuoriporta; 10.40 pm.

The Sands End SW6 £52 444
135 Stephendale Rd 7731 7823 10–1B
A "top-notch gastropub", in the eponymous section of Fulham, that "impresses on all fronts" (not least with its "amazing homemade Scotch eggs"); perhaps the main attraction, though, is a "great twenty something crowd, who make the place swing". / SW6 2PR; www.thesandsend.co.uk; @thesandsend; 11.30 pm, Thu-Sat midnight; set weekday L £32 (FP).

Santa Lucia SW10 £42 322
2 Hollywood Rd 7352 8484 5–3B
"Good pizzas, served with panache" – and "delicious" pasta too – draw Chelsea locals to this "fun" (but "tightly-packed") backstreet spot. / SW10 9HY; www.madeinitalygroup.co.uk; 11.30 pm, Sun 10.30 pm; closed weekday L.

Santa Maria W5 £32 533
15 St Mary's Rd 8579 1462 1–3A
"The best pizza this side of Naples" has made this "wonderfully genuine" outfit world-famous in Ealing; one drawback, though – "it's nigh on impossible to get a table". / W5 5RA; www.santamariapizzeria.com; @SantaMariaPizza; 10.30 pm.

Santini SW1 £70 234
29 Ebury St 7730 4094 2–4B
"Improved" of late, this stalwart swanky Belgravia Italian is a "professional" operation – it's always been "on the pricey side", though, and particularly popular "for business". / SW1W 0NZ; www.santini-restaurant.com; 11 pm, Sun 10 pm; set pre theatre £46 (FP).

Santore EC1 £43 442
59 Exmouth Mkt 7812 1488 9–1A
"A little bit of Italy"; this superb Exmouth Market spot majors in Neapolitan pizza "to die for"; "lovely outside tables on a summer's day" too. / EC1R 4QL; www.santorerestaurant.co.uk; 11 pm.

Sapori Sardi SW6 £48 442
786 Fulham Rd 7731 0755 10–1B
The "most fabulous local"; the Sardinian cuisine "comes straight from the heart" at this two-year-old Fulham spot, and it is not just "tasty" but "extremely reasonably priced" too. / SW6 5SL; www.saporisardi.co.uk; 11 pm; no Amex.

Sarastro WC2 £50 133
126 Drury Ln 7836 0101 2–2D
"Lots to look at while you dine" – and "fantastic entertainment" – justify a trip to this flamboyant operatic-themed Covent Garden haunt; without the opera, though, the whole experience would be eminently "forgettable". / WC2B 5SU; www.sarastro-restaurant.com; @SastroR; 10.30 pm, Sat 11 pm.

Sardo W1 £55 332
45 Grafton Way 7387 2521 2–1B
"Unfussy and well-executed" Sardinian dishes make for an "enjoyable" experience at this Fitzrovia fixture, where the interior is "pleasant but often noisy". / W1T 5DQ; www.sardo-restaurant.com; 11 pm; closed Sat L & Sun.

Sarracino NW6 £42 432
186 Broadhurst Gdns 7372 5889 1–1B
"No better pizza than this!" – served 'al metro' – wins praise from reporters for this West Hampstead trattoria; apparently, "everyone in the kitchen is from round Naples". / NW6 3AY; www.sarracinorestaurant.com; 11 pm; closed weekday L.

Sartoria W1 £59 332
20 Savile Row 7534 7000 3–2C
"Spacious", "comfortable" and "efficient", this Mayfair Italian is a popular business venue, offering some "very enjoyable" cooking; impressive wine too, from the "thoroughly knowledgeable"

sommelier. / W1S 3PR; www.sartoria-restaurant.co.uk; @SartoriaRest; 10.45 pm; closed Sat L & Sun; SRA-2 stars.

Satay House W2 **£35** 3 3 2
13 Sale Pl 7723 6763 6–1D
An "authentically Malaysian" veteran in a Bayswater backwater, offering a consistently "decent" level of cooking. / W2 1PX; www.satay-house.co.uk; 11 pm.

Sauterelle
Royal Exchange EC3 **£72** 3 3 4
Bank 7618 2483 9–2C
"Tucked away on the mezzanine level of the Royal Exchange", this is a D&D Group outpost that's "perfect for business"; "it has worked hard to up its game" in recent times, and the modern French cuisine can be very good. / EC3V 3LR; www.sauterelle-restaurant.co.uk; 9.30 pm; closed Sat & Sun; no trainers; SRA-1 star.

Savoir Faire WC1 **£39** 3 3 2
42 New Oxford St 7436 0707 4–1C
A "welcoming" spot offering "homely French bistro cooking", in a "perfect location near the British Museum"; it's "very reasonably priced" too. / WC1A 1EP; www.savoir.co.uk; 11 pm.

(Savoy Grill)
The Savoy Hotel WC2 **£75** 2 3 3
Strand 7592 1600 4–3D
Once London's unchallenged power-dining scene, this "elegant" room, now a Ramsay outpost, "still delivers the goods", say fans; there are quite a few critics too, though, for whom the "fairly staid" British food "never ends up more than OK", and – apart from the "great-value set lunch" – is "expensive" too. / WC2R 0EU; www.gordonramsay.com/thesavoygrill; @savoygrill; 10.45 pm, Sun 10.15 pm; jacket required; set pre-theatre £49 (FP), set weekday L £51 (FP).

Scalini SW3 **£73** 3 3 3
1-3 Walton St 7225 2301 5–2C
"A long-established Italian that's always buzzing"; the food is "consistent good", if "expensive"... but then it is just a few paces from Harrods. / SW3 2JD; www.scalinionline.com; 11.30 pm, Sun 11 pm; no shorts.

Scandinavian Kitchen
W1 **£16** 4 5 3
61 Great Titchfield St 7580 7161 2–1B
With its "cleverly prepared" open sarnies, "tasty" meatballs, and the "hilarious Scandi-themed pun of the day", this Fitzrovia haunt is "guaranteed to lift the spirits"; want to try this at home? – select from a "concise collection of Nordic food essentials" to take away. / W1W 7PP; www.scandikitchen.co.uk; @scanditwitchen; 7 pm, Sat 6 pm, Sun 4 pm; L only; no Maestro; no booking.

SCOTT'S W1 **£80** 4 5 4
20 Mount St 7495 7309 3–3A
Richard Caring's "stunning" Mayfair glamour-magnet "will leave your guest über-impressed" – it is "one of the slickest operations in London", where the "confident" staff serve up "fresh interpretations of classic fish dishes" with "ease and efficiency". / W1K 2HE; www.scotts-restaurant.com; 10.30 pm, Sun 10 pm; booking: max 6.

Sea Containers
Mondrian London SE1 NEW
20 Upper Ground 0808 234 9523 9–3A
In the first non-US outpost of the trendy Mondrian hotel chain, on the South Bank, a restaurant that's attracted positive early-days commentary, especially for its design. / SE1 9PD; www.mondrianlondon.com; @MondrianLDN.

The Sea Cow SE22 **£31** 3 3 3
37 Lordship Ln 8693 3111 1–4D
Modest feedback nowadays on this "upmarket" East Dulwich chippy, where you squash onto benches, and fish is cooked to order – all positive though! / SE22 8EW; www.theseacow.co.uk; @seacowcrew; 11 pm, Sun & Mon 10 pm; closed Mon L, Tue L & Wed L; no Amex.

Seafresh SW1 **£37** 3 3 1
80-81 Wilton Rd 7828 0747 2–4B
It's "not exactly romantic", but this "efficient" veteran Pimlico chippy rewards investigation of its "wide range of fish" (and a few other dishes too). / SW1V 1DL; www.seafresh-dining.com; 10.30 pm; closed Sun.

The Sea Shell NW1 **£43** 4 4 2
49 Lisson Grove 7224 9000 8–4A
"Top-quality fish (battered or grilled), excellent non-greasy chips and extremely friendly service" – that's the deal at this famous Marylebone chippy; since its "pleasant" makeover a couple of years back, take-away is no longer necessary. / NW1 6UH; www.seashellrestaurant.co.uk; @SeashellRestaur; 10.30 pm; closed Sun; SRA-1 star.

Season Kitchen N4 **£38** 4 4 3
53 Stroud Green Rd 7263 5500 8–1D
A Finsbury Park spot that's "a real find", thanks to its "well thought-through and frequently-changing menu", which does proper justice to its advertised themes of seasonality and local sourcing; "fairly-priced wines" too. / N4 3EF; www.seasonkitchen.co.uk; 10.30 pm, Sun 9 pm; D only.

Seven Park Place SW1 £91 3 4 4
7-8 Park Pl 7316 1600 3–4C
The "nooks and crannies" of this "quirky" but "sumptuous" St James's room add to its possibilities as a business or romantic venue; best to visit for the "good-value lunch", though – evening prices for William Drabble's "high-quality" cuisine can be "alarming". / SW1A 1LP; www.stjameshotelandclub.com; @SevenParkPlace; 10 pm; closed Mon & Sun; set weekday L £55 (FP).

Seven Stars WC2 £30 3 2 4
53 Carey St 7242 8521 2–2D
It's a "tight space", but fans love the "wonderful quirky charm" of this ancient tavern, behind the Royal Courts of Justice, presided over by larger-than-life landlady Roxy Beaujolais; the pub grub's really not bad either. / WC2A 2JB; 9.30 pm.

1701
Bevis Marks Synagogue EC3 £68 4 3 3
Bevis Marks 7621 1701 9–2D
"London has never had kosher food like this!" – with its "traditional-with-a-very-interesting-twist" menu, this year-old venture, in the "lovely and historic" space next to the UK's oldest synagogue, "surpasses expectations"; it's a "fine location for business lunches" too. / EC3A 5DQ; www.restaurant1701.co.uk; @Restaurant1701; 10 pm; closed Sat & Sun.

Shake Shack WC2 £23 2 2 2
23 The Mkt, Covent Garden 3598 1360 4–3D
"Stonking" burgers and "amazing shakes" convince some reporters that top NYC restaurateur Danny Meyer's export to Covent Garden is a real winner; the survey, however, doesn't rate the food much better than Byron's. / WC2E 8RD; www.shakeshack.com/location/london-covent-garden; @shakeshack; 11 pm, Sun 10.30 pm.

Shampers W1 £49 2 4 5
4 Kingly St 7437 1692 3–2D
"The owners set an excellent tone of bonhomie", at this "unchanging" wine bar veteran, just off Carnaby Street; it's "always packed at lunchtime" with "surveyors and professional types", drawn by the "simple but effective" cooking and a wine list with "some real gems". / W1B 5PE; www.shampers.net; 10.45 pm; closed Sun.

Shanghai E8 £36 3 2 4
41 Kingsland High St 7254 2878 1–1C
"My Chinese friend travels from Essex to come here!"; "brilliant dim sum" are the culinary highlight at this former pie 'n' eel shop in Dalston – make sure you sit in the superb tiled section at the front. / E8 2JS; www.shanghaidalston.co.uk; 11 pm; no Amex.

Shanghai Blues WC1 £64 4 2 4
193-197 High Holborn 7404 1668 4–1D
"Perpetually dark", in a moody sort of way, this Holborn Chinese is sometimes hailed as a "hidden gem" – it's a "consistently good" lunchtime dim sum stop, and its jazz evenings can form the basis for a "perfect night out". / WC1V 7BD; www.shanghaiblues.co.uk; 11 pm, Sun 10.30 pm.

The Shed W8 £39 3 3 5
122 Palace Gardens Ter 7229 4024 6–2B
"You feel you are in the country" (almost!) at this "quirky" faux-rustic spot, by Notting Hill Gate; fans praise its "imaginative British tapas", but critics can find the experience "too self-consciously whimsical", given toppish prices and the "uncomfortable" seating. / W8 4RT; www.theshed-restaurant.com; @theshed_resto; 11 pm; closed Mon & Sun; SRA-3 stars.

J SHEEKEY WC2 £70 4 4 4
28-34 St Martin's Ct 7240 2565 4–3B
Deep in the heart of Theatreland, this "peerless" icon (est 1896) is yet again London's most talked-about destination; "straightforward, classical fish and seafood" (most famously, fish pie) is "slickly" served in a "cosseting", if "squeezed", ramble of "snug" and "classy" rooms. / WC2N 4AL; www.j-sheekey.co.uk; @CapriceHoldings; 11.30 pm, Sun 10.30 pm; booking: max 6; set weekday L & Sun L £49 (FP).

J Sheekey Oyster Bar WC2 £63 4 5 5
32-34 St Martin's Ct 7240 2565 4–3B
Expansion has done nothing to dim the charms of this "fabulous" bar attached to the Theatreland legend, where "simply outstanding fish dishes" are "efficiently" served perched at a stool around the glamorous and supremely "buzzy" bar. / WC2N 4AL; www.j-sheekey.co.uk; @CapriceHoldings; 11.30 pm, Sun 10.30 pm; booking: max 3.

Shilpa W6 £31 4 3 1
206 King St 8741 3127 7–2B
"Remarkably good" Keralan cuisine at "a quarter of the cost of more fashionable places" makes this Hammersmith caff a top pick on the "curry-crowded King Street drag" – "don't let the impressively drab setting put you off!" / W6 0RA; www.shilparestaurant.co.uk; 11 pm, Thu-Sat midnight.

The Shiori W2 £86 5 5 3
45 Moscow Rd 7221 9790 6–2C
"As good a Japanese meal as you can get in Kyoto!" – the Takagis' tiny and "peaceful" Bayswater

yearling offers "beautifully refined" kaiseki and "perfect" service too; "you'll need to take out a small mortgage, but it'll be worth it". / W2 4AH; www.theshiori.com; @SHIORIoflondon; 8.30 pm; closed Mon & Sun.

The Ship SW18 **£49** 334
41 Jews Row 8870 9667 10–2B
"When the weather's good, the crowds descend" on this "busy" riverside boozer, by Wandsworth Bridge; it's a popular dining destination at any time, but the "inventive and hearty" barbecue is a particular summer attraction. / SW18 1TB; www.theship.co.uk; @shipwandsworth; 10 pm; no booking, Sun L.

Shoryu Ramen **£27** 323
9 Regent St, SW1 no tel 3–3D
3 Denman St, W1 no tel 3–2D
5 Kingly Ct, W1 no tel 3–2C NEW
"Fast, furious, and packed to the rafters!" – these "basic" and "very noisy" Japanese pit stops major in "wonderful broth and noodles" and "tasty hirata buns". / Regent St 11.30 pm, Sun 10.30 pm – Soho midnight, Sun 10.30 pm; no booking (except Kingly Ct).

Shrimpy's N1 **£50** 333
King's Cross Filling Station, Good's Way 8880 6111 8–3C
"Who knew a former petrol station could be turned into a cool 'beachfront' diner?" – this "fun" outfit, in the heart of redeveloping King's Cross, is just the place for an "epic soft-shell crab burger" or some other "funky" bite. / N1C 4UR; www.shrimpys.co.uk; @shrimpyloves; 11 pm.

Sichuan Folk E1 **£44** 432
32 Hanbury St 7247 4735 12–2C
Dishes will "blow your head off… in a good way" at this East End joint, praised by all for its "real Sichuanese food"; for the uninitiated, "the menu has photos that actually look like the plates served!" / E1 6QR; www.sichuan-folk.co.uk; 10.30 pm; no Amex.

The Sign of the Don EC4 **£55** 234
21 St Swithin's Ln 7626 2606 9–3C
The Don's new neighbour, is "a welcome extension of the original" and widely praised as a "great spot for City lunching", in "mid-price brasserie style"; the food, though, still has a little way to go to measure up to the original. / EC4N 8AD; www.thesignofthedon.com; @TheDonLondon.

Signor Sassi SW1 **£67** 233
14 Knightsbridge Grn 7584 2277 5–1D
This long-established Knightsbridge-crowd Italian still serves up some great pasta and the like; fans proclaim its "lovely" ambience too, cramped and noisy as the setting undoubtedly is. / SW1X 7QL; www.signorsassi.co.uk; 11.30 pm, Sun 10.30 pm.

Silk Road SE5 **£24** 521
49 Camberwell Church St 7703 4832 1–3C
"Just big bold flavours and great tasting food… so long as you like chilli, garlic and cumin!" – this "authentic" and "unusual" Xingjiang café, in Camberwell, is, for those of a culinarily adventurous disposition, "really worth the trip". / SE5 8TR; 10.30 pm; closed Sat L & Sun L; no credit cards.

Simply Fish NW1 **£39** 333
4 Inverness St 7482 2977 8–3B
For "high-quality" fish, regulars tip these "funky" Camden Town and Shoreditch canteens – you choose a fish, and specify the preparation style and accompaniments. / NW1 7HJ; www.simplyfishcamden.co.uk; @wearesimplyfish; 10 pm.

Simpson's Tavern EC3 **£38** 345
38 1/2 Ball Ct, Cornhill 7626 9985 9–2C
"Like going back in time"; this Dickensian City chophouse is currently on top form, with its "efficient" staff dishing up "good-value" scoff that's "like school dinners on a good day" (including some "gorgeous" puddings); popular for breakfast too. / EC3V 9DR; www.simpsonstavern.co.uk; @SimpsonsTavern; 3 pm; L only, closed Sat & Sun.

Simpsons-in-the-Strand WC2 **£77** 122
100 Strand 7836 9112 4–3D
"The home of an unbeatable Full English breakfast", it may be, but otherwise this "stately" temple to the Roast Beef god, by the Savoy, has decidedly "slipped in recent years" – nowadays, "it's just an expensive tourist trap". / WC2R 0EW; www.simpsonsinthestrand.co.uk; 10.45 pm, Sun 9 pm; no trainers.

Singapore Garden NW6 **£46** 432
83a Fairfax Rd 7624 8233 8–2A
"Always packed, even on a weekday, despite its out-of-the-way location" – thanks to its "fresh, tasty, and well-priced" Chinese/Malaysian/Singaporean fare, this "hardy veteran", hidden away in Swiss Cottage, remains one of north London's most popular spots. / NW6 4DY; www.singaporegarden.co.uk; @SingaporeGarden; 11 pm, Fri & Sat 11.30 pm.

64 Degrees
Artist Residence Hotel
SW1 NEW
52 Cambridge St 3262 0501 2–4B
Around the publication date of this guide, a small-plates concept that's a smash hit in Brighton opens in the Smoke; might it bring a bit of a life to a dull part of Pimlico? – time will tell. / SW1V 4QQ; artistresidencelondon.co.uk.

(Gallery)
Sketch W1 **£80** 124
9 Conduit St 7659 4500 3–2C
As a "fun" young-fashionista hangout, this eclectically decorated Mayfair party scene – known for London's funkiest WCs – has certainly shown staying power, but it perennially takes flak for "rubbish" food, and at prices that are "beyond excessive" too. / W1S 2XG; www.sketch.uk.com; 11 pm; booking: max 10.

(Lecture Room)
Sketch W1 **£120** 223
9 Conduit St 7659 4500 3–2C
Inspired by Parisian über-chef Pierre Gagnaire, this "crazy" Mayfair dining room offers "experimental" ("weird") cooking that's often "incredible", but which "occasionally fails dramatically"; it's "way overpriced", naturally. / W1S 2XG; www.sketch.uk.com; @sketchlondon; 10.30 pm; closed Mon, Sat L & Sun; no trainers; booking: max 8; set weekday L £62 (FP).

(The Parlour)
Sketch W1 **£82** 224
9 Conduit St 7659 4533 3–2C
"OMG the cakes are amazing", but "the best thing is actually the decor", say fans of this cute and stylish Mayfair room, best liked for afternoon tea or breakfast; other food can be "very ordinary", though, and service likewise. / W1S 2XG; www.sketch.uk.com; 10 pm; no booking.

Skipjacks HA3 **£40** 442
268-270 Streatfield Rd 8204 7554 1–1A
"A bit more than just a chippy"; this "unpretentious" family-run Harrow veteran of three decades' standing is "a beacon in a desert", and serves "the best fish 'n' chips". / HA3 9BY; 10.30 pm; closed Sun; no Amex.

Skylon
South Bank Centre
SE1 **£59** 123
Belvedere Rd 7654 7800 2–3D
"The view of the Thames is wonderful" and "the decor is straight out of Mad Men", so it's a shame that this "spectacular" South Bank chamber offers such "ordinary" food, and at very high prices too. / SE1 8XX; www.skylonrestaurant.co.uk; @skylonsouthbank; 10.30 pm; closed Sun D; no trainers; max 12; SRA-2 stars.

Skylon Grill SE1 **£57** 123
Belvedere Rd 7654 7800 2–3D
The cheaper option at the D&D Group's massive South Bank dining room fares no better with reporters than its neighbour, but it does at least have the same "fantastic" view. / SE1 8XX; www.skylon-restaurant.co.uk; @skylonsouthbank; 11 pm; closed Sun D; set pre theatre £29 (FP).

Smiths Brasserie E1 **£53** 334
22 Wapping High St 7488 3456 11–1A
"Fabulous views of Tower Bridge and the Shard" add to the appeal of this "Essex-chic" Wapping yearling (offshoot of an outfit in Ongar); it wins consistent praise for its "excellent fish prepared to order", but live music and big groups can make for a "noisy" experience. / E1W 1NJ; smithsrestaurant.com; 10 pm; closed Sun D.

(Top Floor)
Smiths of Smithfield
EC1 **£72** 222
67-77 Charterhouse St 7251 7950 9–1A
"Steak, steak, steak… and lovely views of St Paul's" – the selling points of this business-friendly rooftop dining room, overlooking the City; as ever, though, it takes a fair degree of flak for being "overpriced and underwhelming". / EC1M 6HJ; www.smithsofsmithfield.co.uk; 10.45 pm; closed Sat L & Sun; booking: max 10.

(Dining Room)
Smiths of Smithfield
EC1 **£53** 222
67-77 Charterhouse St 7251 7950 9–1A
"Reliable", "businesslike" and "always buzzy", the first-floor brasserie of this Smithfield warehouse-complex has its fans; service rarely sparkles, though, and the "expensive" meaty fare is often merely "OK". / EC1M 6HJ; www.smithsofsmithfield.co.uk; @thisismiths; 10.45 pm; closed Sat L & Sun; booking: max 12; set weekday L & dinner £34 (FP).

(Ground Floor)
Smiths of Smithfield
EC1 **£33** 224
67-77 Charterhouse St 7251 7950 9–1A
"THE place to catch up the morning after the night before" – "there's always a great buzz in the mornings", at this celebrated Smithfield hangout. / EC1M 6HJ; www.smithsofsmithfield.co.uk; L only; no bookings.

The Smokehouse Islington N1 **£46** 3|4|3
63-69 Canonbury Rd 7354 1144 8–2D
"A reliably great neighbourhood restaurant"; this "off-the-beaten-track" Canonbury yearling is a "friendly" sort of place, where the "hearty" gastropub-style food is "rich and incredibly yummy". / N1 2RG; www.smokehouseislington.co.uk; @smokehouseN1; 10.30 pm.

Social Eating House W1 **£60** 4|4|5
58-59 Poland St 7993 3251 3–2D
"An excellent addition to Atherton's empire" – thanks to its "big and gutsy" dishes, Jason A's "no-frills" Soho yearling has shone ever brighter since its debut; don't miss some "pretty amazing cocktails" in the upstairs "speakeasy". / W1F 7NR; www.socialeatinghouse.com; 10 pm; closed Sun.

Sofra **£36** 2|3|3
1 St Christopher's Pl, W1 7224 4080 3–1A
18 Shepherd St, W1 7493 3320 3–4B
36 Tavistock St, WC2 7240 3773 4–3D
"Always reliable", "always busy" – this Turkish chain remains a handy standby, thanks to its "tasty" mezze and "easy pricing"; the set lunch is a particularly good deal. / www.sofra.co.uk; 11 pm-midnight.

Soho Diner W1 **£38** 2|3|4
19 Old Compton St 7734 5656 4–2A
The former Soho Diner, rebranded but under unchanged ownership, now boasts a clubby new interior and more extensive French-American menu; it remains a very handy drop-in, and its long hours makes it "a rare find in the early hours". / W1D 5JJ; Rated on Editors' visit; www.sohodiner.com; SohoDinerLDN; 11.45 pm.

Soif SW11 **£52** 4|4|3
27 Battersea Rise 7223 1112 10–2C
"Wines for all tastes and pockets" are matched with "delicious and unpretentious French-provincial" dishes at this Terroirs-sibling in Battersea; it has "a good neighbourhood vibe" but "can get noisy when packed". / SW11 1HG; www.soif.co.uk; @soifSW11; 10 pm; closed Mon L, Tue L, Wed L.

Solly's NW11 **£45** 2|2|2
146-150 Golders Green Rd 8455 0004 1–1B
It's a feature of Golders Green life, but this busy Israeli take-away (with upstairs restaurant) inspired little (and mediocre) feedback this year. / NW11 8HE; 10.30 pm; closed Fri D & Sat L; no Amex.

Sông Quê E2 **£34** 2|1|2
134 Kingsland Rd 7613 3222 12–1B
"It's a bit of a canteen, but you will be fed in the best possible way", and at "low prices" too, say fans of this "brusque" Vietnamese, in Shoreditch; sceptics, though, say standards are "slipping" and that its cooking is "not competitive with others in the strip". / E2 8DY; www.sonque.co.uk; 11 pm; no Amex.

Sonny's Kitchen SW13 **£55** 2|2|2
94 Church Rd 8748 0393 10–1A
"Everything's done properly, without show", say fans of this Barnes stalwart, which has long been applauded as "a great local restaurant"; nowadays, however, it's far too "hit and miss" – "with the Olympic now opened opposite, you'd have thought they'd have upped their game". / SW13 0DQ; www.sonnyskitchen.co.uk; Fri-Sat 11 pm, Sun 9.30 pm; set weekday L & dinner £34 (FP).

Sophie's Steakhouse **£53** 2|3|2
29-31 Wellington St, WC2 7836 8836 4–3D
311-313 Fulham Rd, SW10 7352 0088 5–3B
"Consistently attractive over the years", these Covent Garden and Fulham spots have quite a few fans for their "great choice of steaks"; critics, though, can find this a formula which offers "nothing distinctive". / www.sophiessteakhouse.com; SW10 11.45 pm, Sun 11.15 pm; WC2 12.45 am, Sun 11 pm; no booking.

Sotheby's Café W1 **£60** 3|4|3
34-35 New Bond St 7293 5077 3–2C
It's not just the "people-watching" possibilities which make the café off the foyer of the famous Mayfair auction house of interest; the small menu of luxurious snacks is "surprisingly good" too. / W1A 2AA; www.sothebys.com; L only, closed Sat & Sun; booking: max 8.

Source SW11 NEW **£48** 2|3|4
Unit 29, 35-37 Parkgate Rd 7350 0555 5–4C
This "casual" new venture on the site of Ransome's Dock (RIP) has many of the virtues of its predecessor, minus the legendary wine – a "friendly" place (with its own parking!), where the food is somewhere between "decent" (very much our own experience) and "dull". / SW11 4NP; www.sourcebattersea.com; closed Sun D.

Spianata & Co **£11** 4|4|3
Tooley St, SE1 8616 4662 9–4D
41 Brushfield St, E1 7655 4411 12–2B
20 Holborn Viaduct, EC1 7248 5947 9–2A
17 Blomfield St, EC2 7256 9103 9–2C
73 Watling St, EC4 7236 3666 9–2B
"Freshly baked flatbreads" with "gorgeous" fillings, "good snacks and salads" and "the best cappuccino

in the City" win nothing but praise for this small Italian take-away chain. / www.spianata.com; 3.30 pm; EC3 11 pm; closed Sat & Sun; E1 closed Sat; no credit cards; no booking.

Spice Market W Hotel London W1 **£77** 233
10 Wardour St 7758 1088 4–3A
"The main problem is that it's nowhere near as good as its NYC namesake"; there's little actually wrong with Jean-Georges Vongerichten's Leicester Square outpost, but his pan-Asian dining room continues to inspire remarkably little (and mixed) feedback. / W1D 6QF; www.spicemarketlondon.co.uk; @spicemarketLDN; 11 pm, Thu-Sat 11.30 pm; set weekday L & pre-theatre £44 (FP).

Spring Somerset House WC2 NEW
Lancaster Pl 3011 0115 2–2D
Australian chef Skye Gyngell carved a major name when she was at Petersham Nurseries;perhaps she can repeat the trick with her new venue at Somerset House. / WC2R 1LA; springrestaurant.co.uk.

Spuntino W1 **£41** 235
61 Rupert St no tel 3–2D
Russell Norman's "unbelievably cool", "industrial-look" Soho bar (where you eat at the counter) "still does the best sliders", and other "lovely" 'dirty' dishes too; the bills, though, "can rack up quite quickly". / W1D 7PW; www.spuntino.co.uk; 11.30 pm, Sun 10.30 pm.

THE SQUARE W1 **£113** 443
6-10 Bruton St 7495 7100 3–2C
"Discreet, quiet and well-spaced", this Mayfair landmark has long been a top expense-account choice, thanks to Phil Howard's "brilliantly focussed" cuisine, and the "phenomenal" wine list; the experience can seem "a bit soulless", though, and it is of course "astronomically expensive". / W1J 6PU; www.squarerestaurant.com; @square_rest; 9.45 pm, Sat 10.15 pm, Sun 9.30 pm; closed Sun L; booking: max 8; set weekday L £55 (FP).

Sree Krishna SW17 **£27** 432
192-194 Tooting High St 8672 4250 10–2C
"Hasn't changed in years, and that's why we go!" – this Tooting veteran, now in its fourth decade, still serves up some "excellent value" South Indian fare ("especially the dosas"); Mon-Fri, you can BYO. / SW17 0SF; www.sreekrishna.co.uk; @SreeKrishnaUk; 10.45 pm, Fri & Sat 11.45 pm.

Star of India SW5 **£54** 42–
154 Old Brompton Rd 7373 2901 5–2B
The cooking at this long-established Earl's Court subcontinental has been "on a peak" in recent times – let's hope this carries on after the major refurbishment carried out in the summer of 2014! / SW5 0BE; www.starofindia.eu; 11.45 pm, Sun 11.15 pm.

Sticks'n'Sushi **£48** 333
11 Henrietta St, WC2 3141 8800 4–3D
58 Wimbledon Hill Rd, SW19 3141 8800 10–2B
A stylish Danish-Japanese (!) hybrid, in Covent Garden and Wimbledon, that offers an "innovative twist on sushi"; it may be "a bit pricey" but it "does what it does pretty well". / www.sticksnsushi.com; Sun - Tues 10 pm, Wed -Sat 11 pm.

Sticky Fingers W8 **£43** 222
1a Phillimore Gdns 7938 5338 5–1A
Diehard fans still see this veteran Kensington burger-joint (decked out with Bill Wyman's Rolling Stones memorabilia) as "a quirky antidote to the homogenous chains"; in spite of its new menu, though, critics still feel it is in need of a "serious overhaul". / W8 7QR; www.stickyfingers.co.uk; 10.45 pm; set weekday L £19 (FP).

STK Steakhouse ME by Meliá London WC2 **£69** 222
336-337 The Strand 7395 3450 4–3C
On the fringe of Covent Garden, an "extremely loud" and "very expensive" steakhouse – it offers "none of the fun sexiness of the NYC original, nor the more casual excellence of Hawksmoor or Goodman". / WC2R 1HA; www.stkhouse.com; @STKLondon; Mon-Wed 11 pm, Thu-Sat midnight, Sun 10 pm; D only.

Stock Pot **£27** 222
38 Panton St, SW1 7839 5142 4–4A
54 James St, W1 7935 6034 3–1A
273 King's Rd, SW3 7823 3175 5–3C
No one has a bad word to say about these hardy '60s canteens, whose huge range of basic scoff at bargain-basement prices has nourished generations of students, shoppers and those who just can't be bothered to cook. / SW1 11.30 pm, Wed-Sat midnight, Sun 11 pm SW3 10.15 pm, Sun 9.45 pm; no Amex.

Story SE1 **£81** 443
201 Tooley St 7183 2117 9–4D
"Mind-blowing and unique!" – Tom Sellers's "Scandi-style" dining room, not far from Tower Bridge, offers multi-course meals that most reports say are just "out of this world"; for the occasional critic,

though, it is all is a bit too "post-modern/bonkers"! / SE1 2UE; www.restaurantstory.co.uk; @Rest_Story; 9.30 pm; closed Mon & Sun; set weekday L £53 (FP).

Story Deli E2 **£43** 5 2 3
123 Bethnal Green Rd 0791 819 7352 12–2B
Still close to the Brick Lane action (although no longer in the Truman Brewery, where it was once located), this hip hangout is still "worth a visit" for its "really different" thin-crust pizza. / E2 7DG; www.storydeli.com; 10.30 pm; no credit cards.

Strada **£42** 1 2 2
Branches throughout London
These "family-friendy" pizza-and-pasta spots have been very "inconsistent" in recent years, and many long term fans can't help feeling they've "gone off"; can Hugh Osmond (who bought the chain in late-2014) sprinkle on them some of the magic he once helped instil at PizzaExpress? / www.strada.co.uk; 10.30 pm-11 pm; some booking restrictions apply.

Strand Dining Rooms WC2 NEW **£64** 2 4 3
1-3 Grand Buildings, Strand 7930 8855 2–2C
An ambitiously large all-day British brasserie, which opened near Trafalgar Square in the summer of 2014; it couldn't have a much handier location (especially for breakfast or tea), and service tries so hard, but our early-days lunchtime visits found food with no oomph at all. / WC2N 4JF; www.thestranddiningrooms.com; @StrandDining; 11 pm.

Street Kitchen EC2 **£18** 3 3 –
Broadgate Circle no tel 12–2B
For "good-quality take-away", many City worker bees tip this Silver Airstream, near Broadgate Circle, overseen by 'name' chefs Mark Jankel and Jun Tanaka. / EC2; www.streetkitchen.co.uk/home.shtml; @Streetkitchen; L only.

Sufi W12 **£31** 3 3 4
70 Askew Rd 8834 4888 7–1B
"The bread, made in front of you, is worth the trip alone", say fans of his welcoming Persian, in the depths of Shepherd's Bush – a "great-value" local. / W12 9BJ; www.sufirestaurant.com; @SUFIRESTAURANT; 11 pm.

Suk Saran SW19 **£52** 4 2 1
29 Wimbledon Hill Rd 8947 9199 10–2B
Part of a three-strong southwest London chain, this upmarket Wimbledon Town restaurant is a handy Thai option – good food, but service "can be slow and inattentive". / SW19 7NE; www.sukhogroup.com; 10.30 pm; booking: max 25; set weekday L £35 (FP).

Sukho Fine Thai Cuisine SW6 **£53** 5 4 3
855 Fulham Rd 7371 7600 10–1B
"The best Thai food in town" can come as a "surprise" find at this unassuming shop-conversion in deepest Fulham; "charming" service helps offset the "cramped" conditions, though, and it always feels "busy" and "buzzy". / SW6 5HJ; www.sukhogroup.co.uk; 11 pm; set weekday L £35 (FP).

The Summerhouse W9 **£55** 3 3 5
60 Blomfield Rd 7286 6752 8–4A
An "exceptional location", by the canal in Little Venice, makes this simply decorated spot a "superb" and "very romantic" summertime choice; "after a shaky start, the kitchen is turning out consistently good food", with fish the speciality. / W9 2PA; www.thesummerhouse.co.uk; 10.30 pm, Sun 10 pm; no Amex.

Sumosan W1 **£78** 3 2 2
26b Albemarle St 7495 5999 3–3C
"It's never had the pull of Nobu, Novikov or Zuma", but this moody-looking Japanese-fusion spot, in Mayfair, wins praise from its small fan club, particularly for sushi that's "fantastic, even if it's not cheap". / W1S 4HY; www.sumosan.com; @sumosan_; 11.30 pm, Sun 10.30 pm; closed Sat L & Sun L.

The Surprise SW3 **£45** 2 3 4
6 Christchurch Ter 7351 6954 5–3D
"Once a Sloaney watering hole", this "delightful" pub, near the Royal Hospital, has a bright new look nowadays, and serves an "ace tapas-sized menu" that's "great for sharing or filling up". / SW3 4AJ; www.geronimo-inns.co.uk/thesurprise; @TheSurpriseSW3; 10 pm, Sun 9 pm.

Sushisamba EC2 **£78** 3 3 5
Heron Tower, 110 Bishopsgate 3640 7330 9–2D
"A magical lift journey" wafts diners to this "memorable" 38th-39th-floor bar-terrace-restaurant, by Liverpool Street; it ain't no bargain, of course, but this is one of the very best rooms with a view, offering Japanese/South American fusion fare that's sometimes a "wow", and service much improved on the early days. / EC2N 4AY; www.sushisamba.com; Sun-Thu midnight, Fri & Sat 1 am; smart casual.

Sushi Tetsu EC1 **£58** 5 5 3
12 Jerusalem Pas 3217 0090 9–1A
"You are sat at the bar, one of only 7 people, face-to-face with the chef", at this "intense" Clerkenwell one-off, which is run by a "superb husband-and-wife team"; the sushi is "the best in the UK", so it's

no surprise that "getting a table takes real commitment". / EC1V 4JP; www.sushitetsu.co.uk; @SushiTetsuUK; midnight; closed Mon & Sun.

Sushi-Say NW2 **£44** 5 4 2
33b Walm Ln 8459 7512 1–1A
The decor is "simple" and the Willesden Green location obscure, but this unassuming café is "always full" – it's one of the top Japanese restaurants in town, and serves "some of the best sushi ever!" / NW2 5SH; 10 pm, Sat 10.30 pm, Sun 9.30 pm; closed Mon, Tue, Wed L, Thu L & Fri L; no Amex.

The Swan W4 **£46** 4 4 5
119 Acton Ln 8994 8262 7–1A
"In the fabulous garden, it feels like you're on holiday", at this "spacious" and characterful pub, tucked-away on the Chiswick/Acton borders; service is "very warm and welcoming" too, and the Mediterranean cooking is "wonderful". / W4 5HH; www.theswanchiswick.co.uk; @SwanPubChiswick; 10 pm, Fri & Sat 10.30 pm, Sun 10 pm; closed weekday L.

The Swan at the Globe SE1 **£58** 3 3 4
21 New Globe Walk 7928 9444 9–3B
With "the most amazingly romantic view over the Thames and St Paul's", this first-floor South Bank venture makes "a great place for a celebratory occasion"; it offers quite a "limited" British menu, but the results generally hit the spot. / SE1 9DT; www.loveswan.co.uk; @swanabout; 9.45 pm, Sun 4.45 pm; closed Sun D.

Sweet Thursday N1 **£34** 3 3 3
95 Southgate Rd 7226 1727 1–2C
"A superb local pizza restaurant"; this retro-chic two-year-old, in De Beauvoir, offers "excellent" Neapolitan-style thin-crusts; the wine shop at the front "has some real gems" too. / N1 3JS; www.sweetthursday.co.uk; @Pizza_and_Pizza; 10 pm, Sat 10.30 pm, Sun 9 pm.

Sweetings EC4 **£65** 3 2 3
39 Queen Victoria St 7248 3062 9–3B
"The best of the old-school City restaurants"; this "unique" Victorian fish parlour has a "jovial" but "slightly haphazard" air that's "totally English", and its fish and seafood, if "not cheap", is "consistently good" too; arrive early for a table. / EC4N 4SA; www.sweetingsrestaurant.com; 3 pm; L only, closed Sat & Sun; no booking.

T.E.D N1 NEW
47-51 Caledonian Rd 3763 2080 8–3D
'Sustainability' always seems to have been a bit of a King's Cross speciality; Ted Grainger-Smith made quite a hit of a sustainable resturant with Acorn House (now RIP), so perhaps he can do the same again at this summer-2014 newcomer. / N1 9BU; www.tedrestaurants.co.uk; @TEDrestaurant.

Taberna Etrusca EC4 **£50** 3 3 3
9 -11 Bow Churchyard 7248 5552 9–2C
A "thoroughly enjoyable high-end City Italian", in "classic" style; thanks not least to its "reliable" cooking, it's "heaving at lunchtime" – in summer, the al fresco tables are particularly popular. / EC4M 9DQ; www.etruscarestaurants.com; 10 pm; closed Mon D, Sat & Sun.

The Table SE1 **£46** 2 2 2
83 Southwark St 7401 2760 9–4B
Over the road from Tate Modern, this "stylish indie café" – once an architects' practice office canteen – is "very popular for weekend brunch"; "you'll be rammed in on benches though, so it's a place to get caffeinated not relaxed". / SE1 0HX; www.thetablecafe.com; @thetablecafe; 10.30 pm; closed Mon D & Sun D; SRA-2 stars.

Taiwan Village SW6 **£35** 5 5 3
85 Lillie Rd 7381 2900 5–3A
"It might not have the posh decor you'd find in the West End", but this Fulham operation behind an "unlikely-looking shopfront" offers "superb" and "utterly reliable" Chinese dishes; "choose the 'leave it to the chef' menu – he really does know best". / SW6 1UD; www.taiwanvillage.com; 11.30 pm, Sun 10.30 pm; closed weekday L; booking: max 20.

Tajima Tei EC1 **£36** 3 3 3
9-11 Leather Ln 7404 9665 9–2A
A "hidden gem" of a Japanese, not far from Holborn Circus; it's well-known locally for its "good-value" set menu – including "very well-made sushi" – and consequently "jammed at lunchtimes". / EC1N 7ST; www.tajima-tei.co.uk; 10 pm; closed Sat & Sun; no booking, L.

Talad Thai SW15 **£32** 3 2 1
320 Upper Richmond Rd 8246 5791 10–2A
"It's a little bit like a transport caff", but this long-serving Thai canteen, attached to an Asian supermarket in Putney, serves "authentic" scoff at "great-value" prices. / SW15 6TL; www.taladthairestaurant.com; 10.30 pm, Sun 9.30 pm; no Amex.

Tamarind W1 **£75** 4 4 3
20 Queen St 7629 3561 3–3B
"High-end Indian food cooked to perfection" and "incredibly helpful" staff help win rave reports for this "extremely civilised" and "classy" Mayfair stalwart; if there is a reservation, it's the basement

setting. / W1J 5PR; www.tamarindrestaurant.com; 10.45 pm, Sun 10.30 pm; closed Sat L; booking: max 20; set weekday L £47 (FP).

Tandoori Nights SE22 £38 3 4 3
73 Lordship Ln 8299 4077 1–4D
A welcoming East Dulwich fixture, consistently applauded for Indian food that's always "decent", and which locals proclaim outstanding. / SE22 8EP; www.tandoorinightsdulwich.co.uk; 11.30 pm, Fri & Sat midnight; closed weekday L & Sat L.

Tapas Brindisa £43 3 2 3
46 Broadwick St, W1 7534 1690 3–2D
18-20 Southwark St, SE1 7357 8880 9–4C
41-43 Atlantic Rd, SW9 7095 8655 10–2D
"Sociable, bustling, noisy, cramped" – this Borough Market tapas bar can be "a nightmare to get into", but perennially draws the crowds with its "authentic" style and "high-quality, if expensive" dishes; the Soho spin-off is hardly mentioned. / 10.45 pm, Sun 10 pm; W1 booking: max 10.

Taqueria W11 £35 3 4 3
139-143 Westbourne Grove 7229 4734 6–1B
"A far remove from the usual Tex Mex" – this "always buzzing" Notting Hill cantina offers an "interesting" menu majoring in tacos, "admirably complemented" by some "excellent" tequila-based cocktails. / W11 2RS; www.taqueria.co.uk; @TaqueriaUK; 11 pm, Fri & Sat 11.30 pm, Sun 10.30 pm; no Amex; no booking Fri-Sun.

Taro £35 2 3 2
10 Old Compton St, W1 7439 2275 4–2B
61 Brewer St, W1 7734 5826 3–2D
"Vast numbers of diners ensure the food is always super fresh", at these "cheap" Soho canteens, "efficiently run" under "the ever-watchful eye of Mr Taro"; critics find them too "business-like" but the more common verdict is that they're "great value". / www.tarorestaurants.co.uk; 10.30 pm, Sun 9.30 pm; no Amex.

Tartufo SW3 £57 5 4 3
11 Cadogan Gdns 7730 6383 5–2D
"A rare find"; Alexis Gauthier's "restful" and "cleverly designed" yearling may be "buried in a hard-to-find hotel basement, off Sloane Square", but it makes a "brilliant" discovery, thanks to its "friendly" style and "refined" Italian cuisine, and all at "incredibly good-value prices" too. / SW3 2RJ; www.tartufolondon.co.uk; 10 pm; closed Mon & Sun.

Tas £37 2 3 3
22 Bloomsbury St, WC1 7637 4555 2–1C
33 The Cut, SE1 7928 2111 9–4A
76 Borough High St, SE1 7403 8557 9–4C
97-99 Isabella St, SE1 7620 6191 9–4A
37 Farringdon Rd, EC1 7430 9721 9–1A
"Stick to the mezze and you can feast cheaply" – always the best advice, at these "handy" Turkish "standbys", whose "bustling" style add to their appeal; the original branch at The Cut has always been a boon for those going to the Old Vic. / www.tasrestaurant.com; 11.30 pm, Sun 10.30 pm.

Tas Pide SE1 £34 2 3 4
20-22 New Globe Walk 7928 3300 9–3B
Right by the Globe Theatre, this large but cosy Anatolian café is a "reliable" spot, where "you can feast cheaply" on mezze and "tasty" Turkish pizza ('pide'). / SE1 9DR; www.tasrestaurant.com/tas_pide; 11.30 pm, Sun 10.30 pm.

(Whistler Restaurant) Tate Britain SW1 £54 2 3 5
Millbank 7887 8825 2–4C
"Welcome back!" – this "calm" dining room has emerged from an 18-month restoration of its famous Whistler murals… "pretty much the same as it was prior to the closure!"; as ever, the food is only "OK", and the real draw is the "superlative" wine selection at "sensible" prices. / SW1 4RG; www.tate.org.uk; L & afternoon tea only.

(Restaurant, Level 6) Tate Modern SE1 £48 2 2 4
Bankside 7887 8888 9–3B
"Breathtaking" views of the City and St Paul's are the undoubted reason to seek out this "canteen-like" space on the gallery's top floor – the British cuisine ranges from "much better than expected" to "awful". / SE1 9TG; www.tate.org.uk; @TateFood; 9 pm; Sun-Thu closed D, Fri & Sat open L & D; SRA-2 stars.

Taylor St Baristas £15 4 4 3
22 Brooks Mews, W1 7629 3163 3–2B
Unit 3 Westminster Hs, Kew Rd, TW9 07969 798650 1–4A
110 Clifton St, EC2 7929 2207 12–2B
Unit 3, 125 Old Broad St, EC2 7256 8668 9–2C
2 Botolph Alley, EC3 7283 1835 9–3C
"They take coffee seriously", at this small Aussie chain; "surprisingly good" sarnies and other snacks too. / EC2M 4TP; www.taylor-st.com; All branches 5 pm; Old Broad ST, Clifton St, W1, E14 closed Sat & Sun; New St closed Sat; TW9 closed Sun.

Tayyabs E1 £28 4 2 3
83 Fieldgate St 7247 9543 9–2D
"Notwithstanding the chaos, there's nothing to beat the lamb chops" – this "amazing" East End

Pakistani "madhouse" gets "crazily busy", so "get their early, or queue for ages"; but has it expanded too far? – now on three floors, it can feel like it is pushing out curries "on an industrial scale". / E1 1JU; www.tayyabs.co.uk; @itayyabs; 11.30 pm.

Telegraph SW15 **£40** 324
Telegraph Rd 8788 2011 10–2A
"They bill themselves as the leading country pub in London, and I'd say that's a pretty good description" – this "tucked away" Putney Heath pub couldn't be much more leafily located, and its satisfactory scoff makes it a happy weekend or sunny day destination. / SW15 3TU; www.thetelegraphputney.co.uk; 9 pm, Fri & Sat 9.30 pm.

The 10 Cases WC2 **£55** 233
16 Endell St 7836 6801 4–2C
"Limited but fascinating", the wine list is the "star" at this "convivial" Covent Garden two-year-old, explaining why its "crowded" quarters are so "busy, busy, busy"; "decent" food plays a supporting role. / WC2H 9BD; www.the10cases.co.uk; @10cases; 11 pm; closed Sun.

10 Greek Street W1 **£47** 553
10 Greek St 7734 4677 4–2A
"Informal brilliance" has won a huge following for this "well-priced" (but "cramped") Soho two-year-old, which offers "outstanding" dishes from an ever-changing menu, and "great, well priced wines" to go with them; only problem – no dinner reservations. / W1D 4DH; www.10greekstreet.com; @10GreekStreet; 11.30 pm; closed Sun.

Tendido Cero SW5 **£46** 334
174 Old Brompton Rd 7370 3685 5–2B
"Consistently delicious and inventive" tapas ensure this "slick" South Kensington bar is always "buzzing with a sleek thirty-something clientele"... who presumably don't mind prices critics find "mind-boggling". / SW5 0BA; www.cambiodetercio.co.uk; @CambiodTercio; 11 pm.

Tendido Cuatro SW6 **£42** 444
108-110 New King's Rd 7371 5147 10–1B
Cambio de Tercio's "lovely", if cramped, Fulham outpost serves up "terrific tapas", and a "good wine list" too. / SW6 4LY; www.cambiodetercio.co.uk; @Cambiode Tercio; 11 pm, Sun 10.30 pm.

Tentazioni SE1 **£55** 344
2 Mill St 7394 5248 11–2A
"You feel squirrelled away", at this "out-of-the-way" but "welcoming" Italian, near Shad Thames; it's not well-known nowadays but still "really rather good", offering an "amazing range of game pastas", and some "unusual meat dishes" too. / SE1 2BD; www.tentazioni.co.uk; @TentazioniWorld; 10.45 pm, Sun 9 pm; closed Sat L; set weekday L £17 (FP).

The Terrace W8 NEW **£57** 244
33c Holland St 7937 3224 5–1A
Newly resurrected, this "lovely" Kensington local (with tiny, er, terrace) wins praise for its "charming" service and "precise but simple" cooking; for the prices, though, critics can find the food rather "average". / W8 4LX; www.theterraceholIandstreet.co.uk; 10.30 pm; closed Sun.

Terroirs WC2 **£45** 323
5 William IV St 7036 0660 4–4C
"A weird and wonderful wine list with some corkers" (and "some like home brew!") is the undoubted star at this "reassuring" Gallic bistro, near Charing Cross; its "strongly flavoured" small plates inspire more diverse reactions than they used to, though, and service can sometimes be "chaotic". / WC2N 4DW; www.terroirswinebar.com; @terroirswinebar; 11 pm; closed Sun.

Texture W1 **£92** 343
34 Portman St 7224 0028 2–2A
Agnar Sverrisson's cuisine shows some "sophisticated Icelandic twists", and it is complemented by some notably good wines and (especially) champagnes, at this ambitious spot, near Selfridges; some reporters found the place rather "overrated" this year, though, and the high-ceilinged interior is rather "noisy". / W1H 7BY; www.texture-restaurant.co.uk; 10.30 pm; closed Mon & Sun; set weekday L £56 (FP).

Thai Corner Café SE22 **£21** 333
44 North Cross Rd 8299 4041 1–4D
"Very cramped, as so many people try to get in!" – this "cheap 'n' cheerful" East Dulwich BYO is treasured by the locals for "basic Thai scoff that's full of flavour". / SE22 9EU; www.thaicornercafe.co.uk; 10.30 pm; closed Mon L & Tue L; no credit cards.

Thai Square **£41** 222
166-170 Shaftesbury Ave, WC2 7836 7600 4–1B
229-230 Strand, WC2 7353 6980 2–2D
19 Exhibition Rd, SW7 7584 8359 5–2C
347-349 Upper St, N1 7704 2000 8–3D
136-138 Minories, EC3 7680 1111 9–3D
"Reliable and reasonably priced"... "dependable, but oh-so-average" – the broad spectrum of opinion on the outlets of this Thai chain; SW15 has "the best river views". / www.thaisquare.net;

10 pm-11.30 pm; SW1 Fri & Sat 1 am; EC3, EC4 & St Annes Ct closed Sat & Sun, Strand branches and Princess St closed Sun.

Thali SW5 **£44** 442

166 Old Brompton Rd 7373 2626 5–2B

"Consistently great" North Indian dishes are the draw to this crisp-looking Earl's Court venue – "not cheap", but a meal still costs "way less than the super-Indians". / SW5 0BA; www.thali.uk.com; 11.30 pm, Sun 10.30 pm.

Theo Randall InterContinental Hotel W1 **£88** 322

1 Hamilton Pl 7318 8747 3–4A

In the past, Theo Randall's ace Italian cuisine has usually transcended the "sterile and dull" interior of this windowless chamber, in a "corporate" Hyde Park Corner hotel; of late, however, the food has sometimes proved "not as stellar as expected", and service has been a mite "unpredictable" too. / W1J 7QY; www.theorandall.com; @theorandall; 11 pm; closed Sat L & Sun; set dinner £57 (FP).

34 W1 **£78** 333

34 Grosvenor Sq 3350 3434 3–3A

"The cooking is plain but top-class", say fans of Richard Caring's "posh" Mayfair grill-house, hailing "the best steaks… period"; critics, though, feel it's only "OK", and say its "bloated" prices makes it one for "hedgies and the offspring of oligarchs". / W1K 2HD; www.34-restaurant.co.uk; 10.30 pm; set weekday L £50 (FP).

Thirty Six Duke's Hotel SW1 **£85** 221

35-36 Saint James's Pl 7491 4840 3–4C

Feedback for this hotel restaurant "tucked away in a St James backstreet" is again modest and curiously mixed; fans enthuse of an establishment that "truly shines", but critics bemoan the "dire" atmosphere, and food that's "average at best for a place at this level". / SW1A 1NY; www.dukeshotel.com; @dukeshotel; 9.30 pm; closed Mon L & Sun D; set weekday L £50 (FP).

The Thomas Cubitt SW1 **£51** 334

44 Elizabeth St 7730 6060 2–4A

"Permanently thronged with Belgravia's young bloods", this "glammed-up boozer" serves food in both its "charming" upstairs room and on the "bustling" ground floor (where there are some tightly-packed al fresco tables); "it's not cheap, but then it is SW1…" / SW1W 9PA; www.thethomascubitt.co.uk; 10 pm; booking only in restaurant; SRA-3 stars.

3 South Place South Place Hotel EC2 **£60** 233

3 South Pl 3503 0000 12–2A

"For breakfast and convenience, hard to beat!" – this ground-floor brasserie of a D&D Group hotel, by Liverpool Street, makes a useful standby at any time of day; for a more serious lunch or dinner option, however, see 'Angler'. / EC2M 2AF; www.southplacehotel.com; @southplacehotel; 10.30 pm; max 22.

tibits W1 **£35** 323

12-14 Heddon St 7758 4110 3–2C

A Swiss-run veggie, near Piccadilly Circus, where you pay by weight; "the wide variety of wholesome yet comforting food" is "always fresh and interesting"; beware, though – "the pick 'n' mix formula makes it easy to get carried away!" / W1B 4DA; www.tibits.co.uk; 11.30 pm, Sun 10 pm; no Amex; Only bookings for 8+.

Tinello SW1 **£48** 444

87 Pimlico Rd 7730 3663 5–2D

"Subtle and sophisticated" Tuscan dishes are served by "very caring" staff at this "elegant" and "genuinely Italian" restaurant, not far from Sloane Square, which is emerging as an "all-round" favourite for many reporters. / SW1W 8PH; www.tinello.co.uk; @tinello_london; 10.30 pm; closed Sun.

Ting Shangri-La Hotel at the Shard SE1 NEW **£86** 223

Shangri-La Hotel At The Shard 7234 8000 9–4C

"Gorgeous views" distinguish this 35th-floor hotel dining room, but it's otherwise a remarkably "anonymous" venue, lacking any of the sparkle you might expect from the illustrious Shangri-La chain; afternoon teas, though, are "fantastic". / SE1 9RY; www.shangri-la.com; 11.30 pm.

Toasted SE22 **£46** 334

38 Lordship Ln 8693 9021 1–4D

"Another local gem" in the Caves de Pryène (Terroirs and so on) empire – this East Dulwich yearling mixes a "brilliant selection of small plates for sharing" with the wine importer's "lovely draught wines at amazingly reasonable prices". / SE22 8HJ; toastdulwich.co.uk; toastdulwich; 9.45 pm; closed Sun D.

Toff's N10 **£40** 432

38 Muswell Hill Broadway 8883 8656 1–1B

"The freshness and variety of the fish" distinguish this "always-busy", "no-frills" Muswell Hill institution

– north London's top chippy. / N10 3RT; www.toffsfish.co.uk; @toffsfish; 10 pm; closed Sun.

Tokyo Diner WC2 **£26** 2 2 3
2 Newport Pl 7287 8777 4–3B
It's "tatty" and "cramped", but this Chinatown "treasure" has a place in fans' hearts for its "fast, cheap and healthy" bites. / WC2H 7JJ; www.tokyodiner.com; 11.30 pm; no Amex; no booking, Fri & Sat.

Tom's Kitchen **£65** 2 1 1
Somerset House, 150 Strand, WC2 7845 4646 2–2D
27 Cale St, SW3 7349 0202 5–2C
11 Westferry Circus, E14 3011 1555 11–1C
1 Commodity Quay, E1 3011 5433 9–3D
Save as "hustling and bustling" brunch venues (SW3 especially), reporters rarely give solidly positive reports on Tom Aikens's growing bistro chain – prices for the "very average" food can seem "excruciating", and service can be "shambolic"; WC2 has a "wonderful location overlooking the Thames". / 10 pm - 10.45 pm; WC2 closed Sun D.

Tommi's Burger Joint **£18** 4 2 3
30 Thayer St, W1 7224 3828 3–1A
342 Kings Rd, SW3 7349 0691 5–3C
It's a "meaty dream", exclaim fans of this "simple and straightforward" – order-at-the-counter – Marylebone burger parlour (for which you can expect to queue); good ratings for its new Chelsea sibling too.

Tonkotsu **£32** 3 3 3
63 Dean St, W1 7437 0071 4–2A
Arch 334 1a Dunston St, E8 7254 2478 1–2D NEW
You eat "with someone texting at your elbow" amidst the "controlled chaos" of this "cramped" Soho ramen bar, which serves "consistently good noodles to sooth the soul"; it now has a larger branch in Haggerston too.

Tortilla **£18** 3 2 2
Branches throughout London
Just as highly rated as, if less well-known than, Chipotle, these simple outlets offer "a good choice of meats and plenty of interesting fillings" at "competitive prices" – "perfect for some quick refuelling". / www.tortilla.co.uk; W1 & N1 11 pm, Sun 9 pm, SE1 & E14 9 pm, EC3 7 pm, E14 Sun 7 pm; SE1 & EC3 closed Sat & Sun, N1 closed sun; no Amex.

Tosa W6 **£42** 4 2 2
332 King St 8748 0002 7–2B
"It's hard to stop ordering", at this "down-to-earth and authentic" Hammersmith café, which is "always full of Japanese people"; it offers a "good selection of sushi and yakitori" (plus "some more unusual dishes too, for a change"). / W6 0RR; www.tosauk.com; 10.30 pm.

Toto's Walton House SW1 NEW **£79** 3 5 4
Lennox Gardens Mews 7589 0075 5–2C
"Welcome back!" to this "light and airy" resurrected Knightsbridge trattoria, and its "beautifully presented" dishes; oddly – but successfully, it seems – the 'face' of the enterprise is none other than Silvano Giraldin, former maître d' of the very Gallic Gavroche. / SW1 0DP; www.totosrestaurant.com; 11 pm, Sun 10.30 pm.

Tozi SW1 **£41** 3 4 3
8 Gillingham St 7769 9771 2–4B
"What a find in a 'dead' restaurant area!" – this "authentic" and "enjoyable" cicchetti restaurant transcends its potentially anonymous hotel location, near Victoria, and many reporters find they "just keep going back". / SW1V 1HN; www.tozirestaurant.co.uk; @ToziRestaurant; 10 pm.

Tramontana Brindisa EC2 **£37** 3 2 3
152-154 Curtain Rd 7749 9961 12–1B
In Shoreditch, a fairly typical outlet of the Brindisa empire – fans applaud "great small-plate food" (here with something of a Catalan twist) and "excellent cocktails", but critics find some dishes "slightly disappointing", and service so-so. / EC2A 3AT; www.brindisatapaskitchens.com; @brindisa; Mon-Sat 11 pm, Sun 9 pm.

The Tramshed EC2 **£57** 2 2 4
32 Rivington St 7749 0478 12–1B
"An amazing interior with Damien Hirst's 'Cock and Bull' looming overhead" sets the scene at Mark Hix's vast Shoreditch shed; most reports extol the "basic" but "mouthwatering" formula of chicken or steak 'n' chips, but a sizeable minority "just don't get it". / EC2A 3LX; www.chickenandsteak.co.uk; @HIXrestaurants.

Tredwell's WC2 NEW
4 Upper St Martin's Ln 3764 0840 4–3B
From the Marcus Wareing group, a new multi-floor all-day operation, at Seven Dials; early-days press reviews have been notably mixed. / WC2H 9NY; www.tredwells.com.

Trinity SW4 **£68** 4 5 3
4 The Polygon 7622 1199 10–2D
"Outstanding but unassuming", Adam Byatt's "superb" Clapham HQ remains "the best in the area by a mile", thanks to its "seasonal ingredients

prepared with great flair", and "service that makes you feel like a VIP". / SW4 0JG; www.trinityrestaurant.co.uk; @TrinityLondon; 9.45 pm; closed Mon L & Sun D; set weekday L £50 (FP), set Sun L £56 (FP).

Trishna W1 **£65** 4 3 2
15-17 Blandford St 7935 5624 2–1A
"Spellbinding" southwest Indian cuisine has made quite a name for this "basic" ("lacking warmth or charm") Marylebone outpost of a famous Mumbai fish restaurant; this year, however, standards have sometimes seemed a little "inconsistent". / W1U 3DG; www.trishnalondon.com; @TrishnaLondon; 10.45 pm; set weekday L £44 (FP).

Les Trois Garçons E1 **£70** 2 2 2
1 Club Row 7613 1924 12–1C
"Such fun and eccentric decor" has helped make quite a name for this camp East End pub-conversion; its Gallic menu is no bargain, though, and a number of reports of late are of an all-round "mediocre" experience. / E1 6JX; www.lestroisgarcons.com; @lestroisgarcons; 9.30 pm, Sat 10.30 pm; closed Mon L, Tue L, Wed L, Sat L & Sun; need credit card to book; set weekday L £43 (FP).

LA TROMPETTE W4 **£67** 5 4 4
5-7 Devonshire Rd 8747 1836 7–2A
"After a fall from grace post-refurb" (in 2013), this "fabulous" Chiswick "jewel" – sibling to the legendary Chez Bruce – "has recovered its zing"; ratings for its "glorious" Gallic cuisine ("just the right balance of classic and innovative"), "outstanding" wine and "immaculate" service are all impressive. / W4 2EU; www.latrompette.co.uk; @LaTrompetteUK; 10.30 pm, Sun 9.30 pm; set weekday L £48 (FP), set Sun L £53 (FP).

Troubadour SW5 **£43** 2 3 4
263-267 Old Brompton Rd 7370 1434 5–3A
"A piece of '60s history", and perhaps the last redoubt of bohemianism in the SWs! – this "quirky" Earl's Court café (and basement music venue) serves "decent" all-day nosh, including a "wide choice of breakfast dishes". / SW5 9JA; www.troubadour.co.uk; 11 pm.

Trullo N1 **£51** 4 4 4
300-302 St Paul's Rd 7226 2733 8–2D
Hailed as a "baby River Café" by its gigantic north London fan club, Jordan Trullo's "smart but relaxed" Highbury venture serves up an "outstanding" (and "often gutsy") menu, complemented by an "educational treasury" of a wine list; let's hope "creeping prices" don't spoil the fun! / N1 2LH; www.trullorestaurant.com; @Trullo_LDN; 10.30 pm; closed Sun D; no Amex; booking: max 12; set weekday L £37 (FP).

Truscott Arms W9 NEW **£54** 3 3 4
55 Shirland Rd 7266 9198 1–2B
With its "buzzing bar on the ground floor, upstairs dining room and dining conservatory", this Maida Vale gastropub wins all-round praise, including for its gourmet food at "neighbourhood prices". / W9 2JD; www.thetruscottarms.com; @TheTruscottArms; 9 pm; SRA-3 stars.

Tsunami **£49** 5 2 2
93 Charlotte St, W1 7637 0050 2–1C
5-7 Voltaire Rd, SW4 7978 1610 10–1D
"Black cod to die for" and other Asian-fusion wizardry still inspire raves for this Clapham destination (with Fitzrovia spin-off), which fans say is "as good as Nobu"... but half the cost; on the downside, "the decor has seen better days", and service is sometimes "terrible". / www.tsunamirestaurant.co.uk; @Tsunamirest; SW4 10.30 pm, Fri & Sat 11 pm, Sun 9.30 pm; W1 11 pm; SW4 closed Mon - Fri L; W1 closed Sat L and Sun; SW4 no Amex.

28-50 **£53** 3 3 4
15 Maddox St, W1 7495 1505 3–2C
15-17 Marylebone Ln, W1 7486 7922 3–1A
140 Fetter Ln, EC4 7242 8877 9–2A
"The food is fine, but the real story is the wine" – "interesting selections by the glass", and a "killer collector's list of old and rare bottles with modest mark-ups" are making a big hit of this growing bistro chain; it's often hailed as "a good choice for lunch". / www.2850.co.uk; EC4 9.30 pm; W1 Mon-Wed 10 pm, Thu-Sat 10.30 pm, Sun 9.30 pm; EC4 closed Sat-Sun.

21 Bateman Street W1 NEW **£36** 3 4 4
21 Bateman St 7287 6638 4–2A
A "welcome new one-room restaurant", in the heart of Soho, "buzzing with the sound of Greek voices", and offering "unparalleled value for money"; the "rather minimal" menu focusses on charcoal grill-cooked souvlaki "done to perfection". / W1D 3AL; www.21batemanstreet.co.uk; Mon-Thu 11.30 pm, Sat midnight, Sun 10.20 pm.

Two Brothers N3 **£42** 3 3 2
297-303 Regent's Park Rd 8346 0469 1–1B
"Really fresh fish and terrific chips" maintain the reputation of this ever-"popular" Finchley fixture as one of north London's premier chippys. / N3 1DP; www.twobrothers.co.uk; 10 pm, Sun 8 pm; closed Mon.

2 Veneti W1 **£47** 3 4 3
10 Wigmore St 7637 0789 3–1B
"Pleasant and helpful" service and "good-quality, traditional cooking" are mainstays of the simple

formula which makes this "well-spaced" Venetian a useful destination in the "bereft area" round the Wigmore Hall, especially for business. / W1U 2RD; www.2veneti.com; @2Veneti; 10.30 pm, Sat 11 pm; closed Sat L & Sun.

Typing Room Town Hall Hotel E2 NEW **£85** 5 4 4
Patriot Square 7871 0461 1–2D
"A superb replacement for Viajante (RIP)"; "amazing" tasting menus – with "wow" flavours, "fantastic" presentation, and "interesting wine pairings" – are quickly putting this Bethnal Green dining room firmly back on the map; service is notably "attentive" too. / E2 9NF; www.typingroom.com; @TypingRoom; 10.15 pm; closed Mon & Tue; set weekday L £52 (FP).

Umu W1 **£105** 2 1 2
14-16 Bruton Pl 7499 8881 3–2C
"Ouch! Make sure you ask your bank manager first…"; Marlon Abela's discreetly-located but "blingy" Mayfair Japanese offers some "lovely" Kyoto-style kaiseki, but it is losing its way, and the cost is "crazy". / W1J 6LX; www.umurestaurant.com; 10.30 pm; closed Sat L & Sun; no trainers; booking: max 14.

Uni SW1 NEW **£46** 4 4 3
18a, Ebury St 7730 9267 2–4B
A bright Belgravia newcomer, acclaimed in early-days survey reports for its "unusual and creative" Peruvian/Japanese cuisine; "superb sushi" a highlight. / SW1W 0LU; www.restaurantuni.com; @UNIRestaurant; 10 pm.

The Union Café W1 **£45** 2 3 2
96 Marylebone Ln 7486 4860 3–1A
A "reliable" and "no-nonsense" Marylebone fixture, where the food is "good value and always tasty", if arguably "a little uninspiring"; real plus point? – "no silly mark-ups on the wine!" / W1U 2QA; www.brinkleys.com; @BrinkleysR; 10.30 pm; closed Sun.

Union Street Café SE1 **£49** 2 2 2
Harling Hs, Union St 7592 7977 9–4B
"Striving too hard for some sort of industrial chic", Gordon Ramsay's "SoHo-style" Italian yearling, in Borough, is "a bit of a Curate's Egg" – too often, it seems a "pretentious" place where standards are "average" all-round. / SE1 0BS; www.gordonramsay.com/union-street-cafe; @unionstreetcafe; Mon-Fri 10 pm, Sat 9.45 pm, Sun 7.30 pm.

Upstairs SW2 **£57** 4 4 4
89b Acre Ln (door on Branksome Rd) 7733 8855 10–2D
Knock to enter this "fun" Brixton "hidden gem" – "a charming combination of Berlin-style secret venue and French family restaurant", where "gorgeous" cocktails help sustain the "romantic" vibe. / SW2 5TN; www.upstairslondon.com; @upstairsbrixton; 9.30 pm, Thu-Sat 10.30 pm; D only, closed Mon & Sun.

Le Vacherin W4 **£62** 3 3 3
76-77 South Pde 8742 2121 7–1A
"All the French classics" are realised to a "perfectly sound" standard at Malcolm John's "professional but laid-back" bistro, opposite Acton Green; it has the knack of "making a series of small surprises into a very satisfactory all-round experience". / W4 5LF; www.levacherin.co.uk; @Le_Vacherin; 10.15 pm, Fri & Sat 10.45 pm, Sun 9.45; closed Mon L; set always available £38 (FP).

Vanilla Black EC4 **£64** 3 3 3
17-18 Tooks Ct 7242 2622 9–2A
"I didn't believe veggie food could taste this good!"; this "delightful" restaurant, "tucked away" down a Midtown alleyway, inspires consistently positive reports on its "upmarket and imaginative", "if sometimes quirky", cuisine. / EC4A 1LB; www.vanillablack.co.uk; @vanillablack1; 10 pm; closed Sun.

Vapiano **£25** 3 2 3
19-21 Great Portland St, W1 7268 0080 3–1C
90B Southwark St, SE1 7593 2010 9–4B NEW
This (German-owned) Mediterranean self-serve canteen concept may be "a bit odd"… but most reporters find it "very useful" for "a quick, easy and tasty meal"; now in Soho too. / www.vapiano.co.uk.

Vasco & Piero's Pavilion W1 **£58** 4 4 3
15 Poland St 7437 8774 3–1D
"Very unshowy, and often overlooked", this "real old-fashioned Italian" offers "faultless" cooking, "very friendly" service and a "cosy" old-Soho atmosphere – all in all, a "memorable" combination. / W1F 8QE; www.vascosfood.com; @Vasco_and_Piero; 10.15 pm; closed Sat L & Sun.

Veeraswamy W1 **£75** 4 4 4
Victory Hs, 99-101 Regent St 7734 1401 3–3D
London's oldest Indian should be a tourist trap, yet it's anything but – yes it's "a bit expensive",

but the "light and fragrant" cooking, "yummy cocktails" and "sumptuous" modern design make a visit "well worthwhile". / W1B 4RS; www.veeraswamy.com; 10.30 pm, Sun 10 pm; booking: max 14; set pre theatre £48 (FP).

Verden E5 NEW **£42**
181 Clarence Rd 8986 4723 1–1D
A chef of impeccable West End provenance (Scott's) has gone East, to Clapton, to help establish this new meat-, cheese- and wine-specialist bar; early feedback is euphoric, but too scant to justify a survey rating. / E5 8EE; www.verdene5.com; @VerdenE5; midnight; closed Mon.

El Vergel SE1 **£33** 4 3 4
132 Webber St 7401 2308 9–4B
"A great place for a quick lunchtime bite", or brunch – this Latino canteen, near Borough tube, is known for its "deliciously fresh" fare; "I'd think of moving to Southwark just to eat there every day!" / SE1 0QL; www.elvergel.co.uk; 2.45pm, Sat-Sun 3.45 pm; closed D, closed Sun; no Amex.

Il Vicolo SW1 **£50** 3 4 2
3-4 Crown Passage 7839 3960 3–4D
"Tucked away" in a St James's alleyway, this "cheery" Sicilian stalwart is particularly buoyed up by its "always lively" service, but the "traditional" fare is "consistently good" too. / SW1Y 6PP; www.vicolo.co.uk; 10 pm; closed Sat L & Sun.

The Victoria SW14 **£49** 3 4 3
10 West Temple 8876 4238 10–2A
Not far from Richmond Park, Paul Merrett's large hostelry – with a spacious conservatory and a "lovely garden in summer", complete with playground – makes a natural weekend destination; dependable food too, including a BBQ in summer. / SW14 7RT; www.thevictoria.net; @thevictoria_pub; 10 pm, Sat 10 pm; no Amex; set weekday L £38 (FP).

Viet Grill E2 **£38** 4 2 3
58 Kingsland Rd 7739 6686 12–1B
"The best place on the Viet-Town strip" – this "upmarket... for the area" Shoreditch café offers "very tasty and authentic dishes at reasonable prices". / E2 8DP; www.vietnamesekitchen.co.uk; @CayTreVietGrill; 11 pm, Fri & Sat 11.30 pm, Sun 10.30 pm.

Vijay NW6 **£31** 3 4 2
49 Willesden Ln 7328 1087 1–1B
"Real subtlety in the use of herbs as well as spices" – with "fair prices" too – wins a loyal fan base for this South Indian veteran, in Kilburn; they "could improve the decor" though. / NW6 7RF; www.vijayrestaurant.co.uk; 10.45 pm, Fri & Sat 11.45 pm.

Villa Bianca NW3 **£60** 2 2 3
1 Perrins Ct 7435 3131 8–2A
In a cute Hampstead lane, "one of the few remaining traditional Italian silver service restaurants"; while fans (perennially) claim that "it's raised its game again" of late, critics find the food "no more than competent", and "pricey" for what it is too. / NW3 1QS; www.villabiancanw3.com; 11.30 pm, Sun 10.30 pm.

Village East SE1 **£55** 3 2 3
171-173 Bermondsey St 7357 6082 9–4D
A "busy and buzzy" Bermondsey's local eatery, with open kitchen, which – after a recent revamp – is still quite a crowd-pleaser; it makes "a very lively place for a weekend breakfast". / SE1 3UW; www.villageeast.co.uk; @VillageEastSE1; 10 pm, Sun 9.30 pm.

Villandry **£51** 2 2 2
170 Gt Portland St W1 7631 3131 2–1B
11-12 Waterloo Pl SW1 7930 3305 3-3D
NEW
So much missed potential – these "pricey" grand cafés, now with a smart St James's branch to complement the Marylebone original, could easily be the "excellent all-rounders" their fans suggest, but reports overall support those who say the food is "all over the place". / W1W 5QB; www.villandry.com; 10.30 pm; closed Sun D.

Villiers Coffee Co WC2 NEW **£46**
31a Villiers St 7925 2100 2–2D
A summer opening from the same family as the ever-popular Gordon's Wine Bar, just down the street; favourably reviewed in the press, it's potentially a very handy sort of all-day standby in a street that's improved immeasurably in recent years. / WC2N 6ND; @VilliersCoffee.

The Vincent Rooms Westminster Kingsway College SW1 **£32** 3 3 3
76 Vincent Sq 7802 8391 2–4C
"The students got through it, and so did we!" – the elegant dining room of this Westminster college can offer "delicious" food "even though it's cooked and served by catering students"; you have to accept "a few hairy moments", but "who knows, these may be great chefs of the future!" / SW1P 2PD; www.thevincentrooms.com; 7.15 pm; closed Mon D, Tue D, Fri D, Sat & Sun; no Amex.

VQ **£47** 2 3 2
St Giles Hotel, Great Russell St, WC1 7300 3000 4–1A
325 Fulham Rd, SW10 7376 7224 5–3B
"Breakfast, at any time!" – the special feature

of this long-established 24/7 Chelsea diner, which now has an offshoot in Bloomsbury.
/ www.vingtquatre.co.uk; open 24 hours.

Vinoteca **£45** 2 4 4
15 Seymour Pl, W1 7724 7288 2–2A
55 Beak St, W1 3544 7411 3–2D
18 Devonshire Rd, W4 3701 8822 7–2A
7 St John St, EC1 7253 8786 9–1B
"Heaven for wine lovers"; these "cramped" bars are run by staff "with a real passion for inspiring their customers" with their "creative" and very "sensibly-priced" list; the "simple" bistro fare? – "sound but unexciting". / www.vinoteca.co.uk; 11 pm, Seymour Pl Sun 5 pm; EC1 Sun; Seymour Pl Sun D.

Vivat Bacchus **£53** 2 3 2
4 Hay's Ln, SE1 7234 0891 9–4C
47 Farringdon St, EC4 7353 2648 9–2A
"Useful for a get-together after a day in the City", this "relaxed" spot is of special note for its "fantastic" South African wine list, and "amazing array" of cheeses, although its other "simple" fare is generally "dependable" too; the SE1 branch rarely elicits reports. / www.vivatbacchus.co.uk; 9.30 pm; EC4 closed Sat & Sun; SE1 closed Sat L & Sun.

Vivo N1 NEW **£35** 4 4 4
57-58 Upper St 7424 5992 8–3D
"A fantastic addition to Islington" – offering light Italian dishes, "like a sort of poor man's Princi", this "excellent casual dining spot" has inspired only positive comments in its first year of operation; it even boasts a "roof terrace"! / N1 0NY; www.vivotaste.com; @vivo_taste; 11 pm, Fri & Sat 1 am, Sun 10.30 pm.

Vrisaki N22 **£36** 3 3 3
73 Middleton Rd 8889 8760 1–1C
"If you order mezze, the portions are huge" – you'll be pushed to finish – at this quirky old taverna and take-away, which makes an offbeat find in an unassuming Bounds Green street. / N22 8LZ; www.vrisaki.uk.com; @vrisaki; 11.30 pm, Sun 9 pm; closed Mon; no Amex.

Wagamama **£38** 2 3 2
Branches throughout London
This "crowd-pleasing" Asian noodle chain remains "a safe bet" for most reporters (and kids, in particular, undoubtedly "love it"); it's "fallen a long way from where it once was", though, and the food "while fresh, lacks the real taste of the East". / www.wagamama.com; 10 pm-11 pm; EC4 & EC2 closed Sat & Sun; no booking.

Wahaca **£33** 2 3 4
19-23 Charlotte St, W1 7323 2342 2–1C
80-82 Wardour St, W1 7734 0195 3–2D
66 Chandos Pl, WC2 7240 1883 4–4C
68-69 Upper St, N1 3697 7990 8–3D
Southbank Centre, SE1 7928 1876 2–3D
"Vibrant colours and flavours that tingle the taste buds" ensure this "sociable" Mexican street food chain remains a major hit; there are reporters, however, who "just don't get it"… and they are becoming more vocal. / www.wahaca.com; WC2 & W1 & E14 11 pm, Sun 10.30 pm; W12 11 pm, Sun 10 pm; no booking.

The Wallace
The Wallace Collection
W1 **£56** 2 2 5
Hertford Hs, Manchester Sq 7563 9505 3–1A
This Marylebone museum café boasts a "stunning" setting in an "airy" atrium adjoining an 18th-century palazzo; with its "ordinary" cooking and "eccentric" service, though, it can seem a "wasted opportunity". / W1U 3BN; www.thewallacerestaurant.co.uk; Fri & Sat 9.15 pm; Sun-Thu closed D; no Amex.

Waterloo Bar & Kitchen
SE1 **£54** 3 3 2
131 Waterloo Rd 7928 5086 9–4A
A handy standby for Waterloo commuters and Old Vic theatre-goers – a cavernous (and sometimes "noisy") spot where "engaging" staff dish up "tasty" bistro fare. / SE1 8UR; www.barandkitchen.co.uk; 10.30 pm.

The Waterway W9 **£51** 2 1 4
54 Formosa St 7266 3557 8–4A
Thanks to the "perfect canalside location", there's "always a buzz" at this "happening" spot, near Little Venice – sadly, this often seems to mean that the kitchen is "overloaded", and service "hard to get". / W9 2JU; www.thewaterway.co.uk; @thewaterway_; 10.30 pm, Sun 10 pm.

The Wells NW3 **£49** 3 2 4
30 Well Walk 7794 3785 8–1A
This "very consistent" Hampstead hostelry, handy for the Heath, is one of NW3's finest destinations; "it's the place to be if you have a dog, but even without a canine friend it's buzzy and fun". / NW3 1BX; www.thewellshampstead.co.uk; @WellsHampstead; 10 pm, Sun 9.30 pm.

The Wet Fish Café
NW6 **£47** 3 3 3
242 West End Ln 7443 9222 1–1B
"A dream local, with flattering lighting and a well-considered soundtrack" – this former fishmongers' shop in West Hampstead "hits the spot" at any

time, but especially for weekend brunch. / NW6 1LG; www.thewetfishcafe.co.uk; @thewetfishcafe; 10 pm; no Amex.

The Wharf TW11 **£48** 2 3 4
22 Manor Rd 8977 6333 1–4A
It's the "good riverside location", overlooking Teddington Lock, which makes this airy bar/brasserie, with large terrace, a special destination; locals say the cooking's OK too. / TW11 8BG; www.thewharfteddington.com; Mon-Sat 10 pm, Sun 8.30 pm; closed Mon L; set always available £32 (FP), set Sun L £38 (FP).

White Horse SW6 **£51** 2 2 4
1-3 Parsons Grn 7736 2115 10–1B
"A first-rate list of well-chosen beers" and "a great buzzy atmosphere", especially when it's sunny, are the prime attractions of Fulham's famous 'Sloaney Pony'; the food? – "perfectly competent pub grub". / SW6 4UL; www.whitehorsesw6.com; 10.30 pm; no Maestro.

White Rabbit N16 **£27** 4 3 3
15-16 Bradbury St 7682 0163 1–1C
"As clever as any food you will have in smarter postcodes… just with more beards"; this Dalston yearling offers a "beautifully textured" cuisine, and its "very unusual" small plates can be "out of this world". / N16 8JN; www.whiterabbitdalston.com; 9.30 pm; D only, closed Mon.

The White Swan EC4 **£63** 4 4 3
108 Fetter Ln 7242 9696 9–2A
"Very sound", "high-end gastropub-style food" makes this "excellent" Fleet Street pub a "reliably good choice for a business lunch"; the upstairs dining room "is fortunately well-insulated from the noisy bar below". / EC4A 1ES; www.thewhiteswanlondon.com; @thewhiteswanEC4; 10 pm; closed Sat & Sun.

Whits W8 **£48** 3 5 3
21 Abingdon Rd 7938 1122 5–1A
A "very friendly" welcome from the "brilliant" co-owner Eva helps make for a "special evening out" at this "cosy" Kensington side street bistro, which offers "elegant" Gallic dishes in paradoxically "large" portions. / W8 6AH; www.whits.co.uk; @Whitsrestaurant; 10 pm; D only, closed Mon & Sun.

Whyte & Brown W1 NEW **£37** 3 4 4
Kingly Ct, Kingly St 3747 9820 3–2C
A "lovely" atmosphere – "both in the courtyard and inside" – helps make this "buzzy" Carnaby Street newcomer something of a surprise hit; fans say the chicken-centric menu is "a brilliant concept" too. / W1B 5PW; www.whyteandbrown.com; @whyteandbrown; Mon-Sat 10.45 pm, Sun 5.30 pm; closed Sun D.

Wild Honey W1 **£68** 3 3 3
12 St George St 7758 9160 3–2C
"Much improved" since the recent refurbishment, this "relaxed but classy" Mayfair spot is a "good but pricey" fixture, where the food is "reliably interesting", and whose "clubby, wood-panelled intimacy" suits business in particular. / W1S 2FB; www.wildhoneyrestaurant.co.uk; @whrestaurant; 10.30 pm; closed Sun.

Wiltons SW1 **£100** 3 4 4
55 Jermyn St 7629 9955 3–3C
"So wonderfully old-fashioned"; this "very professional" St James's bastion of the Establishment (est 1742, but here only since 1984) offers "perfect Dover sole" and other "first-rate" British seafood; prices are certainly high, though – "best visit on someone else's expenses". / SW1Y 6LX; www.wiltons.co.uk; @wiltons1742; 10.15 pm; closed Sat & Sun; jacket required; set dinner £64 (FP).

The Windmill W1 **£38** 3 2 3
6-8 Mill St 7491 8050 3–2C
"Pie heaven!"; this "time-warped" Young's boozer, near Savile Row, offers pastries with a "huge variety" of fillings, and at "very reasonable prices" too. / W1S 2AZ; www.windmillmayfair.co.uk; @tweetiepie_w1; 9.30 pm, Sat 4 pm; closed Sat & Sun; no Amex.

The Windsor Castle W8 **£43** 2 2 5
114 Campden Hill Rd 7243 8797 6–2B
Consistent but not exciting reports on the food at this old Kensington coaching inn; who cares, though? – it's the delightful walled garden and snug ancient interior that's always been the real attraction. / W8 7AR; www.thewindsorcastlekensington.co.uk; @windsorcastlew8; 10 pm, Sun 9 pm.

The Wine Library EC3 **£26** 1 3 5
43 Trinity Sq 7481 0415 9–3D
A "one-off"; these ancient City cellars offer "a place for wine lovers to explore and relax", and their "eclectic and expert array of wines" (at cost plus a small mark-up) is the "star of the show" – the picnic-style buffet is "just so you can say you had something to eat while you drank"! / EC3N 4DJ; www.winelibrary.co.uk; 8 pm, Mon 6 pm; closed Mon D, Sat & Sun.

Wishbone SW9 **£18** 322
Brixton Village, Coldharbour Ln 7274 0939 10–2D
"It has its detractors but if you go at a quiet time, it's easy to get a table, and the chicken is really good", at this "fancy fried chicken shack", in Brixton Market (part of the MEAT franchise). STOP PRESS – since late summer 2014 now trading as CHICKENliquor. / SW9 8PR; www.wishbonebrixton.co.uk; @wishbonebrixton; closed Mon.

Wolfe's WC2 **£48** 343
30 Gt Queen St 7831 4442 4–1D
Having ridden the burger craze (the '70s one), this stalwart Covent Garden diner de luxe may be in a rather dated style, but it's a "relaxing" sort of place with "consistent" standards; "great lunchtime menu". / WC2B 5BB; www.wolfes-grill.net; @wolfesbargrill; 10 pm, Fri & Sat 10.30 pm, Sun 9 pm.

THE WOLSELEY W1 **£59** 345
160 Piccadilly 7499 6996 3–3C
For pure theatre and excitement, Corbin & King's "splendid", "celeb-packed" London linchpin, by The Ritz, just can't be beat; its brasserie fare is "solid" but "not the most exciting", although the (power) "breakfast event" here is famously "the best in town". / W1J 9EB; www.thewolseley.com; @TheWolseleyRest; midnight, Sun 11 pm; SRA-3 stars.

Wong Kei W1 **£30**
41-43 Wardour St 7437 8408 4–3A
"New management, new staff, new air conditioning, new all-black uniform and new manners!" – this Chinatown landmark reopened under new management as our survey for the year was wrapping up; a proper assessment of the new régime will have to wait till next year. / W1D 6PY; www.wongkeilondon.com; 11.30 pm, Fri & Sat 11.45 pm, Sun 10.30 pm; no credit cards; no booking.

Woodlands **£41** 332
37 Panton St, SW1 7839 7258 4–4A
77 Marylebone Ln, W1 7486 3862 2–1A
102 Heath St, NW3 7794 3080 8–1A
These under-the-radar veggie stalwarts may look dull, but they serve some "unusual and tasty" South Indian dishes. / www.woodlandsrestaurant.co.uk; 10 pm; NW3 no L Mon.

Workshop Coffee EC1 **£45** 433
27 Clerkenwell Rd 7253 5754 9–1A
"Yummy, casual and fun", this Oz-style café in Clerkenwell serves "the best coffee, no question", and an "outstanding brunch" too. / EC1M 5RN; www.workshopcoffee.com; @WorkshopCoffee; 10 pm; closed Mon D, Sat D & Sun D.

Wright Brothers **£53** 433
13 Kingly St, W1 7434 3611 3–2D
11 Stoney St, SE1 7403 9554 9–4C
8 Lamb St, E1 7377 8706 9–2D
"Oysters zinging with the taste of the sea" and other "phenomenal" seafood has made a major hit of the "crowded" but "happy" Borough Market original; its more spacious Soho and, now, Spitalfields spin-offs are good too, if not quite so much fun. / 10.30 pm, Sun 9 pm; booking: max 8.

XO NW3 **£47** 222
29 Belsize Ln 7433 0888 8–2A
"Nothing beats sitting in a booth with friends enjoying the wide range of cocktails", say fans of this "solid" Belsize Park local; as a place to eat, though, it can seem "stale" – "resting on its laurels, in the absence of much local competition". / NW3 5AS; www.rickerrestaurants.com; 10.30 pm.

Yalla Yalla **£35** 334
1 Green's Ct, W1 7287 7663 3–2D
12 Winsley St, W1 7637 4748 3–1C
186 Shoreditch High St, E1 0772 584 1372 8–3C
"Zingy bites served in a minuscule café besieged by irritating queues" – the "crowded" original branch of this Lebanese street food chain, in the sleaziest heart of Soho; other branches rarely inspire commentary. / www.yalla-yalla.co.uk; Green's Court 11 pm, Sun 10 pm; Winsley Street 11.30 pm, Sat 11 pm; W1 Sun.

Yard Sale Pizza E5 NEW **£31**
105 Lower Clapton Rd 3602 9090 1–1D
A popular pop-up goes permanent; this Clapton newcomer seeks to make the pizza experience fun – successfully on the basis of an early-days report. / E5 0NP; www.yardsalepizza.com; @yardsalepizza; 11 pm, Sun 10 pm; closed Mon.

Yashin W8 **£84** 532
1a Argyll Rd 7938 1536 5–1A
With its "superb Japanese food" – "reserve a table upstairs (ground floor) to watch the dishes being expertly prepared" – this "top-notch", Manhattan-esque Kensington operation is generally hailed as "worth the cost", considerable as that is… / W8 7DB; www.yashinsushi.com; 10 pm.

Yashin Ocean House SW7 **£82** 113
117-119 Old Brompton Rd 7373 3990 5–2B
"Overpriced, overrated, weird and not wonderful" – you'd never guess that Yashin's South Kensington offshoot would inspire such a drubbing; fans do applaud its "wonderfully inventive" Japanese-fusion

cuisine, but to foes "it's very unusual... but just not very nice!" / SW7 3RN; www.yashinocean.com; @YashinLondon.

Yauatcha W1 **£72** 4 2 3
Broadwick Hs, 15-17 Broadwick St 7494 8888 3–2D
It's "still serving outstanding dim sum", but this "slick" Soho basement operation is starting to slip; sometimes "slow" or "shirty" service doesn't help, and critics are beginning to feel it's "lost its edge foodwise" too. / W1F 0DL; www.yauatcha.com; @yauatcha; 11.15 pm, Sun 10.30 pm.

The Yellow House SE16 **£44** 3 4 2
126 Lower Rd 7231 8777 11–2A
"The best restaurant in Surrey Quays"; this "family-friendly" spot is of particular note for its "delicious" pizzas, and "the fudge cooked to the chef's mother's recipe" is "amazing" too. / SE16 2UE; www.theyellowhouse.eu; @theyellowhousejazz; 10.30 pm, Sun 9.30 pm; closed Mon, Tue–Sat closed L, Sun open L & D.

Yi-Ban E16 **£45** 4 3 2
London Regatta Ctr, Royal Albert Dock 7473 6699 11–1D
"Fantastic dim sum" draw a good following to this obscurely located waterside Chinese, in deepest Docklands – "a pity it's so far away from the rest of London", but a fab destination for (City Airport) plane-spotters! / E16 2QT; www.yi-ban.co.uk; 10.45 pm.

Yipin China N1 **£42** 5 2 1
70-72 Liverpool Rd 7354 3388 8–3D
"The most sublime Chinese food in the most unprepossessing of surroundings" – that's the trade-off at this "brightly lit and functional" Sichuanese two-year-old, in Islington; "you can eat strangely and wonderfully" but beware – "dishes marked 'mild' are very hot by Western standards!" / N1 0QD; www.yipinchina.co.uk; 11 pm.

Yming W1 **£40** 4 5 3
35-36 Greek St 7734 2721 4–2A
A "haven", an "oasis", "the best Chinese in Soho"... Christine Yau's "effortlessly pleasing" corner "stalwart" has been "consistent for years" – "maitre d' William is the host with the most", and "the food always hits the mark". / W1D 5DL; www.yminglondon.com; 11.45 pm; set weekday L & pre-theatre £25 (FP).

Yo Sushi **£28** 1 1 2
Branches throughout London
With its "sad plates of circulating sushi" and "second- or even third-rate" standards, this gimmicky chain gives "a poor and very overpriced representation of Japanese food"; even those who find the whole show "depressing", though, concede that "kids love it!" / www.yosushi.co.uk; 10.30 pm; no booking.

Yoisho W1 **£45** 3 2 2
33 Goodge St 7323 0477 2–1C
"There is nowhere more authentic", say supporters of this izakaya-style Fitzrovia stalwart; it's particularly known for its grills, although one former fan this year thought they'd become "nothing special". / W1T 2PS; 10.30 pm; D only, closed Sun; no Amex.

York & Albany NW1 **£59** 2 2 4
127-129 Parkway 7388 3344 8–3B
Vanishingly few reports of late on Gordon Ramsay's "cool"-looking and "spacious" operation, in a monumental old tavern near Regent's Park; it's for breakfast and business meetings that it mostly seems to shine. / NW1 7PS; www.gordonramsay.com; @yorkandalbany; 10.30 pm, Sun 8 pm.

Yoshino W1 **£44** 3 4 2
3 Piccadilly Pl 7287 6622 3–3D
"Hidden-away down an alley off Piccadilly", a "quality" Japanese operation all the more worth knowing about in such a central location; those who remember the old days, however, are inclined to regret that it's "not as good as it used to be". / W1J 0DB; www.yoshino.net; 10 pm; closed Sun.

Yum Yum N16 **£40** 3 2 4
187 Stoke Newington High St 7254 6751 1–1D
This large and rather "beautiful" Thai has long been one of Stoke Newington's key destinations for a meal plus a cocktail or two; it still attracts largely favourable reports. / N16 0LH; www.yumyum.co.uk; @yumyum; 10.30 pm, Fri & Sat 11.30 pm.

Zafferano SW1 **£76** 3 3 3
15 Lowndes St 7235 5800 5–1D
"A taste of upper-class Italy!"; this "comfortable" and "intimate" Belgravia classic "has had its ups and downs over the years", but continues to be a "perennial favourite" serving some "top-notch" dishes – even some who say "it used to be better" still feel it's "a treat". / SW1X 9EY; www.zafferanorestaurants.com; 11 pm, Sun 10.30 pm.

Zaffrani N1 **£45** 4 4 3
47 Cross St 7226 5522 8–3D
"Definitely not your typical curry house" – this "classy" Islington spot serves cuisine that's "lighter than traditional Indian fare". / N1 2BB; www.zaffrani-islington.co.uk; 10.30 pm.

Zayna W1 **£50** 4 3 2
25 New Quebec St 7723 2229 2–2A
"Excellent" judiciously spiced curries, mixing flavours Indian and Pakistani, win praise for this handy operation, near Marble Arch; the basement dining room is "far less atmospheric". / W1H 7SF; www.zaynarestaurant.co.uk; 11.15 pm, Fri & Sat 11.45 pm; closed weekday L.

Zero Degrees SE3 **£43** 3 2 2
29-31 Montpelier Vale 8852 5619 1–4D
A "great selection of pizzas" and "very good-quality beer" make for "an interesting combination" at this Blackheath microbrewery; its critics feel there has been a slip in general standards of late, though, with the premises feeling "less welcoming" after recent expansion. / SE3 0TJ; www.zerodegrees.co.uk; @Zerodegreesbeer; midnight, Sun 11.30 pm.

Zest
JW3 NW3 NEW **£48** 3 2 2
341-351 Finchley Rd 7433 8955 1–1B
"Rescuing Jewish cuisine from stodgy, Mittel-European associations", this "dramatic", "high-ceilinged" space, on the Finchley Road, offers "interesting", "Ottolenghi-style" salads and fish dishes; "service is pleasant, but needs to sharpen up". / NW3 6ET; Sun-Thu 9.45 pm; closed Fri & Sat.

Ziani's SW3 **£55** 3 3 3
45 Radnor Walk 7351 5297 5–3C
Peak times are "so noisy and cramped", but Chelsea locals still love this "fun" and "friendly" Italian, which dishes up "home-cooking" from its postage stamp-sized kitchen. / SW3 4BP; www.ziani.co.uk; 11 pm, Sun 10 pm.

Zizzi **£47** 2 2 2
Branches throughout London
"Unexceptional" and "unsophisticated" it undoubtedly is, but this "pleasant" kid-friendly pizza-'n'-pasta chain is still generally rated a "useful, if unspectacular, standby". / www.zizzi.co.uk; 11 pm.

Zoilo W1 **£54** 4 4 3
9 Duke St 7486 9699 3–1A
"Easy to miss, but an excellent find"; this small Argentinean yearling, near Selfridges, "bombs your taste buds with hugely flavourful tapas" – "get a seat at the counter downstairs where it's exciting see all the activity in the open kitchen". / W1U 3EG; www.zoilo.co.uk; @Zoilo_London; 10.30 pm; closed Sun.

Zucca SE1 **£55** 5 4 3
184 Bermondsey St 7378 6809 9–4D
"Unpretentious fine dining at its best!"; this "charming" Bermondsey Italian is "such a 'wow'!" – even if the "crowded" and "canteen-like" setting can be "very noisy", the "impassioned" cooking is "outstanding" and "fairly priced" and "there's a real treat of a wine list". / SE1 3TQ; www.zuccalondon.com; @ZuccaSam; 10 pm; closed Mon & Sun D; no Amex.

Zuma SW7 **£82** 5 3 4
5 Raphael St 7584 1010 5–1C
"If you can cope with the fact that all the customers look like Tamara Ecclestone", what's not to like about this "jaw-droppingly" pricey Knightsbridge glamour-magnet? – the Japanese-fusion fare "may not be classic gastronomy, but it's absolutely wonderful". / SW7 1DL; www.zumarestaurant.com; 10.45 pm, Sun 10.15 pm; booking: max 8.

LONDON INDEXES

BREAKFAST
(with opening times)

Central

Al Duca *(9)*
Athenaeum *(7)*
The Attendant *(8 am, Sat 10 am)*
Aubaine: *Heddon St W1 (8, Sat 10); Dover St W1 (8 am); Oxford St W1 (9.30 am Mon-Sat)*
Baker & Spice: *SW1 (7)*
Balans: *W1 (8)*
Balthazar *(7.30 Mon-Fri, 9 Sat & Sun)*
Bar Italia *(6.30)*
Bentley's *(Mon-Fri 7.30)*
The Berners Tavern *(7)*
Bistro 1: *Beak St W1 (Sun 11)*
Black & Blue: *Berners St W1 (9)*
The Botanist *(8, Sat & Sun 9)*
La Bottega: *Eccleston St SW1 (8, Sat 9); Lower Sloane St SW1 (8, Sat 9, Sun 10)*
Boulestin *(7)*
Boulevard *(9)*
Brasserie Max *(7, Sun 8)*
Browns (Albemarle) *(7, Sun 7.30)*
Café Bohème *(8, Sat & Sun 9)*
Café in the Crypt *(Mon-Sat 8)*
Caffé Vergnano: *WC1 (6.30 am, Sun 8.30 am); WC2 (8, Sun 11)*
Cecconi's *(7 am, Sat & Sun 8 am)*
Christopher's *(Sat & Sun 11.30)*
The Cinnamon Club *(Mon-Fri 7.30)*
Colbert *(8)*
Comptoir Libanais: *Wigmore St W1 (8.30); Broadwick St W1 (8 am)*
Cut *(7am, Sat & Sun 7.30 am)*
Daylesford Organic: *SW1 (8, Sun 10); W1 (9)*
Dean Street Townhouse *(Mon-Fri 7, Sat-Sun 8)*
The Delaunay *(7, Sat & Sun 11)*
Diner: *W1 (10, Sat & Sun 9); WC2 (9.30 am)*
Dishoom: *WC2 (8, Sat & Sun 10)*
Dorchester Grill *(7, Sat & Sun 8)*
Ed's Easy Diner: *Sedley Pl, 14 Woodstock St W1 (Sat 9.30 am)*
Fernandez & Wells: *Beak St W1 (7.30, sat& sun 9); Lexington St W1 (7 am); St Anne's Ct W1 (8, sat 10); WC2 (8am, sat-sun 9am)*
Flat White *(8, Sat & Sun 9)*
Fleet River Bakery *(7, Sat 9)*
The Fountain (Fortnum's) *(7.30, Sun 11)*
Franco's *(7, Sat 8)*
La Fromagerie Café *(8, Sat 9, Sun 10)*
Fuzzy's Grub: *SW1 (7)*
Gelupo *(Sat & Sun 12)*
The Goring Hotel *(7, Sun 7.30)*
Grazing Goat *(7.30)*
Hélène Darroze *(Sat 11)*
Holborn Dining Room *(Mon - Fri 7, Sat & Sun 8)*
Homage *(7)*
Hush: *WC1 (8 am)*
Indigo *(6.30)*
Inn the Park *(8, Sat & Sun 9)*
JW Steakhouse *(6.30, Sat & Sun 7)*
Kaffeine *(7.30, Sat 8.30, Sun 9.30)*
Kaspar's Seafood and Grill *(7)*
Kazan (Cafe): *Wilton Rd SW1 (8 am, Sun 9 am)*
Konditor & Cook: *WC1 (9.30); W1 (9.30, Sun 10.30)*
Kopapa *(8.30, Sat & Sun 10)*
Koya-Bar *(Mon-Fri 8.30, Sat & Sun 9:30)*
Ladurée: *W1 (9); SW1 (Mon - Sat 9, Sun noon - 1.30)*
Langan's Brasserie *(7 Mon-Fri)*
Lantana Cafe: *W1 (8, Sat & Sun 9)*
Maison Bertaux *(8.30, Sun 9.15)*
maze Grill *(6.45)*
Monmouth Coffee Company: *WC2 (8)*
The National Dining Rooms *(10)*
National Gallery Café *(8, Sat & Sun 10)*
Natural Kitchen: *Marylebone High St W1 (8, Sat 9, Sun 11)*
Nopi *(8, Sat & Sun 10)*
Nordic Bakery: *Dorset St W1 (8 am, Sat-Sun 9); Golden Sq W1 (Mon-Fri 8, Sat 9, Sun 11)*
The Northall *(6.30, Sat & Sun 7)*
Noura: *William St SW1 (8)*
One-O-One *(7)*
The Only Running Footman *(7.30, Sat & Sun 9.30)*
The Orange *(8)*
Ottolenghi: *SW1 (8, Sun 9)*
Ozer *(8)*
The Pantechnicon *(Sat & Sun 9)*
Paramount *(7)*
The Portrait *(10)*
Princi *(8, Sun 8.30)*
The Providores *(9am)*
Providores (Tapa Room) *(9, Sat & Sun 10)*
Rib Room *(7, Sun 8)*
Riding House Café *(7.30, Sat & Sun 9)*
The Ritz Restaurant *(7, Sun 8)*
Roux at the Landau *(7)*
Royal Academy *(10)*
Scandinavian Kitchen *(8, Sat & Sun 10)*
Simpsons-in-the-Strand *(Mon-Fri 7.30)*
The Sketch (Parlour) *(Mon-Fri 8, Sat 10)*
Sophie's Steakhouse: *all branches (Sat & Sun 11)*
Sotheby's Café *(9.30)*
Spice Market *(7, Sat & Sun 8)*
Stock Pot: *SW1 (9.30)*
Strand Dining Rooms *(7, Sat & Sun 8)*
Tate Britain (Rex Whistler) *(Sat-Sun 10)*
Taylor St Baristas: *W1 (8 am)*
Thirty Six *(7)*
tibits *(9, Sun 11.30)*
Tom's Kitchen: *WC2 (Sat & Sun 10)*
Villandry *(Sat 8 am, Sun 9 am)*
The Wallace *(10)*
Wolfe's *(9)*
The Wolseley *(7, Sat & Sun 8)*
Yalla Yalla: *Green's Ct W1 (Sat-Sun 10)*

West

Adams Café *(7.30 am)*
Angelus *(10)*
Annie's: *W4 (Tue - Thu 10, Fri & Sat 10.30, Sun 10)*
Aubaine: *SW3 (8, Sun 9); W8 (Mon-Sat 8 am, 9 am Sun)*
Baker & Spice: *all west branches (7, Sun 8)*
Balans: *W4, W8 (8)*
Beirut Express: *W2 (7)*
Best Mangal: *SW6 (10-12)*
Bibendum Oyster Bar *(8.30 Mon-Fri, Sat 9)*
La Brasserie *(8)*
Bumpkin: *SW7 (11 am)*
Bush Dining Hall *(Tue-Fri 8.30 am)*
Chelsea Bun Diner *(7, Sun 9)*
Clarke's *(8)*
Comptoir Libanais: *SW7 (8.30 am); W12 (9.30)*
Daylesford Organic: *W11 (8, Sun 11)*
Electric Diner *(8)*
Gallery Mess *(Sat & Sun 10)*
Geales Chelsea Green: *SW3 (9 am Sat & Sun)*
Granger & Co: *W11 (7)*
The Hampshire Hog *(8, Sat& Sun 9)*
The Henry Root *(Sat & Sun 9)*
High Road Brasserie *(7, Sat & Sun 8)*
Joe's Brasserie *(Sat & Sun 11)*
Julie's *(10)*
Kensington Square Kitchen *(8, Sun 9.30)*
Kurobuta *(9)*
Lisboa Pâtisserie *(7)*
Lucky Seven *(Mon noon, Tue-Thu 10, Fri-Sun 9)*
Mona Lisa *(7)*
Ottolenghi: *W11 (8, Sun 8.30)*
Pappa Ciccia: *Fulham High St SW6 (7 am)*
Pavilion *(24 hrs)*
Pellicano *(mon-fri 7-10 sat-sun 8-11)*
Pizza East Portobello: *W10 (8)*
PJ's Bar and Grill *(Sat & Sun 10)*
Ranoush: *W8 (10); W2 (9); SW3 (noon)*
Raoul's Café & Deli: *W11 (8.30); W9 (8.30 am)*
Rivea *(7)*
Sam's Brasserie *(9)*

BRUNCH MENUS

Central

BUSINESS

Central

Murano
Nobu
The Northall
One-O-One
Orrery
Osteria Dell'Angolo
The Pantechnicon
Paramount
Pétrus
Pied à Terre
Quilon
Quirinale
Quo Vadis
Rib Room
Roka: *Charlotte St W1*
Roux at Parliament Square
Roux at the Landau
Rules
Santini
Sartoria
Savoy Grill
Scott's
Seven Park Place
J Sheekey
Simpsons-in-the-Strand
The Square
Tamarind
Theo Randall
Thirty Six
2 Veneti
Veeraswamy
Il Vicolo
The Wallace
Wild Honey
Wiltons
The Wolseley
Zafferano

West

Bibendum
The Frontline Club
Gallery Mess
Gaucho: *all branches*
Gordon Ramsay
The Ledbury
Manicomio: *all branches*
Outlaw's Seafood and Grill
Pavilion
Poissonnerie de l'Avenue
Racine
Sam's Brasserie
La Trompette
Zuma

North

Frederick's
Landmark (Winter Gdn)
Rotunda Bar & Restaurant
St Pancras Grand
York & Albany

South

La Barca
Blueprint Café
Brigade
Butlers Wharf Chop House
Cannizaro House
Gaucho: *all branches*
The Glasshouse
Hutong
Magdalen
Oblix
Oxo Tower (Brass')
Oxo Tower (Rest')
Le Pont de la Tour
Roast
Skylon
Vivat Bacchus: *all branches*
Zucca

East

L'Anima
Barbecoa
Bevis Marks
Bleeding Heart
Boisdale of Canary Wharf
Café du Marché
Chamberlain's
The Chancery
Chinese Cricket Club
Chiswell Street Dining Rms
Cinnamon Kitchen
City Miyama
Club Gascon
Coq d'Argent
The Don
Eyre Brothers
Fish Market
Forman's
The Fox and Anchor
Galvin La Chapelle
Gaucho: *all branches*
Goodman: *all branches*
Hawksmoor: *all east branches*
High Timber
The Hoxton Grill
Lutyens
Manicomio: *all branches*
The Mercer
Moro
New Street Grill
1901
Northbank
One Canada Square
1 Lombard Street
Paternoster Chop House
Plateau
Portal
Roka: *E14*
The Royal Exchange Grand Café
St John
Sauterelle
1701
Smiths (Top Floor)
Smiths (Dining Rm)
Sweetings
Taberna Etrusca
28-50: *EC4*
Vivat Bacchus: *all branches*
The White Swan

BYO

(Bring your own wine at no or low – less than £3 – corkage. Note for £5-£15 per bottle, you can normally negotiate to take your own wine to many, if not most, places.)

Central

Cyprus Mangal
Food for Thought
Golden Hind
India Club
Patogh
Ragam

West

Adams Café
Alounak: *all branches*
Café 209
Chelsea Bun Diner
Faanoos: *all branches*
Fez Mangal
Fitou's Thai Restaurant
Miran Masala
Mirch Masala: *all branches*
Pappa Ciccia: *Munster Rd SW6*

North

Ali Baba
Chutneys
Diwana Bhel-Poori House
Huong-Viet
Jai Krishna
Rugoletta
Toff's
Vijay

South

Apollo Banana Leaf
Cah-Chi: *all branches*
Faanoos: *all branches*
Hot Stuff
Kaosarn: *SW9*
Lahore Karahi
Lahore Kebab House: *all branches*
Mien Tay: *all branches*
Mirch Masala: *all branches*
The Paddyfield
Sree Krishna
Thai Corner Café

East

CHILDREN

(h – high or special chairs
m – children's menu
p – children's portions
e – weekend entertainments
o – other facilities)

Central

East

ENTERTAINMENT
(Check times before you go)

Central

LATE
(open to midnight or later; may be earlier Sunday)

Harbour City *(Fri & Sat midnight)*
Hard Rock Café
Inamo*: SW1 (Fri & Sat 12.30 am)*
Joe Allen *(Fri & Sat 12.45 am)*
Levant *(Fri & Sat midnight)*
Maroush*: W1 (12.30 am)*
MEATLiquor *(Fri & Sat 1 am)*
Carom at Meza *(2 am, Thu-Sat 3 am)*
Mr Kong *(2.45 am, Sun 1.45 am)*
New Mayflower *(4 am)*
ping pong*: Gt Marlborough St W1*
La Porchetta Pizzeria*: WC1 (Sat & Sun midnight)*
Princi
Randall & Aubin *(Sat midnight)*
Rossopomodoro*: WC2*
San Carlo Cicchetti
J Sheekey
J Sheekey Oyster Bar
Shoryu Ramen*: Denman St W1*
Sofra*: all branches*
Sophie's Steakhouse*: all branches (12.45 am, not Sun)*
STK Steakhouse *(Thu-Sat mignight)*
21 Bateman Street *(Sat only)*
VQ*: all branches (24 hours)*
The Wolseley

West

Anarkali
Balans*: W8*
Basilico*: SW6*
Beirut Express*: SW7 ; W2 (2 am)*
Best Mangal*: SW6 ; North End Rd W14 (midnight, Sat 1 am)*
Buona Sera*: all branches*
Gifto's *(Sat & Sun midnight)*
Halepi
Khan's *(Sat & Sun midnight)*
Maroush*: I) 21 Edgware Rd W2 (1.45 am); VI) 68 Edgware Rd W2 (12.30 am); SW3 (3.30 am)*
Mirch Masala*: all branches*
Il Pagliaccio
ping pong*: W2*
Pizza East Portobello*: W10 (Fri & Sat midnight)*
Ranoush*: SW3 ; W8 (1.30 am); W2 (2.30 am)*
Rossopomodoro*: SW10*
The Sands End *(Thu-Sat midnight)*
Shilpa *(Thu-Sat midnight)*
Sophie's Steakhouse*: all branches (12.45 am, not Sun)*
VQ*: all branches (24 hours)*

North

Ali Baba
Banners *(Fri & Sat midnight)*
Basilico*: N1, NW3*
Bistro Aix
Chilango*: N1 (Fri & Sat midnight)*
Dirty Burger*: NW5 (Mon-Thu midnight, Fri & Sat 1 am)*
Gallipoli*: all branches (Fri & Sat midnight)*
Gem *(Fri & Sat midnight)*
Mangal II *(1 am)*
Meat Mission
Le Mercury *(12.30 am, not Sun)*
Pizzeria Pappagone
La Porchetta Pizzeria*: NW1 (Fri & Sat midnight); N4 (Sat & Sun midnight); N1 (weekends midnight)*
The Salt House *(Fri & Sat midnight)*
Vivo *(Fri & Sat 1 am)*
Yum Yum *(Fri & Sat midnight)*

South

Basilico*: SW11*
Boqueria *(Fri & Sat midnight)*
Buona Sera*: all branches*
Caffé Vergnano*: SE1*
Cah-Chi*: SW18 (not Sat & Sun)*
Champor-Champor
Dirty Burger*: SW8 (Fri & Sat 2 am)*
Everest Inn
Fish in a Tie
Gastro
Indian Moment *(Fri & Sat midnight)*
Lahore Karahi
Lahore Kebab House*: all branches*
Mirch Masala*: all branches*
Nazmins
Tandoori Nights *(Fri & Sat midnight)*
Tsunami*: SW4 (Fri-Sun midnight)*
Zero Degrees

East

Bird *(Thu-Sat 12.30 am)*
Brick Lane Beigel Bake *(24 hours)*
Cellar Gascon
The Diner*: EC2 (not Sun & Mon)*
Elephant Royale *(Fri & Sat midnight)*
Hoi Polloi *(Thu-Sat 1 am)*
The Jugged Hare *(Thu-Sat midnight)*
Lahore Kebab House*: all branches*
Mangal 1 *(midnight, Sat-Sun 1 am)*
Mirch Masala*: all branches*
Pizza East*: E1 (Thu midnight, Fri & Sat 1 am)*
La Porchetta Pizzeria*: EC1 (Sat & Sun midnight)*
Rocket*: E14*
Sushisamba *(midnight, Fri & Sat 1 am)*
Sushi Tetsu
Verden

OUTSIDE TABLES
(* particularly recommended)

Central

A Wong
Al Duca
Al Hamra
Al Sultan
Andrew Edmunds
Antidote
aqua nueva
L'Artiste Musclé
Atari-Ya*: W1*
The Attendant
Aubaine*: Heddon St W1, Dover St W1*
Aurora
L'Autre Pied
Baker & Spice*: SW1*
Bam-Bou
Bank Westminster
Bar Italia
Il Baretto
Barrafina*: W1*
Barrica
Beiteddine
Benito's Hat*: Goodge St W1*
Bentley's
Bistro 1*: Frith St W1, WC2*
Bonnie Gull
The Botanist
La Bottega*: Lower Sloane St SW1, Eccleston St SW1*
Boudin Blanc
Brasserie Max
Café Bohème
Café des Amis
Cantina Laredo
Le Caprice
Caraffini
Cecconi's
Ceviche
Chisou*: W1*
Ciao Bella
Cigala
Colbert
Comptoir Libanais*: Wigmore St W1*
Da Mario
Daylesford Organic*: SW1*
Dean Street Townhouse
Dehesa
Delfino
dim T*: W1*
Diner*: W1*
Dishoom*: WC2*
Donostia
Ducksoup
Ed's Easy Diner*: Moor St W1*
Fairuz
Flat White
Fleet River Bakery
Franco's
Galvin Bistrot de Luxe
Le Garrick
Gelupo
Golden Hind
Goodman*: W1*
Gordon's Wine Bar*
Goya
Grazing Goat
Great Queen Street

Grumbles
Hard Rock Café
Hardy's Brasserie
Hush*:W1*
Inn the Park
Ishtar
JW Steakhouse
Kaffeine
Kazan*: all branches*
The Keeper's House
Kopapa
Ladurée*: SW1, W1*
The Lady Ottoline
Lantana Cafe*:W1*
The Lockhart
Maison Bertaux
Marani
Mildreds
Mishkin's
Momo
Mon Plaisir
Motcombs
Nizuni
The Norfolk Arms
Noura*: Hobart Pl SW1*
Olivocarne
Olivomare
Opera Tavern
The Orange
Orrery
Ozer
The Pantechnicon
Pescatori*: Charlotte St W1*
Piccolino*:W1**
El Pirata
Pizza Pilgrims*: Dean St W1*
La Porchetta Pizzeria*:WC1*
La Poule au Pot
Prix Fixe
The Providores
Providores (Tapa Room)
The Queens Arms
Quo Vadis
Le Relais de Venise L'Entrecôte*:W1*
Reubens
Roka*: Charlotte St W1*
Royal Academy
Salaam Namaste
Salt Yard
Santini
Sardo
Savoir Faire
Scandinavian Kitchen
Scott's
Shampers
J Sheekey
J Sheekey Oyster Bar
Sofra*: Shepherd St W1, WC2*
Soho Diner
Tapas Brindisa Soho*:W1*
Taro*: Brewer St W1*
Tate Britain (Rex Whistler)
The 10 Cases
The Thomas Cubitt
tibits
Tinello
Tom's Kitchen*:WC2*
Toto's
Trishna
Tsunami*:W1*
Vapiano*:W1*
Villandry
Vinoteca Seymour Place*: Seymour Pl W1*
The Wallace
Wolfe's
Yalla Yalla*: Green's Ct W1*

West

The Abingdon
The Admiral Codrington
Al-Waha
Anarkali
Angelus
The Anglesea Arms
The Anglesea Arms
Annie's*: all branches*
The Atlas*
Aubaine*: SW3*
Babylon
Baker & Spice*: SW3*
Balans*:W12, W4*
Beach Blanket Babylon*:W11*
Beirut Express*: SW7*
Belvedere
Best Mangal*: SW6, North End Rd W14*
Bibendum Oyster Bar
Big Easy*: SW3*
Bird in Hand
Black & Blue*:W8*
Bluebird
Bombay Palace
La Bouchée
La Brasserie
Brinkley's
Bumpkin*: SW3, SW7*
Cambio de Tercio
Canta Napoli*:W4*
Capote Y Toros
The Carpenter's Arms*
Casa Brindisa
Casa Malevo
Charlotte's Place
Chelsea Bun Diner
Cibo
Le Colombier
The Cow
Cumberland Arms
The Dartmouth Castle
Daylesford Organic*:W11*
La Delizia Limbara
Duke of Sussex
Durbar
E&O
Edera
Eelbrook*
Electric Diner
The Enterprise
Essenza
La Famiglia*
Fat Boy's*: all west branches*
Fire & Stone*:W12*
First Floor
Foxtrot Oscar
Gallery Mess
The Gate*:W6*
Geales*:W8*
Haché*: SW10*
The Hampshire Hog*
The Havelock Tavern
The Henry Root
Hereford Road
Hole in the Wall*
Indian Zing
Joe's Brasserie
Julie's
Karma
Kateh
Kensington Square Kitchen
The Kensington Wine Rooms
Khan's
Kurobuta
The Ladbroke Arms
Made in Italy*: SW3*
The Mall Tavern
The Malt House
Manicomio*: all branches*
Maxela
Mazi
Mediterraneo
Medlar
Mona Lisa
Noor Jahan*:W2*
The Oak W12*: all branches*
Polish Club
Osteria Basilico
Il Pagliaccio
Pappa Ciccia*: Fulham High St SW6*
Paradise by Way of Kensal Green
Pellicano
Pentolina
The Phene
Poissonnerie de l'Avenue
Il Portico
Princess Victoria
Queen's Head*
Raoul's Café & Deli*:W11*;W9*
The Real Greek*:W12*
The Red Pepper
Riccardo's
The River Café
Rocca Di Papa*: SW7*
Royal China*: SW6*
Saigon Saigon
The Sands End
Santa Lucia
Santa Maria
The Shed
The Summerhouse*
The Swan*
Tartufo

North

South

East

PRIVATE ROOMS

*** particularly recommended**

Central

West

North

South

ROMANTIC

ROOMS WITH A VIEW

NOTABLE WINE LISTS

Gordon's Wine Bar
Green Man & French Horn
The Greenhouse
Hardy's Brasserie
Hibiscus
The Ivy
Kai Mayfair
Latium
Locanda Locatelli
Marcus
Olivo
Olivomare
Opera Tavern
Orrery
Otto's
Pétrus
Pied à Terre
The Providores
Providores (Tapa Room)
Quo Vadis
The Ritz Restaurant
Salt Yard
Sardo
Sartoria
Savoy Grill
Shampers
Sotheby's Café
The Square
Tate Britain (Rex Whistler)
The 10 Cases
10 Greek Street
Terroirs
Texture
28-50: *all branches*
The Union Café
Vinoteca Seymour Place: *all branches*
Wild Honey
Zafferano

West
Albertine
Angelus
Bibendum
Brinkley's
Cambio de Tercio
Clarke's
Le Colombier
L'Etranger
The Frontline Club
Garnier
Gordon Ramsay
Joe's Brasserie
The Kensington Wine Rooms
The Ledbury
Locanda Ottomezzo
The Mall Tavern
Margaux
Medlar
Popeseye: *all branches*
Princess Victoria
Racine
The River Café
Tendido Cuatro
La Trompette
Vinoteca: *all branches*
White Horse

North
La Collina
Prawn On The Lawn
Sweet Thursday
Trullo

South
Brula
Cantina Vinopolis
Chez Bruce
Emile's
Enoteca Turi
40 Maltby Street
Fulham Wine Rooms
The Glasshouse
José
Magdalen
Meson don Felipe
Pizarro
Le Pont de la Tour
Popeseye: *all branches*
Riva
RSJ
Soif
Tentazioni
Toasted
Vivat Bacchus: *all branches*
Zucca

East
Bleeding Heart
Brawn
Cellar Gascon
Club Gascon
Comptoir Gascon
Coq d'Argent
The Don
Eyre Brothers
High Timber
The Jugged Hare
Moro
Portal
The Quality Chop House
Sager & WIlde
St John Bread & Wine
The Sign of the Don
Smiths (Top Floor)
28-50: *all branches*
Typing Room
Vinoteca: *all branches*
Vivat Bacchus: *all branches*
The Wine Library

Palomar
Rivea
The New Angel
Typing Room

LONDON CUISINES

An asterisk (*) after an entry indicates exceptional or very good cooking

AMERICAN

Central
The Avenue *(SW1)*
Big Easy *(WC2)*
Bodean's *(W1)*
Bubbledogs *(W1)*
Christopher's *(WC2)*
Hard Rock Café *(W1)*
Hubbard & Bell *(WC1)*
Jackson & Rye *(W1)*
Jamie's Diner *(W1)*
Joe Allen *(WC2)*
The Lockhart *(W1)*
Mishkin's *(WC2)*
Pitt Cue Co *(W1)**
Soho Diner *(W1)*
Spuntino *(W1)*
The Chiltern Firehouse *(W1)*

West
Big Easy *(SW3)*
Bodean's *(SW6)*
Dirty Bones *(W8)*
Electric Diner *(W11)*
Lucky Seven *(W2)*
Sticky Fingers *(W8)*

North
Chicken Shop *(NW5)*
Karpo *(NW1)*
Pond *(N16)*
Q Grill *(NW1)*
Red Dog Saloon *(N1)*
Shrimpy's *(N1)*

South
Bodean's *(SW4)*
Chicken Shop *(SW17)*
Oblix *(SE1)*
Red Dog South *(SW4)*
Wishbone *(SW9)*

East
Bodean's *(EC3)*
Chicken Shop & Dirty Burger *(E1)*
The Hoxton Grill *(EC2)*

AUSTRALIAN

Central
Lantana Cafe *(W1)*

West
Granger & Co *(W11)*

East
Granger & Co *(EC1)*
Lantana Cafe *(EC1)*

BELGIAN

Central
Belgo *(WC2)*

North
Belgo Noord *(NW1)*

BRITISH, MODERN

Central
Alyn Williams *(W1)**
Andrew Edmunds *(W1)*
The Angel & Crown *(WC2)*
The Ape & Bird *(WC2)*
Arbutus *(W1)**
Athenaeum *(W1)*
Aurora *(W1)*
Axis *(WC2)*
Balthazar *(WC2)*
Bank Westminster *(SW1)*
Barnyard *(W1)*
Bellamy's *(W1)*
The Berners Tavern *(W1)*
The Blind Pig *(W1)**
Bob Bob Ricard *(W1)*
The Botanist *(SW1)*
Brasserie Max *(WC2)*
Le Caprice *(SW1)*
Coopers Restaurant & Bar *(WC2)*
Criterion *(W1)*
Daylesford Organic *(SW1,W1)*
Dean Street Townhouse *(W1)*
Le Deuxième *(WC2)*
Dorchester Grill *(W1)*
Ducksoup *(W1)*
Ebury Rest' & Wine Bar *(SW1)*
Fera at Claridge's *(W1)**
The Fifth Floor Restaurant *(SW1)*
Gordon's Wine Bar *(WC2)*
The Goring Hotel *(SW1)*
Grazing Goat *(W1)*
Ham Yard Restaurant *(W1)*
Hardy's Brasserie *(W1)*
Heddon Street Kitchen *(W1)*
Hix *(W1)*
Homage *(WC2)*
Hush *(W1,WC1)*
Indigo *(WC2)*
Inn the Park *(SW1)*
The Ivy *(WC2)*
Kettners *(W1)*
Langan's Brasserie *(W1)*
Little Social *(W1)*
Natural Kitchen *(W1)*
Newman Street Tavern *(W1)*
The Norfolk Arms *(WC1)**
The Northall *(SW1)*
The Only Running Footman *(W1)*
The Orange *(SW1)*
Ozer *(WC2)*
The Pantechnicon *(SW1)*
Paramount *(WC1)*
Picture *(W1)*
Pollen Street Social *(W1)**
The Portrait *(WC2)*
Quaglino's *(SW1)*
The Queens Arms *(SW1)**
Quo Vadis *(W1)*
Randall & Aubin *(W1)**
Roux at Parliament Square *(SW1)*
Roux at the Landau *(W1)*
Seven Park Place *(SW1)*
Seven Stars *(WC2)*
1707 *(W1)*
Shampers *(W1)*
64 Degrees *(SW1)*
Social Eating House *(W1)**
Sotheby's Café *(W1)*
Spring *(WC2)*
Tate Britain (Rex Whistler) *(SW1)*
10 Greek Street *(W1)**
Thirty Six *(SW1)*
The Thomas Cubitt *(SW1)*
Tom's Kitchen *(WC2)*
Tredwell's *(WC2)*
The Union Café *(W1)*
Villandry *(W1)*
The Vincent Rooms *(SW1)*
Vinoteca *(W1)*
VQ *(WC1)*
Whyte & Brown *(W1)*
Wild Honey *(W1)*
The Wolseley *(W1)*

West
The Abingdon *(W8)*
The Anglesea Arms *(W6)**
The Anglesea Arms *(SW7)*
Babylon *(W8)*
Beach Blanket Babylon *(W11)*
Belvedere *(W8)*
Bluebird *(SW3)*
The Brackenbury *(W6)**
Brinkley's *(SW10)*
The Builders Arms *(SW3)*
Bush Dining Hall *(W12)*
The Cadogan Arms *(SW3)*
The Carpenter's Arms *(W6)*
City Barge *(W4)**
Clarke's *(W8)*
The Cow *(W2)*
The Dartmouth Castle *(W6)*
Daylesford Organic *(W11)*
The Dock Kitchen *(W10)*
Duke of Sussex *(W4)*
The Enterprise *(SW3)*
First Floor *(W11)*
The Five Fields *(SW3)**
The Frontline Club *(W2)*
Harwood Arms *(SW6)**
The Havelock Tavern *(W14)*
Hedone *(W4)**
The Henry Root *(SW10)*
High Road Brasserie *(W4)*
Hole in the Wall *(W4)*
Joe's Brasserie *(SW6)*
Julie's *(W11)*
Kensington Place *(W8)**
Kensington Square Kitchen *(W8)*

Kitchen W8 *(W8)**
The Ladbroke Arms *(W11)*
Launceston Place *(W8)*
The Ledbury *(W11)**
The Magazine Restaurant *(W2)*
The Mall Tavern *(W8)*
Marianne *(W2)**
Medlar *(SW10)**
New Tom's *(W11)*
Paradise by Way of Kensal Green *(W10)*
Pavilion *(W8)*
The Phene *(SW3)*
Princess Victoria *(W12)*
Queen's Head *(W6)*
Rabbit *(SW3)*
Sam's Brasserie *(W4)*
The Sands End *(SW6)**
The Shed *(W8)*
The Terrace *(W8)*
Tom's Kitchen *(SW3)*
Truscott Arms *(W9)*
VQ *(SW10)*
Vinoteca *(W4)*
The Waterway *(W9)*
White Horse *(SW6)*
Whits *(W8)*

North

The Albion *(N1)*
Bald Faced Stag *(N2)*
Bradley's *(NW3)*
The Bull *(N6)*
Caravan King's Cross *(N1)*
The Clissold Arms *(N2)*
The Drapers Arms *(N1)*
The Duke of Cambridge *(N1)*
The Engineer *(NW1)*
The Fellow *(N1)*
Frederick's *(N1)*
Grain Store *(N1)*
The Haven *(N20)*
The Horseshoe *(NW3)*
The Junction Tavern *(NW5)*
Juniper Dining *(N5)*
Landmark (Winter Gdn) *(NW1)*
LeCoq *(N1)**
Made In Camden *(NW1)*
Mango Room *(NW1)*
Market *(NW1)**
The North London Tavern *(NW6)*
Odette's *(NW1)*
The Old Bull & Bush *(NW3)*
Parlour *(NW10)**
Pig & Butcher *(N1)**
Plum + Spilt Milk *(N1)*
Rising Sun *(NW7)*
Rotunda Bar & Restaurant *(N1)*
St Pancras Grand *(NW1)*
Season Kitchen *(N4)**
T.E.D *(N1)*
The Wells *(NW3)*
The Wet Fish Cafe *(NW6)*
White Rabbit *(N16)**

South

Abbeville Kitchen *(SW4)*
Albion *(SE1)*
Aqua Shard *(SE1)*
The Bingham *(TW10)*
Bistro Union *(SW4)*
Blueprint Café *(SE1)*
The Bolingbroke *(SW11)*
The Brown Dog *(SW13)*
Brunswick House Cafe *(SW8)*
The Camberwell Arms *(SE5)**
Cannizaro House *(SW19)*
Cantina Vinopolis *(SE1)*
Chapters *(SE3)*
Chez Bruce *(SW17)**
Claude's Kitchen *(SW6)**
The Crooked Well *(SE5)*
The Dairy *(SW4)**
The Dartmouth Arms *(SE23)*
The Depot *(SW14)*
Earl Spencer *(SW18)*
Edwins *(SE1)*
Elliot's Cafe *(SE1)**
Emile's *(SW15)**
Entrée *(SW11)**
40 Maltby Street *(SE1)**
Franklins *(SE22)*
Garrison *(SE1)*
The Glasshouse *(TW9)**
Inside *(SE10)**
Lamberts *(SW12)**
The Lido Cafe *(SE24)*
Linnea *(TW9)**
Magdalen *(SE1)**
Menier Chocolate Factory *(SE1)*
The Old Brewery *(SE10)*
Olympic Café *(SW13)*
Oxo Tower (Rest') *(SE1)*
The Palmerston *(SE22)*
Peckham Refreshment Rms *(SE15)*
Petersham Hotel *(TW10)*
Petersham Nurseries *(TW10)*
Le Pont de la Tour *(SE1)*
Rivington Grill *(SE10)*
RSJ *(SE1)*
Sea Containers *(SE1)*
Skylon *(SE1)*
Skylon Grill *(SE1)*
Sonny's Kitchen *(SW13)*
Source *(SW11)*
Story *(SE1)**
The Swan at the Globe *(SE1)*
The Table *(SE1)*
Tate Modern (Level 7) *(SE1)*
The Dysart Petersham *(TW10)**
Trinity *(SW4)**
Union Street Café *(SE1)*
The Victoria *(SW14)*
Waterloo Bar & Kitchen *(SE1)*
The Wharf *(TW11)*

East

The Anthologist *(EC2)*
Balans *(E20)*
Beach Blanket Babylon *(E1)*
Bevis Marks *(E1)*
Bird *(E2)**
Bird of Smithfield *(EC1)*
Bistrotheque *(E2)*
Blackfoot *(EC1)*
The Boundary *(E2)*
Bread Street Kitchen *(EC4)*
Caravan *(EC1)*
The Chancery *(EC4)*
Chiswell Street Dining Rms *(EC1)*
City Social *(EC2)**
The Clove Club *(EC1)**
The Don *(EC4)*
Duck & Waffle *(EC2)*
Eat 17 *(E17)*
The Empress *(E9)*
Foxlow *(EC1)*
Gin Joint *(EC2)*
The Gun *(E14)*
High Timber *(EC4)*
Hilliard *(EC4)**
Hixter *(EC2)*
Hoi Polloi *(E1)*
The Jugged Hare *(EC1)*
Lyle's *(E1)**
The Mercer *(EC2)*
Merchants Tavern *(EC2)**
The Modern Pantry *(EC1)*
The Morgan Arms *(E3)**
The Narrow *(E14)*
1901 *(EC2)*
Northbank *(EC4)*
Notes *(EC2)*
One Canada Square *(E14)*
1 Lombard Street *(EC3)*
The Peasant *(EC1)*
Princess of Shoreditch *(EC2)*
Raw Duck *(E8)*
Rivington Grill *(EC2)*
Rochelle Canteen *(E2)**
Sager & Wilde *(E2)*
The Sign of the Don *(EC4)*
Smiths Brasserie *(E1)*
Smiths (Ground Floor) *(EC1)*
Street Kitchen *(EC2)*
3 South Place *(EC2)*
Tom's Kitchen *(E1, E14)*
Vinoteca *(EC1)*
The White Swan *(EC4)**

BRITISH, TRADITIONAL

Central

Boisdale *(SW1)*
Browns (Albemarle) *(W1)*
Corrigan's Mayfair *(W1)*
Dinner *(SW1)*
The Fountain (Fortnum's) *(W1)*
Fuzzy's Grub *(SW1)*
Great Queen Street *(WC2)*
Green's *(SW1)*

The Guinea Grill *(W1)*
Hardy's Brasserie *(W1)*
Holborn Dining Room *(WC1)*
The Keeper's House *(W1)*
The Lady Ottoline *(WC1)*
The National Dining Rooms *(WC2)*
Rib Room *(SW1)*
Rules *(WC2)*
Savoy Grill *(WC2)*
Scott's *(W1)**
Simpsons-in-the-Strand *(WC2)*
Strand Dining Rooms *(WC2)*
Wiltons *(SW1)*
The Windmill *(W1)*

West
The Brown Cow *(SW6)**
Bumpkin *(SW3, SW7, W11)*
Ffiona's *(W8)*
The Hampshire Hog *(W6)*
Hereford Road *(W2)*
Maggie Jones's *(W8)*
The Malt House *(SW6)**
The Surprise *(SW3)*

North
Bull & Last *(NW5)**
Gilbert Scott *(NW1)*
Kentish Canteen *(NW5)*
St Johns *(N19)*

South
The Anchor & Hope *(SE1)**
Butlers Wharf Chop House *(SE1)*
Canteen *(SE1)*
Canton Arms *(SW8)*
Fox & Grapes *(SW19)*
The Lord Northbrook *(SE12)*
Roast *(SE1)*

East
Albion *(E2)*
Bumpkin *(E20)*
Canteen *(E1, E14)*
The Fox and Anchor *(EC1)*
Fuzzy's Grub *(EC4)*
George & Vulture *(EC3)*
Hix Oyster & Chop House *(EC1)*
Paternoster Chop House *(EC4)*
E Pellicci *(E2)*
The Quality Chop House *(EC1)**
St John *(EC1)**
St John Bread & Wine *(E1)**
Simpson's Tavern *(EC3)*
Sweetings *(EC4)*

EAST & CENT. EUROPEAN
Central
The Delaunay *(WC2)*
Gay Hussar *(W1)*
The Wolseley *(W1)*

North
Kipferl *(N1)*

FISH & SEAFOOD
Central
Belgo Centraal *(WC2)*
Bellamy's *(W1)*
Bentley's *(W1)*
Bonnie Gull *(W1)**
Bubba Gump Shrimp Company *(W1)*
Burger & Lobster *(W1)*
Fishworks *(W1)*
Green's *(SW1)*
Kaspar's Seafood and Grill *(WC2)*
Loch Fyne *(WC2)*
Olivomare *(SW1)**
One-O-One *(SW1)**
The Pantechnicon *(SW1)*
Pescatori *(W1)*
Quaglino's *(SW1)*
Randall & Aubin *(W1)**
Rib Room *(SW1)*
Royal China Club *(W1)**
Scott's *(W1)**
J Sheekey *(WC2)**
J Sheekey Oyster Bar *(WC2)**
Wiltons *(SW1)*
Wright Brothers *(W1)**

West
Bibendum Oyster Bar *(SW3)*
Big Easy *(SW3)*
Le Café Anglais *(W2)*
Chez Patrick *(W8)*
The Cow *(W2)*
Geales *(W8)*
Kensington Place *(W8)**
Mandarin Kitchen *(W2)**
Outlaw's Seafood and Grill *(SW3)**
Poissonnerie de l'Avenue *(SW3)**
The Summerhouse *(W9)*

North
Belgo Noord *(NW1)*
Bradley's *(NW3)*
Carob Tree *(NW5)**
Olympus Fish *(N3)**
Prawn On The Lawn *(N1)**
Simply Fish *(NW1)*
Toff's *(N10)**

South
Applebee's Cafe *(SE1)*
Cornish Tiger *(SW11)**
fish! *(SE1)*
Gastro *(SW4)*
The Lobster House *(SW18)*
Lobster Pot *(SE11)**
Le Querce *(SE23)**
Wright Brothers *(SE1)**

East
Angler *(EC2)*
Bonnie Gull Seafood Cafe *(EC1)**
Burger & Lobster *(EC1)*
Chamberlain's *(EC3)*
Fish Central *(EC1)*
Fish Market *(EC2)*
Forman's *(E3)**
The Grapes *(E14)*
Hix Oyster & Chop House *(EC1)*
Loch Fyne *(EC3)*
Orpheus *(EC3)**
The Royal Exchange Grand Café *(EC3)*
Sweetings *(EC4)*
Wright Brothers *(E1)**

FRENCH
Central
Alain Ducasse *(W1)*
Antidote *(W1)**
L'Artiste Musclé *(W1)*
L'Atelier de Joel Robuchon *(WC2)*
Aubaine *(W1)*
L'Autre Pied *(W1)**
The Balcon *(SW1)*
Bar Boulud *(SW1)*
Bellamy's *(W1)*
Blanchette *(W1)*
Boudin Blanc *(W1)*
Boulestin *(SW1)*
Boulevard *(WC2)*
Brasserie Chavot *(W1)*
Brasserie Zédel *(W1)*
Café Bohème *(W1)*
Café des Amis *(WC2)*
Chabrot Bistrot d'Amis *(SW1)*
Le Cigalon *(WC2)*
Clos Maggiore *(WC2)**
Colbert *(SW1)*
Compagnie des Vins S. *(WC2)**
Les Deux Salons *(WC2)*
Elena's L'Etoile *(W1)*
L'Escargot *(W1)*
Galvin at Windows *(W1)*
Galvin Bistrot de Luxe *(W1)*
Le Garrick *(WC2)*
Gauthier Soho *(W1)**
Le Gavroche *(W1)**
Green Man & French Horn *(WC2)*
The Greenhouse *(W1)**
Hélène Darroze *(W1)*
Hibiscus *(W1)*
Koffmann's *(SW1)**
Marcus *(SW1)*
maze *(W1)*
Mon Plaisir *(WC2)*
Orrery *(W1)*
Otto's *(WC1)**
La Petite Maison *(W1)**
Pétrus *(SW1)**
Pied à Terre *(W1)**
La Poule au Pot *(SW1)*
Prix Fixe *(W1)*
Randall & Aubin *(W1)**
Le Relais de Venise L'Entrecôte *(W1)*
The Ritz Restaurant *(W1)*
Savoir Faire *(WC1)*

Savoy Grill *(WC2)*
Sketch (Lecture Rm) *(W1)*
Sketch (Gallery) *(W1)*
The Square *(W1)**
Terroirs *(WC2)*
28-50 *(W1)*
Villandry *(W1)*
The Wallace *(W1)*

West
Albertine *(W12)*
Angelus *(W2)*
Aubaine *(SW3,W8)*
Belvedere *(W8)*
Bibendum *(SW3)*
La Bouchée *(SW7)*
La Brasserie *(SW3)*
Le Café Anglais *(W2)*
Charlotte's Bistro *(W4)*
Charlotte's Place *(W5)*
Cheyne Walk Brasserie *(SW3)*
Chez Patrick *(W8)*
Le Colombier *(SW3)*
L'Etranger *(SW7)*
Garnier *(SW5)*
Gordon Ramsay *(SW3)*
Les Gourmets Des Ternes *(W9)*
The Pig's Ear *(SW3)*
Poissonnerie de l'Avenue *(SW3)**
Quantus *(W4)*
Racine *(SW3)*
La Trompette *(W4)**
Le Vacherin *(W4)*
Whits *(W8)*

North
L'Absinthe *(NW1)*
The Almeida *(N1)*
Les Associés *(N8)*
L'Aventure *(NW8)**
Bistro Aix *(N8)**
Blue Legume *(N1, N16, N8)*
Bradley's *(NW3)*
La Cage Imaginaire *(NW3)*
Le Coq *(N1)*
Le Mercury *(N1)*
Michael Nadra *(NW1)**
Mill Lane Bistro *(NW6)*
Oslo Court *(NW8)**
Le Sacré-Coeur *(N1)*
The Wells *(NW3)*

South
Augustine Kitchen *(SW11)**
Bellevue Rendez-Vous *(SW17)*
Brasserie Toulouse-Lautrec *(SE11)*
Brula *(TW1)**
La Buvette *(TW9)*
Casse-Croute *(SE1)**
Gastro *(SW4)*
Gazette *(SW11, SW12, SW15)*
The Lawn Bistro *(SW19)*
Lobster Pot *(SE11)**
Ma Cuisine *(TW9)*
Le P'tit Normand *(SW18)*
Soif *(SW11)**
Toasted *(SE22)*
Upstairs *(SW2)**

East
Bistrot Bruno Loubet *(EC1)*
Bleeding Heart *(EC1)*
Brawn *(E2)**
Café du Marché *(EC1)*
Café Pistou *(EC1)*
Cellar Gascon *(EC1)*
Chabrot Bistrot des Halles *(EC1)*
Club Gascon *(EC1)**
Comptoir Gascon *(EC1)*
Coq d'Argent *(EC2)*
The Don *(EC4)*
Galvin La Chapelle *(E1)**
Lutyens *(EC4)*
Plateau *(E14)*
Provender *(E11)**
Relais de Venise L'Entrecôte *(E14, EC2)*
The Royal Exchange Grand Café *(EC3)*
Sauterelle *(EC3)*
Les Trois Garçons *(E1)*
28-50 *(EC4)*

FUSION
Central
Bubbledogs Kitchen Table *(W1)**
Kopapa *(WC2)*
Providores (Tapa Room) *(W1)*
Uni *(SW1)**

West
E&O *(W11)*
Eight Over Eight *(SW3)*
L'Etranger *(SW7)*

North
XO *(NW3)*

South
Champor-Champor *(SE1)*
Tsunami *(SW4)**
Village East *(SE1)*

East
Caravan *(EC1)*
Penkul & Banks *(EC2)**

GAME
Central
Boisdale *(SW1)*
Rules *(WC2)*
Wiltons *(SW1)*

West
Harwood Arms *(SW6)**

North
San Daniele del Friuli *(N5)*

GREEK
Central
Ergon *(W1)**
Real Greek *(W1,WC2)*
21 Bateman Street *(W1)*

West
Halepi *(W2)*
Mazi *(W8)*
The Real Greek *(W12)*

North
Carob Tree *(NW5)**
Lemonia *(NW1)*
Vrisaki *(N22)*

South
Real Greek *(SE1)*

East
Kolossi Grill *(EC1)*
Real Greek *(E1)*

HUNGARIAN
Central
Gay Hussar *(W1)*

INTERNATIONAL
Central
Balans *(W1)*
Boulevard *(WC2)*
Café in the Crypt *(WC2)*
Canvas *(SW1)*
Colony Grill Room *(W1)*
Cork & Bottle *(WC2)*
Ember Yard *(W1)*
Fischer's *(W1)*
Gordon's Wine Bar *(WC2)*
Grumbles *(SW1)*
Carom at Meza *(W1)**
Motcombs *(SW1)*
National Gallery Café *(WC2)*
The Providores *(W1)**
Rextail *(W1)*
Rocket *(WC2)*
Sarastro *(WC2)*
Stock Pot *(SW1,W1)*
The 10 Cases *(WC2)*
Terroirs *(WC2)*

West
The Andover Arms *(W6)*
Annie's *(W4)*
Balans *(W12,W4,W8)*
Chelsea Bun Diner *(SW10)*
Eelbrook *(SW6)*
Foxtrot Oscar *(SW3)*
Gallery Mess *(SW3)*
The Kensington Wine Rooms *(W8)*
Margaux *(SW5)*
Michael Nadra *(W4)**
Mona Lisa *(SW10)*
The New Angel *(W2)**
One Kensington *(W8)*

Rivea *(SW7)*
Stock Pot *(SW3)*
Troubadour *(SW5)*
The Windsor Castle *(W8)*

North
Banners *(N8)*
8 Hoxton Square *(N1)*
The Haven *(N20)*
The Old Bull & Bush *(NW3)*
The Orange Tree *(N20)*
Primeur *(N5)*

South
Annie's *(SW13)*
Brigade *(SE1)*
Hudsons *(SW15)*
Joanna's *(SE19)*
The Light House *(SW19)*
London House *(SW11)**
Rabot 1745 *(SE1)*
The Rooftop Cafe *(SE1)*
The Ship *(SW18)*
Telegraph *(SW15)*
The Clink *(SW2)*
Ting *(SE1)*
Vivat Bacchus *(SE1)*
The Wharf *(TW11)*
The Yellow House *(SE16)*

East
LMNT *(E8)*
Les Trois Garçons *(E1)*
Typing Room *(E2)**
Verden *(E5)*
Vivat Bacchus *(EC4)*
The Wine Library *(EC3)*

IRISH
East
Lutyens *(EC4)*

ITALIAN
Central
Al Duca *(SW1)*
Alloro *(W1)*
Amico Bio *(WC1)*
Assunta Madre *(W1)*
Babbo *(W1)*
Il Baretto *(W1)*
Bocca Di Lupo *(W1)**
La Bottega *(SW1,WC2)*
Briciole *(W1)*
C London *(W1)*
Caffè Caldesi *(W1)*
Caffé Vergnano *(WC2)*
Caraffini *(SW1)*
Cecconi's *(W1)*
Ciao Bella *(WC1)*
Como Lario *(SW1)*
Il Convivio *(SW1)**
Da Mario *(WC2)*
Polpo *(WC2)*
Dehesa *(W1)**
Delfino *(W1)*
Franco's *(SW1)*
La Genova *(W1)*
Gustoso *(SW1)*
Latium *(W1)**
Locanda Locatelli *(W1)*
Made in Italy *(W1)*
Mele e Pere *(W1)*
Murano *(W1)**
Novikov (Italian restaurant) *(W1)*
Obika *(W1)*
Oliveto *(SW1)**
Olivo *(SW1)**
Olivocarne *(SW1)**
Olivomare *(SW1)**
Opera Tavern *(WC2)**
Orso *(WC2)*
Osteria Dell'Angolo *(SW1)*
Ottolenghi *(SW1)**
Pescatori *(W1)*
Piccolino *(W1)*
La Polenteria *(W1)*
Polpo *(W1)*
La Porchetta Pizzeria *(WC1)*
Princi *(W1)*
Quattro Passi *(W1)*
Quirinale *(SW1)**
Café Murano *(SW1)**
Rossopomodoro *(WC2)*
Sale e Pepe *(SW1)*
Salt Yard *(W1)*
San Carlo Cicchetti *(W1)*
Santini *(SW1)*
Sardo *(W1)*
Sartoria *(W1)*
Signor Sassi *(SW1)*
Theo Randall *(W1)*
Tinello *(SW1)**
Toto's *(SW1)*
Tozi *(SW1)*
2 Veneti *(W1)*
Vapiano *(W1)*
Vasco & Piero's Pavilion *(W1)**
Il Vicolo *(SW1)*
Zafferano *(SW1)*

West
Aglio e Olio *(SW10)*
L'Amorosa *(W6)*
Assaggi *(W2)**
Bird in Hand *(W14)*
La Bottega *(SW7)*
Buona Sera *(SW3)*
Canta Napoli *(W4)*
Cibo *(W14)**
Da Mario *(SW7)*
Daphne's *(SW3)*
La Delizia Limbara *(SW3)**
Edera *(W11)*
Essenza *(W11)*
La Famiglia *(SW10)*
Frantoio *(SW10)*
Locanda Ottomezzo *(W8)*
Lucio *(SW3)*
Made in Italy *(SW3)*
Manicomio *(SW3)*
Mediterraneo *(W11)*
Mona Lisa *(SW10)*
Napulé *(SW6)**
Nuovi Sapori *(SW6)*
The Oak W12 *(W12,W2)**
Obika *(SW3)*
Osteria Basilico *(W11)*
Ottolenghi *(W11,W8)**
Il Pagliaccio *(SW6)*
Pappa Ciccia *(SW6)**
Pellicano *(SW3)*
Pentolina *(W14)**
Polpo *(W11)*
Il Portico *(W8)*
Portobello Ristorante *(W11)*
The Red Pepper *(W9)**
Riccardo's *(SW3)*
The River Café *(W6)*
Rossopomodoro *(SW10)*
Santa Lucia *(SW10)*
Scalini *(SW3)*
Tartufo *(SW3)**
Ziani's *(SW3)*

North
Artigiano *(NW3)*
L'Artista *(NW11)*
Il Bacio *(N16, N5)*
La Collina *(NW1)**
Fabrizio *(N19)*
Fifteen *(N1)*
500 *(N19)*
Ostuni *(NW6)*
Ottolenghi *(N1)**
Pizzeria Oregano *(N1)**
Pizzeria Pappagone *(N4)*
La Porchetta Pizzeria *(N1, N4, NW1)*
Rugoletta *(N2)**
The Salt House *(NW8)*
San Daniele del Friuli *(N5)*
Sarracino *(NW6)**
Trullo *(N1)**
Villa Bianca *(NW3)*
Vivo *(N1)**
York & Albany *(NW1)*

South
A Cena *(TW1)*
Al Forno *(SW15, SW19)*
Antico *(SE1)**
Antipasto & Pasta *(SW11)*
Artusi *(SE15)**
La Barca *(SE1)*
Bibo *(SW15)**
Al Boccon di'vino *(TW9)**
Buona Sera *(SW11)*
Canta Napoli *(TW11)*
Donna Margherita *(SW11)**
Enoteca Turi *(SW15)**
Lorenzo *(SE19)*
Numero Uno *(SW11)*
Osteria Antica Bologna *(SW11)*

Pizza Metro *(SW11)**
Le Querce *(SE23)**
Riva *(SW13)*
San Lorenzo Fuoriporta *(SW19)*
Sapori Sardi *(SW6)**
The Table *(SE1)*
Tentazioni *(SE1)*
Vapiano *(SE1)*
Zucca *(SE1)**

East

Amico Bio *(EC1)*
L'Anima *(EC2)*
L' Anima Cafe *(EC2)*
Apulia *(EC1)*
Il Bordello *(E1)**
Coco Di Mama *(EC4)**
Fabrizio *(EC1)**
La Figa *(E14)*
Lardo *(E8)*
Manicomio *(EC2)*
Obika *(E14)*
E Pellicci *(E2)*
Piccolino *(EC2)*
Polpo *(EC1)*
La Porchetta Pizzeria *(EC1)*
Rotorino *(E8)*
Santore *(EC1)**
Taberna Etrusca *(EC4)*

MEDITERRANEAN

Central

About Thyme *(SW1)*
Bistro 1 *(W1,WC2)*
Dabbous *(W1)**
Hummus Bros *(W1,WC1)*
Massimo *(SW1)*
Nopi *(W1)**
The Norfolk Arms *(WC1)**
Riding House Café *(W1)*

West

The Atlas *(SW6)**
Cumberland Arms *(W14)**
Locanda Ottomezzo *(W8)*
Made in Italy *(SW3)*
Mediterraneo *(W11)*
Raoul's Cafe *(W9)*
Raoul's Café & Deli *(W11,W6)*
The Swan *(W4)**
Troubadour *(SW5)*

North

Blue Legume *(N16)*
The Little Bay *(NW6)*

South

Cantina Vinopolis *(SE1)*
Fish in a Tie *(SW11)*
The Fox & Hounds *(SW11)**
The Little Bay *(SW11)*
Oxo Tower (Brass') *(SE1)*
Peckham Bazaar *(SE15)*
The Wharf *(TW11)*

East

The Eagle *(EC1)**
Hummus Bros *(EC1, EC2)*
The Little Bay *(EC1)*
Morito *(EC1)**
Portal *(EC1)*
Rocket *(E14, EC2)*
Vinoteca *(EC1)*

ORGANIC

Central

Daylesford Organic *(SW1,W1)*

West

Daylesford Organic *(W11)*

North

The Duke of Cambridge *(N1)*

East

Smiths (Dining Rm) *(EC1)*

POLISH

West

Daquise *(SW7)*
Polish Club *(SW7)*
Patio *(W12)*

South

Baltic *(SE1)*

PORTUGUESE

West

Lisboa Pâtisserie *(W10)**

East

Eyre Brothers *(EC2)**
The Gun *(E14)*
Portal *(EC1)*

RUSSIAN

Central

Bob Bob Ricard *(W1)*

SCANDINAVIAN

Central

Nordic Bakery *(W1)*
Scandinavian Kitchen *(W1)**
Texture *(W1)*

SCOTTISH

Central

Boisdale *(SW1)*

East

Boisdale of Canary Wharf *(E14)*

SPANISH

Central

Ametsa *(SW1)*
aqua nueva *(W1)*
Barrafina *(W1,WC2)**
Barrica *(W1)**
Bilbao Berria *(SW1)*
Cigala *(WC1)*
Copita *(W1)*
Dehesa *(W1)**
Donostia *(W1)**
Drakes Tabanco *(W1)*
Fino *(W1)**
Goya *(SW1)*
Ibérica *(W1)*
Navarro's *(W1)*
Opera Tavern *(WC2)**
El Pirata *(W1)*
Salt Yard *(W1)*
Tapas Brindisa Soho *(W1)*

West

Cambio de Tercio *(SW5)**
Capote Y Toros *(SW5)**
Casa Brindisa *(SW7)*
Duke of Sussex *(W4)*
Notting Hill Kitchen *(W11)*
El Pirata de Tapas *(W2)*
Tendido Cero *(SW5)*
Tendido Cuatro *(SW6)**

North

Bar Esteban *(N8)**
La Bota *(N8)*
Café del Parc *(N19)**
Camino *(N1)*
El Parador *(NW1)**

South

Alquimia *(SW15)*
Angels & Gypsies *(SE5)*
Boqueria *(SW2)**
don Fernando's *(TW9)*
José *(SE1)**
Lola Rojo *(SW11)*
Meson don Felipe *(SE1)*
Pizarro *(SE1)*
Tapas Brindisa *(SE1, SW9)*

East

Bravas *(E1)**
Eyre Brothers *(EC2)**
Ibérica *(E14, EC1)*
Morito *(EC1)**
Moro *(EC1)**
Tramontana Brindisa *(EC2)*

STEAKS & GRILLS

Central

Black & Blue *(W1)*
Bodean's *(W1)*
Christopher's *(WC2)*
Cut *(W1)*
Flat Iron *(W1,WC2)**
Gaucho *(W1)*
Goodman *(W1)*
The Guinea Grill *(W1)*
Hawksmoor *(W1,WC2)**
JW Steakhouse *(W1)*
MASH Steakhouse *(W1)*
maze Grill *(W1)*

Carom at Meza *(W1)**
Le Relais de Venise L'Entrecôte *(W1)*
Rib Room *(SW1)*
Rowley's *(SW1)*
Sophie's Steakhouse *(WC2)*
STK Steakhouse *(WC2)*
34 *(W1)*
Wolfe's *(WC2)*

West
The Admiral Codrington *(SW3)*
Black & Blue *(W8)*
Bodean's *(SW6)*
Casa Malevo *(W2)**
Gaucho *(SW3)*
Haché *(SW10)*
Hawksmoor Knightsbridge *(SW3)**
Kings Road Steakhouse *(SW3)*
Maxela *(SW7)**
PJ's Bar and Grill *(SW3)*
Popeseye *(W14)*
Sophie's Steakhouse *(SW10)*

North
Haché *(NW1)*
The Smokehouse Islington *(N1)*

South
Archduke Wine Bar *(SE1)*
Black & Blue *(SE1)*
Bodean's *(SW4)*
Buenos Aires Café *(SE10, SE3)*
Butcher & Grill *(SW11)*
Cattle Grid *(SW12)*
Cornish Tiger *(SW11)**
Gaucho *(SE1)*
Popeseye *(SW15)*

East
Barbecoa *(EC4)*
Buen Ayre *(E8)**
Clutch *(E2)**
Gaucho *(EC1)*
Goodman *(E14)*
Goodman City *(EC2)*
Hawksmoor *(E1, EC2)**
Hill & Szrok *(E8)*
Hix Oyster & Chop House *(EC1)*
M *(EC2)*
New Street Grill *(EC2)*
Relais de Venise L'Entrecôte *(E14, EC2)*
Simpson's Tavern *(EC3)*
Smiths (Top Floor) *(EC1)*
Smiths (Dining Rm) *(EC1)*
Smiths (Ground Floor) *(EC1)*
The Tramshed *(EC2)*

VEGETARIAN

Central
Amico Bio *(WC1)*
Chettinad *(W1)*
Food for Thought *(WC2)**
Hummus Bros *(W1, WC1)*
Malabar Junction *(WC1)*
Masala Zone *(W1)*
Mildreds *(W1)**
Orchard *(WC1)*
Ragam *(W1)**
Rasa Maricham *(WC1)**
Sagar *(W1)*
tibits *(W1)*
Woodlands *(SW1, W1)*

West
The Gate *(W6)*
Masala Zone *(SW5, W2)*
Sagar *(W6)*

North
Chutneys *(NW1)*
Diwana Bhel-Poori House *(NW1)*
Jai Krishna *(N4)**
Manna *(NW3)*
Masala Zone *(N1)*
Rani *(N3)*
Rasa *(N16)**
Vijay *(NW6)*
Woodlands *(NW3)*

South
Blue Elephant *(SW6)*
Ganapati *(SE15)**
Le Pont de la Tour *(SE1)*
Sree Krishna *(SW17)**

East
Amico Bio *(EC1)*
The Gate *(EC1)*
Hummus Bros *(EC2)*
Vanilla Black *(EC4)*

AFTERNOON TEA

Central
Athenaeum *(W1)*
The Diamond Jub' Salon (Fortnum's) *(W1)*
The Fountain (Fortnum's) *(W1)*
La Fromagerie Café *(W1)*
Ladurée *(SW1, W1, WC2)*
Maison Bertaux *(W1)**
Notes *(WC2)*
Ritz (Palm Court) *(W1)*
Royal Academy *(W1)*
The Sketch (Parlour) *(W1)*
Villandry *(W1)*
The Wallace *(W1)*
The Wolseley *(W1)*
Yauatcha *(W1)**

North
Kenwood (Brew House) *(NW3)*
Landmark (Winter Gdn) *(NW1)*

South
Cannizaro House *(SW19)*
San Lorenzo Fuoriporta *(SW19)*

East
Ladurée *(EC3)*

BURGERS, ETC

Central
Bar Boulud *(SW1)*
Beast *(W1)*
Black & Blue *(W1)*
Bobo Social *(W1)*
Burger & Lobster *(SW1, W1)*
Diner *(W1, WC2)*
Dub Jam *(WC2)**
Ed's Easy Diner *(W1)*
Five Guys *(WC2)*
Goodman *(W1)*
Hard Rock Café *(W1)*
Hawksmoor *(W1, WC2)**
Honest Burgers *(W1)**
Joe Allen *(WC2)*
Kettners *(W1)*
MEATLiquor *(W1)*
MEATmarket *(WC2)**
Opera Tavern *(WC2)**
Patty and Bun *(W1)**
Shake Shack *(WC2)*
Tommi's Burger Joint *(W1)**
Wolfe's *(WC2)*

West
The Admiral Codrington *(SW3)*
Big Easy *(SW3)*
Black & Blue *(W8)*
Diner *(SW7)*
Haché *(SW10)*
Honest Burgers *(W11)**
Lucky Seven *(W2)*
Sticky Fingers *(W8)*
Tommi's Burger Joint *(SW3)**
Troubadour *(SW5)*

North
The Diner *(NW1)*
Dirty Burger *(NW5)**
Duke's Brew & Que *(N1)*
Ed's Easy Diner *(NW1)*
Haché *(NW1)*
Harry Morgan's *(NW8)*
Honest Burgers *(NW1)**
Meat Mission *(N1)**
Red Dog Saloon *(N1)*
The Rib Man *(N1)**

South
Black & Blue *(SE1)*
Cattle Grid *(SW12)*
Dip & Flip *(SW11)**
Dirty Burger *(SW8)**
Ed's Easy Diner *(SW18)*
Haché *(SW4)*
Honest Burgers *(SW17, SW9)**
The Old Brewery *(SE10)*
Village East *(SE1)*

East

Big Apple Hot Dogs *(EC1)**
Burger & Lobster *(EC1, EC4)*
Comptoir Gascon *(EC1)*
The Diner *(EC2)*
Goodman *(E14)*
Goodman City *(EC2)*
Haché *(EC2)*
Hawksmoor *(E1, EC2)**
Patty and Bun *(EC2)**
Smiths (Dining Rm) *(EC1)*

FISH & CHIPS

Central

Golden Hind *(W1)*
North Sea Fish *(WC1)*
Seafresh *(SW1)*

West

Geales *(W8)*
Geales Chelsea Green *(SW3)*
Kerbisher & Malt *(W5, W6)*

North

The Fish & Chip Shop *(N1)**
Nautilus *(NW6)**
The Sea Shell *(NW1)**
Skipjacks *(HA3)**
Toff's *(N10)**
Two Brothers *(N3)*

South

Brady's *(SW18)*
Fish Club *(SW11, SW4)**
Kerbisher & Malt *(SW14, SW4)*
Masters Super Fish *(SE1)**
Moxon's Fish Bar *(SW12)**
Olley's *(SE24)**
The Sea Cow *(SE22)*

East

Ark Fish *(E18)**
Faulkner's *(E8)**

ICE CREAM

Central

Gelupo *(W1)**

PIZZA

Central

Il Baretto *(W1)*
Bianco43 *(WC2)*
Bocconcino *(W1)*
Delfino *(W1)*
Fire & Stone *(WC2)*
Homeslice *(WC2)**
Kettners *(W1)*
Made in Italy *(W1)*
Oliveto *(SW1)**
The Orange *(SW1)*
Piccolino *(W1)*
Pizza Pilgrims *(W1)**
La Porchetta Pizzeria *(WC1)*
Princi *(W1)*
Rossopomodoro *(WC2)*

West

Basilico *(SW6)**
Bird in Hand *(W14)*
Buona Sera *(SW3)*
Canta Napoli *(W4)*
Da Mario *(SW7)*
La Delizia Limbara *(SW3)**
Fire & Stone *(W12)*
Franco Manca *(W4)**
Made in Italy *(SW3)*
The Oak W12 *(W12, W2)**
Osteria Basilico *(W11)*
Il Pagliaccio *(SW6)*
Pappa Ciccia *(SW6)**
Pizza East Portobello *(W10)**
Portobello Ristorante *(W11)*
The Red Pepper *(W9)**
Rocca Di Papa *(SW7)*
Rossopomodoro *(SW10)*
Santa Lucia *(SW10)*
Santa Maria *(W5)**

North

Il Bacio *(N16, N5)*
Basilico *(N1, N8, NW3)**
Fabrizio *(N19)*
Pizza East *(NW5)**
Pizzeria Oregano *(N1)**
Pizzeria Pappagone *(N4)*
La Porchetta Pizzeria *(N1, N4, NW1)*
Rossopomodoro *(N1, NW1)*
Sacro Cuore *(NW10)**
Sweet Thursday *(N1)*

South

Al Forno *(SW15, SW19)*
Basilico *(SW11)**
Bianco43 *(SE10, SE3)*
Buona Sera *(SW11)*
Donna Margherita *(SW11)**
Eco *(SW4)*
Franco Manca *(SW11, SW12, SW9)**
Gourmet Pizza Company *(SE1)*
The Gowlett *(SE15)**
Lorenzo *(SE19)*
Pizza Metro *(SW11)**
Pizzeria Rustica *(TW9)**
Rocca Di Papa *(SE21)*
Rossopomodoro *(SW18)*
San Lorenzo Fuoriporta *(SW19)*
The Yellow House *(SE16)*
Zero Degrees *(SE3)*

East

Il Bordello *(E1)**
La Figa *(E14)*
Franco Manca *(E20)**
GB Pizza *(EC1)**
Piccolino *(EC2)*
Pizza East *(E1)**
La Porchetta Pizzeria *(EC1)*
Rocket *(E14, EC2)*
Story Deli *(E2)**
Yard Sale Pizza *(E5)*

SANDWICHES, CAKES, ETC

Central

The Attendant *(W1)**
Baker & Spice *(SW1)*
Bar Italia *(W1)*
Caffé Vergnano *(WC1)*
Fernandez & Wells *(W1, WC2)*
Flat White *(W1)**
Fleet River Bakery *(WC2)*
La Fromagerie Café *(W1)*
Fuzzy's Grub *(SW1)*
Kaffeine *(W1)*
Konditor & Cook *(W1, WC1)*
Ladurée *(SW1, W1)*
Maison Bertaux *(W1)**
Monmouth Coffee Company *(WC2)**
Natural Kitchen *(W1)*
Nordic Bakery *(W1)*
Notes *(WC2)*
Royal Academy *(W1)*
Scandinavian Kitchen *(W1)**
The Sketch (Parlour) *(W1)*
Taylor St Baristas *(W1)**
Villiers Coffee Co *(WC2)*

West

Baker & Spice *(SW3, W9)*
Lisboa Pâtisserie *(W10)**

North

Ginger & White *(NW3)*
Greenberry Cafe *(NW1)*
Kenwood (Brew House) *(NW3)*
Notes *(N7)*

South

Caffé Vergnano *(SE1)*
Fulham Wine Rooms *(SW6)*
Konditor & Cook *(SE1)*
Monmouth Coffee Company *(SE1, SE16)**
Orange Pekoe *(SW13)*
Spianata & Co *(SE1)**
Taylor St Baristas *(TW9)**

East

Brick Lane Beigel Bake *(E1)**
Caffé Vergnano *(EC4)*
Department of Coffee *(EC1)*
Dose *(EC1)**
Fuzzy's Grub *(EC2, EC3, EC4)*
Konditor & Cook *(EC3)*
Look Mum No Hands! *(EC1)*
Natural Kitchen *(EC4)*
Nusa Kitchen *(EC1, EC2)**
Prufrock Coffee *(EC1)**
Spianata & Co *(E1, EC1, EC2, EC4)**
Taylor St Baristas *(EC2, EC3)**
Workshop Coffee *(EC1)**

SALADS
Central
Kaffeine *(W1)*
Natural Kitchen *(W1)*

West
Beirut Express *(SW7, W2)**

East
Natural Kitchen *(EC3, EC4)*

ARGENTINIAN
Central
Gaucho *(W1)*
Zoilo *(W1)**

West
Casa Malevo *(W2)**
Gaucho *(SW3)*
Quantus *(W4)*

South
Buenos Aires Café *(SE10, SE3)*
Gaucho *(SE1)*

East
Buen Ayre *(E8)**
Gaucho *(EC1)*

BRAZILIAN
East
Sushisamba *(EC2)*

MEXICAN/TEXMEX
Central
Benito's Hat *(W1, WC2)*
La Bodega Negra *(W1)*
Cantina Laredo *(WC2)**
Chilango *(WC2)*
Chipotle *(W1, WC2)*
Lupita *(WC2)*
Peyote *(W1)*
Wahaca *(W1, WC2)*

West
Taqueria *(W11)*

North
Benito's Hat *(N1)*
Chilango *(N1)*
Chipotle *(N1)*
Wahaca *(N1)*

South
Wahaca *(SE1)*

East
Benito's Hat *(EC1)*
Chilango *(E1, EC2, EC4)*
Daddy Donkey *(EC1)**
DF Mexico *(E1)*

PERUVIAN
Central
Ceviche *(W1)**
Coya *(W1)**
Lima *(W1)**
Lima Floral *(WC2)*
Pachamama *(W1)*

East
Andina *(E2)**
Sushisamba *(EC2)*

SOUTH AMERICAN
West
Quantus *(W4)*

South
El Vergel *(SE1)**

AFRO-CARIBBEAN
Central
Jamaica Patty Co. *(WC2)*

North
Mango Room *(NW1)*

MOROCCAN
West
Adams Café *(W12)*

NORTH AFRICAN
Central
Momo *(W1)*

West
Azou *(W6)**

SOUTH AFRICAN
Central
Bunnychow *(W1)*

East
Bunnychow *(E1)*

TUNISIAN
West
Adams Café *(W12)*

EGYPTIAN
North
Ali Baba *(NW1)*

ISRAELI
Central
Gaby's *(WC2)*
The Palomar *(W1)**

North
Solly's *(NW11)*

KOSHER
Central
Reubens *(W1)*

North
Kaifeng *(NW4)*
Solly's *(NW11)*
Zest *(NW3)*

East
Bevis Marks *(E1)*
Brick Lane Beigel Bake *(E1)**

LEBANESE
Central
Al Hamra *(W1)*
Al Sultan *(W1)*
Beiteddine *(SW1)*
Comptoir Libanais *(W1)*
Fairuz *(W1)**
Levant *(W1)*
Maroush *(W1)**
Noura *(SW1, W1)*
Yalla Yalla *(W1)*

West
Al-Waha *(W2)*
Beirut Express *(SW7, W2)**
Chez Abir *(W14)**
Comptoir Libanais *(SW7, W12)*
Maroush *(W2)**
Maroush *(SW3)**
Ranoush *(SW3, W2, W8)**

South
Arabica Bar and Kitchen *(SE1)*
Meza *(SW17)**
Palmyra *(TW9)**

East
Comptoir Libanais *(E20)*
Yalla Yalla *(E1)*

MIDDLE EASTERN
Central
Honey & Co *(W1)**
Patogh *(W1)*

North
Solly's *(NW11)*

East
Morito *(EC1)**
Nusa Kitchen *(EC4)**
Pilpel *(E1, EC4)**
1701 *(EC3)**

PERSIAN
West
Alounak *(W14, W2)*
Faanoos *(W4)*
Kateh *(W9)**
Sufi *(W12)*

North
Gilak *(N19)*

South
Faanoos *(SW14)*

SYRIAN
West
Abu Zaad *(W12)*

TURKISH
Central
Cyprus Mangal *(SW1)**
Ishtar *(W1)*
Kazan *(SW1)*
Sofra *(W1, WC2)*
Tas *(WC1)*

West
Best Mangal *(SW6, W14)**
Fez Mangal *(W11)**

North
Antepliler *(N1, N4)*
Gallipoli *(N1)*
Gem *(N1)*
Izgara *(N3)*
Mangal II *(N16)*

South
Ev Restaurant, Bar & Deli *(SE1)*
Tas Pide *(SE1)*

East
Haz *(E1, EC2, EC3)*
Mangal 1 *(E8)**
Tas *(EC1)*

AFGHANI
North
Afghan Kitchen *(N1)**

BURMESE
West
Mandalay *(W2)*

CHINESE
Central
A Wong *(SW1)**
Ba Shan *(W1)**
Baozi Inn *(WC2)*
Bar Shu *(W1)**
The Bright Courtyard *(W1)*
Chilli Cool *(WC1)**
China Tang *(W1)*
Er Mei *(WC2)**
The Four Seasons *(W1)**
Golden Dragon *(W1)*
The Grand Imperial *(SW1)*
Hakkasan Mayfair *(W1)**
Harbour City *(W1)*
Hunan *(SW1)**
Joy King Lau *(WC2)*
Kai Mayfair *(W1)**
Ken Lo's Memories *(SW1)*
Mr Chow *(SW1)*
Mr Kong *(WC2)*
New Mayflower *(W1)**
New World *(W1)*
Plum Valley *(W1)**
Princess Garden *(W1)**
Royal China *(W1)**
Royal China Club *(W1)**
Shanghai Blues *(WC1)**
Wong Kei *(W1)*
Yauatcha *(W1)**
Yming *(W1)**

West
The Four Seasons *(W2)**
Gold Mine *(W2)*
Good Earth *(SW3)*
Mandarin Kitchen *(W2)**
Min Jiang *(W8)**
North China *(W3)**
Pearl Liang *(W2)*
Royal China *(SW6, W2)**
Taiwan Village *(SW6)**

North
Good Earth *(NW7)*
Green Cottage *(NW3)*
Gung-Ho *(NW6)*
Kaifeng *(NW4)*
Phoenix Palace *(NW1)*
Singapore Garden *(NW6)**
Yipin China *(N1)**

South
Dalchini *(SW19)*
Dragon Castle *(SE17)*
Four Regions *(TW9)*
Good Earth *(SW17)*
Hutong *(SE1)*
Silk Road *(SE5)**

East
Chinese Cricket Club *(EC4)**
Gourmet San *(E2)**
HKK *(EC2)**
Lotus Chinese Floating Restaurant *(E14)*
Royal China *(E14)**
Shanghai *(E8)*
Sichuan Folk *(E1)**
Yi-Ban *(E16)**

CHINESE, DIM SUM
Central
The Bright Courtyard *(W1)*
dim T *(W1)*
Golden Dragon *(W1)*
The Grand Imperial *(SW1)*
Hakkasan Mayfair *(W1)**
Harbour City *(W1)*
Joy King Lau *(WC2)*
Leong's Legends *(W1)*
New World *(W1)*
ping pong *(W1)*
Princess Garden *(W1)**
Royal China *(W1)**
Royal China Club *(W1)**
Shanghai Blues *(WC1)**
Yauatcha *(W1)**

West
Bo Lang *(SW3)*
Min Jiang *(W8)**
Pearl Liang *(W2)*
ping pong *(W2)*
Royal China *(SW6, W2)**

North
dim T *(N6, NW3)*
Phoenix Palace *(NW1)*

South
dim T *(SE1)*
Dragon Castle *(SE17)*
ping pong *(SE1)*

East
Lotus Chinese Floating Restaurant *(E14)*
ping pong *(EC4)*
Royal China *(E14)**
Shanghai *(E8)*
Yi-Ban *(E16)**

GEORGIAN
Central
Marani *(W1)*

North
Little Georgia Café *(N1)*

East
Little Georgia Café *(E2)*

INDIAN
Central
Amaya *(SW1)**
Benares *(W1)*
Chettinad *(W1)*
Chor Bizarre *(W1)**
The Cinnamon Club *(SW1)*
Cinnamon Soho *(W1)**
Dishoom *(WC2)**
Gaylord *(W1)*
Gymkhana *(W1)**
Imli Street *(W1)*
India Club *(WC2)*
Malabar Junction *(WC1)*
Masala Zone *(W1, WC2)*
Mint Leaf *(SW1)*
Moti Mahal *(WC2)**
La Porte des Indes *(W1)*
Punjab *(WC2)*
Ragam *(W1)**
Red Fort *(W1)*
Roti Chai *(W1)**
Sagar *(W1, WC2)*
Salaam Namaste *(WC1)*
Salloos *(SW1)**
Tamarind *(W1)**

Trishna *(W1)**
Veeraswamy *(W1)**
Woodlands *(SW1,W1)*
Zayna *(W1)**

West
Anarkali *(W6)*
Bombay Brasserie *(SW7)**
Bombay Palace *(W2)**
Brilliant *(UB2)*
Chakra *(W11)*
Chutney Mary *(SW10)**
Durbar *(W2)*
Gifto's *(UB1)*
The Greedy Buddha *(SW6)*
Indian Zing *(W6)**
Karma *(W14)**
Khan's *(W2)**
Madhu's *(UB1)**
Malabar *(W8)**
Masala Zone *(SW5,W2)*
Miran Masala *(W14)**
Mirch Masala *(UB1)*
Noor Jahan *(SW5,W2)**
The Painted Heron *(SW10)**
Potli *(W6)**
Rasoi *(SW3)**
Sagar *(W6)*
Star of India *(SW5)**
Thali *(SW5)**

North
Chutneys *(NW1)*
Delhi Grill *(N1)**
Dishoom *(N1)**
Diwana Bhel-Poori House *(NW1)*
Eriki *(NW3)**
Great Nepalese *(NW1)*
Guglee *(NW3, NW6)*
Indian Rasoi *(N2)**
Jai Krishna *(N4)**
Kadiri's *(NW10)**
Masala Zone *(N1)*
Paradise Hampstead *(NW3)**
Rani *(N3)*
Ravi Shankar *(NW1)**
Roots at N1 *(N1)**
Vijay *(NW6)*
Woodlands *(NW3)*
Zaffrani *(N1)**

South
Apollo Banana Leaf *(SW17)**
Babur *(SE23)**
Bengal Clipper *(SE1)*
Chutney *(SW18)**
Dalchini *(SW19)*
Everest Inn *(SE3)**
Ganapati *(SE15)**
Holy Cow *(SW11)**
Hot Stuff *(SW8)*
Indian Moment *(SW11)*
Indian Ocean *(SW17)**
Indian Zilla *(SW13)**
Kennington Tandoori *(SE11)**
Lahore Karahi *(SW17)**
Lahore Kebab House *(SW16)**
Ma Goa *(SW15)**
Mango Food of India *(SE1)*
Mirch Masala *(SW16, SW17)*
Nazmins *(SW18)*
Sree Krishna *(SW17)**
Tandoori Nights *(SE22)*

East
Café Spice Namaste *(E1)**
Cinnamon Kitchen *(EC2)**
Dishoom *(E2)**
Lahore Kebab House *(E1)**
Mint Leaf *(EC2)*
Mirch Masala *(E1)*
Needoo *(E1)**
Tayyabs *(E1)**

INDIAN, SOUTHERN

Central
India Club *(WC2)*
Malabar Junction *(WC1)*
Quilon *(SW1)**
Ragam *(W1)**
Rasa Maricham *(WC1)**
Rasa Samudra *(W1)**
Sagar *(W1,WC2)*
Woodlands *(SW1,W1)*

West
Sagar *(W6)*
Shilpa *(W6)**

North
Chutneys *(NW1)*
Rani *(N3)*
Rasa *(N16)**
Vijay *(NW6)*
Woodlands *(NW3)*

South
Ganapati *(SE15)**
Sree Krishna *(SW17)**

JAPANESE

Central
Abeno *(WC1,WC2)*
aqua kyoto *(W1)*
Atari-Ya *(W1)**
Bone Daddies *(W1)*
Chisou *(W1)**
Chotto Matte *(W1)**
Defune *(W1)*
Dinings *(W1)**
Eat Tokyo *(WC1,WC2)**
Flesh and Buns *(WC2)*
Hazuki *(WC2)*
Ippudo London *(WC2)*
Kiku *(W1)**
Kikuchi *(W1)**
Koya *(W1)**
Koya-Bar *(W1)**
Kulu Kulu *(W1,WC2)*
Matsuri *(SW1)*
Nizuni *(W1)**
Nobu *(W1)**
Nobu Berkeley *(W1)*
Roka *(W1,WC2)**
Sakana-tei *(W1)**
Sake No Hana *(SW1)*
Sakura *(W1)*
Shoryu Ramen *(SW1,W1)*
Sticks'n'Sushi *(WC2)*
Sumosan *(W1)*
Taro *(W1)*
Tokyo Diner *(WC2)*
Tonkotsu *(W1)*
Tsunami *(W1)**
Umu *(W1)*
Yoisho *(W1)*
Yoshino *(W1)*

West
Atari-Ya *(W5)**
Chisou *(SW3,W4)**
Eat Tokyo *(W6,W8)**
Inaho *(W2)**
Kiraku *(W5)**
Kulu Kulu *(SW7)*
Kurobuta *(W2)**
Maguro *(W9)**
The Shiori *(W2)**
Tosa *(W6)**
Yashin *(W8)**
Yashin Ocean House *(SW7)*
Zuma *(SW7)**

North
Akari *(N1)**
Asakusa *(NW1)**
Atari-Ya *(NW4, NW6)**
Bento Cafe *(NW1)**
Dotori *(N4)**
Eat Tokyo *(NW11)**
Jin Kichi *(NW3)**
Sushi-Say *(NW2)**

South
Fujiyama *(SW9)**
Hashi *(SW20)**
Matsuba *(TW9)**
Sticks'n'Sushi *(SW19)*
Tsunami *(SW4)**

East
City Miyama *(EC4)*
K10 *(EC2)**
Pham Sushi *(EC1)**
Roka *(E14)**
Sushisamba *(EC2)*
Sushi Tetsu *(EC1)**
Tajima Tei *(EC1)*
Tonkotsu East *(E8)*

KOREAN

Central

Asadal *(WC1)*
Bibimbap Soho *(W1)*
Kimchee *(WC1)**
Koba *(W1)*

North

Dotori *(N4)**

South

Cah-Chi *(SW18, SW20)**

East

On The Bab *(EC1)**

MALAYSIAN

Central

C&R Cafe *(W1)**
Spice Market *(W1)*

West

Satay House *(W2)*

North

Singapore Garden *(NW6)**

South

Champor-Champor *(SE1)*

PAKISTANI

Central

Salloos *(SW1)**

West

Miran Masala *(W14)**
Mirch Masala *(UB1)*

South

Lahore Karahi *(SW17)**
Lahore Kebab House *(SW16)**
Mirch Masala *(SW16, SW17)*

East

Lahore Kebab House *(E1)**
Mirch Masala *(E1)*
Needoo *(E1)**
Tayyabs *(E1)**

PAN-ASIAN

Central

Banana Tree Canteen *(W1)*
Buddha-Bar London *(SW1)*
dim T *(SW1,W1)*
East Street *(W1)*
Hare & Tortoise *(WC1)*
Inamo *(SW1,W1)*
The Noodle House *(WC2)*
Novikov (Asian restaurant) *(W1)*
Spice Market *(W1)*

West

Banana Tree Canteen *(W2,W9)*
E&O *(W11)*
Eight Over Eight *(SW3)*
Hare & Tortoise *(W14,W5)*

North

dim T *(N6, NW3)*
Gilgamesh *(NW1)*
XO *(NW3)*

South

The Banana Tree Canteen *(SW11)*
dim T *(SE1)*
Hare & Tortoise *(SW15)*

East

Banana Tree Canteen *(EC1)*
Hare & Tortoise *(EC4)*

THAI

Central

Busaba Eathai *(SW1,W1,WC2)*
C&R Cafe *(W1)**
Crazy Bear *(W1)*
Mango Tree *(SW1)*
Patara *(W1)*
Spice Market *(W1)*
Thai Square *(WC2)*

West

Addie's Thai Café *(SW5)*
Bangkok *(SW7)*
C&R Cafe *(W2)**
Café 209 *(SW6)*
Churchill Arms *(W8)*
Esarn Kheaw *(W12)**
Fat Boy's *(W4,W5)*
Fitou's Thai Restaurant *(W10)**
101 Thai Kitchen *(W6)**
Patara *(SW3)*
Sukho Fine Thai Cuisine *(SW6)**
Thai Square *(SW7)*

North

Isarn *(N1)**
Thai Square *(N1)*
Yum Yum *(N16)*

South

The Begging Bowl *(SE15)**
Blue Elephant *(SW6)*
Fat Boy's *(SW14,TW1,TW8)*
Kaosarn *(SW11, SW9)**
The Paddyfield *(SW12)*
The Pepper Tree *(SW4)**
Suk Saran *(SW19)**
Talad Thai *(SW15)*
Thai Corner Café *(SE22)*

East

Busaba Eathai *(EC1)*
Elephant Royale *(E14)*
Thai Square City *(EC3)*

VIETNAMESE

Central

Bam-Bou *(W1)*
Cây Tre *(W1)*
House of Ho *(W1)**
Pho *(W1)*

West

Pho *(W12)*
Saigon Saigon *(W6)*

North

Huong-Viet *(N1)*
Salvation In Noodles *(N1)**

South

Cafe East *(SE16)**
Mien Tay *(SW11)**
The Paddyfield *(SW12)*

East

Cây Tre *(EC1)*
City Càphê *(EC2)**
Mien Tay *(E2)**
Pho *(E1, EC1)*
Sông Quê *(E2)*
Viet Grill *(E2)**

Take your love of food further

ACTION AGAINST HUNGER

Because those who love food, give food

Action Against Hunger works with hundreds of restaurants across the UK with one aim: to end child hunger worldwide. Be part of something bigger and take your love of food further. Find out why we are the food and drink industry's charity of choice.

Save lives whilst gaining:

- Positive PR and Marketing
- Employee engagement
- Customer satisfaction

Caroline Dyer
0208 293 6133
c.dyer@actionagainsthunger.org.uk
lovefoodgivefood.org

In association with:

OpenTable

delicious. MAGAZINE

Registered charity No. 1047501

LONDON AREA OVERVIEWS

CENTRAL

Soho, Covent Garden & Bloomsbury (Parts of W1, all WC2 and WC1)

£80+	L'Atelier de Joel Robuchon	*French*	333
	MASH Steakhouse	*Steaks & grills*	332
	Roka	*Japanese*	534
£70+	Christopher's	*American*	323
	Brasserie Max	*British, Modern*	343
	Homage	"	112
	The Ivy	"	233
	Paramount	"	224
	Rules	*British, Traditional*	345
	Savoy Grill	"	233
	Simpsons-in-the-Strand	"	122
	Kaspar's Seafood and Grill	*Fish & seafood*	333
	J Sheekey	"	444
	Yauatcha	*Chinese*	423
	aqua kyoto	*Japanese*	222
	Spice Market	*Pan-Asian*	233
£60+	Axis	*British, Modern*	223
	Balthazar	"	124
	Bob Bob Ricard	"	345
	Hix	"	222
	Indigo	"	233
	Kettners	"	223
	Social Eating House	"	445
	Tom's Kitchen	"	211
	Strand Dining Rooms	*British, Traditional*	243
	J Sheekey Oyster Bar	*Fish & seafood*	455
	Clos Maggiore	*French*	455
	L'Escargot	"	– – –
	Gauthier Soho	"	554
	Bocca Di Lupo	*Italian*	544
	aqua nueva	*Spanish*	222
	Hawksmoor	*Steaks & grills*	443
	STK Steakhouse	"	222
	Ladurée	*Afternoon tea*	222
	Shanghai Blues	*Chinese*	424
	Moti Mahal	*Indian*	443
	Red Fort	"	332
£50+	Big Easy	*American*	222
	Jamie's Diner	"	212
	Joe Allen	"	124

	Arbutus	*British, Modern*	442
	Aurora	*"*	334
	Coopers	*"*	333
	Dean Street Townhouse	*"*	334
	Le Deuxième	*"*	221
	Ducksoup	*"*	223
	Ham Yard Restaurant	*"*	222
	Hush	*"*	223
	The Portrait	*"*	224
	Quo Vadis	*"*	344
	Holborn Dining Room	*British, Traditional*	223
	The Lady Ottoline	*"*	223
	The National Dining Rms	*"*	112
	The Delaunay	*East & Cent. Euro*	345
	Wright Brothers	*Fish & seafood*	433
	Antidote	*French*	543
	Café des Amis	*"*	122
	Compagnie des Vins S.	*"*	422
	Les Deux Salons	*"*	122
	Mon Plaisir	*"*	234
	Otto's	*"*	454
	Randall & Aubin	*"*	445
	Kopapa	*Fusion*	222
	Ember Yard	*International*	333
	Sarastro	*"*	133
	The 10 Cases	*"*	233
	Mele e Pere	*Italian*	222
	Orso	*"*	332
	Vasco & Piero's Pavilion	*"*	443
	Nopi	*Mediterranean*	544
	Sophie's Steakhouse	*Steaks & grills*	232
	Cantina Laredo	*Mexican/TexMex*	443
	Lima Floral	*Peruvian*	– – –
	Bar Shu	*Chinese*	412
	Chotto Matte	*Japanese*	424
	Flesh and Buns	*"*	322
	Patara	*Thai*	333
	House of Ho	*Vietnamese*	432
£40+	Bodean's	*American*	222
	Jackson & Rye	*"*	112
	Mishkin's	*"*	123
	Spuntino	*"*	235
	Belgo	*Belgian*	243
	Andrew Edmunds	*British, Modern*	345
	The Angel & Crown	*"*	223
	The Ape & Bird	*"*	– – –
	The Norfolk Arms	*"*	432
	Shampers	*"*	245

10 Greek Street	"	553
Vinoteca	"	244
VQ	"	232
Great Queen Street	*British, Traditional*	333
Loch Fyne	*Fish & seafood*	222
Café Bohème	*French*	234
Le Cigalon	"	333
Le Garrick	"	223
Green Man & French Horn	"	344
Terroirs	"	323
Real Greek	*Greek*	222
Gay Hussar	*Hungarian*	234
Balans	*International*	243
Boulevard	"	233
Cork & Bottle	"	234
National Gallery Café	"	312
Rocket	"	333
Ciao Bella	*Italian*	243
Da Mario	"	223
Dehesa	"	434
Made in Italy	"	334
Obika	"	221
San Carlo Cicchetti	"	333
Barrafina	*Spanish*	555
Cigala	"	332
Copita	"	324
Opera Tavern	"	444
Tapas Brindisa Soho	"	323
Mildreds	*Vegetarian*	434
Orchard	"	333
Burger & Lobster	*Burgers, etc*	323
Wolfe's	"	343
Bianco43	*Pizza*	322
Fire & Stone	"	222
Villiers Coffee Co	*Sandwiches, cakes, etc*	– – –
La Bodega Negra	*Mexican/TexMex*	234
Ceviche	*Peruvian*	433
The Palomar	*Israeli*	454
Ba Shan	*Chinese*	412
Harbour City	"	211
New Mayflower	"	432
Plum Valley	"	423
Yming	"	453
Cinnamon Soho	*Indian*	432
Dishoom	"	434
Malabar Junction	"	323
Abeno	*Japanese*	332
Hazuki	"	222
Sticks'n'Sushi	"	333

	Asadal	*Korean*	322
	Inamo	*Pan-Asian*	222
	Thai Square	*Thai*	222
£35+	Soho Diner	*American*	234
	The Blind Pig	*British, Modern*	444
	Whyte & Brown	*"*	344
	Blanchette	*French*	354
	Brasserie Zédel	*"*	245
	Prix Fixe	*"*	344
	Savoir Faire	*"*	332
	21 Bateman Street	*Greek*	344
	Polpo	*Italian*	235
	La Polenteria	*"*	343
	Amico Bio	*Vegetarian*	222
	Honest Burgers	*Burgers, etc*	444
	North Sea Fish	*Fish & chips*	332
	Rossopomodoro	*Pizza*	222
	Lupita	*Mexican/TexMex*	323
	Gaby's	*Israeli*	332
	Yalla Yalla	*Lebanese*	334
	Sofra	*Turkish*	233
	Tas	*"*	233
	Er Mei	*Chinese*	443
	Joy King Lau	*"*	322
	New World	*"*	323
	Leong's Legends	*Chinese, Dim sum*	323
	Imli Street	*Indian*	344
	Sagar	*"*	322
	Salaam Namaste	*"*	332
	Rasa Maricham	*Indian, Southern*	443
	Koya	*Japanese*	443
	Taro	*"*	232
	Kimchee	*Korean*	423
	Banana Tree Canteen	*Pan-Asian*	222
	The Noodle House	*"*	– – –
	Busaba Eathai	*Thai*	224
	Cây Tre	*Vietnamese*	333
	Pho	*"*	333
£30+	Seven Stars	*British, Modern*	324
	Café in the Crypt	*International*	223
	Gordon's Wine Bar	*"*	235
	Carom at Meza	*"*	443
	Caffé Vergnano	*Italian*	333
	La Porchetta Pizzeria	*"*	333
	Princi	*"*	324
	Diner	*Burgers, etc*	133
	Ed's Easy Diner	*"*	123

	MEATmarket	"	422
	Caffé Vergnano	Sandwiches, cakes, etc	333
	Fernandez & Wells	"	324
	Wahaca	Mexican/TexMex	234
	Chilli Cool	Chinese	411
	The Four Seasons	"	411
	Golden Dragon	"	322
	Mr Kong	"	333
	Wong Kei	"	– – –
	ping pong	Chinese, Dim sum	223
	Masala Zone	Indian	343
	Koya-Bar	Japanese	444
	Kulu Kulu	"	311
	Tonkotsu	"	333
	Bibimbap Soho	Korean	333
	Hare & Tortoise	Pan-Asian	323
	C&R Cafe	Thai	422
£25+	Pitt Cue Co	American	544
	Bar Italia	Sandwiches, cakes, etc	345
	Konditor & Cook	"	342
	Benito's Hat	Mexican/TexMex	342
	Comptoir Libanais	Lebanese	222
	India Club	Indian	321
	Punjab	"	333
	Shoryu Ramen	Japanese	323
	Tokyo Diner	"	223
£20+	Bistro 1	Mediterranean	244
	Flat Iron	Steaks & grills	454
	Food for Thought	Vegetarian	442
	Dub Jam	Burgers, etc	443
	Shake Shack	"	222
	Homeslice	Pizza	532
	Pizza Pilgrims	"	444
	Fleet River Bakery	Sandwiches, cakes, etc	323
	Bone Daddies	Japanese	344
	Eat Tokyo	"	422
£15+	La Bottega	Italian	344
	Hummus Bros	Mediterranean	332
	Nordic Bakery	Scandinavian	333
	Maison Bertaux	Afternoon tea	423
	Notes	Sandwiches, cakes, etc	244
	Chilango	Mexican/TexMex	322
	Chipotle	"	332
	Baozi Inn	Chinese	322

£10+	Five Guys	*Burgers, etc*	322
	Gelupo	*Ice cream*	523
	Flat White	*Sandwiches, cakes, etc*	444
	Monmouth Coffee Co	*"*	554
	Jamaica Patty Co.	*Afro-Caribbean*	322
	Bunnychow	*South African*	– – –

Mayfair & St James's (Parts of W1 and SW1)

£150+	Quattro Passi	*Italian*	222
£140+	Fera at Claridge's	*British, Modern*	455
£130+	Le Gavroche	*French*	555
£120+	Alain Ducasse	*French*	232
	The Greenhouse	*"*	444
	Hélène Darroze	*"*	234
	Hibiscus	*"*	332
	The Ritz Restaurant	*"*	345
	Sketch (Lecture Rm)	*"*	223
£110+	The Square	*French*	443
	Cut	*Steaks & grills*	222
£100+	Wiltons	*British, Traditional*	344
	C London	*Italian*	112
	Novikov (Italian restaurant)	*"*	111
	Umu	*Japanese*	212
	Novikov (Asian restaurant)	*Pan-Asian*	123
£90+	Dorchester Grill	*British, Modern*	231
	Seven Park Place	*"*	344
	Galvin at Windows	*French*	235
	Murano	*Italian*	444
	Kai Mayfair	*Chinese*	442
	Benares	*Indian*	333
	Nobu, Park Ln	*Japanese*	422
	Nobu, Berkeley St	*"*	322
£80+	Alyn Williams	*British, Modern*	442
	Athenaeum	*"*	333
	Pollen Street Social	*"*	443
	Thirty Six	*"*	221
	Browns (Albemarle)	*British, Traditional*	233
	Corrigan's Mayfair	*"*	222

	Bentley's	*Fish & seafood*	333
	Scott's	*"*	454
	maze	*French*	222
	La Petite Maison	*"*	434
	Sketch (Gallery)	*"*	124
	Assunta Madre	*Italian*	322
	Theo Randall	*"*	322
	Rextail	*International*	122
	The Sketch (Parlour)	*Sandwiches, cakes, etc*	224
	Hakkasan Mayfair	*Chinese*	424
	Matsuri	*Japanese*	331
	Roka	*"*	534
£70+	Le Caprice	*British, Modern*	344
	Little Social	*"*	333
	Green's	*British, Traditional*	344
	Babbo	*Italian*	222
	Cecconi's	*"*	224
	Franco's	*"*	343
	Gaucho	*Steaks & grills*	211
	JW Steakhouse	*"*	222
	maze Grill	*"*	111
	34	*"*	333
	Coya	*Peruvian*	423
	Momo	*North African*	225
	China Tang	*Chinese*	223
	Tamarind	*Indian*	443
	Veeraswamy	*"*	444
	Sumosan	*Japanese*	322
£60+	Bellamy's	*British, Modern*	344
	The Berners Tavern	*"*	335
	Criterion	*"*	225
	Langan's Brasserie	*"*	224
	The Only Running Footman	*"*	222
	Quaglino's	*"*	– – –
	Sotheby's Café	*"*	343
	Wild Honey	*"*	333
	The Fountain (Fortnum's)	*British, Traditional*	232
	The Keeper's House	*"*	323
	Boulestin	*French*	222
	Brasserie Chavot	*"*	333
	Alloro	*Italian*	242
	La Genova	*"*	222
	Goodman	*Steaks & grills*	333
	The Guinea Grill	*"*	333
	Hawksmoor	*"*	443
	Rowley's	*"*	223
	Ladurée	*Afternoon tea*	222

Price	Restaurant	Cuisine	Rating
	Peyote	*Mexican/TexMex*	332
	Marani	*Georgian*	332
	Chor Bizarre	*Indian*	443
	Gymkhana	"	544
	Sake No Hana	*Japanese*	212
£50+	The Avenue	*American*	133
	Hush	*British, Modern*	223
	Inn the Park	"	224
	The Wolseley	"	345
	Fishworks	*Fish & seafood*	322
	Pescatori	"	322
	Aubaine	*French*	111
	Boudin Blanc	"	223
	28-50	"	334
	Piccolino	*Italian*	222
	Café Murano	"	444
	Sartoria	"	332
	Il Vicolo	"	342
	Diamond Jub' Salon)	*Afternoon tea*	355
	Delfino	*Pizza*	322
	Royal Academy	*Sandwiches, cakes, etc*	122
	Al Hamra	*Lebanese*	322
	Noura	"	222
	Princess Garden	*Chinese*	433
	Mint Leaf	*Indian*	323
	Chisou	*Japanese*	422
	Kiku	"	542
	Patara	*Thai*	333
£40+	Hard Rock Café	*American*	324
	1707	*British, Modern*	343
	L'Artiste Musclé	*French*	224
	Al Duca	*Italian*	222
	Ritz (Palm Court)	*Afternoon tea*	345
	Burger & Lobster	*Burgers, etc*	323
	Al Sultan	*Lebanese*	321
	Woodlands	*Indian*	332
	Yoshino	*Japanese*	342
	Inamo	*Pan-Asian*	222
£35+	The Windmill	*British, Traditional*	323
	El Pirata	*Spanish*	235
	tibits	*Vegetarian*	323
	Sofra	*Turkish*	233
	Rasa Samudra	*Indian, Southern*	443
	Sakana-tei	*Japanese*	442
	Busaba Eathai	*Thai*	224

£30+	Ed's Easy Diner	*Burgers, etc*	1 2 3
	Sakura	*Japanese*	2 2 2
£25+	Stock Pot	*International*	2 2 2
	Shoryu Ramen	*Japanese*	3 2 3
£15+	La Bottega	*Italian*	3 4 4
	Taylor St Baristas	*Sandwiches, cakes, etc*	4 4 3
£10+	Fuzzy's Grub	*Sandwiches, cakes, etc*	3 2 2

Fitzrovia & Marylebone (Part of W1)

£110+	Beast	*Burgers, etc*	3 2 3
£90+	Roux at the Landau	*British, Modern*	3 3 3
	Pied à Terre	*French*	5 5 3
	Bubbledogs (Kitchen Table @)	*Fusion*	4 5 4
	Texture	*Scandinavian*	3 4 3
£80+	The Chiltern Firehouse	*American*	2 2 5
	L'Autre Pied	*French*	4 4 2
	Hakkasan	*Chinese*	4 2 4
	Roka	*Japanese*	5 3 4
£70+	Orrery	*French*	3 4 4
	Locanda Locatelli	*Italian*	3 3 4
	Gaucho	*Steaks & grills*	2 1 1
£60+	Galvin Bistrot de Luxe	*French*	3 4 4
	The Providores	*International*	4 2 2
	Il Baretto	*Italian*	2 2 2
	Dabbous	*Mediterranean*	4 3 2
	Royal China Club	*Chinese*	4 4 3
	La Porte des Indes	*Indian*	3 3 4
	Trishna	"	4 3 2
	Defune	*Japanese*	3 2 1
	Crazy Bear	*Thai*	2 2 4
£50+	The Lockhart	*American*	2 2 2
	Grazing Goat	*British, Modern*	3 2 3
	Fishworks	*Fish & seafood*	3 2 2
	Pescatori	"	3 2 2
	Aubaine	*French*	1 1 1
	Elena's L'Etoile	"	1 1 1
	28-50	"	3 3 4

	Restaurant	Cuisine	Ratings
	Villandry	"	222
	The Wallace	"	225
	Providores (Tapa Room)	*Fusion*	323
	Fischer's	*International*	233
	Caffè Caldesi	*Italian*	342
	Latium	"	453
	Sardo	"	332
	Riding House Café	*Mediterranean*	224
	Fino	*Spanish*	444
	Black & Blue	*Steaks & grills*	222
	Zoilo	*Argentinian*	443
	Lima	*Peruvian*	422
	Reubens	*Kosher*	322
	Fairuz	*Lebanese*	433
	Levant	"	223
	The Bright Courtyard	*Chinese*	342
	Gaylord	*Indian*	332
	Zayna	"	432
	Dinings	*Japanese*	541
	Kikuchi	"	521
	Bam-Bou	*Vietnamese*	335
£40+	Barnyard	*British, Modern*	332
	Daylesford Organic	"	224
	Hardy's Brasserie	"	224
	Newman Street Tavern	"	323
	Ozer	"	232
	The Union Café	"	232
	Vinoteca Seymour Place	"	244
	Bonnie Gull	*Fish & seafood*	544
	Ergon	*Greek*	443
	Real Greek	"	222
	Briciole	*Italian*	334
	Made in Italy	"	334
	Obika	"	221
	2 Veneti	"	343
	Barrica	*Spanish*	434
	Donostia	"	544
	Drakes Tabanco	"	343
	Ibérica	"	323
	Navarro's	"	224
	Salt Yard	"	343
	Le Relais de Venise	*Steaks & grills*	323
	Maroush	*Lebanese*	422
	Ishtar	*Turkish*	343
	Royal China	*Chinese*	422
	Roti Chai	*Indian*	443
	Woodlands	"	332
	Nizuni	*Japanese*	442

	Tsunami	"	522
	Yoisho	"	322
	Koba	*Korean*	323
£35+	Lantana Cafe	*Australian*	334
	Natural Kitchen	*British, Modern*	323
	MEATLiquor	*Burgers, etc*	323
	La Fromagerie Café	*Sandwiches, cakes, etc*	324
	Natural Kitchen	*Salads*	323
	Yalla Yalla	*Lebanese*	334
	Sofra	*Turkish*	233
	Sagar	*Indian*	322
	dim T	*Pan-Asian*	223
	East Street	"	334
	Pho	*Vietnamese*	333
£30+	Bubbledogs	*American*	234
	Picture	*British, Modern*	352
	Wahaca	*Mexican/TexMex*	234
	Honey & Co	*Middle Eastern*	443
	ping pong	*Chinese, Dim sum*	223
	Chettinad	*Indian*	343
	Atari-Ya	*Japanese*	521
£25+	Stock Pot	*International*	222
	Vapiano	*Italian*	323
	Golden Hind	*Fish & chips*	342
	Benito's Hat	*Mexican/TexMex*	342
	Comptoir Libanais	*Lebanese*	222
	Ragam	*Indian*	541
£20+	Patty and Bun	*Burgers, etc*	423
	Patogh	*Middle Eastern*	322
£15+	Nordic Bakery	*Scandinavian*	333
	Scandinavian Kitchen	"	453
	Tommi's Burger Joint	*Burgers, etc*	423
	Nordic Bakery	*Sandwiches, cakes, etc*	333
	Chipotle	*Mexican/TexMex*	332
£10+	The Attendant	*Sandwiches, cakes, etc*	444
	Kaffeine	"	345

Belgravia, Pimlico, Victoria & Westminster (SW1, except St James's)

Price	Restaurant	Cuisine	Ratings
£110+	Marcus	*French*	333
£100+	Dinner	*British, Traditional*	333
	Rib Room	*Steaks & grills*	332
£90+	One-O-One	*Fish & seafood*	531
	Pétrus	*French*	444
£80+	The Goring Hotel	*British, Modern*	355
	Koffmann's	*French*	553
	Ametsa	*Spanish*	231
	Mr Chow	*Chinese*	332
£70+	Roux at Parliament Square	*British, Modern*	342
	Santini	*Italian*	234
	Toto's	"	354
	Zafferano	"	333
	Massimo	*Mediterranean*	244
	Amaya	*Indian*	543
	The Cinnamon Club	"	334
	Buddha-Bar London	*Pan-Asian*	123
£60+	Bank Westminster	*British, Modern*	322
	The Botanist	"	111
	The Fifth Floor Restaurant	"	333
	The Northall	"	343
	Olivomare	*Fish & seafood*	532
	Bar Boulud	*French*	334
	Colbert	"	123
	La Poule au Pot	"	335
	Motcombs	*International*	233
	Sale e Pepe	*Italian*	223
	Signor Sassi	"	233
	Boisdale	*Scottish*	334
	Ladurée	*Afternoon tea*	222
	Oliveto	*Pizza*	422
	The Grand Imperial	*Chinese*	322
	Hunan	"	531
	Ken Lo's Memories	"	343
	Quilon	*Indian, Southern*	432
	Salloos	*Pakistani*	442
£50+	Ebury Rest' & Wine Bar	*British, Modern*	223
	The Orange	"	334
	The Pantechnicon	"	334

	Tate Britain (Rex Whistler)	"	235
	The Thomas Cubitt	"	334
	The Balcon	*French*	223
	Chabrot Bistrot d'Amis	"	343
	Caraffini	*Italian*	253
	Il Convivio	"	443
	Olivo	"	442
	Olivocarne	"	442
	Osteria Dell'Angolo	"	342
	Quirinale	"	442
	About Thyme	*Mediterranean*	342
	Beiteddine	*Lebanese*	332
	Noura	"	222
	Mango Tree	*Thai*	112
£40+	Daylesford Organic	*British, Modern*	224
	The Queens Arms	"	444
	Uni	*Fusion*	443
	Grumbles	*International*	233
	Como Lario	*Italian*	223
	Gustoso	"	353
	Ottolenghi	"	533
	Tinello	"	444
	Tozi	"	343
	Bilbao Berria	*Spanish*	343
	Goya	"	232
	Burger & Lobster	*Burgers, etc*	323
	Baker & Spice	*Sandwiches, cakes, etc*	222
	Kazan	*Turkish*	333
£35+	Seafresh	*Fish & chips*	331
	dim T	*Pan-Asian*	223
£30+	The Vincent Rooms	*British, Modern*	333
	Cyprus Mangal	*Turkish*	431
	A Wong	*Chinese*	433
£15+	La Bottega	*Italian*	344

WEST

Chelsea, South Kensington, Kensington, Earl's Court & Fulham (SW3, SW5, SW6, SW7, SW10 & W8)

Price	Restaurant	Cuisine	Ratings
£120+	Gordon Ramsay	*French*	343
£100+	Rasoi	*Indian*	544
£80+	Bibendum	*French*	234
	Yashin	*Japanese*	532
	Yashin Ocean House	"	113
	Zuma	"	534
£70+	Babylon	*British, Modern*	244
	The Five Fields	"	554
	Launceston Place	"	344
	Cheyne Walk Bras'	*French*	333
	L'Etranger	"	342
	One Kensington	*International*	231
	Scalini	*Italian*	333
	Gaucho	*Steaks & grills*	211
	Min Jiang	*Chinese*	535
£60+	The Abingdon	*British, Modern*	334
	Bluebird	"	123
	Clarke's	"	332
	Kitchen W8	"	543
	Medlar	"	543
	Pavilion	"	343
	Tom's Kitchen	"	211
	Bibendum Oyster Bar	*Fish & seafood*	243
	Outlaw's Seafood and Grill	"	442
	Poissonnerie de l'Av.	"	432
	Belvedere	*French*	224
	Racine	"	222
	Margaux	*International*	333
	Rivea	"	242
	Daphne's	*Italian*	– – –
	La Famiglia	"	222
	Lucio	"	222
	Manicomio	"	323
	Pellicano	"	353
	Locanda Ottomezzo	*Mediterranean*	343
	Cambio de Tercio	*Spanish*	434
	Hawksmoor Knightsbridge	*Steaks & grills*	443
	Bo Lang	*Chinese, Dim sum*	233

£50+	Big Easy	*American*	222
	Brinkley's	*British, Modern*	334
	The Enterprise	"	233
	Harwood Arms	"	433
	The Henry Root	"	223
	Kensington Place	"	453
	The Sands End	"	444
	The Terrace	"	244
	White Horse	"	224
	Bumpkin	*British, Traditional*	322
	Ffiona's	"	233
	Maggie Jones's	"	235
	The Malt House	"	443
	Aubaine	*French*	111
	La Brasserie	"	224
	Le Colombier	"	344
	Garnier	"	342
	The Pig's Ear	"	223
	Mazi	*Greek*	322
	Foxtrot Oscar	*International*	222
	Gallery Mess	"	222
	The Kensington Wine Rms	"	223
	Frantoio	*Italian*	223
	Il Portico	"	253
	Tartufo	"	543
	Ziani's	"	333
	Polish Club	*Polish*	234
	The Admiral Codrington	*Steaks & grills*	222
	Black & Blue	"	222
	Kings Road Steakhouse	"	211
	PJ's Bar and Grill	"	234
	Sophie's Steakhouse	"	232
	Good Earth	*Chinese*	332
	Bombay Brasserie	*Indian*	444
	Chutney Mary	"	454
	The Painted Heron	"	532
	Star of India	"	42–
	Chisou	*Japanese*	422
	Eight Over Eight	*Pan-Asian*	333
	Patara	*Thai*	333
	Sukho Fine Thai Cuisine	"	543
£40+	Bodean's	*American*	222
	Sticky Fingers	"	222
	The Anglesea Arms	*British, Modern*	224
	The Builders Arms	"	334
	The Cadogan Arms	"	331
	Joe's Brasserie	"	243
	The Mall Tavern	"	223
	The Phene	"	123

	VQ	"	2 3 2
	Whits	"	3 5 3
	The Brown Cow	*British, Traditional*	4 4 4
	The Surprise	"	2 3 4
	La Bouchée	*French*	2 2 4
	Chez Patrick	"	3 5 4
	Balans	*International*	2 4 3
	Troubadour	"	2 3 4
	The Windsor Castle	"	2 2 5
	Aglio e Olio	*Italian*	3 3 2
	Da Mario	"	2 3 3
	Made in Italy	"	3 3 4
	Napulé	"	4 4 3
	Nuovi Sapori	"	3 4 3
	Obika	"	2 2 1
	Ottolenghi	"	5 3 3
	Pappa Ciccia	"	4 3 3
	Riccardo's	"	2 2 2
	The Atlas	*Mediterranean*	4 4 4
	Daquise	*Polish*	2 3 2
	Capote Y Toros	*Spanish*	4 3 4
	Casa Brindisa	"	2 2 2
	Tendido Cero	"	3 3 4
	Tendido Cuatro	"	4 4 4
	Maxela	*Steaks & grills*	4 3 3
	Geales	*Fish & chips*	2 1 2
	La Delizia Limbara	*Pizza*	4 4 3
	Rocca Di Papa	"	2 2 3
	Santa Lucia	"	3 2 2
	Baker & Spice	*Sandwiches, cakes, etc*	2 2 2
	Beirut Express	*Lebanese*	4 2 2
	Maroush	"	4 2 2
	Ranoush	"	4 3 2
	Royal China	*Chinese*	4 2 2
	Malabar	*Indian*	4 4 2
	Thali	"	4 4 2
	Bangkok	*Thai*	3 2 2
	Thai Square	"	2 2 2
£35+	Dirty Bones	*American*	– – –
	The Shed	*British, Modern*	3 3 5
	Buona Sera	*Italian*	2 3 3
	Il Pagliaccio	"	2 3 3
	Haché	*Steaks & grills*	3 3 4
	Basilico	*Pizza*	4 4 1
	Rossopomodoro	"	2 2 2
	Best Mangal	*Turkish*	4 4 3
	Taiwan Village	*Chinese*	5 5 3
	Noor Jahan	*Indian*	4 4 4
	Churchill Arms	*Thai*	3 3 5

Price	Restaurant	Cuisine	Ratings
£30+	Kensington Square Kitchen	*British, Modern*	344
	Chelsea Bun Diner	*International*	323
	Diner	*Burgers, etc*	133
	The Greedy Buddha	*Indian*	322
	Masala Zone	*"*	343
	Kulu Kulu	*Japanese*	311
	Addie's Thai Café	*Thai*	332
£25+	Mona Lisa	*International*	333
	Stock Pot	*"*	222
	Comptoir Libanais	*Lebanese*	222
£20+	Eat Tokyo	*Japanese*	422
	Café 209	*Thai*	235
£15+	La Bottega	*Italian*	344
	Tommi's Burger Joint	*Burgers, etc*	423

Notting Hill, Holland Park, Bayswater, North Kensington & Maida Vale (W2, W9, W10, W11)

Price	Restaurant	Cuisine	Ratings
£130+	The Ledbury	*British, Modern*	554
£90+	Marianne	*British, Modern*	443
£80+	The New Angel	*International*	443
	The Shiori	*Japanese*	553
£70+	Angelus	*French*	354
	Assaggi	*Italian*	442
£60+	Beach Blanket Babylon	*British, Modern*	123
	Julie's	*"*	115
	Edera	*Italian*	343
	Chakra	*Indian*	211
	E&O	*Pan-Asian*	323
£50+	The Cow	*British, Modern*	344
	The Dock Kitchen	*"*	345
	The Frontline Club	*"*	333
	The Ladbroke Arms	*"*	314
	The Magazine Restaurant	*"*	235
	New Tom's	*"*	– – –
	Truscott Arms	*"*	334
	The Waterway	*"*	214
	Bumpkin	*British, Traditional*	322
	The Summerhouse	*Fish & seafood*	335
	Le Café Anglais	*French*	334

Price	Restaurant	Cuisine	Ratings
	Les Gourmets Des Ternes	"	– – –
	Essenza	*Italian*	3 3 3
	Mediterraneo	"	3 3 3
	The Oak	"	4 4 4
	Osteria Basilico	"	3 3 4
	Casa Malevo	*Argentinian*	4 3 3
	Bombay Palace	*Indian*	5 2 1
	Kurobuta	*Japanese*	4 2 3
£40+	Electric Diner	*American*	2 4 4
	Lucky Seven	"	3 3 3
	Granger & Co	*Australian*	2 3 4
	Daylesford Organic	*British, Modern*	2 2 4
	First Floor	"	3 2 5
	Paradise, Kensal Green	"	3 4 5
	Hereford Road	*British, Traditional*	3 3 2
	Halepi	*Greek*	3 4 2
	Ottolenghi	*Italian*	5 3 3
	Portobello Ristorante	"	3 4 4
	Raoul's Cafe	*Mediterranean*	2 2 3
	El Pirata de Tapas	*Spanish*	3 3 2
	Pizza East Portobello	*Pizza*	4 3 4
	The Red Pepper	"	4 2 2
	Baker & Spice	*Sandwiches, cakes, etc*	2 2 2
	Al-Waha	*Lebanese*	3 2 1
	Beirut Express	"	4 2 2
	Maroush	"	4 2 2
	Ranoush	"	4 3 2
	Kateh	*Persian*	5 4 3
	Mandarin Kitchen	*Chinese*	4 1 1
	Pearl Liang	"	3 2 2
	Royal China	"	4 2 2
	Inaho	*Japanese*	4 3 2
£35+	Polpo	*Italian*	2 3 5
	Honest Burgers	*Burgers, etc*	4 4 4
	Taqueria	*Mexican/TexMex*	3 4 3
	Noor Jahan	*Indian*	4 4 4
	Maguro	*Japanese*	4 4 3
	Satay House	*Malaysian*	3 3 2
	Banana Tree Canteen	*Pan-Asian*	2 2 2
£30+	Notting Hill Kitchen	*Spanish*	2 3 2
	Alounak	*Persian*	3 2 3
	The Four Seasons	*Chinese*	4 1 1
	Gold Mine	"	3 2 1
	ping pong	*Chinese, Dim sum*	2 2 3
	Durbar	*Indian*	3 3 3
	Masala Zone	"	3 4 3
	C&R Cafe	*Thai*	4 2 2

£25+	Mandalay	*Burmese*	331
	Fitou's Thai Restaurant	*Thai*	432
£20+	Fez Mangal	*Turkish*	543
	Khan's	*Indian*	422
£5+	Lisboa Pâtisserie	*Sandwiches, cakes, etc*	442

Hammersmith, Shepherd's Bush, Olympia, Chiswick, Brentford & Ealing (W4, W5, W6, W12, W13, W14, TW8)

£90+	The River Café	*Italian*	323
£80+	Hedone	*British, Modern*	543
£60+	La Trompette	*French*	544
	Le Vacherin	*"*	333
£50+	The Anglesea Arms	*British, Modern*	424
	The Brackenbury	*"*	432
	High Road Brasserie	*"*	223
	The Hampshire Hog	*British, Traditional*	223
	Charlotte's Bistro	*French*	343
	Charlotte's Place	*"*	343
	Michael Nadra	*International*	531
	Cibo	*Italian*	453
	The Oak W12	*"*	444
	Popeseye	*Steaks & grills*	342
	Chisou	*Japanese*	422
£40+	Bush Dining Hall	*British, Modern*	123
	The Carpenter's Arms	*"*	334
	City Barge	*"*	445
	The Dartmouth Castle	*"*	343
	Duke of Sussex	*"*	324
	The Havelock Tavern	*"*	323
	Hole in the Wall	*"*	233
	Princess Victoria	*"*	344
	Sam's Brasserie	*"*	344
	Vinoteca	*"*	244
	The Real Greek	*Greek*	222
	The Andover Arms	*International*	244
	Annie's	*"*	234
	Balans	*"*	243
	L'Amorosa	*Italian*	– – –
	Pentolina	*"*	454
	Cumberland Arms	*Mediterranean*	443
	Raoul's Café & Deli	*"*	223

 FSA Ratings: from [1] (Poor) to [5] (Exceptional)

Price	Restaurant	Cuisine	Ratings
	The Swan	"	445
	The Gate	Vegetarian	322
	Bird in Hand	Pizza	344
	Fire & Stone	"	222
	Azou	North African	444
	North China	Chinese	443
	Indian Zing	Indian	543
	Karma	"	442
	Tosa	Japanese	422
	Saigon Saigon	Vietnamese	343
£35+	Queen's Head	British, Modern	224
	Canta Napoli	Italian	332
	Patio	Polish	355
	Quantus	South American	354
	Best Mangal	Turkish	443
	Brilliant	Indian	333
	Madhu's	"	433
	Potli	"	434
	Sagar	"	322
	Kiraku	Japanese	532
	Fat Boy's	Thai	233
	Pho	Vietnamese	333
£30+	Albertine	French	244
	Santa Maria	Pizza	533
	Adams Café	Moroccan	254
	Chez Abir	Lebanese	432
	Alounak	Persian	323
	Sufi	"	334
	Anarkali	Indian	332
	Shilpa	Indian, Southern	431
	Atari-Ya	Japanese	521
	Hare & Tortoise	Pan-Asian	323
	Esarn Kheaw	Thai	431
	101 Thai Kitchen	"	421
£25+	Comptoir Libanais	Lebanese	222
	Faanoos	Persian	324
£20+	Franco Manca	Pizza	433
	Abu Zaad	Syrian	332
	Eat Tokyo	Japanese	422
	Miran Masala	Pakistani	542
	Mirch Masala	"	311
£15+	Kerbisher & Malt	Fish & chips	332
	Gifto's	Indian	322

NORTH

Hampstead, West Hampstead, St John's Wood, Regent's Park, Kilburn & Camden Town (NW postcodes)

Price	Restaurant	Cuisine	Ratings
£80+	Landmark (Winter Gdn)	*British, Modern*	234
£70+	Gilgamesh	*Pan-Asian*	223
£60+	Bull & Last	*British, Traditional*	433
	Gilbert Scott	*"*	224
	L'Aventure	*French*	455
	Oslo Court	*"*	454
	Villa Bianca	*Italian*	223
	Kaifeng	*Chinese*	322
£50+	Q Grill	*American*	332
	Bradley's	*British, Modern*	222
	The Engineer	*"*	223
	Market	*"*	432
	Odette's	*"*	334
	St Pancras Grand	*"*	222
	Michael Nadra	*French*	531
	La Collina	*Italian*	432
	York & Albany	*"*	224
	Manna	*Vegetarian*	232
	Good Earth	*Chinese*	332
	Phoenix Palace	*"*	322
£40+	Karpo	*American*	321
	Belgo Noord	*Belgian*	243
	The Horseshoe	*British, Modern*	323
	The Junction Tavern	*"*	344
	The North London Tavern	*"*	333
	The Old Bull & Bush	*"*	323
	Parlour	*"*	443
	Rising Sun	*"*	343
	The Wells	*"*	324
	The Wet Fish Cafe	*"*	333
	Kentish Canteen	*British, Traditional*	243
	L'Absinthe	*French*	232
	La Cage Imaginaire	*"*	334
	Mill Lane Bistro	*"*	332
	Lemonia	*Greek*	234
	Artigiano	*Italian*	333
	Ostuni	*"*	233
	The Salt House	*"*	212
	Sarracino	*"*	432

	Harry Morgan's	*Burgers, etc*	222
	Nautilus	*Fish & chips*	441
	The Sea Shell	*"*	442
	Skipjacks	*"*	442
	Pizza East	*Pizza*	434
	Greenberry Cafe	*Sandwiches, cakes, etc*	333
	Mango Room	*Afro-Caribbean*	332
	Solly's	*Israeli*	222
	Zest	*Kosher*	322
	Green Cottage	*Chinese*	311
	Gung-Ho	*"*	342
	Eriki	*Indian*	432
	Woodlands	*"*	332
	Jin Kichi	*Japanese*	543
	Sushi-Say	*"*	542
	Singapore Garden	*Malaysian*	432
	XO	*Pan-Asian*	222
£35+	Made In Camden	*British, Modern*	333
	Simply Fish	*Fish & seafood*	333
	L'Artista	*Italian*	244
	El Parador	*Spanish*	444
	Haché	*Steaks & grills*	334
	Honest Burgers	*Burgers, etc*	444
	Basilico	*Pizza*	441
	Rossopomodoro	*"*	222
	Asakusa	*Japanese*	522
	Bento Cafe	*"*	442
	dim T	*Pan-Asian*	223
£30+	Chicken Shop	*American*	344
	Carob Tree	*Greek*	454
	La Porchetta Pizzeria	*Italian*	333
	The Little Bay	*Mediterranean*	234
	The Diner	*Burgers, etc*	133
	Ed's Easy Diner	*"*	123
	Sacro Cuore	*Pizza*	434
	Kenwood (Brew House)	*Sandwiches, cakes, etc*	225
	Chutneys	*Indian*	222
	Diwana B-P House	*"*	321
	Great Nepalese	*"*	342
	Guglee	*"*	344
	Paradise Hampstead	*"*	454
	Ravi Shankar	*"*	432
	Vijay	*"*	342
	Atari-Ya	*Japanese*	521
£20+	Ali Baba	*Egyptian*	322

	Kadiri's	*Indian*	432
	Eat Tokyo	*Japanese*	422
£15+	Ginger & White	*Sandwiches, cakes, etc*	334
£10+	Dirty Burger	*Burgers, etc*	444

Hoxton, Islington, Highgate, Crouch End, Stoke Newington, Finsbury Park, Muswell Hill & Finchley (N postcodes)

£60+	Frederick's	*British, Modern*	234
	Fifteen Restaurant	*Italian*	111
£50+	Shrimpy's	*American*	333
	The Duke of Cambridge	*British, Modern*	233
	Grain Store	"	323
	The Haven	"	222
	Rotunda Bar & Restaurant	"	213
	The Almeida	*French*	222
	Bistro Aix	"	433
	Trullo	*Italian*	444
£40+	Red Dog Saloon	*American*	323
	The Albion	*British, Modern*	224
	Bald Faced Stag	"	333
	The Bull	"	224
	Caravan King's Cross	"	324
	The Clissold Arms	"	344
	The Drapers Arms	"	323
	The Fellow	"	333
	Juniper Dining	"	332
	LeCoq	"	444
	Pig & Butcher	"	433
	Plum + Spilt Milk	"	233
	St Johns	*British, Traditional*	335
	Kipferl	*East & Cent. Euro*	333
	Les Associés	*French*	342
	Blue Legume	"	223
	Le Coq	"	343
	Banners	*International*	345
	8 Hoxton Square	"	332
	The Orange Tree	"	123
	Primeur	"	– – –
	500	*Italian*	342
	Ottolenghi	"	533
	Pizzeria Oregano	"	443
	San Daniele	"	343

	Camino	*Spanish*	233
	The Smokehouse Islington	*Steaks & grills*	343
	Duke's Brew & Que	*Burgers, etc*	323
	The Fish & Chip Shop	*Fish & chips*	444
	Toff's	*"*	432
	Two Brothers	*"*	332
	Il Bacio	*Pizza*	322
	Yipin China	*Chinese*	521
	Dishoom	*Indian*	434
	Roots at N1	*"*	553
	Zaffrani	*"*	443
	Isarn	*Thai*	432
	Thai Square	*"*	222
	Yum Yum	*"*	324
£35+	Season Kitchen	*British, Modern*	443
	Le Sacré-Coeur	*French*	234
	Vrisaki	*Greek*	333
	Pizzeria Pappagone	*Italian*	334
	Rugoletta	*"*	442
	Vivo	*"*	444
	Bar Esteban	*Spanish*	533
	Café del Parc	*"*	444
	Basilico	*Pizza*	441
	Rossopomodoro	*"*	222
	Gilak	*Persian*	332
	Antepliler	*Turkish*	322
	Gallipoli	*"*	343
	Mangal II	*"*	332
	Little Georgia Café	*Georgian*	323
	Indian Rasoi	*Indian*	443
	Rasa	*Indian, Southern*	443
	Akari	*Japanese*	423
	dim T	*Pan-Asian*	223
	Huong-Viet	*Vietnamese*	322
£30+	Olympus Fish	*Fish & seafood*	441
	Le Mercury	*French*	234
	La Porchetta Pizzeria	*Italian*	333
	La Bota	*Spanish*	343
	Meat Mission	*Burgers, etc*	433
	Fabrizio	*Pizza*	342
	Sweet Thursday	*"*	333
	Wahaca	*Mexican/TexMex*	234
	Gem	*Turkish*	344
	Izgara	*"*	321
	Delhi Grill	*Indian*	433
	Masala Zone	*"*	343
	Salvation In Noodles	*Vietnamese*	443

£25+	White Rabbit	*British, Modern*	433
	Prawn On The Lawn	*Fish & seafood*	453
	Benito's Hat	*Mexican/TexMex*	342
	Afghan Kitchen	*Afghani*	421
	Rani	*Indian*	322
	Dotori	*Korean*	422
£15+	Notes	*Sandwiches, cakes, etc*	244
	Chilango	*Mexican/TexMex*	322
	Chipotle	*"*	332
	Jai Krishna	*Indian*	432
£10+	The Rib Man	*Burgers, etc*	534

SOUTH

South Bank (SE1)

Price	Restaurant	Cuisine	Ratings
£80+	Oblix	*American*	225
	Aqua Shard	*British, Modern*	114
	Oxo Tower (Rest')	*"*	112
	Story	*"*	443
	Ting	*International*	223
£70+	Le Pont de la Tour	*British, Modern*	223
	Rabot 1745	*International*	233
	Oxo Tower (Brass')	*Mediterranean*	122
	Gaucho	*Steaks & grills*	211
	Hutong	*Chinese*	224
£60+	Butlers W'f Chop-house	*British, Traditional*	222
	Roast	*"*	222
	La Barca	*Italian*	222
£50+	Cantina Vinopolis	*British, Modern*	222
	Elliot's Cafe	*"*	433
	Magdalen	*"*	443
	Menier Chocolate Factory	*"*	123
	Skylon	*"*	123
	Skylon Grill	*"*	123
	The Swan at the Globe	*"*	334
	Waterloo Bar & Kitchen	*"*	332
	fish!	*Fish & seafood*	222
	Wright Brothers	*"*	433
	Village East	*Fusion*	323
	Vivat Bacchus	*International*	232
	Tentazioni	*Italian*	344
	Zucca	*"*	543
	Baltic	*Polish*	323
	Archduke Wine Bar	*Steaks & grills*	222
	Black & Blue	*"*	222
£40+	Albion	*British, Modern*	222
	Blueprint Café	*"*	325
	Edwins	*"*	334
	40 Maltby Street	*"*	444
	Garrison	*"*	333
	RSJ	*"*	342
	The Table	*"*	222
	Tate Modern (Level 7)	*"*	224
	Union Street Café	*"*	222
	The Anchor & Hope	*British, Traditional*	533

	Canteen	"	111
	Applebee's Cafe	*Fish & seafood*	322
	Champor-Champor	*Fusion*	323
	Real Greek	*Greek*	222
	Brigade	*International*	323
	The Rooftop Cafe	"	345
	Antico	*Italian*	443
	José	*Spanish*	545
	Meson don Felipe	"	224
	Pizarro	"	344
	Tapas Brindisa	"	323
	Arabica Bar and Kitchen	*Lebanese*	343
	Bengal Clipper	*Indian*	333
	Mango Food of India	"	322
£35+	Casse-Croute	*French*	445
	Ev Restaurant, Bar & Deli	*Turkish*	233
	dim T	*Pan-Asian*	223
£30+	Masters Super Fish	*Fish & chips*	411
	Gourmet Pizza Co.	*Pizza*	223
	Caffé Vergnano	*Sandwiches, cakes, etc*	333
	Wahaca	*Mexican/TexMex*	234
	El Vergel	*South American*	434
	Tas Pide	*Turkish*	234
	ping pong	*Chinese, Dim sum*	223
£25+	Vapiano	*Italian*	323
	Konditor & Cook	*Sandwiches, cakes, etc*	342
£10+	Monmouth Coffee Co	*Sandwiches, cakes, etc*	554
	Spianata & Co	"	443

Greenwich, Lewisham, Dulwich & Blackheath (All SE postcodes, except SE1)

£60+	Lobster Pot	*Fish & seafood*	432
£50+	The Camberwell Arms	*British, Modern*	444
	Chapters	"	232
	The Palmerston	"	332
	Rivington Grill	"	223
	Buenos Aires Café	*Argentinian*	333
	Babur	*Indian*	543
£40+	The Crooked Well	*British, Modern*	344
	Franklins	"	333

Price	Restaurant	Cuisine	Ratings
	Inside	"	441
	The Lido Cafe	"	223
	The Old Brewery	"	234
	Brasserie Toulouse-Lautrec	*French*	343
	Toasted	"	334
	Joanna's	*International*	344
	The Yellow House	"	342
	Artusi	*Italian*	432
	Lorenzo	"	343
	Le Querce	"	442
	Peckham Bazaar	*Mediterranean*	333
	Angels & Gypsies	*Spanish*	223
	Olley's	*Fish & chips*	432
	Bianco43	*Pizza*	322
	Rocca Di Papa	"	223
	Zero Degrees	"	322
	Ganapati	*Indian*	544
	Kennington Tandoori	"	443
£35+	The Dartmouth Arms	*British, Modern*	223
	Peckham Refreshment Rms	"	333
	The Lord Northbrook	*British, Traditional*	344
	Dragon Castle	*Chinese*	311
	Everest Inn	*Indian*	444
	Tandoori Nights	"	343
	The Begging Bowl	*Thai*	545
£30+	The Sea Cow	*Fish & chips*	333
	The Gowlett	*Pizza*	434
£20+	Silk Road	*Chinese*	521
	Thai Corner Café	*Thai*	333
	Cafe East	*Vietnamese*	422
£10+	Monmouth Coffee Company	*Sandwiches, cakes, etc*	554

Battersea, Brixton, Clapham, Wandsworth Barnes, Putney & Wimbledon (All SW postcodes south of the river)

Price	Restaurant	Cuisine	Ratings
£60+	Cannizaro House	*British, Modern*	234
	Chez Bruce	"	554
	Trinity	"	453
	The Lawn Bistro	*French*	222
	Riva	*Italian*	342
	San Lorenzo Fuoriporta	"	222
£50+	Abbeville Kitchen	*British, Modern*	342

	The Brown Dog	"	333
	Entrée	"	443
	Sonny's Kitchen	"	222
	Fox & Grapes	*British, Traditional*	222
	The Lobster House	*Fish & seafood*	223
	Soif	*French*	443
	Upstairs	"	444
	The Light House	*International*	233
	London House	"	454
	Bibo	*Italian*	433
	Enoteca Turi	"	443
	Numero Uno	"	344
	Alquimia	*Spanish*	342
	Popeseye	*Steaks & grills*	342
	Fulham Wine Rooms	*Sandwiches, cakes, etc*	234
	Good Earth	*Chinese*	332
	Suk Saran	*Thai*	421
£40+	Bodean's	*American*	222
	Red Dog South	"	323
	Bistro Union	*British, Modern*	223
	The Bolingbroke	"	323
	Brunswick House Cafe	"	225
	Claude's Kitchen	"	444
	The Dairy	"	544
	The Depot	"	235
	Earl Spencer	"	323
	Emile's	"	442
	Lamberts	"	554
	Olympic Café	"	223
	Source	"	234
	The Victoria	"	343
	Canton Arms	*British, Traditional*	334
	Augustine Kitchen	*French*	441
	Bellevue Rendez-Vous	"	333
	Gastro	"	215
	Le P'tit Normand	"	343
	Annie's	*International*	234
	Hudsons	"	223
	The Ship	"	334
	Telegraph	"	324
	Antipasto & Pasta	*Italian*	342
	Donna Margherita	"	433
	Ost. Antica Bologna	"	333
	Pizza Metro	"	443
	Sapori Sardi	"	442
	The Fox & Hounds	*Mediterranean*	444
	Lola Rojo	*Spanish*	323
	Tapas Brindisa	"	323

 FSA Ratings: from [1] (Poor) to [5] (Exceptional)

	Butcher & Grill	*Steaks & grills*	223
	Cattle Grid	*"*	323
	Cornish Tiger	*"*	443
	Indian Zilla	*Indian*	553
	Ma Goa	*"*	442
	Sticks'n'Sushi	*Japanese*	333
	Tsunami	*"*	522
	Blue Elephant	*Thai*	323
£35+	Gazette	*French*	224
	Buona Sera	*Italian*	233
	Fish in a Tie	*Mediterranean*	344
	Haché	*Burgers, etc*	334
	Honest Burgers	*"*	444
	Fish Club	*Fish & chips*	442
	Al Forno	*Pizza*	244
	Basilico	*"*	441
	Eco	*"*	334
	Rossopomodoro	*"*	222
	Dalchini	*Chinese*	342
	Indian Moment	*Indian*	343
	Nazmins	*"*	344
	Hashi	*Japanese*	443
	Cah-Chi	*Korean*	432
	The Banana Tree Canteen	*Pan-Asian*	222
	Fat Boy's	*Thai*	233
£30+	Chicken Shop	*American*	344
	The Clink	*International*	235
	The Little Bay	*Mediterranean*	234
	Boqueria	*Spanish*	444
	Ed's Easy Diner	*Burgers, etc*	123
	Brady's	*Fish & chips*	333
	Chutney	*Indian*	442
	Indian Ocean	*"*	443
	Hare & Tortoise	*Pan-Asian*	323
	Talad Thai	*Thai*	321
	Mien Tay	*Vietnamese*	422
£25+	Dip & Flip	*Burgers, etc*	432
	Moxon's Fish Bar	*Fish & chips*	543
	Orange Pekoe	*Sandwiches, cakes, etc*	344
	Faanoos	*Persian*	324
	Holy Cow	*Indian*	433
	Sree Krishna	*"*	432
	Fujiyama	*Japanese*	432
	Lahore Kebab House	*Pakistani*	522
	Kaosarn	*Thai*	434

Price	Restaurant	Cuisine	Ratings
	The Pepper Tree	"	443
	The Paddyfield	Vietnamese	332
£20+	Franco Manca	Pizza	433
	Apollo Banana Leaf	Indian	511
	Hot Stuff	"	332
	Lahore Karahi	Pakistani	422
	Mirch Masala SW17	"	311
£15+	Wishbone	American	322
	Kerbisher & Malt	Fish & chips	332
	Meza	Lebanese	443
£10+	Dirty Burger	Burgers, etc	444

Outer western suburbs Kew, Richmond, Twickenham, Teddington

Price	Restaurant	Cuisine	Ratings
£80+	The Bingham	British, Modern	334
£70+	Petersham Nurseries	British, Modern	214
£60+	The Glasshouse	British, Modern	553
	Petersham Hotel	"	355
	The Dysart Petersham	"	442
	Al Boccon di'vino	Italian	435
£50+	A Cena	Italian	333
£40+	Linnea	British, Modern	543
	The Wharf	"	234
	Brula	French	444
	La Buvette	"	334
	Ma Cuisine	"	343
	don Fernando's	Spanish	232
	Palmyra	Lebanese	432
	Four Regions	Chinese	332
	Matsuba	Japanese	432
£35+	Canta Napoli	Italian	332
	Pizzeria Rustica	Pizza	443
	Fat Boy's	Thai	233
£15+	Taylor St Baristas	Sandwiches, cakes, etc	443

EAST

Smithfield & Farringdon (EC1)

Price	Restaurant	Cuisine	Ratings
£70+	The Clove Club	*British, Modern*	444
	Club Gascon	*French*	433
	Gaucho	*Steaks & grills*	211
	Smiths (Top Floor)	*"*	222
£60+	Bird of Smithfield	*British, Modern*	223
	Chiswell Street Dining Rms	*"*	222
	The Jugged Hare	*"*	333
	St John	*British, Traditional*	442
	Bonnie Gull Seafood Cafe	*Fish & seafood*	433
	Bleeding Heart	*French*	335
	Moro	*Spanish*	544
£50+	The Modern Pantry	*British, Modern*	333
	Bistrot Bruno Loubet	*French*	333
	Café du Marché	*"*	345
	Fabrizio	*Italian*	442
	Portal	*Portuguese*	344
	Hix	*Steaks & grills*	322
	Smiths (Dining Rm)	*"*	222
	Sushi Tetsu	*Japanese*	553
£40+	Granger & Co	*Australian*	234
	Blackfoot	*British, Modern*	332
	Caravan	*"*	324
	Foxlow	*"*	333
	The Peasant	*"*	334
	Vinoteca	*"*	244
	The Fox and Anchor	*British, Traditional*	335
	The Quality Chop House	*"*	454
	Chabrot Bistrot des Halles	*French*	222
	Comptoir Gascon	*"*	334
	Santore	*Italian*	442
	Ibérica	*Spanish*	323
	The Gate	*Vegetarian*	322
	Burger & Lobster	*Burgers, etc*	323
	Workshop Coffee	*Sandwiches, cakes, etc*	433
£35+	Lantana Cafe	*Australian*	334
	Cellar Gascon	*French*	333
	Apulia	*Italian*	331
	Polpo	*"*	235
	Morito	*Spanish*	444
	Amico Bio	*Vegetarian*	222

Price	Restaurant	Cuisine	Ratings
	Tas	*Turkish*	233
	Pham Sushi	*Japanese*	541
	Tajima Tei	*"*	333
	On The Bab	*Korean*	434
	Banana Tree Canteen	*Pan-Asian*	222
	Busaba Eathai	*Thai*	224
	Cây Tre	*Vietnamese*	333
	Pho	*"*	333
£30+	Smiths (Ground Floor)	*British, Modern*	224
	Fish Central	*Fish & seafood*	332
	Kolossi Grill	*Greek*	344
	La Porchetta Pizzeria	*Italian*	333
	The Eagle	*Mediterranean*	434
	The Little Bay	*"*	234
	Look Mum No Hands!	*Sandwiches, cakes, etc*	334
£25+	GB Pizza	*Pizza*	443
	Benito's Hat	*Mexican/TexMex*	342
£15+	Hummus Bros	*Mediterranean*	332
	Department of Coffee	*Sandwiches, cakes, etc*	334
	Daddy Donkey	*Mexican/TexMex*	432
£10+	Big Apple Hot Dogs	*Burgers, etc*	44–
	Dose	*Sandwiches, cakes, etc*	442
	Nusa Kitchen	*"*	442
	Prufrock Coffee	*"*	433
	Spianata & Co	*"*	443

The City (EC2, EC3, EC4)

Price	Restaurant	Cuisine	Ratings
£80+	Hixter	*British, Modern*	333
£70+	City Social	*British, Modern*	454
	1 Lombard Street	*"*	212
	Angler	*Fish & seafood*	334
	Chamberlain's	*"*	332
	Coq d'Argent	*French*	223
	Lutyens	*"*	222
	Sauterelle	*"*	334
	L'Anima	*Italian*	333
	HKK	*Chinese*	553
	Sushisamba	*Japanese*	335
£60+	Bread Street Kitchen	*British, Modern*	232
	The Don	*"*	343

	Duck & Waffle	"	225
	The Mercer	"	322
	1901	"	113
	3 South Place	"	233
	The White Swan	"	443
	Sweetings	*Fish & seafood*	323
	Manicomio	*Italian*	323
	Barbecoa	*Steaks & grills*	223
	Goodman City	"	333
	Hawksmoor	"	443
	Vanilla Black	*Vegetarian*	333
	Ladurée	*Afternoon tea*	222
	1701	*Middle Eastern*	433
£50+	The Hoxton Grill	*American*	224
	The Chancery	*British, Modern*	342
	Gin Joint	"	233
	High Timber	"	344
	Merchants Tavern	"	444
	Northbank	"	333
	Rivington Grill	"	223
	The Sign of the Don	"	234
	Paternoster Chop House	*British, Traditional*	333
	Fish Market	*Fish & seafood*	343
	The Royal Exchange	*French*	224
	28-50	"	334
	Vivat Bacchus	*International*	232
	Piccolino	*Italian*	222
	Taberna Etrusca	"	333
	Eyre Brothers	*Spanish*	434
	New Street Grill	*Steaks & grills*	234
	The Tramshed	"	224
	Chinese Cricket Club	*Chinese*	421
	Cinnamon Kitchen	*Indian*	443
	Mint Leaf	"	323
	City Miyama	*Japanese*	331
£40+	Bodean's	*American*	222
	The Anthologist	*British, Modern*	343
	Princess of Shoreditch	"	343
	George & Vulture	*British, Traditional*	235
	Loch Fyne	*Fish & seafood*	222
	Orpheus	"	431
	Penkul & Banks	*Fusion*	442
	L' Anima Cafe	*Italian*	343
	Rocket	*Mediterranean*	333
	Relais de Venise L'Entrecôte	*Steaks & grills*	323
	Burger & Lobster	*Burgers, etc*	323
	Thai Square City	*Thai*	222

£35+	Simpson's Tavern	*British, Traditional*	345
	Tramontana Brindisa	*Spanish*	323
	Haché	*Burgers, etc*	334
	Natural Kitchen	*Salads*	323
	Haz	*Turkish*	233
	K10	*Japanese*	432
£30+	The Diner	*Burgers, etc*	133
	Caffé Vergnano	*Sandwiches, cakes, etc*	333
	ping pong	*Chinese, Dim sum*	223
	Hare & Tortoise	*Pan-Asian*	323
£25+	Hilliard	*British, Modern*	422
	The Wine Library	*International*	135
	Konditor & Cook	*Sandwiches, cakes, etc*	342
£20+	Patty and Bun	*Burgers, etc*	423
£15+	Notes	*British, Modern*	244
	Street Kitchen	*"*	33–
	Hummus Bros	*Mediterranean*	332
	Taylor St Baristas	*Sandwiches, cakes, etc*	443
	Chilango	*Mexican/TexMex*	322
£10+	Coco Di Mama	*Italian*	432
	Fuzzy's Grub	*Sandwiches, cakes, etc*	322
	Nusa Kitchen	*"*	442
	Spianata & Co	*"*	443
	Nusa Kitchen	*Middle Eastern*	442
	City Càphê	*Vietnamese*	432
£5+	Pilpel	*Middle Eastern*	442

East End & Docklands (All E postcodes)

£80+	Typing Room	*International*	544
	Roka	*Japanese*	534
£70+	Galvin La Chapelle	*French*	445
	Les Trois Garçons	*"*	222
£60+	Beach Blanket Babylon	*British, Modern*	123
	The Boundary	*"*	222
	Lyle's	*"*	442
	One Canada Square	*"*	231
	Tom's Kitchen	*"*	211

	Plateau	*French*	133
	Boisdale of Canary Wharf	*Scottish*	343
	Goodman	*Steaks & grills*	333
	Hawksmoor	*"*	443
	Bevis Marks	*Kosher*	222
£50+	Bistrotheque	*British, Modern*	324
	The Gun	*"*	335
	Hoi Polloi	*"*	233
	The Narrow	*"*	112
	Smiths Brasserie	*"*	334
	Bumpkin	*British, Traditional*	322
	St John Bread & Wine	*"*	534
	Forman's	*Fish & seafood*	433
	Wright Brothers	*"*	433
	Il Bordello	*Italian*	454
	Buen Ayre	*Argentinian*	422
	Café Spice Namaste	*Indian*	443
	Elephant Royale	*Thai*	222
£40+	Balans	*British, Modern*	243
	The Empress	*"*	343
	The Morgan Arms	*"*	434
	Rochelle Canteen	*"*	444
	Albion	*British, Traditional*	222
	Canteen	*"*	111
	The Grapes	*Fish & seafood*	125
	Brawn	*French*	534
	Real Greek	*Greek*	222
	Verden	*International*	– – –
	La Figa	*Italian*	333
	Obika	*"*	221
	Rotorino	*"*	223
	Rocket	*Mediterranean*	333
	Bravas	*Spanish*	434
	Ibérica	*"*	323
	Hill & Szrok	*Steaks & grills*	– – –
	Relais de Venise L'Entrecôte	*"*	323
	Ark Fish	*Fish & chips*	542
	Pizza East	*Pizza*	434
	Story Deli	*"*	523
	Lotus	*Chinese*	322
	Royal China	*"*	422
	Sichuan Folk	*"*	432
	Yi-Ban	*"*	432
	Dishoom	*Indian*	434

£35+	Chicken Shop & Dirty Burger	*American*	– – –
	Eat 17	*British, Modern*	345
	Provender	*French*	432
	LMNT	*International*	235
	Lardo	*Italian*	324
	Andina	*Peruvian*	434
	Yalla Yalla	*Lebanese*	334
	Haz	*Turkish*	233
	Shanghai	*Chinese*	324
	Little Georgia Café	*Georgian*	323
	Pho	*Vietnamese*	333
	Viet Grill	*"*	423
£30+	Bird	*British, Modern*	443
	Clutch	*Steaks & grills*	444
	Faulkner's	*Fish & chips*	432
	Yard Sale Pizza	*Pizza*	– – –
	DF Mexico	*Mexican/TexMex*	334
	Mangal 1	*Turkish*	532
	Tonkotsu East	*Japanese*	333
	Mien Tay	*Vietnamese*	422
	Sông Quê	*"*	212
£25+	Comptoir Libanais	*Lebanese*	222
	Gourmet San	*Chinese*	421
	Lahore Kebab House	*Pakistani*	522
	Needoo	*"*	432
	Tayyabs	*"*	423
£20+	Sager & Wilde	*British, Modern*	344
	E Pellicci	*Italian*	245
	Franco Manca	*Pizza*	433
	Mirch Masala	*Pakistani*	311
£15+	Chilango	*Mexican/TexMex*	322
£10+	Spianata & Co	*Sandwiches, cakes, etc*	443
	Bunnychow	*South African*	– – –
£5+	Brick Lane Beigel Bake	*Sandwiches, cakes, etc*	531
	Pilpel	*Middle Eastern*	442

LONDON MAPS

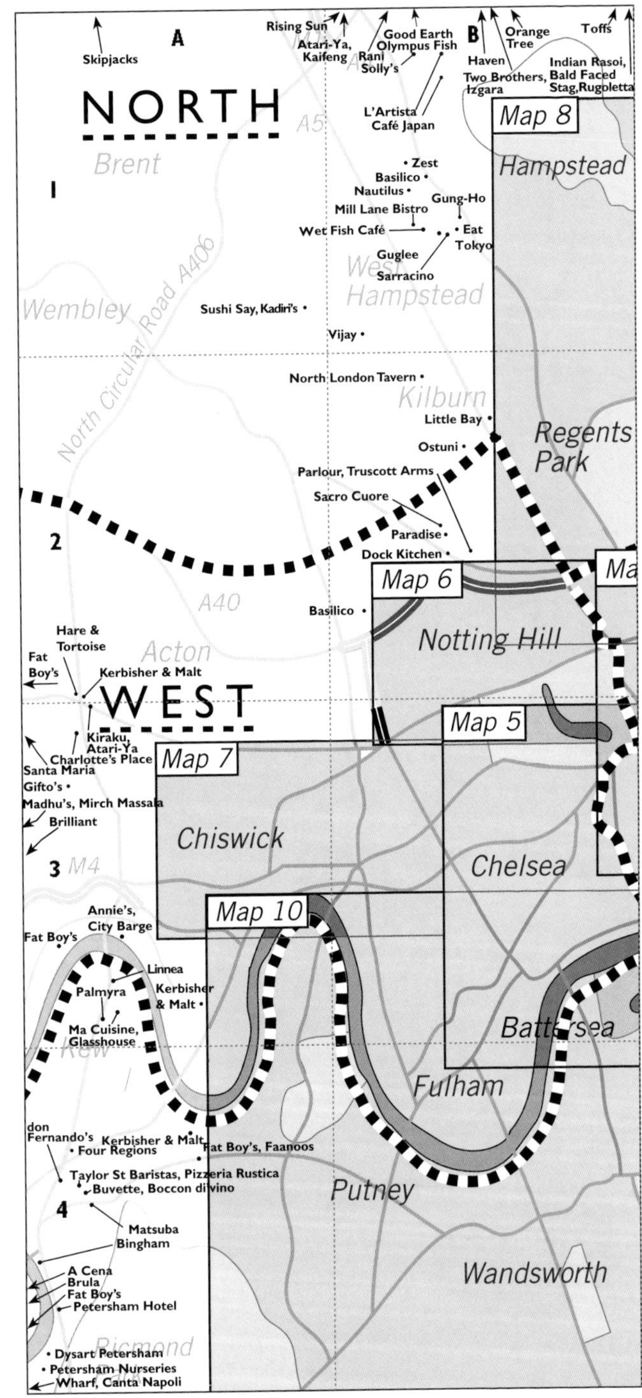
A
B
1
2
3
4
NORTH
WEST
Skipjacks
Rising Sun
Atari-Ya, Kaifeng
Rani
Good Earth
Olympus Fish
Solly's
Orange Tree
Toffs
Haven
Two Brothers, Izgara
Indian Rasoi, Bald Faced Stag, Rugoletta
L'Artista
Café Japan
Map 8
Hampstead
Brent
A5
Zest
Basilico
Nautilus
Gung-Ho
Mill Lane Bistro
Wet Fish Café
Eat Tokyo
Guglee
Sarracino
West Hampstead
Wembley
North Circular Road A406
Sushi Say, Kadiri's
Vijay
North London Tavern
Kilburn
Little Bay
Regents Park
Ostuni
Parlour, Truscott Arms
Sacro Cuore
Paradise
Dock Kitchen
Map 6
A40
Basilico
Notting Hill
Hare & Tortoise
Acton
Fat Boy's
Kerbisher & Malt
Kiraku, Atari-Ya
Charlotte's Place
Santa Maria
Map 5
Map 7
Gifto's
Madhu's, Mirch Massala
Brilliant
Chiswick
Chelsea
M4
Annie's, City Barge
Fat Boy's
Map 10
Linnea
Palmyra
Kerbisher & Malt
Ma Cuisine, Glasshouse
Kew
Battersea
Fulham
don Fernando's
Four Regions
Kerbisher & Malt
Fat Boy's, Faanoos
Taylor St Baristas, Pizzeria Rustica
Buvette, Boccon di vino
Putney
Matsuba
Bingham
Wandsworth
A Cena
Brula
Fat Boy's
Petersham Hotel
Dysart Petersham
Richmond
Petersham Nurseries
Wharf, Canta Napoli

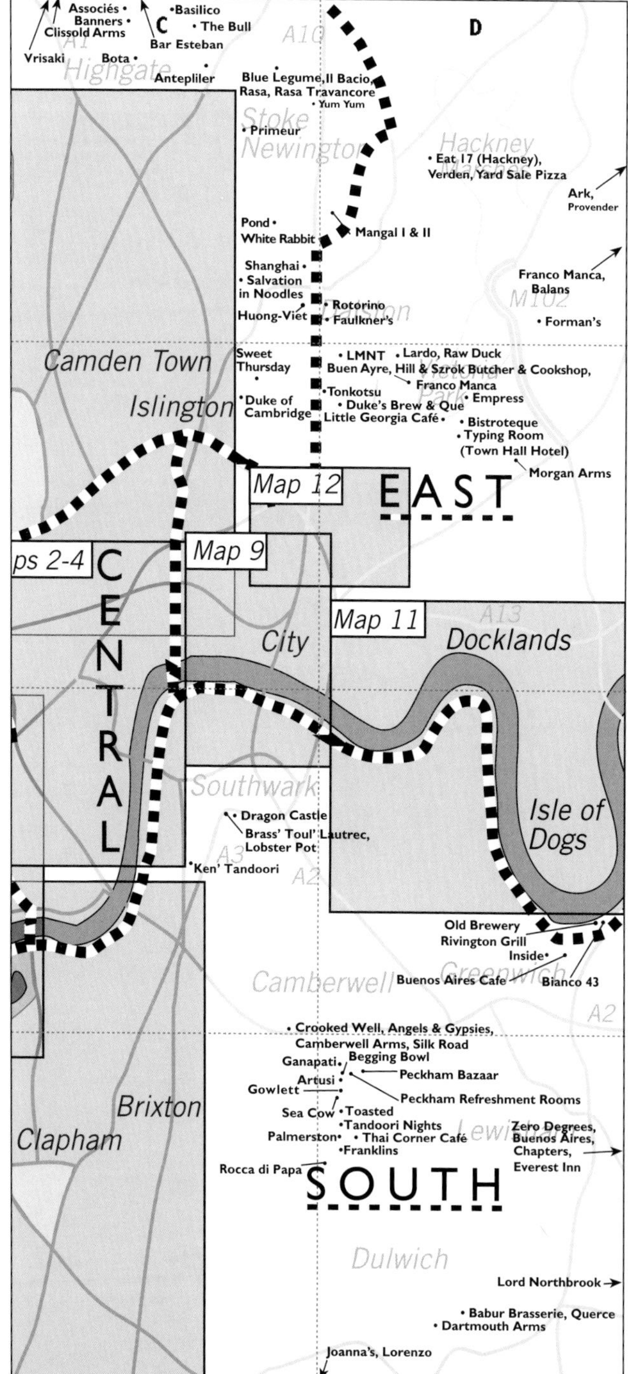

Associés
Banners
Clissold Arms
Vrisaki
Bota
Basilico
The Bull
Bar Esteban
Antepliler
C
D
A1
A10
Highgate
Blue Legume, Il Bacio,
Rasa, Rasa Travancore
Yum Yum
Stoke
Newington
Primeur
Hackney
Eat 17 (Hackney),
Verden, Yard Sale Pizza
Ark,
Provender
Pond
White Rabbit
Mangal I & II
Shanghai
Salvation
in Noodles
Huong-Viet
Rotorino
Faulkner's
Dalston
Franco Manca,
Balans
M102
Forman's
Camden Town
Sweet
Thursday
LMNT
Lardo, Raw Duck
Buen Ayre, Hill & Szrok Butcher & Cookshop,
Franco Manca
Islington
Duke of
Cambridge
Tonkotsu
Duke's Brew & Que
Little Georgia Café
Empress
Bistroteque
Typing Room
(Town Hall Hotel)
Morgan Arms
Map 12
EAST
ps 2-4
CENTRAL
Map 9
Map 11
A13
City
Docklands
Southwark
Dragon Castle
Brass' Toul' Lautrec,
Lobster Pot
Ken' Tandoori
A3
A2
Isle of
Dogs
Old Brewery
Rivington Grill
Inside
Camberwell
Buenos Aires Cafe
Greenwich
Bianco 43
A2
Crooked Well, Angels & Gypsies,
Camberwell Arms, Silk Road
Ganapati
Begging Bowl
Peckham Bazaar
Artusi
Gowlett
Peckham Refreshment Rooms
Sea Cow
Toasted
Tandoori Nights
Brixton
Clapham
Palmerston
Thai Corner Café
Franklins
Lewisham
Zero Degrees,
Buenos Aires,
Chapters,
Everest Inn
Rocca di Papa
SOUTH
Dulwich
Lord Northbrook
Babur Brasserie, Querce
Dartmouth Arms
Joanna's, Lorenzo

MAP 2 – WEST END OVERVIEW

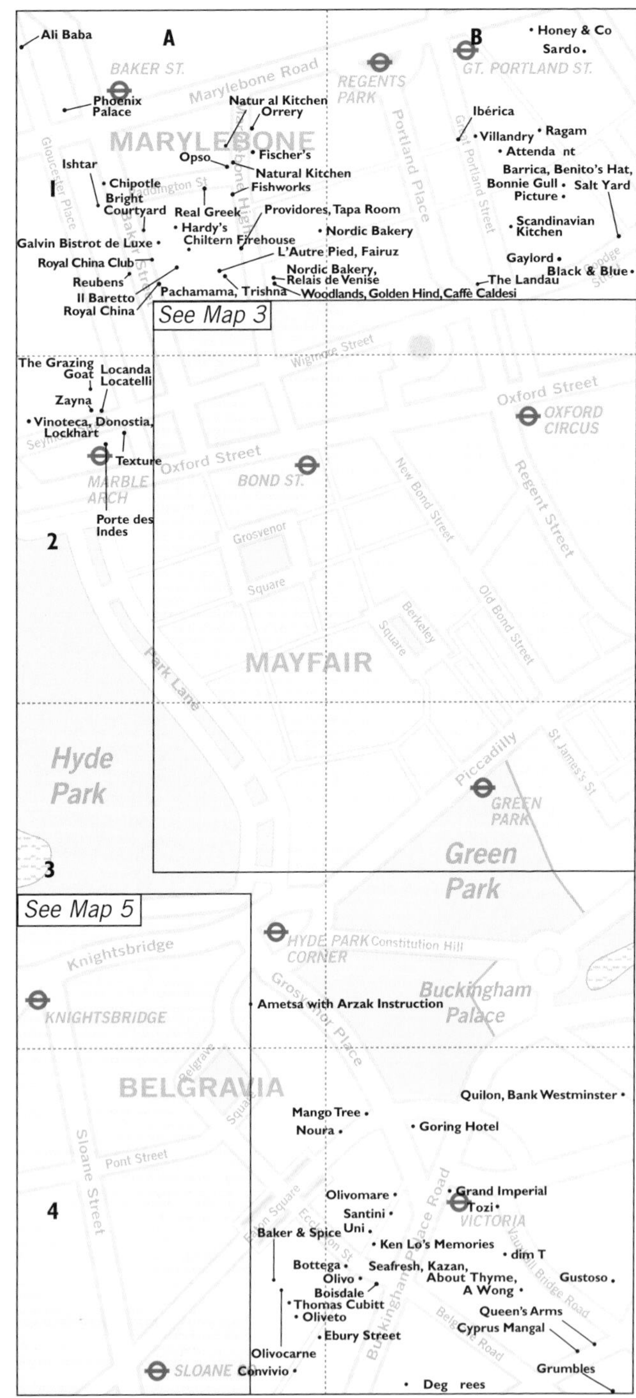

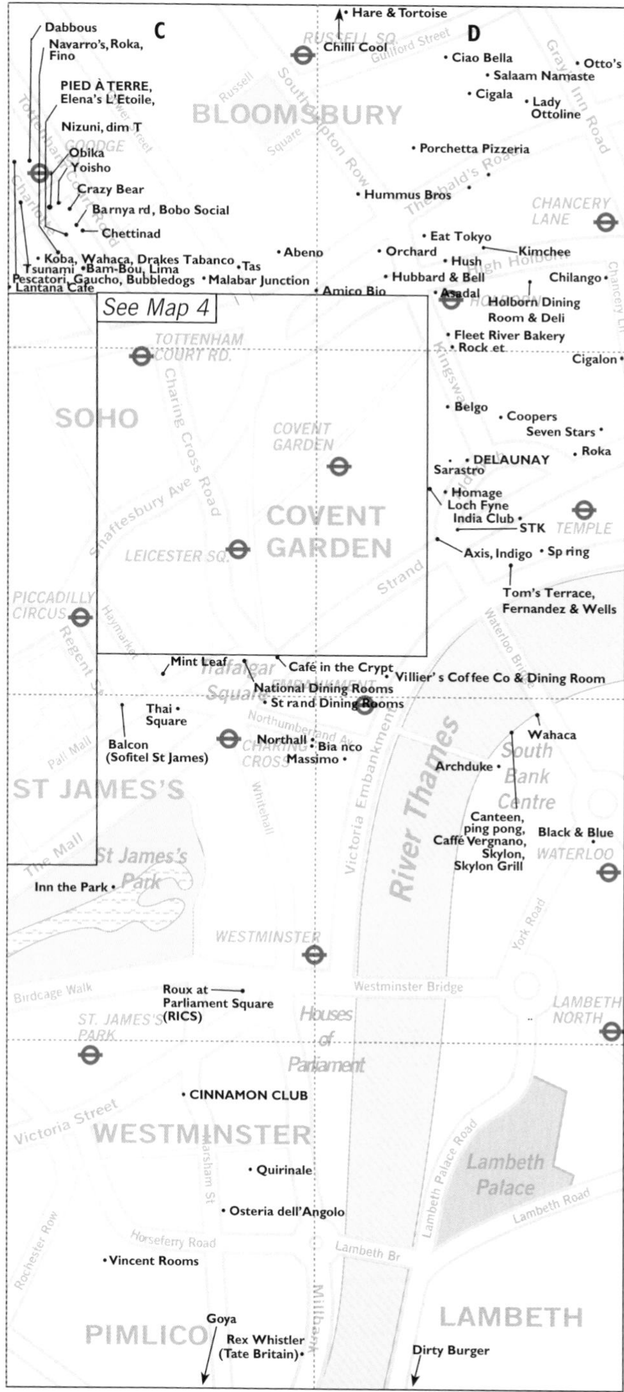
C
D
Hare & Tortoise
Dabbous
Navarro's, Roka, Fino
PIED À TERRE, Elena's L'Etoile,
Nizuni, dim T
Obika
Yoisho
Crazy Bear
Barnya rd, Bobo Social
Chettinad
Koba, Wahaca, Drakes Tabanco
Tsunami
Bam-Bou, Lima
Pescatori, Gaucho, Bubbledogs
Lantana Cafe
Tas
Malabar Junction
Abeno
Chilli Cool
RUSSELL SQ.
Guilford Street
Ciao Bella
Otto's
Salaam Namaste
Cigala
Lady Ottoline
BLOOMSBURY
GOODGE
Gray's Inn Road
Southampton Row
Porchetta Pizzeria
Hummus Bros
Theobald's Road
CHANCERY LANE
Eat Tokyo
Orchard
Hush
Kimchee
High Holborn
Hubbard & Bell
Chilango
Amico Bio
Asadal
Holborn Dining Room & Deli
See Map 4
TOTTENHAM COURT RD.
Fleet River Bakery
Rock et
Cigalon
SOHO
Charing Cross Road
Kingsway
Belgo
Coopers
Seven Stars
COVENT GARDEN
DELAUNAY
Roka
Sarastro
Homage
Loch Fyne
India Club
STK
TEMPLE
Shaftesbury Ave
COVENT GARDEN
LEICESTER SQ.
Axis, Indigo
Sp ring
Strand
Tom's Terrace, Fernandez & Wells
PICCADILLY CIRCUS
Haymarket
Regent St
Waterloo Bridge
Mint Leaf
Café in the Crypt
Trafalgar Square
Villier's Coffee Co & Dining Room
National Dining Rooms
EMBANKMENT
St rand Dining Rooms
Thai Square
Balcon (Sofitel St James)
Northumberland Av
Northall
Bia nco
Massimo
CHARING CROSS
Pall Mall
Wahaca
South Bank Centre
Archduke
River Thames
ST JAMES'S
Whitehall
Victoria Embankment
Canteen, ping pong, Caffé Vergnano, Skylon, Skylon Grill
Black & Blue
WATERLOO
The Mall
St James's Park
Inn the Park
WESTMINSTER
York Road
Birdcage Walk
Westminster Bridge
Roux at Parliament Square (RICS)
ST. JAMES'S PARK
Houses of Parliament
LAMBETH NORTH
CINNAMON CLUB
Victoria Street
WESTMINSTER
Marsham St
Lambeth Palace Road
Quirinale
Lambeth Palace
Osteria dell'Angolo
Lambeth Road
Rochester Row
Horseferry Road
Lambeth Br
Vincent Rooms
Millbank
LAMBETH
Goya
PIMLICO
Rex Whistler (Tate Britain)
Dirty Burger

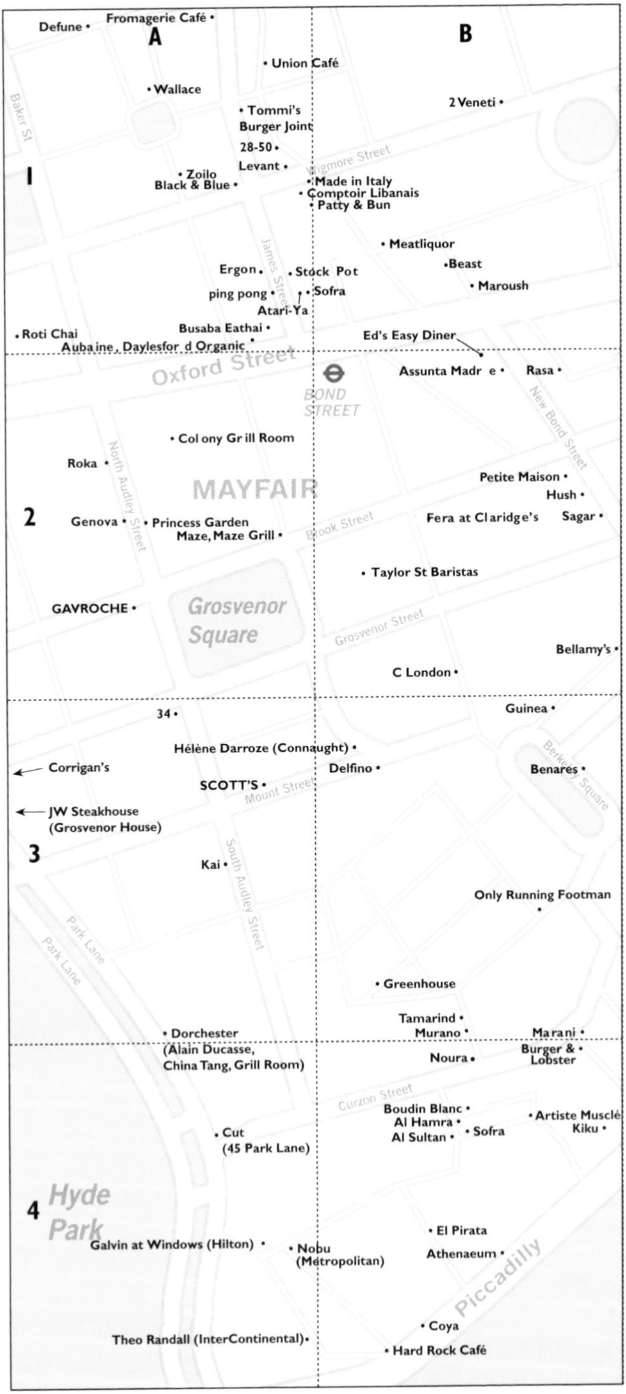

MAP 3 – MAYFAIR, ST. JAMES'S & WEST SOHO

A
B

1
Defune
Fromagerie Café
Union Café
Wallace
Baker St
Tommi's Burger Joint
2 Veneti
28-50
Levant
Wigmore Street
Zoilo
Black & Blue
Made in Italy
Comptoir Libanais
Patty & Bun
Meatliquor
Beast
Ergon
James Street
Stock Pot
Maroush
ping pong
Sofra
Atari-Ya
Busaba Eathai
Roti Chai
Aubaine, Daylesford Organic
Ed's Easy Diner

Oxford Street
BOND STREET
Assunta Madre
Rasa
New Bond Street

2
Colony Grill Room
Roka
North Audley Street
MAYFAIR
Petite Maison
Hush
Genova
Princess Garden
Maze, Maze Grill
Brook Street
Fera at Claridge's
Sagar
Taylor St Baristas
GAVROCHE
Grosvenor Square
Grosvenor Street
Bellamy's
C London

3
Guinea
34
Hélène Darroze (Connaught)
Corrigan's
Delfino
Benares
Berkeley Square
SCOTT'S
Mount Street
JW Steakhouse (Grosvenor House)
Kai
South Audley Street
Only Running Footman
Park Lane
Park Lane
Greenhouse
Tamarind
Murano
Marani
Dorchester (Alain Ducasse, China Tang, Grill Room)

4
Noura
Burger & Lobster
Curzon Street
Boudin Blanc
Al Hamra
Al Sultan
Sofra
Artiste Musclé
Kiku
Cut (45 Park Lane)
Hyde Park
El Pirata
Galvin at Windows (Hilton)
Nobu (Metropolitan)
Athenaeum
Piccadilly
Coya
Theo Randall (InterContinental)
Hard Rock Café

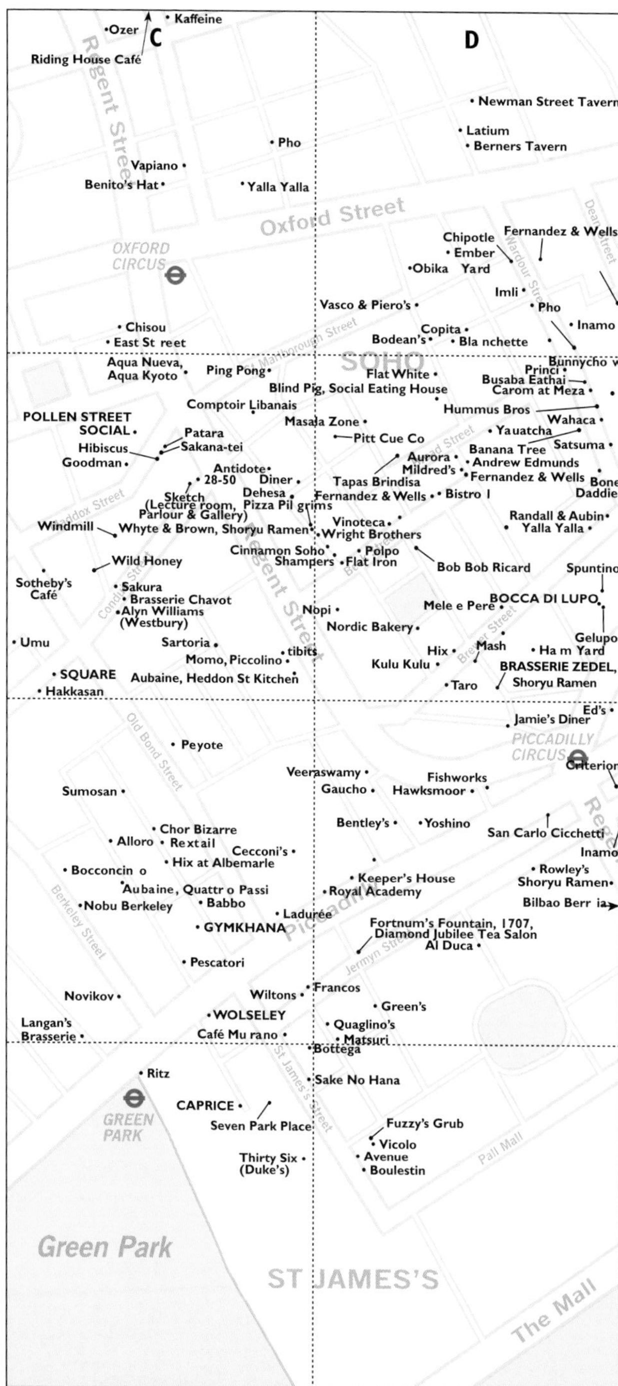

C
D
Ozer
Kaffeine
Riding House Café
Newman Street Tavern
Latium
Berners Tavern
Pho
Vapiano
Benito's Hat
Yalla Yalla
Oxford Street
OXFORD CIRCUS
Chipotle
Fernandez & Wells
Ember
Obika
Yard
Imli
Vasco & Piero's
Pho
Inamo
Chisou
East St reet
Copita
Bodean's
Bla nchette
SOHO
Aqua Nueva, Aqua Kyoto
Ping Pong
Flat White
Princi
Bunnycho w
Busaba Eathai
Carom at Meza
Blind Pig, Social Eating House
Comptoir Libanais
Hummus Bros
POLLEN STREET SOCIAL
Masala Zone
Wahaca
Yauatcha
Patara
Pitt Cue Co
Satsuma
Hibiscus
Sakana-tei
Banana Tree
Goodman
Aurora
Andrew Edmunds
Mildred's
Antidote
28-50
Diner
Tapas Brindisa
Fernandez & Wells
Bone Daddies
Sketch (Lecture room, Parlour & Gallery)
Dehesa
Pizza Pil grims
Fernandez & Wells
Bistro I
Randall & Aubin
Windmill
Whyte & Brown, Shoryu Ramen
Vinoteca
Wright Brothers
Yalla Yalla
Cinnamon Soho
Polpo
Wild Honey
Shampers
Flat Iron
Bob Bob Ricard
Spuntino
Sotheby's Café
Sakura
Brasserie Chavot
Alyn Williams (Westbury)
Nopi
Mele e Pere
BOCCA DI LUPO
Regent Street
Nordic Bakery
Umu
Sartoria
tibits
Hix
Mash
Gelupo
Ham Yard
Momo, Piccolino
Kulu Kulu
BRASSERIE ZEDEL, Shoryu Ramen
SQUARE
Aubaine, Heddon St Kitchen
Taro
Hakkasan
Ed's
Jamie's Diner
PICCADILLY CIRCUS
Peyote
Criterion
Veeraswamy
Fishworks
Gaucho
Hawksmoor
Sumosan
Bentley's
Yoshino
San Carlo Cicchetti
Chor Bizarre
Alloro
Rextail
Cecconi's
Inamo
Hix at Albemarle
Bocconcin o
Keeper's House
Rowley's
Aubaine, Quattr o Passi
Royal Academy
Shoryu Ramen
Nobu Berkeley
Babbo
Bilbao Berr ia
Ladurée
GYMKHANA
Piccadilly
Fortnum's Fountain, 1707, Diamond Jubilee Tea Salon
Al Duca
Pescatori
Jermyn Street
Francos
Novikov
Wiltons
Green's
WOLSELEY
Quaglino's
Langan's Brasserie
Café Mu rano
Matsuri
Bottega
Ritz
Sake No Hana
CAPRICE
GREEN PARK
Seven Park Place
Fuzzy's Grub
Vicolo
Thirty Six (Duke's)
Avenue
Boulestin
Pall Mall
Green Park
ST JAMES'S
The Mall

MAP 4 – EAST SOHO, CHINATOWN & COVENT GARDEN

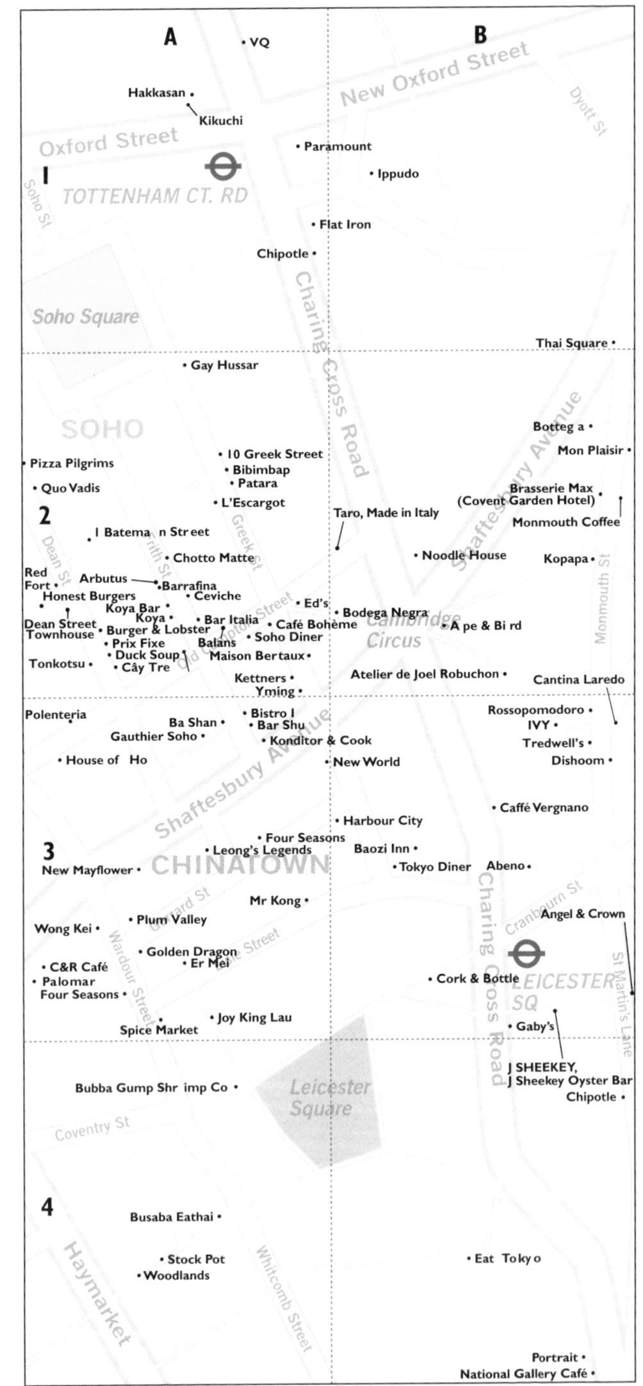

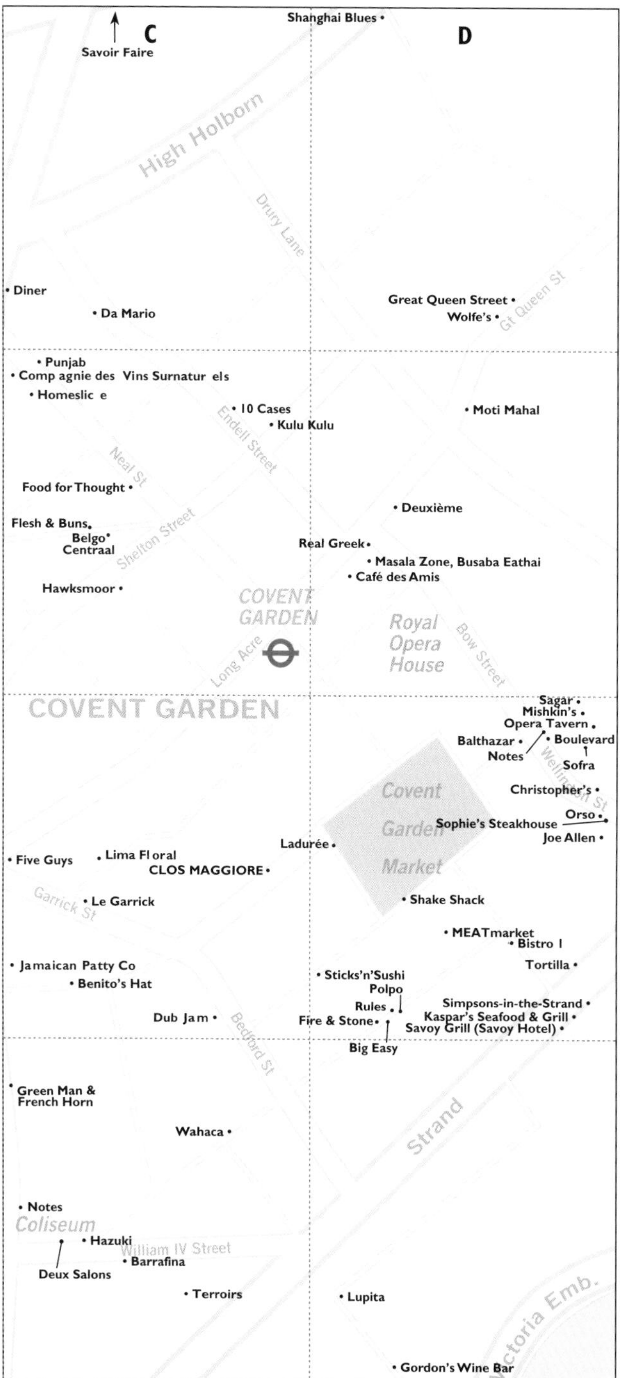

C
D
Savoir Faire
Shanghai Blues
High Holborn
Drury Lane
Diner
Da Mario
Great Queen Street
Wolfe's
Gt Queen St
Punjab
Compagnie des Vins Surnaturels
Homeslice
10 Cases
Kulu Kulu
Moti Mahal
Endell Street
Neal St
Food for Thought
Deuxième
Flesh & Buns
Belgo Centraal
Shelton Street
Real Greek
Masala Zone, Busaba Eathai
Café des Amis
Hawksmoor
COVENT GARDEN
Royal Opera House
Bow Street
Long Acre
COVENT GARDEN
Sagar
Mishkin's
Opera Tavern
Balthazar
Boulevard
Notes
Sofra
Wellington St
Christopher's
Covent Garden Market
Orso
Sophie's Steakhouse
Joe Allen
Ladurée
Five Guys
Lima Floral
CLOS MAGGIORE
Garrick St
Le Garrick
Shake Shack
MEATmarket
Bistro 1
Tortilla
Jamaican Patty Co
Benito's Hat
Sticks'n'Sushi
Polpo
Rules
Simpsons-in-the-Strand
Kaspar's Seafood & Grill
Dub Jam
Fire & Stone
Savoy Grill (Savoy Hotel)
Bedford St
Big Easy
Green Man & French Horn
Wahaca
Strand
Notes
Coliseum
Hazuki
William IV Street
Barrafina
Deux Salons
Terroirs
Lupita
Victoria Emb.
Gordon's Wine Bar

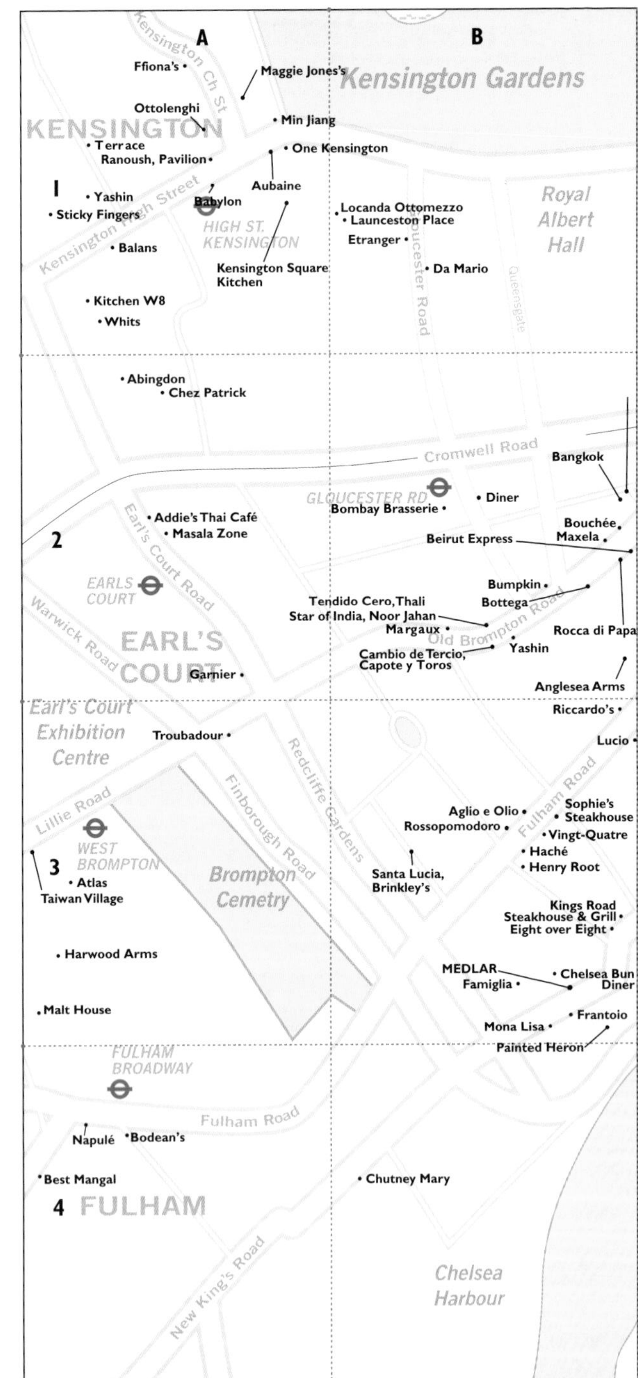
A
B
1
2
3
4
Kensington Gardens
KENSINGTON
Kensington Ch St
Ffiona's
Maggie Jones's
Ottolenghi
Min Jiang
Terrace
Ranoush, Pavilion
One Kensington
Aubaine
Yashin
Babylon
Sticky Fingers
Kensington High Street
HIGH ST. KENSINGTON
Locanda Ottomezzo
Launceston Place
Etranger
Royal Albert Hall
Balans
Kensington Square Kitchen
Da Mario
Gloucester Road
Queensgate
Kitchen W8
Whits
Abingdon
Chez Patrick
Cromwell Road
Bangkok
GLOUCESTER RD
Bombay Brasserie
Diner
Addie's Thai Café
Masala Zone
Bouchée
Maxela
Beirut Express
Earl's Court Road
EARLS COURT
Bumpkin
Bottega
Tendido Cero, Thali
Star of India, Noor Jahan
Margaux
Old Brompton Road
Rocca di Papa
Warwick Road
EARL'S COURT
Yashin
Cambio de Tercio,
Capote y Toros
Garnier
Anglesea Arms
Earl's Court Exhibition Centre
Riccardo's
Troubadour
Lucio
Redcliffe Gardens
Finborough Road
Fulham Road
Lillie Road
Aglio e Olio
Sophie's Steakhouse
Rossopomodoro
Vingt-Quatre
WEST BROMPTON
Haché
Henry Root
Atlas
Taiwan Village
Brompton Cemetry
Santa Lucia,
Brinkley's
Kings Road Steakhouse & Grill
Eight over Eight
Harwood Arms
MEDLAR
Famiglia
Chelsea Bun Diner
Malt House
Frantoio
Mona Lisa
Painted Heron
FULHAM BROADWAY
Fulham Road
Napulé
Bodean's
Best Mangal
Chutney Mary
FULHAM
New King's Road
Chelsea Harbour

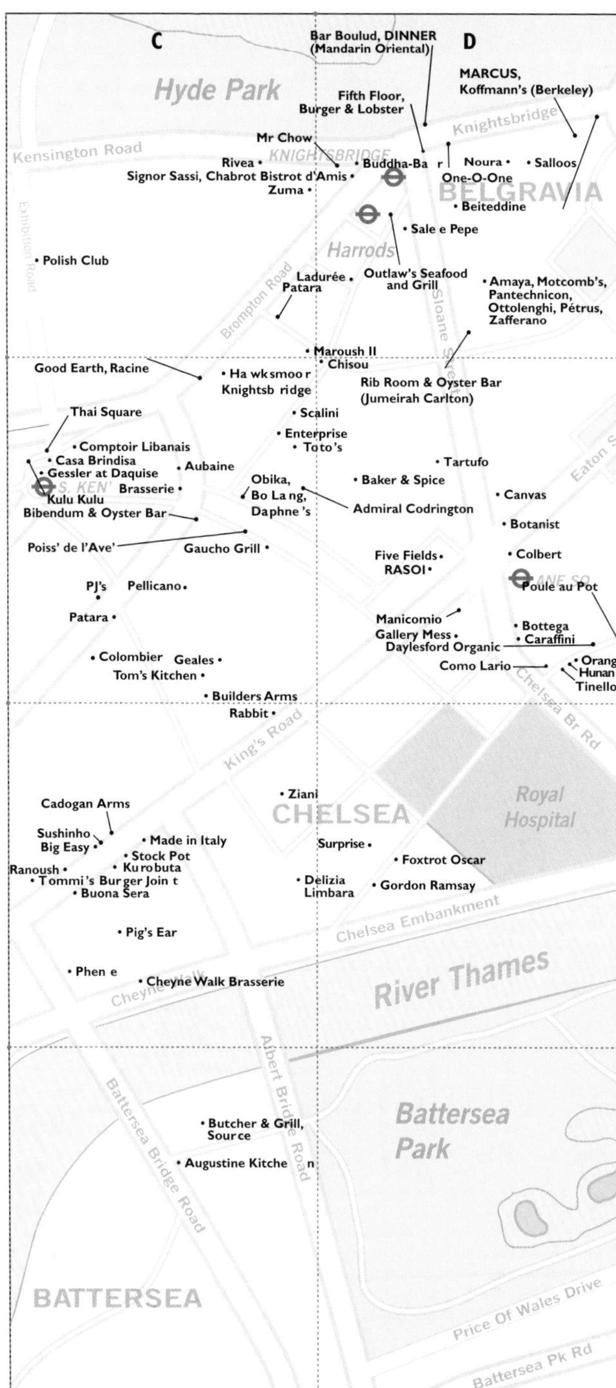
C
D
Hyde Park
Bar Boulud, DINNER
(Mandarin Oriental)
MARCUS,
Koffmann's (Berkeley)
Fifth Floor,
Burger & Lobster
Knightsbridge
Mr Chow
Kensington Road
KNIGHTSBRIDGE
Rivea
Buddha-Bar
Noura
Salloos
Signor Sassi, Chabrot Bistrot d'Amis
One-O-One
Zuma
BELGRAVIA
Beiteddine
Exhibition Road
Sale e Pepe
Harrods
Polish Club
Ladurée
Patara
Outlaw's Seafood
and Grill
Amaya, Motcomb's,
Pantechnicon,
Ottolenghi, Pétrus,
Zafferano
Brompton Road
Sloane Street
Maroush II
Chisou
Good Earth, Racine
Hawksmoor
Knightsbridge
Rib Room & Oyster Bar
(Jumeirah Carlton)
Thai Square
Scalini
Enterprise
Toto's
Comptoir Libanais
Casa Brindisa
Tartufo
Aubaine
Gessler at Daquise
Obika,
Baker & Spice
Eaton Sq
S. KEN'
Brasserie
Kulu Kulu
Bo Lang,
Canvas
Bibendum & Oyster Bar
Daphne's
Admiral Codrington
Botanist
Poiss' de l'Ave'
Gaucho Grill
Five Fields
Colbert
RASOI
PJ's
Pellicano
Poule au Pot
Patara
Manicomio
Bottega
Gallery Mess
Caraffini
Daylesford Organic
Colombier
Geales
Como Lario
Orange
Hunan
Tom's Kitchen
Tinello
Chelsea Br Rd
Builders Arms
Rabbit
King's Road
Ziani
Cadogan Arms
CHELSEA
Royal
Hospital
Sushinho
Made in Italy
Big Easy
Surprise
Stock Pot
Foxtrot Oscar
Ranoush
Kurobuta
Tommi's Burger Joint
Delizia
Limbara
Gordon Ramsay
Buona Sera
Chelsea Embankment
Pig's Ear
River Thames
Phene
Cheyne Walk Brasserie
Cheyne Walk
Albert Bridge Road
Battersea Bridge Road
Battersea
Park
Butcher & Grill,
Source
Augustine Kitchen
BATTERSEA
Price Of Wales Drive
Battersea Pk Rd

MAP 6 – NOTTING HILL & BAYSWATER

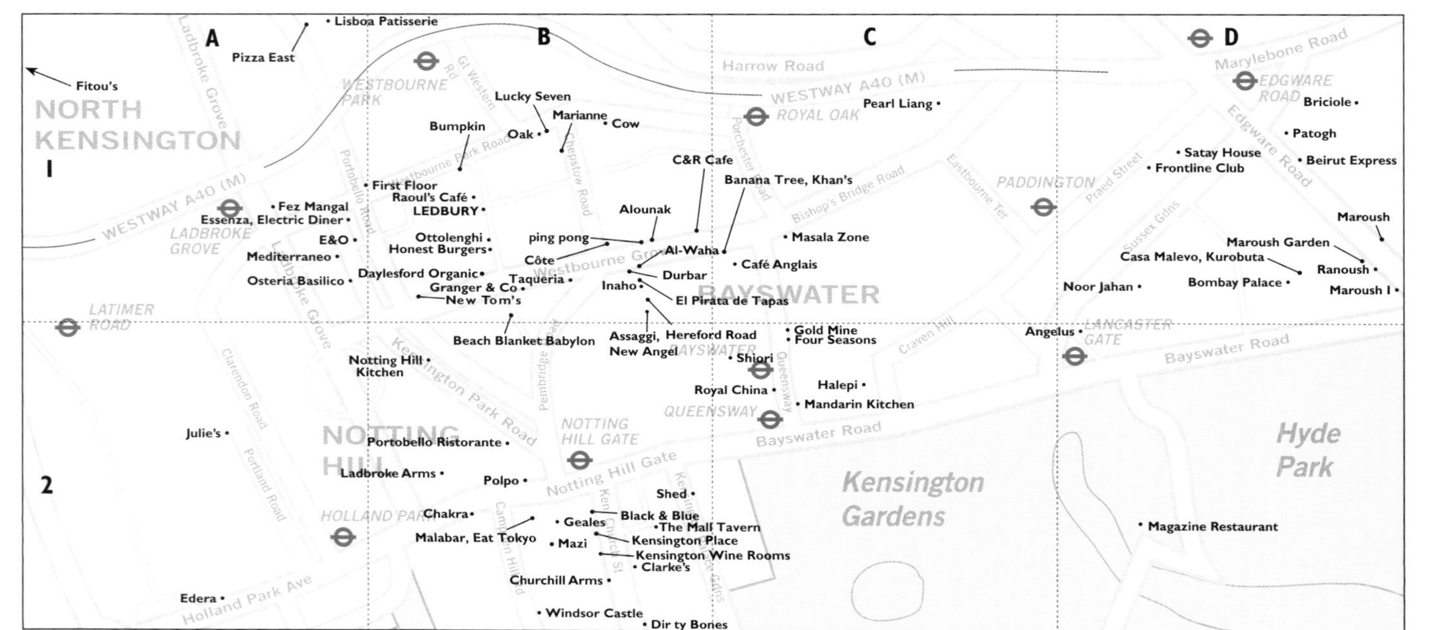

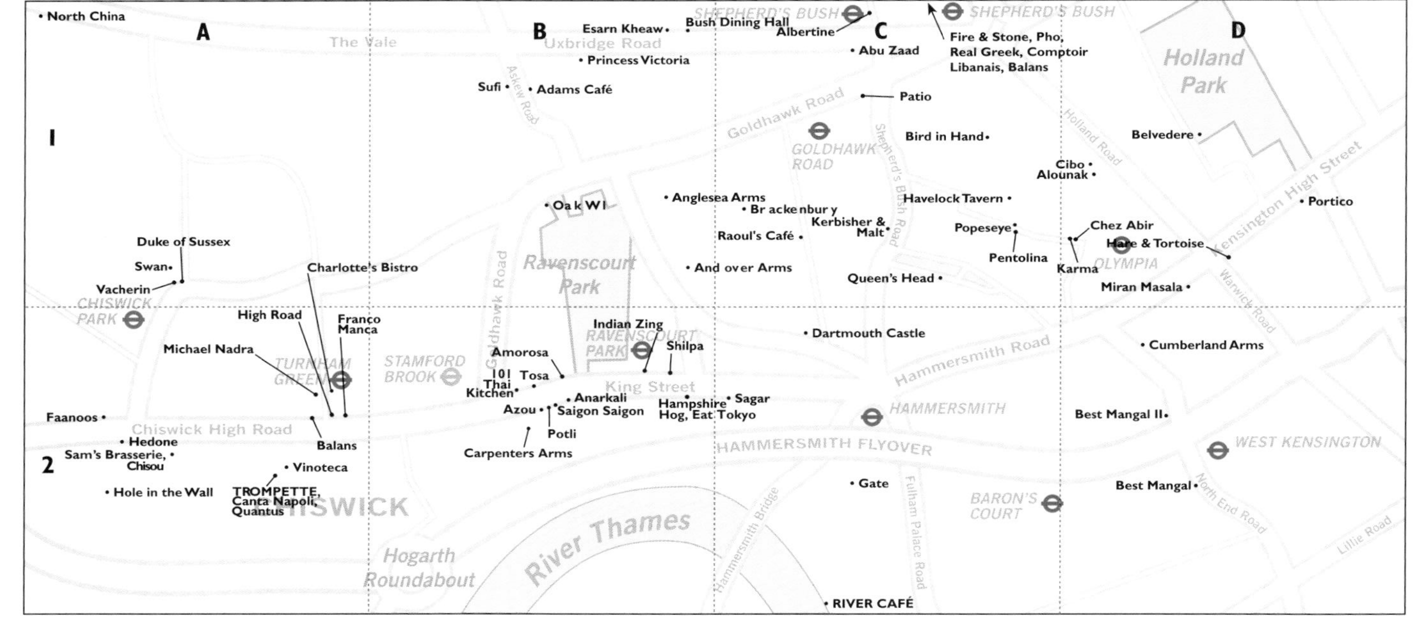

MAP 7 – HAMMERSMITH & CHISWICK

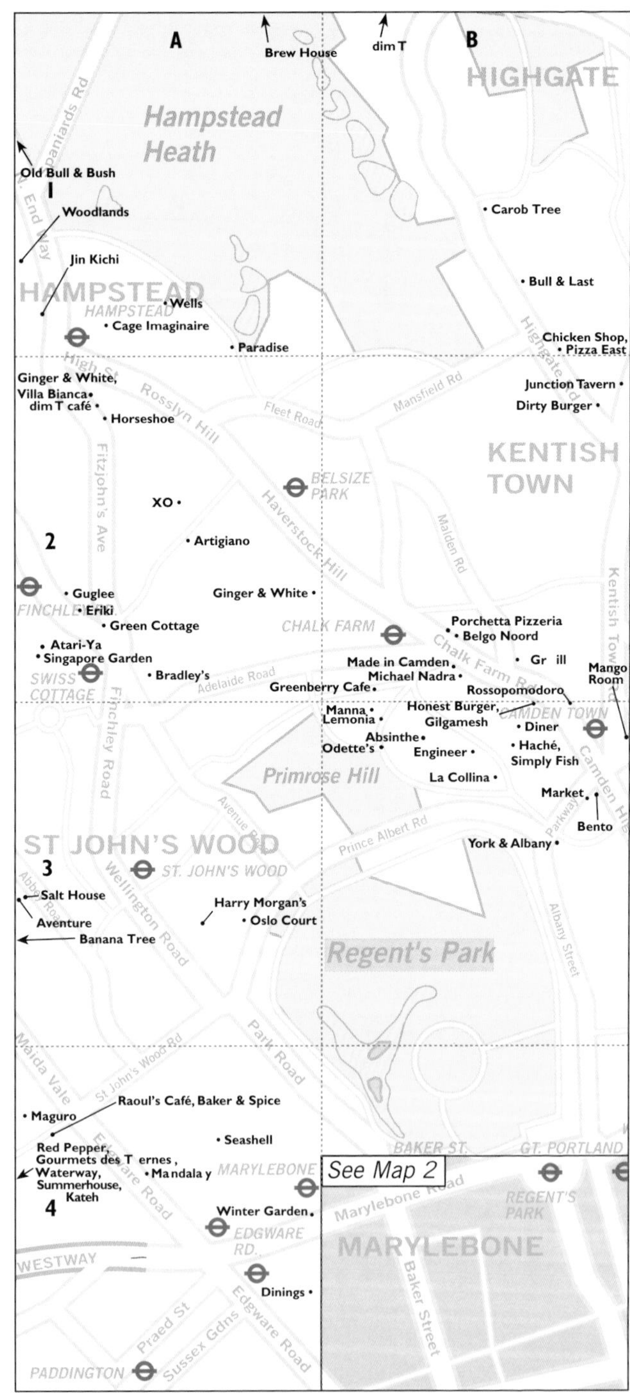
A
B
Brew House
dim T
HIGHGATE
Hampstead Heath
Spaniards Rd
Old Bull & Bush
1
N. End Way
Woodlands
Jin Kichi
HAMPSTEAD
HAMPSTEAD
Wells
Cage Imaginaire
Paradise
Carob Tree
Bull & Last
Highgate Rd
Chicken Shop,
Pizza East
Junction Tavern
Dirty Burger
Ginger & White,
Villa Bianca
dim T café
Horseshoe
High St
Rosslyn Hill
Fleet Road
Mansfield Rd
KENTISH TOWN
BELSIZE PARK
Fitzjohn's Ave
Haverstock Hill
Malden Rd
XO
Artigiano
2
Guglee
FINCHLEY RD.
Eriki
Green Cottage
Ginger & White
CHALK FARM
Kentish Town Rd
Porchetta Pizzeria
Belgo Noord
Atari-Ya
Singapore Garden
Bradley's
Adelaide Road
SWISS COTTAGE
Made in Camden
Michael Nadra
Greenberry Cafe
Chalk Farm Rd
Gr ill
Mango Room
Rossopomodoro
Manna
Lemonia
Honest Burger,
Gilgamesh
CAMDEN TOWN
Diner
Absinthe
Odette's
Engineer
Haché,
Simply Fish
Finchley Road
Primrose Hill
La Collina
Market
Camden High St
Bento
Parkway
Avenue Rd
Prince Albert Rd
York & Albany
ST JOHN'S WOOD
3
ST. JOHN'S WOOD
Abbey Road
Salt House
Aventure
Banana Tree
Wellington Road
Harry Morgan's
Oslo Court
Albany Street
Regent's Park
Maida Vale
St John's Wood Rd
Park Road
Raoul's Café, Baker & Spice
Maguro
Seashell
Red Pepper,
Gourmets des T ernes ,
Waterway,
Summerhouse,
Kateh
Edgware Road
Ma ndala y
MARYLEBONE
See Map 2
BAKER ST.
GT. PORTLAND
REGENT'S PARK
Marylebone Road
4
Winter Garden
EDGWARE RD.
MARYLEBONE
WESTWAY
Baker Street
Dinings
Praed St
Sussex Gdns
Edgware Road
PADDINGTON

MAP 8 – HAMPSTEAD, CAMDEN TOWN & ISLINGTON

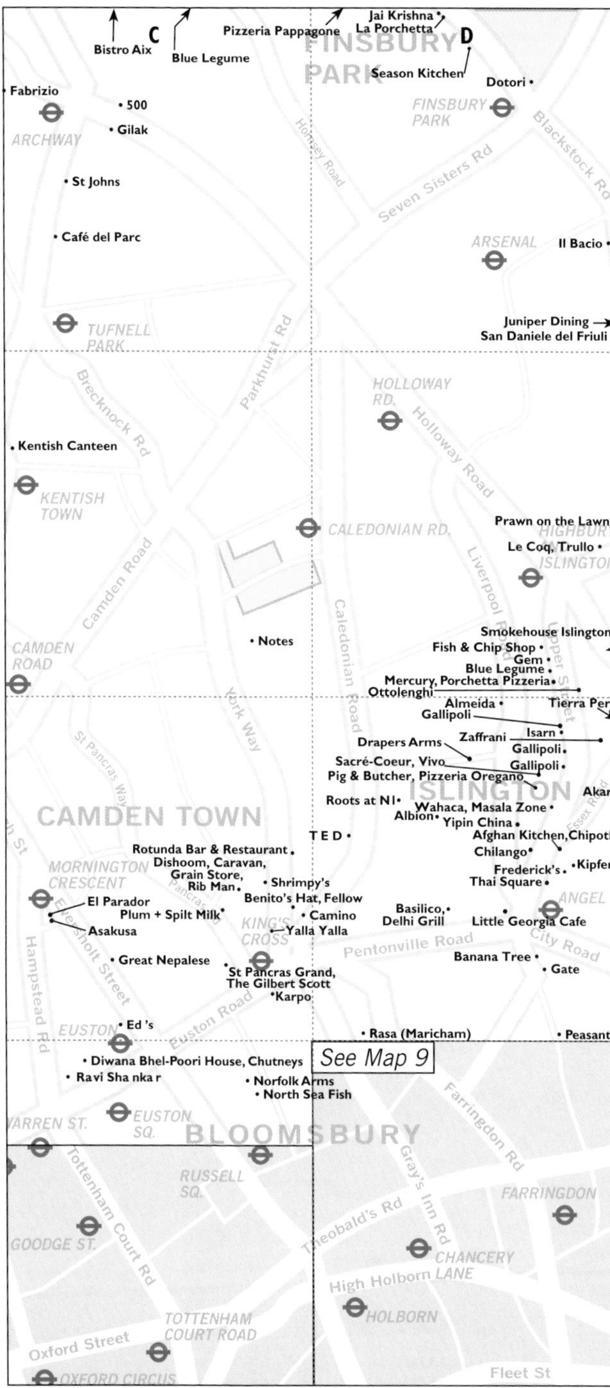

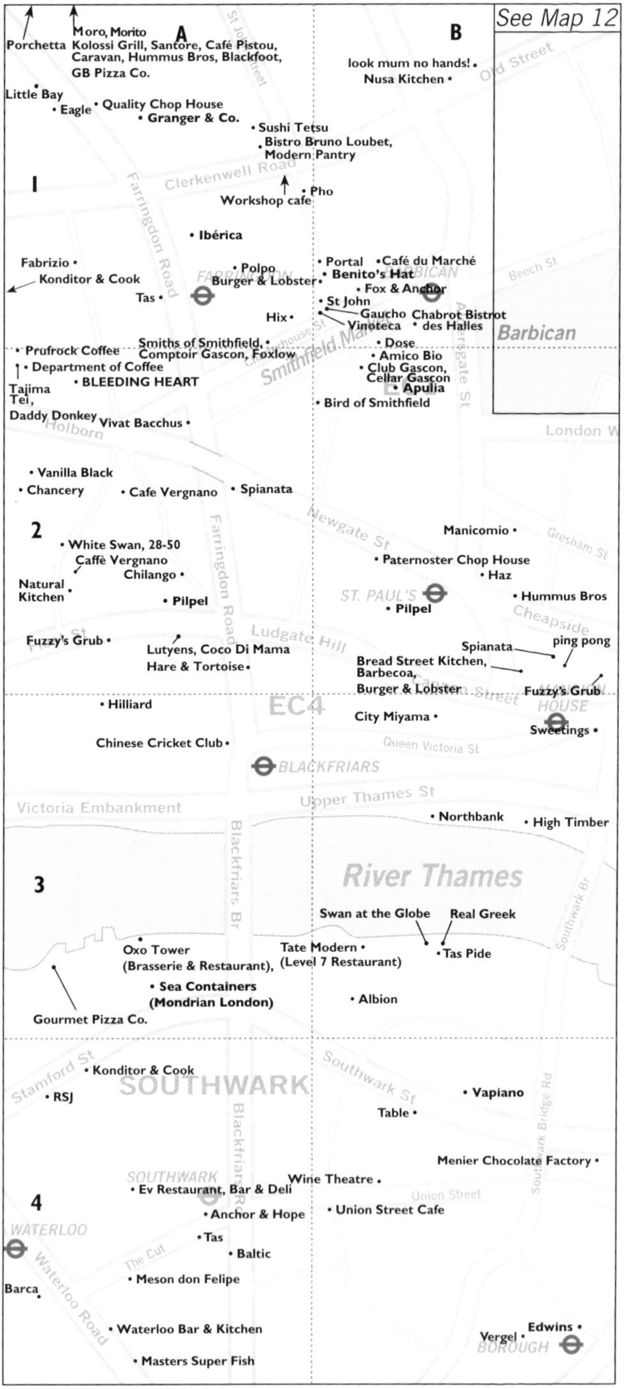

A
B
See Map 12

Porchetta
Moro, Morito
Kolossi Grill, Santore, Café Pistou,
Caravan, Hummus Bros, Blackfoot,
GB Pizza Co.
look mum no hands!
Nusa Kitchen
Old Street
St John Street
Little Bay
Eagle
Quality Chop House
Granger & Co.
Sushi Tetsu
Bistro Bruno Loubet,
Modern Pantry
Clerkenwell Road

1

Pho
Workshop cafe
Farringdon Road
Ibérica
Fabrizio
Konditor & Cook
Polpo
Burger & Lobster
FARRINGDON
Portal
Café du Marché
Benito's Hat
BARBICAN
Beech St
Fox & Anchor
Tas
St John
Hix
Gaucho
Vinoteca
Chabrot Bistrot
des Halles
Barbican
Smiths of Smithfield,
Comptoir Gascon, Foxlow
Charterhouse St
Smithfield Market
Prufrock Coffee
Department of Coffee
Dose
Amico Bio
Club Gascon,
Cellar Gascon
Apulia
EC1
Aldersgate St
Tajima
Tei,
BLEEDING HEART
Bird of Smithfield
Daddy Donkey
Vivat Bacchus
Holborn
London Wall
Vanilla Black
Chancery
Cafe Vergnano
Spianata
Newgate St

2

White Swan, 28-50
Caffè Vergnano
Chilango
Natural
Kitchen
Farringdon Road
Pilpel
Manicomio
Gresham St
Paternoster Chop House
Haz
ST. PAUL'S
Hummus Bros
Pilpel
Cheapside
Fleet St
Fuzzy's Grub
Lutyens, Coco Di Mama
Hare & Tortoise
Ludgate Hill
Spianata
ping pong
Bread Street Kitchen,
Barbecoa,
Burger & Lobster
Cannon Street
Fuzzy's Grub
MANSION
HOUSE
Hilliard
EC4
City Miyama
Sweetings
Chinese Cricket Club
Queen Victoria St
BLACKFRIARS
Upper Thames St
Victoria Embankment
Northbank
High Timber
Blackfriars Br
River Thames

3

Swan at the Globe
Real Greek
Southwark Br
Oxo Tower
(Brasserie & Restaurant),
Tate Modern
(Level 7 Restaurant)
Tas Pide
Sea Containers
(Mondrian London)
Albion
Gourmet Pizza Co.
Stamford St
Konditor & Cook
Southwark St
SOUTHWARK
RSJ
Vapiano
Table
Blackfriars Rd
Southwark Bridge Rd
Menier Chocolate Factory
SOUTHWARK
Wine Theatre
Ev Restaurant, Bar & Deli
Union Street

4

Anchor & Hope
Union Street Cafe
WATERLOO
Tas
Baltic
The Cut
Meson don Felipe
Barca
Waterloo Road
Waterloo Bar & Kitchen
Edwins
Vergel
BOROUGH
Masters Super Fish

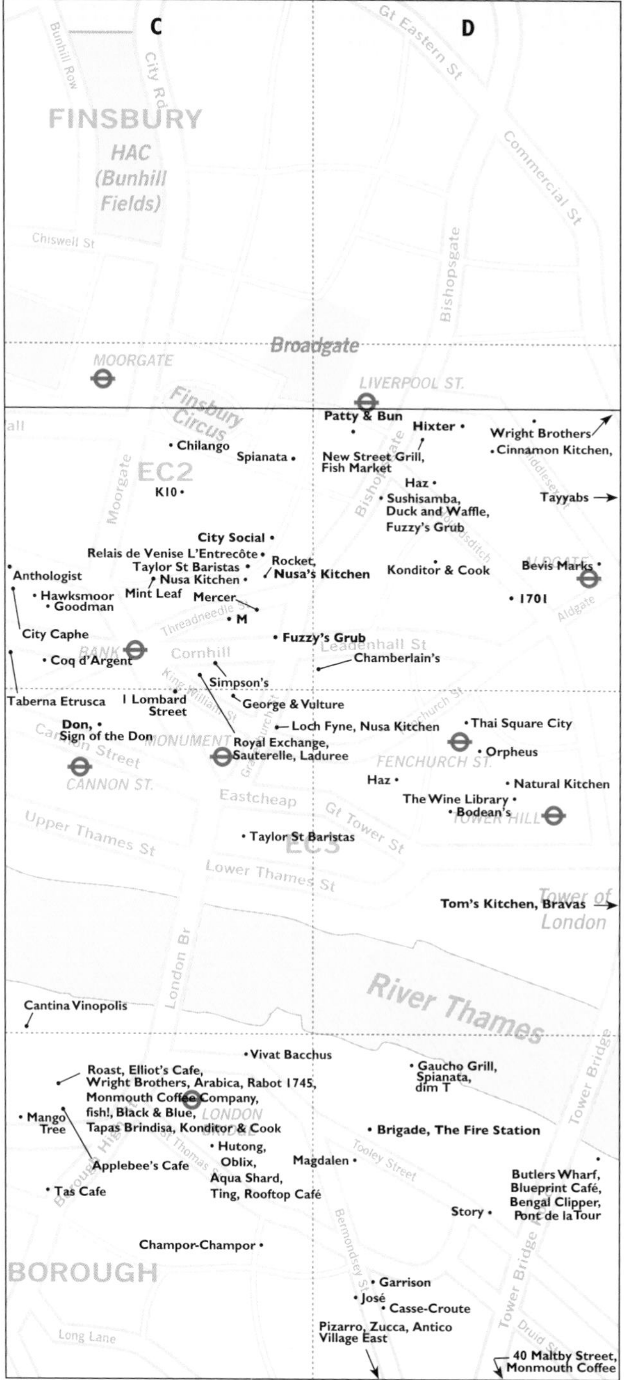

C
D
Bunhill Row
City Rd
Gt Eastern St
FINSBURY
HAC (Bunhill Fields)
Commercial St
Chiswell St
Bishopsgate
Broadgate
MOORGATE
LIVERPOOL ST.
Finsbury Circus
Patty & Bun
Hixter
Wright Brothers
Cinnamon Kitchen,
Chilango
Spianata
New Street Grill, Fish Market
EC2
Moorgate
Haz
K10
Sushisamba, Duck and Waffle, Fuzzy's Grub
Tayyabs
City Social
Relais de Venise L'Entrecôte
Rocket, Nusa's Kitchen
Taylor St Baristas
Nusa Kitchen
Konditor & Cook
Bevis Marks
ALDGATE
Anthologist
Hawksmoor
Goodman
Mint Leaf
Mercer
1701
Threadneedle St
M
Aldgate
City Caphe
Fuzzy's Grub
Leadenhall St
BANK
Coq d'Argent
Cornhill
Chamberlain's
King William St
Simpson's
Taberna Etrusca
1 Lombard Street
George & Vulture
Fenchurch St
Don, Sign of the Don
Loch Fyne, Nusa Kitchen
Thai Square City
Cannon Street
MONUMENT
Royal Exchange, Sauterelle, Laduree
Orpheus
CANNON ST.
FENCHURCH ST.
Haz
Natural Kitchen
Eastcheap
The Wine Library
Bodean's
TOWER HILL
Upper Thames St
Gt Tower St
Taylor St Baristas
EC3
Lower Thames St
Tom's Kitchen, Bravas
Tower of London
London Br
River Thames
Cantina Vinopolis
Vivat Bacchus
Tower Bridge
Roast, Elliot's Cafe, Wright Brothers, Arabica, Rabot 1745, Monmouth Coffee Company, fish!, Black & Blue, Tapas Brindisa, Konditor & Cook
Gaucho Grill, Spianata, dim T
Mango Tree
LONDON BRIDGE
Brigade, The Fire Station
Hutong, Oblix, Aqua Shard, Ting, Rooftop Café
Magdalen
Tooley Street
Applebee's Cafe
Borough High St
St Thomas St
Tas Cafe
Butlers Wharf, Blueprint Café, Bengal Clipper, Pont de la Tour
Story
Bermondsey St
Champor-Champor
BOROUGH
Tower Bridge Rd
Garrison
José
Casse-Croute
Druid St
Long Lane
Pizarro, Zucca, Antico Village East
40 Maltby Street, Monmouth Coffee

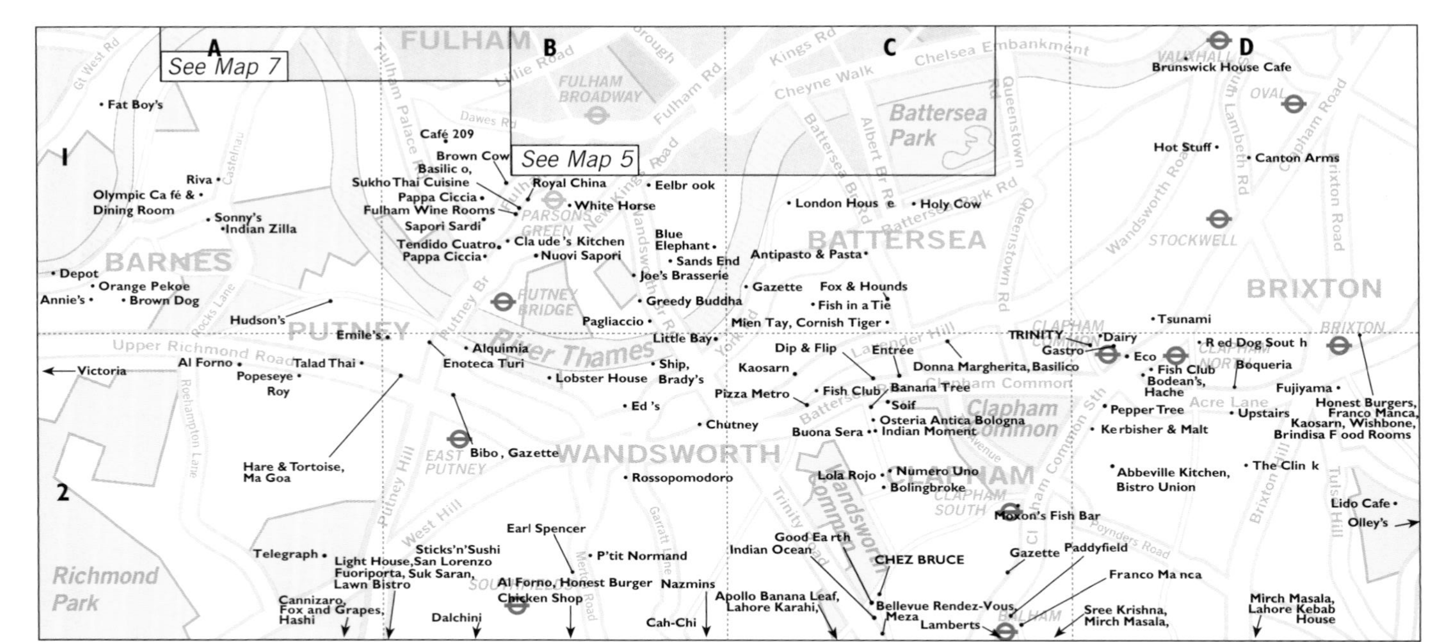
A
See Map 7
B
See Map 5
C
D
1
2
FULHAM
BARNES
PUTNEY
WANDSWORTH
BATTERSEA
CLAPHAM
BRIXTON
Battersea Park
Clapham Common
Wandsworth Common
Richmond Park
River Thames
Fat Boy's
Riva
Olympic Café & Dining Room
Sonny's
Indian Zilla
Depot
Orange Pekoe
Annie's
Brown Dog
Hudson's
Emile's
Victoria
Al Forno
Talad Thai
Popeseye
Roy
Hare & Tortoise, Ma Goa
Telegraph
Light House, San Lorenzo Fuoriporta, Suk Saran, Lawn Bistro
Sticks'n'Sushi
Cannizaro, Fox and Grapes, Hashi
Café 209
Brown Cow
Basilico,
Sukho Thai Cuisine
Pappa Ciccia
Fulham Wine Rooms
Sapori Sardi
Tendido Cuatro
Pappa Ciccia
Royal China
White Horse
Claude's Kitchen
Nuovi Sapori
Eelbrook
Blue Elephant
Sands End
Joe's Brasserie
Greedy Buddha
Pagliaccio
Alquimia
Enoteca Turi
Lobster House
Little Bay
Ship, Brady's
Ed's
Chutney
Bibo, Gazette
Rossopomodoro
Earl Spencer
P'tit Normand
Al Forno, Honest Burger
Chicken Shop
Nazmins
Dalchini
Cah-Chi
London House
Holy Cow
Antipasto & Pasta
Gazette
Fox & Hounds
Fish in a Tie
Mien Tay, Cornish Tiger
Dip & Flip
Kaosarn
Pizza Metro
Fish Club
Entrée
Banana Tree
Soif
Osteria Antica Bologna
Buona Sera
Indian Moment
Donna Margherita, Basilico
Lola Rojo
Numero Uno
Bolingbroke
Good Earth
Indian Ocean
CHEZ BRUCE
Apollo Banana Leaf, Lahore Karahi,
Bellevue Rendez-Vous, Meza
Lamberts
Gazette
Paddyfield
Franco Manca
Sree Krishna, Mirch Masala,
Moxon's Fish Bar
TRINITY
Dairy
Gastro
Eco
Fish Club
Bodean's, Hache
Red Dog South
Boqueria
Pepper Tree
Kerbisher & Malt
Upstairs
Abbeville Kitchen, Bistro Union
The Clink
Tsunami
Fujiyama
Honest Burgers, Franco Manca, Kaosarn, Wishbone, Brindisa Food Rooms
Lido Cafe
Olley's
Mirch Masala, Lahore Kebab House
Brunswick House Cafe
Hot Stuff
Canton Arms
VAUXHALL
OVAL
STOCKWELL
FULHAM BROADWAY
PARSONS GREEN
PUTNEY BRIDGE
EAST PUTNEY
CLAPHAM COMMON
CLAPHAM NORTH
CLAPHAM SOUTH
BALHAM
Gt West Rd
Castelnau
Rocks Lane
Upper Richmond Road
Roehampton Lane
Putney Hill
West Hill
Putney Br
Fulham Palace Rd
Dawes Rd
Lillie Road
Fulham Rd
New Kings Road
Wandsworth Br Rd
Garratt Lane
Merton Road
Kings Rd
Cheyne Walk
Chelsea Embankment
Battersea Br Rd
Albert Br Rd
Battersea Park Rd
Queenstown Rd
Lavender Hill
Trinity Road
Clapham Common Sth
Poynders Road
Acre Lane
Brixton Hill
Tulse Hill
Wandsworth Road
South Lambeth Rd
Clapham Road
Brixton Road

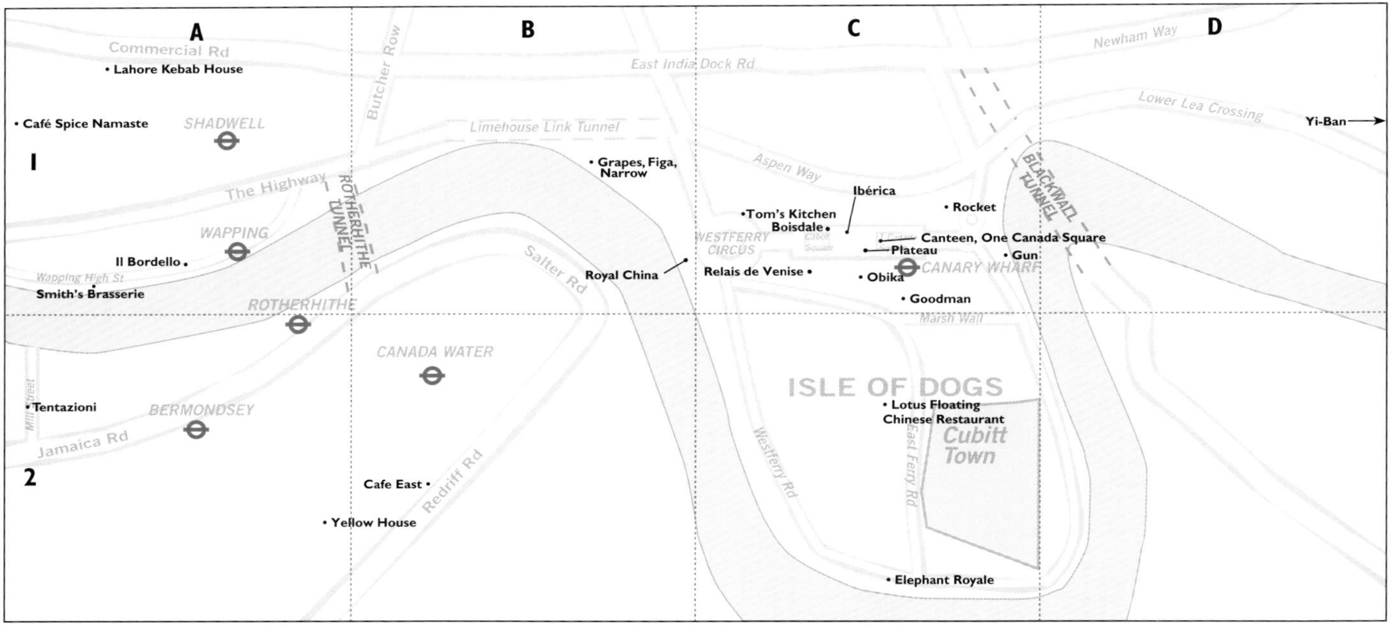

MAP 11 – EAST END & DOCKLANDS

A
B
C
D
1
2

Commercial Rd
• Lahore Kebab House
• Café Spice Namaste
SHADWELL
Butcher Row
East India Dock Rd
Newham Way
Lower Lea Crossing
Yi-Ban
Limehouse Link Tunnel
• Grapes, Figa, Narrow
The Highway
ROTHERHITHE TUNNEL
Aspen Way
BLACKWALL TUNNEL
Ibérica
• Rocket
• Tom's Kitchen
Boisdale •
WESTFERRY CIRCUS
Cabot Square
Canteen, One Canada Square
Plateau
• Gun
WAPPING
Il Bordello •
Wapping High St
Smith's Brasserie
Salter Rd
Royal China
Relais de Venise •
• Obika
CANARY WHARF
• Goodman
ROTHERHITHE
Marsh Wall
CANADA WATER
ISLE OF DOGS
• Lotus Floating Chinese Restaurant
Mill Street
• Tentazioni
BERMONDSEY
Jamaica Rd
Westferry Rd
East Ferry Rd
Cubitt Town
Cafe East •
Redriff Rd
• Yellow House
• Elephant Royale

MAP 12 – SHOREDITCH & BETHNAL GREEN

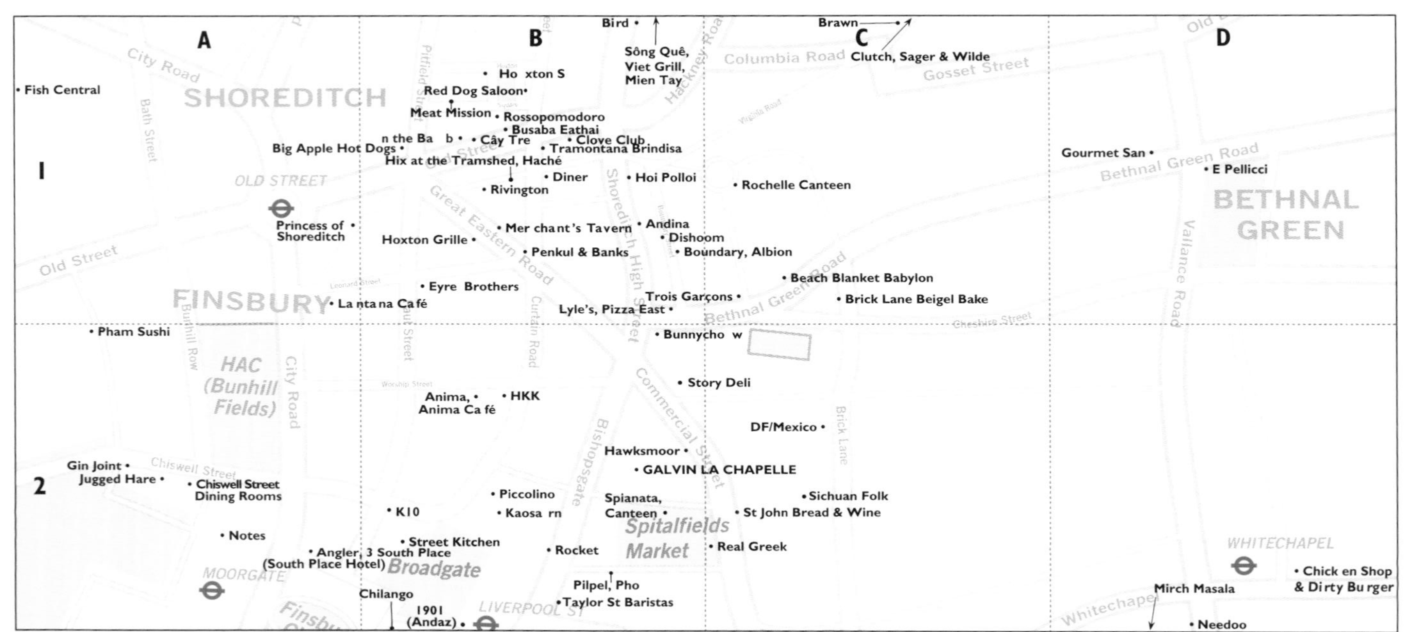

UK SURVEY RESULTS & TOP SCORERS

These are the restaurants outside London that were mentioned most frequently by reporters (last year's position is shown in brackets). For the list of London's most mentioned restaurants, see page 16.

1 **Le Manoir aux Quat' Saisons** (1)
Great Milton, Oxon
2 **Waterside Inn** (3)
Bray, Berks
3 **L'Enclume** (5)
Cartmel, Cumbria
4 **Fat Duck** (2)
Bray, Berks
5 **Hand & Flowers** (4)
Marlow, Bucks

6 **Sportsman** (7)
Whitstable, Kent
7= **Chapter One** (9)
Locksbottom, Kent
7= **Hind's Head** (8)
Bray, Berks
9 **Northcote** (10)
Langho, Lancs
10 **Gidleigh Park** (11)
Chagford, Devon

11 **Seafood Restaurant** (6)
Padstow, Cornwall
12 **Artichoke** (18)
Amersham, Bucks
13= **Restaurant Nathan Outlaw** (20)
Rock, Cornwall
13= **Midsummer House** (12)
Cambridge, Cambs
15= **Great House** (13=)
Lavenham, Suffolk

15= **French Restaurant, Midland Hotel** (-)
Manchester, Greater Manchester
17= **Mr Underhill's** (-)
Ludlow, Shropshire
17= **Restaurant Sat Bains** (13=)
Nottingham, Notts
19= **Reads** (-)
Faversham, Kent
19= **Magpie** (-)
Whitby, N Yorks

Le Manoir aux Quat' Saisons

Waterside Inn

Northcote

Seafood Restaurant

TOP SCORERS

All restaurants whose food rating is **5***; plus restaurants whose price is £50+ with a food rating of* **4**.

Price	Restaurant	Ratings
£240+	The Fat Duck *(Bray)*	454
£200+	Waterside Inn *(Bray)*	554
£190+	Le Manoir aux Quat' Saisons *(Great Milton)*	554
£130+	Gidleigh Park *(Chagford)*	554
	Midsummer House *(Cambridge)*	543
	Andrew Fairlie *(Auchterarder)*	444
£120+	L'Enclume *(Cartmel)*	554
	Restaurant Nathan Outlaw *(Rock)*	553
£110+	Restaurant Sat Bains *(Nottingham)*	543
	Bath Priory Hotel *(Bath)*	445
	The Latymer *(Bagshot)*	444
£100+	André Garrett At Cliveden *(Taplow)*	444
	The Dining Room *(Easton Grey)*	443
	Winteringham Fields *(Winteringham)*	433
£90+	Casamia *(Bristol)*	554
	Martin Wishart *(Loch Lomond)*	554
	Mr Underhill's *(Ludlow)*	554
	Restaurant Martin Wishart *(Edinburgh)*	554
	Simon Radley *(Chester)*	554
	The Pass Restaurant *(Horsham)*	554
	Fraiche *(Oxton)*	543
	Burgh Island Hotel *(Bigbury-on-Sea)*	445
	Kinloch Lodge *(Sleat)*	435
	Fischers at Baslow Hall *(Baslow)*	454
	21212 *(Edinburgh)*	444
	Yorke Arms *(Ramsgill-in-Nidderdale)*	444
	Lords of the Manor *(Upper Slaughter)*	434
	Holbeck Ghyll *(Windermere)*	424
£80+	Northcote *(Langho)*	554
	Ocean Restaurant *(Jersey)*	554
	Manchester House *(Manchester)*	544
	Drakes *(Ripley)*	543
	Harry's Place *(Great Gonerby)*	552
	Bybrook Restaurant *(Castle Combe)*	443
	Kinloch House *(Blairgowrie)*	443

	L'Ortolan *(Shinfield)*	4 4 3
	Seafood Restaurant *(Padstow)*	4 3 3
	Morston Hall *(Morston)*	4 2 3
	Bohemia *(Jersey)*	4 4 2
	The Peat Inn *(Cupar)*	4 4 2
£70+	Hambleton Hall *(Hambleton)*	5 4 5
	Raby Hunt *(Summerhouse)*	5 4 5
	Hipping Hall *(Kirkby Lonsdale)*	5 5 4
	Read's *(Faversham)*	5 5 4
	The Castle Terrace *(Edinburgh)*	5 5 4
	The Harrow at Little Bedwyn *(Marlborough)*	5 5 4
	The Neptune *(Old Hunstanton)*	5 5 4
	Tyddyn Llan *(Llandrillo)*	5 5 4
	Monachyle Mhor *(Balquhidder)*	5 4 4
	Number One *(Edinburgh)*	5 4 4
	The Hambrough *(Ventnor)*	5 4 4
	Le Champignon Sauvage *(Cheltenham)*	5 5 3
	Purnells *(Birmingham)*	5 5 3
	Artichoke *(Amersham)*	5 4 3
	Ormer *(Jersey)*	5 4 3
	The Crown at Whitebrook *(Whitebrook)*	5 2 3
	Michael Caines *(Exeter)*	5 3 2
	Samuel's *(Masham)*	4 5 5
	The Three Chimneys *(Dunvegan)*	4 4 5
	The Crazy Bear *(Stadhampton)*	4 3 5
	Paul Ainsworth at Number 6 *(Padstow)*	4 5 4
	Driftwood Hotel *(Rosevine)*	4 4 4
	Longueville Manor *(Jersey)*	4 4 4
	Michael Caines *(Chester)*	4 4 4
	Middlethorpe Hall *(York)*	4 4 4
	The Alderley *(Alderley Edge)*	4 4 4
	The Cross *(Kingussie)*	4 4 4
	The Peacock *(Rowsley)*	4 4 4
	Dining Room *(Aylesbury)*	4 3 4
	Black Swan *(Oldstead)*	4 4 3
	Fallowfields *(Kingston Bagpuize)*	4 4 3
	Restaurant James Sommerin *(Penarth)*	4 4 3
	Cotto *(Cambridge)*	4 3 3
	Hand & Flowers *(Marlow)*	4 3 3
	Restaurant Mark Greenaway *(Edinburgh)*	4 2 3
	Lumière *(Cheltenham)*	4 4 2
	JSW *(Petersfield)*	4 3 2
	Van Zeller *(Harrogate)*	4 3 1

TOP SCORERS

£60+	Braidwoods *(Dalry)*	554
	Caldesi in Campagna *(Bray)*	554
	Checkers *(Montgomery)*	554
	Fairyhill *(Reynoldston)*	554
	Little Barwick House *(Barwick)*	554
	Sienna *(Dorchester)*	554
	The Butcher's Arms *(Eldersfield)*	554
	The Kitchin *(Edinburgh)*	554
	Craig Millar @ 16 West End *(St Monans)*	544
	Elephant Restaurant & Brasserie *(Torquay)*	544
	The Albannach *(Lochinver)*	544
	The Mason's Arms *(Knowstone)*	544
	The Old Inn *(Drewsteignton)*	544
	The Seahorse *(Dartmouth)*	544
	Menu Gordon Jones *(Bath)*	553
	Michael Caines *(Manchester)*	553
	The Box Tree *(Ilkley)*	553
	Lavender House *(Brundall)*	543
	Little Fish Market *(Brighton)*	543
	The Old Passage Inn *(Arlingham)*	543
	The Vanilla Pod *(Marlow)*	543
	The Walnut Tree *(Llandewi Skirrid)*	543
	Wilks *(Bristol)*	552
	Loves *(Birmingham)*	542
	Chino Latino *(Nottingham)*	532
	Ubiquitous Chip *(Glasgow)*	455
	Hotel Tresanton *(St Mawes)*	445
	Le Talbooth *(Dedham)*	445
	The Star Inn *(Harome)*	445
	The Wellington Arms *(Baughurst)*	445
	Seafood Restaurant *(St Andrews)*	435
	The Dining Room *(Ashbourne)*	454
	The Mirabelle *(Eastbourne)*	454
	Black Swan *(Helmsley)*	444
	Brockencote Hall *(Chaddesley Corbett)*	444
	Crab & Lobster *(Asenby)*	444
	Hassop Hall *(Hassop)*	444
	La Parmigiana *(Glasgow)*	444
	Restaurant 23 *(Leamington Spa)*	444
	Rogano *(Glasgow)*	444
	Silver Darling *(Aberdeen)*	444
	The Feathered Nest Inn *(Nether Westcote)*	444
	Tuddenham Mill *(Tuddenham)*	444
	Amberley Castle *(Amberley)*	434
	La Capanna *(Cobham)*	434
	Bluebells *(Sunningdale)*	453

	The Restaurant at Drakes *(Brighton)*	4 5 3
	Edmunds *(Birmingham)*	4 4 3
	Opus Restaurant *(Birmingham)*	4 4 3
	Park Restaurant *(Sutton on the Forest)*	4 4 3
	Plas Bodegroes *(Pwllheli)*	4 4 3
	Smith's Brasserie *(Ongar)*	4 4 3
	The Dysart Arms *(Richmond)*	4 4 3
	The Loft Restaurant *(Beaumaris)*	4 4 3
	Alec's *(Brentwood)*	4 3 3
	Ondine *(Edinburgh)*	4 3 3
	Thackeray's *(Tunbridge Wells)*	4 3 3
	The Hind's Head *(Bray)*	4 3 3
	The Marquis *(Alkham)*	4 3 3
	Blunos *(Bath)*	4 2 3
	Orwells *(Shiplake)*	4 2 3
	The Bildeston Crown *(Bildeston)*	4 2 3
	5 North Street *(Winchcombe)*	4 4 2
	Lasan *(Birmingham)*	4 3 2
	Roger Hickman's *(Norwich)*	4 3 2
	The Cross at Kenilworth *(Kenilworth)*	4 3 2
	The Olive Tree *(Bath)*	4 3 2
£50+	Maison Bleue *(Bury St Edmunds)*	5 5 4
	Gilpin Lodge *(Windermere)*	5 4 5
	The Jetty *(Christchurch)*	5 4 5
	The Oyster Box *(Jersey)*	5 4 5
	The Pipe & Glass Inn *(Beverley)*	5 4 5
	Chez Roux *(Inverness)*	5 5 4
	Freemasons at Wiswell *(Wiswell)*	5 5 4
	Great House *(Lavenham)*	5 5 4
	No 7 Fish Bistro *(Torquay)*	5 5 4
	Tailors *(Warwick)*	5 5 4
	The Sportsman *(Whitstable)*	5 5 4
	The Stockbridge *(Edinburgh)*	5 5 4
	Yalbury Cottage *(Lower Bockhampton)*	5 5 4
	Bilash *(Wolverhampton)*	5 4 4
	Carpenter's Arms *(Sunninghill)*	5 4 4
	Chapter One *(Locksbottom)*	5 4 4
	Jeremy's at Borde Hill *(Haywards Heath)*	5 4 4
	Margot's *(Padstow)*	5 4 4
	Pea Porridge *(Bury St Edmunds)*	5 4 4
	The Wheatsheaf *(Bath)*	5 4 4
	Crannog *(Fort William)*	5 3 4
	House of Tides *(Newcastle upon Tyne)*	5 3 4
	Gingerman *(Brighton)*	5 5 3
	Rogan & Co *(Cartmel)*	5 5 3

The West House *(Biddenden)*	553
Verveine Fishmarket Restaurant *(Milford-on-Sea)*	553
Wedgwood *(Edinburgh)*	553
Haywards Restaurant *(Epping)*	543
London House *(Old Woking)*	543
Mithas *(Edinburgh)*	543
Riverside *(Bridport)*	543
The Creel *(Orkney Islands)*	543
The Willow Tree *(Taunton)*	543
Wild Thyme *(Chipping Norton)*	543
Restaurant Tristan *(Horsham)*	533
The Sweet Olive *(Aston Tirrold)*	533
Le Langhe *(York)*	523
Bosquet *(Kenilworth)*	552
Lanterna *(Scarborough)*	552
Apicius *(Cranbrook)*	542
Terre à Terre *(Brighton)*	542
The Kings Head *(Leighton Buzzard)*	532
Coast *(Saundersfoot)*	445
Pierhouse Hotel *(Port Appin)*	445
The Chesil Rectory *(Winchester)*	445
The Sir Charles Napier *(Chinnor)*	445
Timberyard *(Edinburgh)*	445
Hix Oyster & Fish House *(Lyme Regis)*	435
Chez Roux *(Gullane)*	454
Damson *(Salford)*	454
Darleys *(Derby)*	454
Retro *(Teddington)*	454
The Honours *(Edinburgh)*	454
The Pheasant Hotel *(Harome)*	454
60 Hope Street *(Liverpool)*	444
Castellamare *(Swansea)*	444
Friends *(Pinner)*	444
Rafters *(Sheffield)*	444
Restaurant 27 *(Portsmouth)*	444
Shaun Dickens at The Boathouse *(Henley-on-Thames)*	444
Stovell's *(Chobham)*	444
The Nut Tree Inn *(Murcott)*	444
Whitstable Oyster Fishery Co. *(Whitstable)*	434
Good Earth *(Esher)*	443
Sebastian's *(Oswestry)*	443
St Petroc's Hotel & Bistro *(Padstow)*	443
The French Table *(Surbiton)*	443
The Oystercatcher *(Portmahomack)*	443
63 Tay Street *(Perth)*	433
La Luna *(Godalming)*	452

	Cinnamon Culture *(Bromley)*	432
	Dining Room *(Rock)*	432
	The Crab at Chieveley *(Newbury)*	412
£40+	The Gunton Arms *(Norwich)*	554
	Wheelers Oyster Bar *(Whitstable)*	554
	The Pig *(Pensford)*	545
	Yu And You *(Copster Green)*	545
	Adam's *(Birmingham)*	554
	Austells *(St Austell)*	554
	Café 21 *(Newcastle upon Tyne)*	554
	Les Mirabelles *(Nomansland)*	554
	Orchid *(Harrogate)*	554
	Prithvi *(Cheltenham)*	554
	Scran & Scallie *(Edinburgh)*	554
	Spice Merchant *(Henley-on-Thames)*	554
	Sukhothai *(Leeds)*	554
	The Berkeley Arms *(Wymondham)*	554
	The Red Lion *(Britwell Salome)*	554
	Wallfish Bistro *(Bristol)*	554
	Crabshakk *(Glasgow)*	544
	Indian Summer *(Brighton)*	544
	Indian Zest *(Sunbury on Thames)*	544
	Jew's House Restaurant *(Lincoln)*	544
	Loch Leven Seafood Café *(Onich)*	544
	Rick Stein's Café *(Padstow)*	544
	The Cove Restaurant & Bar *(Falmouth)*	544
	The Crown Inn *(Snape)*	544
	The Grassington House Hotel *(Grassington)*	544
	The Old Boat House *(Amble)*	544
	The Parkers Arms *(Newton-in-Bowland)*	544
	The Plough at Bolnhurst *(Bolnhurst)*	544
	El Gato Negro Tapas *(Ripponden)*	553
	The Wild Mushroom *(Westfield)*	553
	Acorn Vegetarian Kitchen *(Bath)*	543
	Café Fish *(Tobermory)*	543
	Gandolfi Fish *(Glasgow)*	543
	Riverford Field Kitchen *(Buckfastleigh)*	543
	Rose Garden *(Manchester)*	543
	The Apron Stage *(Stanley)*	543
	The Chilli Pickle *(Brighton)*	533
	Yang Sing *(Manchester)*	533
	Maliks *(Cookham)*	523
	Flinty Red *(Bristol)*	542
	Graveley's Fish & Chip Restaurant *(Harrogate)*	542
	Magpie Café *(Whitby)*	542

	The Feathers Inn *(Hedley On The Hill)*	5 4 2
	Webbe's at The Fish Cafe *(Rye)*	5 4 2
	Sojo *(Oxford)*	5 3 2
	The Ambrette *(Margate)*	5 3 2
£30+	The Vineyard Cafe *(Totnes)*	5 4 5
	Food by Breda Murphy *(Whalley)*	5 5 4
	Green Café *(Ludlow)*	5 5 4
	JoJo *(Whitstable)*	5 5 4
	Mezzet *(East Molesey)*	5 5 4
	Oli's Thai *(Oxford)*	5 5 4
	Albarino *(Broadstairs)*	5 4 4
	Hare Inn *(Scawton)*	5 4 4
	Prashad *(Leeds)*	5 4 4
	The Palm *(Froxfield)*	5 4 4
	White Swan at Fence *(Fence)*	5 4 4
	Hansa's *(Leeds)*	5 4 3
	Stein's Fish & Chips *(Padstow)*	5 4 3
	Great Kathmandu *(Manchester)*	5 3 3
	The Company Shed *(West Mersea)*	5 2 3
	My Sichuan *(Oxford)*	5 1 3
	Ebi Sushi *(Derby)*	5 4 2
	Yuzu *(Manchester)*	5 4 2
	Baipo *(Ipswich)*	5 3 1
£20+	Anstruther Fish Bar *(Anstruther)*	5 4 3
	Crab Shack *(Teignmouth)*	5 4 3
	McDermotts Fish & Chips *(Croydon)*	5 4 3
	Sole Bay Fish Company *(Southwold)*	5 4 3
	The Fish House *(Ludlow)*	5 4 3
	The Mint Room *(Bath)*	5 4 3
	PR Massala *(St Ives)*	5 3 3
	Fuji Hiro *(Leeds)*	5 4 2
	Karachi *(Bradford)*	5 4 2
	Pizza 500 *(Brighton)*	5 4 1
	Jyoti *(Birmingham)*	5 4 2
£10+	The Greedy Cow *(Margate)*	5 4 4
	This & That *(Manchester)*	5 2 2

Blunos

Charlton Arms

RJS

UK DIRECTORY

ABERAERON, CEREDIGION 4–3C

Harbourmaster £48 2 1 4
Quay Pde SA46 0BT (01545) 570755
A location "at the top of one of the prettiest streets in Britain" is the "obvious draw" of this restaurant-with-rooms; it's "so near to the sea there is never any doubt about the freshness of the fish", but the food (and "hit-and-miss" service) have otherwise elicited somewhat mixed reports of late.
*/ **Details:** www.harbour-master.com; @hmaberaeron; 9 pm; no Amex. **Accommodation:** 13 rooms, from £110.*

The Hive On The Quay £44 Ⓣ
Cadwgan Pl SA46 0BU (01545) 570445
Tipped especially for its "good-value seafood", a large and buzzing harbourside restaurant… and, yes, they do sell honey ice cream!
*/ **Details:** www.thehiveaberaeron.com; 9 pm; closed Mon & Sun D; no Amex.*

ABERDEEN, ABERDEENSHIRE 9–2D

Marcliffe Hotel £59 Ⓣ
North Deeside Rd AB15 9YA (01224) 861000
Tipped for "excellent cooking" and a "beautiful setting too" – the dining room of a small but grand hotel with "high standards" ("and just the right ambience for business").
*/ **Details:** www.marcliffe.com; 8.30 pm.*

Moonfish Cafe £46 Ⓣ
AB10 1HP (01224) 644166
"A great addition to the Aberdeen scene"; this small but central restaurant, in the Merchant Quarter, is tipped for "wonderful" cooking, "creative in its use of local produce", and its "different and interesting" wines; it can get "very busy".
*/ **Details:** www.moonfishcafe.co.uk.*

Silver Darling £62 4 4 4
Pocra Quay, North Pier AB11 5DQ
(01224) 576229
"Probably the best seafood restaurant in Aberdeen", this "modern glass structure atop an old stone base" (a former harbour control building) offers "great views" over the water too.
*/ **Details:** www.thesilverdarling.co.uk; 9 pm; closed Sat L & Sun; children: +16 after 8 pm.*

ABERGAVENNY, MONMOUTHSHIRE 2–1A

The Angel Hotel £50 2 3 4
15 Cross St NP7 5EN (01873) 857121
A "relaxed" former coaching inn which "never ceases to please" with its "reliable" cooking of "modern staples"; breakfast is merely "superb", but the afternoon tea is "historic".
*/ **Details:** www.angelhotelabergavenny.com; @lovetheangel; 10 pm. **Accommodation:** 35 rooms, from £101.*

The Hardwick £58 3 3 3
Old Raglan Rd NP7 9AA (01873) 854220
Stephen Terry has a fine CV and his rural gastropub (with rooms) has won renown for its "genuinely classy" cooking; even fans feel it's "perhaps a victim of its own popularity", though, and a disgruntled minority now finds it "hugely disappointing".
*/ **Details:** www.thehardwick.co.uk; @The_Hardwick; 10 pm, Sun 9 pm; no Amex. **Accommodation:** 8 rooms, from £150.*

ABERYSTWYTH, POWYS 4–3C

Gwesty Cymru £44 Ⓣ
19 Marine Ter SY23 2AZ (01970) 612252
Not many reports, but this seafront hotel is tipped as "the best place to eat in the region" (not, it must be admitted, the most demanding test), offering "excellent steak, lamb and fish", and "Welsh hospitality" too.
*/ **Details:** www.gwestycymru.com; @gwestyc; 9 pm; closed Tue L; no Amex; children: 5+. **Accommodation:** 8 rooms, from £85.*

Ultracomida £32 Ⓣ
31 Pier St SY23 2LN (01970) 630686
Behind an "excellent" deli, a "bright and lively" spot tipped for a superb tapas selection from which you can eat "as cheaply or expensively as you want"; "friendly student service" too.
*/ **Details:** www.ultracomida.com; 9 pm; Mon-Thu & Sat L only, Fri open L & D, closed Sun.*

ACHILTIBUIE, ROSSSHIRE 9–1B

Summer Isles Hotel £80 2 2 2
IV26 2YG (01854) 622282
"A very beautiful setting overlooking the Summer Isles" helps make this remote hotel of long standing "a great getaway place"; the style, though, can seem "stuffy" or "old-fashioned", and the cuisine does not always live up to its ambitions.
*/ **Details:** www.summerisleshotel.com; @SummerIslesHot; 25m N of Ullapool on A835; 8 pm; Closed from 1st Nov - 1st Apr; no Amex; no jeans; children: 8+. **Accommodation:** 13 rooms, from £155.*

ALBOURNE, WEST SUSSEX 3–4B

The Ginger Fox £46 3 4 3
Muddleswood Road BN6 9EA
(01273) 857888
As you might expect, this rural outpost of Brighton's Gingerman empire maintains a "high standard" – "the menu changes monthly and the fish, in particular, is always good".
*/ **Details:** www.gingermanrestaurants.com; @gingerfox; 10 pm, Sun 9 pm.*

ALDEBURGH, SUFFOLK 3–1D

Aldeburgh Fish And Chips £15 232
225 High St IP15 5DB (01728) 454685
"An institution for the Chelsea-on-Sea brigade", this famous ("long queues") chippy dishes up "good fish and chips to eat on the sea wall with the other trippers and the seagulls"; naysayers insist, however, that the food "comes nowhere near the standard reported".
/ **Details:** *www.aldeburghfishandchips.co.uk; 8 pm; no credit cards.*

The Lighthouse £43 343
77 High St IP15 5AU (01728) 453377
"Still going strong" – Aldeburgh's "busy" favourite is "always fun", and the food is "lovely" too, but it's the "wonderful warm service" and "dependable high standards" that make it such a stalwart.
/ **Details:** *www.lighthouserestaurant.co.uk; 10 pm.*

Regatta £43 332
171-173 High St IP15 5AN (01728) 452011
"Always fresh fish", and a "good selection" too – this "reliable" and popular stalwart remains one of the town's leading lights; it probably helps that service is "agreeable" too.
/ **Details:** *www.regattaaldeburgh.com; @AldeburghR; 10 pm.*

ALDERLEY EDGE, CHESHIRE 5–2B

The Alderley
Alderley Edge Hotel £74 444
Macclesfield Rd SK9 7BJ (01625) 583033
A "very professional" operation, deep in the Cheshire bling belt, where Chris Holland's cooking is "always of high quality"; "there's a lovely atmosphere" too, "whether it's a busy Sunday or a quiet midweek lunch".
/ **Details:** *www.alderleyedgehotel.com; @AlderleyHotel; 9.45 pm; closed Sun D.*

ALDFORD, CHESHIRE 5–3A

The Grosvenor Arms £40 334
Chester Rd CH3 6HJ (01244) 620228
One of the earlier members of the ever-expanding Brunning & Price chain, this large – but "comfortable" and extremely "characterful" – inn, on the Duke of Westminster's estate, is a "friendly" place, on which reports remain consistently upbeat.
/ **Details:** *www.grosvenorarms-aldford.co.uk; 6m S of Chester on B5130; 10 pm, Sun 9 pm.*

ALKHAM, KENT 3–3D

The Marquis £61 433
Alkham Valley Rd CT15 7DF (01304) 873410
A "smart modern pub-conversion in a picturesque location", where chef Charlie Lakin's "healthy obsession with locally sourced-produce" often leads to the creation of "amazing" dishes; the lunch menu, in particular, offers "incredible value".
/ **Details:** *www.themarquisatalkham.co.uk; 9.30 pm, Sun 8.30 pm; children: 8+ at D.* **Accommodation:** *10 rooms, from £95.*

ALLOSTOCK, CHESHIRE 4–2B

Three Greyhounds £34 Ⓣ
Holmes Chapel Rd WA16 9JY
(01565) 723455
A popular Georgian freehouse, with an attractive garden, and "eclectic" decor; fans say the food is "first-rate", and even a sceptic who found the fare "unexciting", said it was "adequate... and the beer was good!"
/ **Details:** *www.thethreegreyhoundsinn.co.uk; 9.15 pm, Fri & Sat 9.45 pm, Sun 8.45 pm.*

ALNWICK, NORTHUMBERLAND 8–1B

Treehouse
Alnwick Castle £43 335
Denwick Ln NE66 1YU (01665) 511350
"A magical experience, dining up in the stars!"; it's the "amazing" setting – a huge treehouse adjacent to the Castle's new gardens – which makes a visit to this elevated restaurant a "most enjoyable" experience; biggest surprise? – the food is "fine" too!
/ **Details:** *www.alnwickgarden.com; 9.15 pm; closed Mon D, Tue D & Wed D.*

ALRESFORD, HAMPSHIRE 2–3D

Caracoli £30 333
15 Broad St SO24 9AR (01962) 738730
"A haven in this charming town"; this cookware shop café, part of an über-modern city-centre building (and one of three branches locally), wins plaudits for its "tasty salads and sandwiches" and some "scrummy indulgences" too.
/ **Details:** *www.caracoli.co.uk; 2.30 pm; L only; no Amex; no booking.*

ALSTONEFIELD, DERBYSHIRE 5–3C

The George £38 Ⓣ
DE6 2FX (01335) 310205
"In a beautiful quiet village, amidst some of the nicest Peak District scenery", this is tipped as "the country pub straight from Central Casting"; "good local beef and game, as well as good soups at lunch".
/ **Details:** *www.thegeorgeatalstonefield.com.*

ALVESTON, WARWICKSHIRE 2–1C

Baraset Barn £46 244
1 Pimlico Lane CV37 7RJ (01789) 295510
A lavish and extensive contemporary gastroboozer of particular note for its "buzzy" atmosphere; – "the food's quite good" and there's "an interesting menu selection" too, but "it's the decor which makes

the place". / ***Details:*** *www.barasetbarn.co.uk; @TheBarasetBarn; 9.30 pm, Sat 10 pm; closed Sun D; no Amex.*

AMBERLEY, WEST SUSSEX 3–4A

Amberley Castle **£65** 4 3 4
BN18 9LT (01798) 831992
"A first-class experience in a magical setting"; Robby Jenks is an ex-Gidleigh Park chef, and the cooking at this "real" medieval castle (complete with portcullis!) is "excellent"; lunchtime, in particular, is "absolutely fantastic value".
/ ***Details:*** *www.amberleycastle.co.uk; @amberleycastle; N of Arundel on B2139; 9 pm; no jeans or trainers; booking: max 6; children: 12+.*
Accommodation: *19 rooms, from £265.*

AMBLE, NORTHUMBERLAND 8–1B

The Old Boat House **£49** 5 4 4
NE65 0AA (01665) 711232
"The best place by far to eat between Edinburgh and Newcastle!"; "a converted shack on the edge of the harbour" is the location for this "wonderful" new waterside fish restaurant, which inspires a hymn of praise.

AMBLESIDE, CUMBRIA 7–3D

Drunken Duck **£57** 3 2 4
Barngates LA22 0NG (01539) 436347
This "friendly" gastropub and microbrewery offers not just "a wide variety of real ales" (many brewed on the premises), but some "imaginatively cooked" dishes too; at "frantic" peak times, the restaurant can be a better bet than the bar (and "if you sit outside, the view is super").
/ ***Details:*** *www.drunkenduckinn.co.uk; @DrunkenDuckInn; 3m from Ambleside, towards Hawkshead; 9 pm; no Amex; booking: max 10 (D only).*
Accommodation: *17 rooms, from £105.*

Fellini's **£39** 4 3 3
Church St LA22 0BT (01539) 432487
A "very attractively laid-out" dining room where the "inventive" cuisine "reminds carnivores that vegetarians can also eat impressively well"; don't miss "great film-and-food deals" in tandem with the boutique cinema next door.
/ ***Details:*** *www.fellinisambleside.com; 10 pm; no Amex.*

Old Stamp House **£52** 4 4 2
LA22 0BU (015394) 32775
"A very promising newcomer", in an historic building, where Ryan Blackburn "prepares interesting dishes from fresh, local ingredients, with skill and imagination"; these are delivered to table by his brother "with aplomb".
/ ***Details:*** *www.oldstamphouse.com.*

Zeffirelli's **£34** 3 3 3
Compston Rd LA22 9AD (01539) 433845
"If you want or need a quick pit stop" en route to the attached jazz bar or cinema (combined tickets are available) this "relaxed" and "family-friendly" Italian offers some "delicious" food – "all veggie but you'd never know"; there's now a chic new 'vegetarian' venue, Fellini's, on site too.
/ ***Details:*** *www.zeffirellis.com; 10 pm; no Amex.*

AMERSHAM, BUCKINGHAMSHIRE 3–2A

Artichoke **£78** 5 4 3
9 Market Sq HP7 0DF (01494) 726611
"In the beautiful cobbled streets of Old Amersham", these converted 17th century cottages are "well worth a detour"; Laurie Gear's "presence at the pass in the open kitchen gives a wonderfully personal feel to the place", and his "intense" and "creative" cuisine is amongst the UK's best.
/ ***Details:*** *www.theartichokerestaurant.co.uk; 9.15 pm, Fri & Sat 9.30 pm; closed Mon & Sun; no shorts.*

Gilbey's **£50** 2 3 3
1 Market Sq HP7 0DF (01494) 727242
"Varied wine from their own vineyard" and a "cosy" style add to the appeal of this "personal" venture, named after the gin dynasty which owns it; reports aren't entirely consistent, but it is mainly praised for "competent food at a not unreasonable price".
/ ***Details:*** *www.gilbeygroup.com; @GilbeysAmersham; 9.30 pm, Sat 9.45 pm, Sun 8.45 pm.*

ANSTRUTHER, FIFE 9–4D

Anstruther Fish Bar **£25** 5 4 3
42-44 Shore St KY10 3AQ (01333) 310518
"Still the best fish 'n' chips in Scotland!" – "the speed with which the long queue of patrons is kept moving in spite of each order being fried individually is always impressive".
/ ***Details:*** *www.anstrutherfishbar.co.uk; 10 pm; no Amex; no booking.*

APPLECROSS, HIGHLAND 9–2B

Applecross Inn **£39** 4 4 4
Shore St IV54 8LT (01520) 744262
"Just the welcoming food and service you need after a long, mountainous drive or scenic hike!" – this "cosy" inn lives up to its long-standing reputation, not least for "the freshest of fish".
/ ***Details:*** *www.applecross.uk.com; off A896, S of Shieldaig; 9 pm; no Amex; need 6+ to book.*
Accommodation: *7 rooms, from £90.*

APPLEDORE, DEVON 1–2C

The Coffee Cabin **£10** 4 5 5
EX39 1QS (01237) 475843
"A real find"; this "relaxing" new café offers not just "amazing" coffee (and a view of the estuary), but many "delicious" homemade cakes too –

few reports fail to mention "Richard's amazing Victoria sponge"!

ARLINGHAM, GLOUCESTERSHIRE 2–2B

The Old Passage Inn **£66** **5 4 3**
Passage Rd GL2 7JR (01452) 740547
In a "brilliant (but remote) location overlooking a bend in the Severn", a restaurant-with-rooms that's particularly rated for its "fresh, flavoursome fish dishes"; "Severn Bore Breakfasts – coinciding with the local natural phenomenon, a rapidly moving 2 metre-wave – a speciality".
*/ **Details:** www.theoldpassage.com; 9 pm; closed Mon & Sun D. **Accommodation:** 2 rooms, from £80.*

ARUNDEL, WEST SUSSEX 3–4A

Sage Of Arundel **£65** Ⓣ
2-8 Castle Mews BN18 9DG (01903) 883477
*A rather charming town-centre café-gallery-restaurant; it has a new chef of late, but is tipped as still offering "the most relaxed fine dining for miles around". / **Details:** www.sageofarundel.com.*

The Town House **£46** **4 4 4**
65 High St BN18 9AJ (01903) 883847
"Consistently good" food, and "friendly" service too – this restaurant-with-room, overlooking the castle, inspires very positive reports; only problem? – "it's getting a little bit too popular!"
*/ **Details:** www.thetownhouse.co.uk; @thetownhousearundel; 9.30 pm; closed Mon & Sun. **Accommodation:** 4 + family room rooms, from £95.*

ASCOT, BERKSHIRE 3–3A

Restaurant Coworth Park
Coworth Park **£103** **3 5 4**
Blacknest Rd SL5 7SE (01344) 876 600
"The place to go to enjoy a special meal!"; the Dorchester Collection's country house hotel elicits raves for its "fabulous location, perfect service and often superb cooking and presentation"; lunch is a highlight… which is handy as this is a place that's particularly "expensive in the evening".
*/ **Details:** www.coworthpark.com; @CoworthParkUK; 9.45 pm; closed Mon & Sun D.*
***Accommodation:** 17 rooms, from £.*

ASENBY, NORTH YORKSHIRE 8–4C

Crab & Lobster **£65** **4 4 4**
Dishforth Rd YO7 3QL (01845) 577286
*In a "lovely building full of character" (thanks not least to its rich assortment of bric-à-brac), this "quirky village restaurant-with-rooms" is a "most enjoyable" veteran destination, where the menus are almost invariably "well-executed" and "tasty". / **Details:** www.crabandlobster.co.uk; at junction of Asenby Rd & Topcliffe Rd; 9 pm, Sat 9.30 pm. **Accommodation:** 17 rooms, from £160.*

ASHBOURNE, DERBYSHIRE 5–3C

The Dining Room **£66** **4 5 4**
33 St.John's St DE6 1GP (01335) 300666
"Ambitious" cooking that's amongst "the best in Derbyshire" makes this "cosy" husband-and-wife-run spot, in a "lovely old house", well worth seeking out; "delicious home-made sourdough bread" attracts particular praise.
*/ **Details:** www.thediningroomashbourne.co.uk; 7 pm; D only, closed Mon–Wed & Sun; no Amex; children: 12+. **Accommodation:** 1 room, at about £120.*

ASTON TIRROLD, OXFORDSHIRE 2–2D

The Sweet Olive **£52** **5 3 3**
Baker St OX11 9DD (01235) 851272
*"Simply delicious" Gallic food – with "loads of specials rattled off" by front of house Stephane Brun – ensure that a visit to this "lovely" gastropub is always "a treat". / **Details:** www.sweet-olive.com; half a mile off the A417 between Streatley & Wantage; 9 pm; closed 2 weeks in February, and 3 weeks in July.*

AUCHTERARDER, PERTH AND KINROSS 9–3C

Andrew Fairlie
Gleneagles Hotel **£132** **4 4 4**
PH3 1NF (01764) 694267
*"Without a doubt, one of Britain's best restaurants"; this renowned dining room "spells luxury from the moment you enter its fashionably muted and spacious interior", and its cuisine is "truly outstanding" – it is also "frighteningly expensive", though, and there were a couple of "anticlimactic" reports this year. / **Details:** www.andrewfairlie.co.uk; @AndrewFairlie1; 10 pm; L only, closed Sun; children: 12+.*

Jon & Fernanda's **£49** Ⓣ
34 High St PH3 1DB (01764) 662442
"A great way to get away from the formality and prices of Gleneagles but still get an excellent dinner with friendly service"; this "consistent" spot – run by refugees from the big house – is a tip well worth knowing about.
*/ **Details:** www.jonandfernandas.co.uk; 9 pm; D only, closed Mon & Sun; no Amex; children: 10+.*

Strathearn Restaurant
Gleneagles Hotel **£83** Ⓣ
PH3 1NF (01764) 662231
Perhaps unfairly overshadowed by Andrew Fairlie, this grand hotel's more "traditional" number two venue inspires only modest feedback, but it is still tipped as "one of the UK's great dining rooms", offering "a fantastic all-round experience"; breakfast is, naturally, "superb".

/ **Details:** www.gleneagles.com; 10 pm; D only, ex Sun open L & D. **Accommodation:** 232 rooms, from £245

AUSTWICK, LANCASHIRE 5–1B

The Game Cock Inn £41 Ⓣ
LA2 8BB (015242) 51226
"A typical village green pub, but with a Breton chef and Norman sous-chef" – it's tipped for "outstanding slow-cooked meat from local farms and classic French desserts… wow!"
*/ **Details:** www.gamecockinn.co.uk/.*

AXMINSTER, DEVON 2–4A

River Cottage Canteen £40 333
Trinity Sq EX13 5AN (01297) 630 300
"Good simple food" – with "great use of local produce" – makes Hugh Fearnley-Whittingstall's "relaxed" (and kid-friendly) dining room, behind a deli, a hit for with practically all who comment on it, sometimes "slow" service notwithstanding; brunch here is "almost an institution".
*/ **Details:** www.rivercottage.net; 8.30 pm; closed Mon D & Sun D; SRA-84%.*

AYLESBURY, BUCKINGHAMSHIRE 3–2A

Dining Room Hartwell House £79 434
Oxford Rd HP17 8NR (01296) 747444
"Perfect for special occasions"; the "lovely" country house that once accommodated Louis XVIII in exile is a "wonderfully comfortable" hotel nowadays, offering food that's "well above-average".
*/ **Details:** www.hartwell-house.com/wine-and-dine/; 2m W of Aylesbury on A418; 9.45 pm; no jeans or trainers; children: 4+. **Accommodation:** 50 rooms, from £290.*

AYLESFORD, KENT 3–3C

Hengist £54 Ⓣ
7-9 High St ME20 7AX (01622) 885800
Relaunched and reconfigured under new ownership, a village restaurant once of some renown – early reporters tip it as (even) "better than before".
*/ **Details:** www.hengistrestaurant.co.uk; @TheHengist; 9 pm, Fri-Sat 9.30 pm; closed Sun D; no Amex.*

BAGSHOT, SURREY 3–3A

The Latymer Pennyhill Park Hotel £111 444
London Rd GU19 5EU (01276) 471774
"A procession of stunning dishes" typifies Michael Wignall's "exciting" cuisine – "a genuine tour de force combining flavours with incredible complexity and subtlety"; this country house hotel dining room is "up there with the best in the UK".
*/ **Details:** www.pennyhillpark.co.uk; @PennyHillPark; 9.15 pm, Fri & Sat 9.30 pm; closed Mon, Tue L, Sat L & Sun; booking: max 8; children: 12+.*
***Accommodation:** 123 rooms, from £315.*

BAKEWELL, DERBYSHIRE 5–2C

The Monsal Head Hotel £41 333
DE45 1NL (01629) 640250
*Stunning views over Monsal Dale and its railway viaduct set the scene at this hotel and inn, in the Peak District National Park; "food and beer are reliably good", but service at busy times can be "slow". / **Details:** www.monsalhead.com; 9.30 pm, Sun 9 pm; no Amex. **Accommodation:** 7 rooms, from £90.*

Piedaniels £49 343
Bath St DE45 1BX (01629) 812687
It's the "very good-value lunch and midweek menus" which continue to inspire most reporter feedback on this "calm" and "slightly old-fashioned" restaurant – a smart sort of place, which can seem "on the expensive side" at other times.
*/ **Details:** www.piedaniels-restaurant.com; 10.30 pm, open on Sun only 2 weekends per month; closed Mon & Sun D.*

BALLANTRAE, SOUTH AYRSHIRE 7–2A

Glenapp Castle £94 Ⓣ
KA26 0NZ (01465) 831212
*If you're looking for a tip for a "fantastic" setting, you won't do much better than this Baronial castle; it inspires surprisingly little survey commentary, but the food, if hardly inexpensive, is said to be "very good". / **Details:** www.glenappcastle.com; @GlenappCastle; 9.30 pm; children: 5+ after 7 pm.*
***Accommodation:** 17 rooms, from £430.*

BALLATER, ABERDEENSHIRE 9–3C

Darroch Learg £65 Ⓣ
56 Braemar Rd AB35 5UX (01339) 755443
*A "reliable" traditionally furnished hillside country house hotel in Deeside, tipped for its "beautiful" and "unusual" approach to the use of "excellent local produce". / **Details:** www.darrochlearg.co.uk; on A93 W of Ballater; 9 pm; D only, ex Sun open L & D; no Amex. **Accommodation:** 12 rooms, from £140.*

BALQUHIDDER, PERTH AND KINROSS 9–3C

Monachyle Mhor £74 544
FK19 8PQ (01877) 384622
*Few, but uniformly ecstatic, reports on this family-run hotel and restaurant in the Trossachs National Park, and its outstanding handling of local produce; "the tricky location, down a narrow lochside road, only adds to the charm". / **Details:** www.mhor.net; take the Kings House turning off the A84; 8.45 pm.*
***Accommodation:** 14 rooms, from £195.*

BANGOR, COUNTY DOWN 10–1D

The Boat House **£48**
BT20 5HA (028) 9146 9253
"Beautifully restored", this former lifeboat station, run by two Dutch brothers (front/back of house) is tipped for "some of the best food in Northern Ireland" (and "great value" too); the wine list and the gin bar are also singled out for the thumbs up. / **Details:** *www.theboathouseni.co.uk.*

BARNET, HERTFORDSHIRE 3–2B

Savoro **£42** 444
206 High St EN5 5SZ (020) 8449 9888
"Seriously the best restaurant in the area"; located in a small hotel, this "truly excellent" venture attracts rave reviews for its "brilliant" food (desserts are "simply stunning"), "classy setting" and "incredible value for money"; it can get "madly buzzy". / **Details:** *www.savoro.co.uk; 9.45 pm; closed Sun D.* **Accommodation:** *9 rooms, from £75.*

BARNSLEY, GLOUCESTERSHIRE 2–2C

Barnsley House **£58** 354
GL7 5EE (01285) 740000
The greige dining room of this contemporary boutique hotel, sister venue to The Village Pub, is well received by all who comment on it, thanks to its "well-presented" menu; "lovely" gardens too. / **Details:** *www.barnsleyhouse.com; @Barnsley_House; 9 pm, Sat & Sun 9.30 pm; children: 14+ after 7.30 pm.* **Accommodation:** *18 rooms, from £290.*

The Village Pub **£46** 343
GL7 5EF (01285) 740421
This "nice little boozer" and gastropub with a "Farrow & Ball 21st-century look" is owned by the people at Barnsley House, just across the road; it's a "real gem, especially if you like a good pint", and there's a "nice selection of homemade dishes" on offer too. / **Details:** *www.thevillagepub.co.uk; @The_Village_Pub; 9.30 pm, Sun 9 pm.* **Accommodation:** *6 rooms, from £130.*

BARRASFORD, NORTHUMBERLAND 8–2A

Barrasford Arms **£41** 343
NE48 4AA (01434) 681237
A "well-kept country pub with real ale and rooms", which offers not just "lovely" garden views over the Northumbria National Park but also locally-sourced dishes "presented to a high standard". / **Details:** *www.barrasfordarms.co.uk; 9 pm; closed Mon L & Sun D; no Amex; children: 18 + in bar after 9.30pm.* **Accommodation:** *7 rooms, from £85.*

BARTON-ON-SEA, HAMPSHIRE 2–4C

Pebble Beach **£54** 444
Marine Drive BH25 7DZ (01425) 627777
With a "great location on the clifftop", this "rather sophisticated" venue offers "first-rate" (if rather "pricey") seafood dishes by chef Pierre Chevillard; it's especially nice when you can "sit outside, overlooking the Solent". / **Details:** *www.pebblebeach-uk.com; @pebblebeachUK; 9 pm, Fri & Sat 9.30 pm.* **Accommodation:** *4 rooms, from £99.95.*

BARWICK, SOMERSET 2–3B

Little Barwick House **£68** 554
BA22 9TD (01935) 423902
"Breathtaking attention to detail" makes Tim & Emma Ford's "lovely" restaurant-with-rooms a "brilliant find" for all who comment on it; it can sometimes seem a touch "formal". / **Details:** *www.littlebarwickhouse.co.uk; take the A37 Yeovil to Dorchester road, turn left at the brown sign for Little Barwick House; Tue-Fri 9 pm, Sat 9.30 pm; closed Mon, Tue L & Sun; children: 5+ .* **Accommodation:** *6 rooms, from £69 pp.*

BASLOW, DERBYSHIRE 5–2C

Fischers at Baslow Hall **£96** 454
Calver Rd DE45 1RR (01246) 583259
Max and Susan Fischer's "lovely" country house hotel, near Chatsworth, is a "slick" and sometimes "innovative" operation, to the extent that almost all reporters find a visit here a "memorable" occasion; the occasional off-day, however, is not entirely unknown. / **Details:** *www.fischers-baslowhall.co.uk; on the A623; 8.30 pm; no jeans or trainers.* **Accommodation:** *11 rooms, from £180.*

Rowley's **£53** 444
Church Ln DE45 1RY (01246) 583880
"Hard to beat"; this pub-conversion on the edge of the Chatsworth Estate, run by the Fischers of Baslow Hall, has upped its game of late and now receives rave reviews for its "accomplished" ("modern bistro") cooking – "I have never had a better fish soup!". / **Details:** *www.rowleysrestaurant.co.uk; @RowleysBaslow; closed Mon & Sun D; no Amex.*

BATH, SOMERSET 2–2B

Acorn Vegetarian Kitchen **£45** 543
2 North Parade Pas BA1 1NX
(01225) 446059
"Taken over from the old Demuth's (RIP) and, surprisingly, better"; this "superb vegetarian", in a cute alley in the heart of the city, is a "real treat" – "anyone would love it, unless they're really determined to eat meat". / **Details:** *www.acornvegetariankitchen.co.uk.*

Bath Priory Hotel **£110** 4 4 5
Weston Rd BA1 2XT (01225) 331922
"Sam Moody trained with Michael Caines at Gidleigh Park, and it shows" – the dishes presented in the "beautiful" dining room of this country house hotel are often "superb"; even fans, though, can find the experience a touch "overpriced". / **Details:** *www.thebathpriory.co.uk; @Thebathpriory; 9.30 pm; no jeans or trainers; children: 5+ L, 12+ D.* **Accommodation:** *33 rooms, from £205.*

Bistro La Barrique **£40** Ⓣ
31 Barton St BA1 1HG (01225) 463861
Tipped as a venue handy for the Theatre Royal, a Gallic small plates specialist whose features include an "extraordinary-value" lunch menu, and a "very pleasant" courtyard for warm evenings. / **Details:** *www.bistrolabarrique.co.uk; 10 pm, Fri-Sat 10.30 pm; closed Sun; no Amex.*

Blunos County Hotel **£62** 4 2 3
18-19 Pulteney Rd BA2 4EZ (01225) 425003
"Great to have Martin Blunos back in Bath!"; his new hotel dining room arguably "would benefit from more professional service" but "it's early days", and this star chef's seafood specialities are already tipped as "the best in town, by a long way"; "lovely terrace". / **Details:** *www.blunosrestaurant.com.*

Casanis **£51** 4 4 4
4 Saville Row BA1 2QP (01225) 780055
Despite the odd sceptic, this scenic restaurant wins plenty of praise for its "faultless" cooking – "French bistro food at it's best!" – and "improved" comfort of late too. / **Details:** *www.casanis.co.uk; @CasanisBistro; 10 pm; closed Mon & Sun; no Amex.*

The Circus **£44** 4 5 3
34 Brock St BA1 2LN (01225) 466020
"One of the best places to eat in Bath… which has few enough good places!" – this family-owned bistro, near the Royal Crescent, is a "reliable" spot offering "fresh" and "varied" cooking, so it's no surprise that it's often "very busy"; "ground-floor seating is best, but most tables there are for two". / **Details:** *www.thecircuscafeandrestaurant.co.uk; @CircusBath; 10 pm; closed Sun; no Amex; children: 7+ at D.*

Clayton's Kitchen **£47** 4 4 3
BA1 2EN (01225) 585 100
"Fabulous food, great service and a nice relaxed atmosphere, in the centre of Bath" – no wonder this "very pleasant" spot has had a warm reception from all who have commented on it; chef Rob Clayton kicked off his career back in 1988 at Ménage à Trois SW3 – that really is a blast from the past! / **Details:** *www.theporter.co.uk/claytons-kitchen.*

The Eastern Eye **£40** Ⓣ
8a Quiet St BA1 2JS (01225) 422323
Not many Indian restaurants are tipped for the grandeur of their Georgian settings, but this is the exception – "a must for any visitor"! / **Details:** *www.easterneye.co.uk; 11.30 pm.*

Gascoyne Place **£42** 4 4 2
1 Sawclose BA1 1EY (01225) 445854
"It looks as if it's hardly worth a second glance", but this Georgian inn is praised by all reporters as a "gem", offering "consistently delicious cooking of the first order", and at "very reasonable prices" too. / **Details:** *www.gascoyneplace.co.uk; 9.30 pm, Fri-Sun 10 pm; no Amex.*

Hare & Hounds **£43** 4 3 4
Lansdown Rd BA1 5TJ (01225) 482682
"Food worthy of the stunning views" makes this gastropub just outside the city a "real destination for tourists and locals", and "a great place to start or end a walk" too. / **Details:** *www.hareandhoundsbath.com; 9.30 pm, sun 9 pm; no Amex.*

Hon Fusion **£32** Ⓣ
25 Claverton Buildings BA2 4LD (01225) 446020
Not far from Bath Spa railway station, a Widcombe restaurant, run by a family from Hong Kong; it's "popular with the Chinese community", and serves a "wide variety of dishes" – "some great, some unpredictable". / **Details:** *www.honfusion.com; 11 pm; no Amex.*

Menu Gordon Jones **£64** 5 5 3
2 Wellsway BA2 3AQ (01225) 480871
"No fancy table appointment or stuffiness, just amazing food served by knowledgeable staff in a relaxed environment" – that's the deal at this "intimate" venture whose "superb tasting menu and associated wine-matching" would "be of note even in the capital"… perhaps especially for its "very good pricing". / **Details:** *www.menugordonjones.co.uk; 9 pm; closed Mon & Sun; no Amex.*

The Mint Room **£29** 5 4 3
BA2 3EB (01225) 446656
"An Indian menu with more variety than usual, and served with fine-dining flair" – dishes which are "spiced to perfection" make this lavish purpose-built restaurant, just outside the city-centre, undoubtedly "the best in town"; indeed, one reporter had their "best-ever Indian meal" there! / **Details:** *www.themintroom.co.uk.*

The Olive Tree Queensberry Hotel **£65** 4 3 2
Russell St BA1 2QF (01225) 447928
"Knocks most London restaurants for six", say fans, so it's curious that this hotel dining room doesn't elicit more feedback… perhaps due to the muted

basement location; Chris Cleghorn's food is "superb", though, and "whoever selects the wines clearly knows their stuff".
/ **Details:** *www.thequeensberry.co.uk; @olivetreebath; 9.30 pm; Mon-Thu D only, Fri-Sun open L & D.* **Accommodation:** *29 rooms, from £125.*

The Pump Room **£47** Ⓣ
Stall St BA1 1LZ (01225) 444477
"The best breakfasts", and afternoon tea is an "experience" – top tips to make the best of your (inevitable) visit to this famously beautiful Georgian room, at the heart of the city.
/ **Details:** *www.searcys.co.uk; @searcysbars; L only; no booking, Sat & Sun.*

The Wheatsheaf **£50** 544
Combe Hay BA2 7EG (01225) 833504
Just outside the city, a "quiet dining pub" (with rooms) which "always meets expectations" – a "very worthwhile gastronomic detour", it offers "great beer" too!" too!
/ **Details:** *www.wheatsheafcombehay.com; 9.30 pm; closed Mon & Sun D; no Amex.* **Accommodation:** *3 rooms, from £120.*

Yen Sushi **£34** Ⓣ
11-12 Bartlett St BA1 2QZ (01225) 333313
Need a "reliable fallback for a quick utilitarian lunch"? – look no further than this handily-located standby, which offers "big bowls of soup and noodles", plus "better sushi than average".
/ **Details:** *www.yensushi.co.uk; 10.30 pm.*

BAUGHURST, HAMPSHIRE 2–3D

The Wellington Arms **£60** 445
Baughurst Rd RG26 5LP (0118) 982 0110
Jason King & Simon Page's "immaculate" country restaurant-with-rooms scores high praise for its "excellent" cuisine based on local ingredients, "including many from their own kitchen garden" – "rich and greedy" puddings are of particular note.
/ **Details:** *www.thewellingtonarms.com; @WellingtonArms; 9.30 pm; closed Sun D; no Amex.* **Accommodation:** *2 rooms, from £130.*

BAWTRY, SOUTH YORKSHIRE 5–2D

The Dower House **£36** 433
Market Pl DN10 6JL (0130) 271 9696
"A great selection of authentic Indian food" and "efficient" service too – the all-round standards of this popular town-centre Indian are "difficult to match". / **Details:** *www.dower-house.com; 10.30 pm; children: 5+.*

BEACONSFIELD, BUCKINGHAMSHIRE 3–3A

The Cape Etc. **£49** 435
6A Station Rd HP9 1NN (01494) 681137
"Great fish and meat and amazing South African wines" are the hallmarks of this rather theatrical New Town fixture; "shame it only opens for dinner, and then only on Friday and Saturday".
/ **Details:** *www.thecapeonline.com; 9.30 pm; closed Mon D, Tue D, Wed D, Thu D & Sun D; no Amex.*

Crazy Bear **£65** 225
75 Wycombe End HP9 1LX (01494) 673086
"They aim to be different", at this flashy restaurant-with-rooms, which offers "a real wacky experience with its OTT but exquisite decor", but it's as a drinking den that it scores best – the Anglo-Thai food, despite recent improvement, is still "not as good as expected for the price".
/ **Details:** *www.crazybeargroup.co.uk/beaconsfield; @CrazyBearGroup; 10 pm; closed Mon & Sun L; children: bar, not after 6pm.* **Accommodation:** *19 rooms, from £220.*

The Royal Standard of England **£40** 344
Brindle Ln HP9 1XS (01494) 673382
"For a pub as old as this the food and service are excellent" – England's oldest freehouse by and large lives up even to its rather grandiose name.
/ **Details:** *www.rsoe.co.uk; 10 pm, Sun 9 pm; no Amex.*

Spice Merchant **£50** 322
33 London End HP9 2HW (01494) 675474
"A real find"; "feeling very different from your average Indian restaurant", this "lovely" contemporary venue offers food of "reliable, good quality".
/ **Details:** *www.spicemerchantgroup.com; 11 pm, Sun 9.30 pm; no Amex.*

BEARSTED, KENT 3–3C

Fish On The Green **£53** 443
Church Ln ME14 4EJ (01622) 738 300
"A real find in a beautiful location"; "brilliant" fish is the highlight you might hope at this "consistently happy" destination, which is particularly worth seeking out for its "very good value" set lunch menu. / **Details:** *www.fishonthegreen.com; 9.30 pm, Fri & Sat 10 pm; closed Mon & Sun D; no Amex.*

BEAULIEU, HAMPSHIRE 2–4D

The Terrace Montagu Arms Hotel **£100** 342
SO42 7ZL (01590) 612324
A grand and "pricey" New Forest inn where the food and wine is often "of the very best" (with the cheeseboard coming in for particular approval); the odd reporter feels the dining room, though, is "not especially atmospheric" (even if it does have daytime views of the "pretty" small garden).
/ **Details:** *www.montaguarmshotel.co.uk; @themontaguarms; 9 pm; closed Mon & Tue L; no jeans or trainers; children: 11+ D.* **Accommodation:** *22 rooms, from £143.*

BEAUMARIS, ISLE OF ANGLESEY 4–1C

The Loft Restaurant Ye Olde Bull's Head £67 4 4 3
Castle St LL58 8AP (01248) 810329
Apart from an "old-fashioned" bar, this "comfortable" old coaching inn boasts not only this smart upper-floor dining room, but also a "lovely and airy" (cheaper) modern brasserie – both attract praise across the board.
*/ **Details:** www.bullsheadinn.co.uk; @bullsheadinn; on the High Street; 9.30 pm; D only, closed Mon & Sun; no jeans; children: 7+ at D. **Accommodation:** 26 rooms, from £105.*

BEELEY, DERBYSHIRE 5–2C

Devonshire Arms £42 2 2 3
Devonshire Sq DE4 2NR (01629) 733259
Near Chatsworth, a grand estate inn where fans find "simple but hearty" fare of "a good standard"; service, though, can be "offhand", and critics feel the menu "promises more than it delivers".
*/ **Details:** www.devonshirebeeley.co.uk; 9.30 pm; bookings for breakfast. **Accommodation:** 14 rooms, from £125.*

BELFAST, COUNTY ANTRIM 10–1D

Bubbacue £18 T
12 Callender St BT7 1JR (028) 9027 8220
'Slow-cooked BBQ from the Deep South' – that's the proposition that's making quite a name for this daytime and early-evening operation, near City Hall.
*/ **Details:** www.bubbacue.com.*

Coppi £39 T
2 St Anne's Sq BT1 2LD (028) 9031 1959
Looking for "Belfast's tastiest and least expensive snacks?" – this Cathedral Quarter Italian is quite possibly the top tip; it also offers a "good selection of wine by the glass".
*/ **Details:** http://www.coppi.co.uk/.*

Ginger £45 T
7-8 Hope St BT2 5EE (0871) 426 7885
*Tipped for its "fabulous" food ("using the best of Northern Irish produce") – Simon McCance's bohemian bistro, handily sited near the Europa Hotel. / **Details:** www.gingerbistro.com; 9.30 pm, Mon 9 pm, Fri & Sat 10 pm; closed Mon L & Sun; no Amex.*

James Street South £53 T
21 James Street South BT2 7GA
(028) 9043 4310
Niall McKenna's venture is one of the few bringing fine dining to the city centre; fans do tip it as a "totally enjoyable" destination, but reports are few and include the odd let-down.
*/ **Details:** www.jamesstreetsouth.co.uk; @jamesstsouth; 10.45 pm; closed Sun.*

Mourne Seafood Bar £42 4 4 4
34-36 Bank St BT1 1HL (028) 9024 8544
"The best seafood restaurant in Northern Ireland"; "always good", and "always friendly", it's "always busy" too – no one seems terribly to mind that the tables are rather "cramped".
*/ **Details:** www.mourneseafood.com; Mon 5 pm, Tue & Wed 9.30 pm, Thu, Fri & Sat 10.30 pm, Sun 6 pm; closed Mon D & Sun D; no booking at L.*

Ox £39 4 4 3
1 Oxford St BT1 3LA (028) 9031 4121
*"An excellent addition to Belfast"; appropriately enough, it was meeting at the fabled Arpège (Paris) which gave rise to this trendy (but "cavernous") city-centre spot, where the chef "pays homage to local ingredients and makes vegetables as important as meat or fish"; prices are relatively reasonable too, especially for lunch. / **Details:** http://oxbelfast.com/.*

Il Pirata £33 4 4 4
279-281 Upper Newtownards Rd BT4 3JF
(028) 9067 3421
"My go-to restaurant when I want to treat myself but not spend too much" – this "good rustic Italian", in Ballyhackamore Village, is a "casual" and "inviting" spot, "somewhat in the mould of London's Polpo" ("and perhaps better!").
*/ **Details:** www.facebook.com/ilPirataBelfast; @ilpiratabelfast; 10 pm; no Amex.*

Sole Seafood £39 4 3 3
BT9 7GT (028) 9066 2224
"A cheap and cheerful BYO spot where there's nothing cheap about the quality of the food"; its "simple and delicious fish dishes" are "generally very good" – at peak times however "service is a little stretched, as is the kitchen".
*/ **Details:** www.soleseafood.com.*

Tedfords Restaurant £53 4 3 2
5 Donegall Quay BT1 3EA (028) 90434000
*Surprisingly "wonderful" food often rewards visitors to this large restaurant near the Waterfront Hall ("great pre-theatre"); "always ask for a table upstairs", though – "the atmosphere is so much better". / **Details:** www.tedfordsrestaurant.com; @tedfords; 9.30 pm; closed Mon, Tue L, Sat L & Sun.*

BEMBRIDGE, ISLE OF WIGHT

Fox's Restaurant £40 T
PO35 5SD (01983) 872626
"Very difficult to beat" – this High Street outfit, with a pleasant garden, is tipped for its "consistent cooking" and a "good, if short, wine list"; "no wonder the locals wish to keep it to themselves!"

BERKHAMSTED, HERTFORDSHIRE 3–2A

The Gatsby £54 T
97 High St HP4 2DG (01442) 870403
"Art Deco decor, a sophisticated bar, a pianist…" –

this former cinema foyer is tipped as "just the thing for romance"; the food can be "excellent" too. / **Details:** *www.thegatsby.net; 10.30 pm, Sun 9.30 pm; no Amex; booking: max 10.*

BEVERLEY, EAST YORKSHIRE 6–2A

The Pipe & Glass Inn **£57** 5|4|5
West End HU17 7PN (01430) 810246
"First-class food in a traditional inn" – "always on the mark", James & Kate Mackenzie's "outstanding" rustic gastroboozer inspires a hymn of praise which (and this is very rare) includes not a single off-note; actually there is one complaint – "wish we lived nearer!".
/ **Details:** *www.pipeandglass.co.uk; @pipeandglass; 9.30 pm; closed Mon & Sun D.*

Westwood Bar & Grill **£54** 3|3|3
New Walk HU17 7AE (01482) 881999
"A very reasonably priced restaurant, serving top-notch food" that's "locally sourced" and "seasonal" too; a "friendly" sort of place, it inspires only positive reports. / **Details:** *www.thewestwood.co.uk; @The_Westwood; 9.30 pm; closed Mon & Sun D; no Amex.*

Whites **£45** 4|3|3
12-12a North Bar Without HU17 7AB
(01482) 866121
An ex-Winteringham Fields chef-patron dishes up some "consistently interesting" dishes – "beautifully cooked and presented" too – at this ambitious small restaurant.
/ **Details:** *www.whitesrestaurant.co.uk; @Whitesbeverley; 9 pm; closed Mon & Sun D; no Amex.* **Accommodation:** *4 rooms, from £85.*

BEXLEY, KENT 3–3B

Miller & Carter Bexley **£47** Ⓣ
DA5 1PQ (01322) 552748
The Jacobean barn setting adds a touch of class to a visit to this outpost of a small chain, which is tipped for its "varied" menu including "good steaks" and its "perfectly cooked and seasoned" burgers; "attentive" service too.
/ **Details:** *www.millerandcarter.co.uk/millerandcarerbexley/.*

BIDDENDEN, KENT 3–4C

The West House **£59** 5|5|3
28 High St TN27 8AH (01580) 291341
Graham Garrett offers "a top dining experience", at this ancient building in "one of Kent's prettiest villages" – "amazingly textured and flavoursome" cooking, backed up by a "beautifully written and engaging wine list"; the occasional doubter, though, does wonder if it is slightly over-praised.
/ **Details:** *www.thewesthouserestaurant.co.uk; @grahamgarrett; Tue-Fri 9 pm, Sat 10 pm; closed Mon, Sat L & Sun D; no Amex.*

BIDFORD ON AVON, WARWICKSHIRE 2–1C

The Bridge **£45** 4|3|4
High St B50 4BG (01789) 773700
"Simply the best restaurant in this corner of Warkwickshire"; this riverside restaurant (with al fresco seating) is praised not just for its "perfect" location, but for its "consistent" standards too.
/ **Details:** *www.thebridgeatbidford.com/; 9 pm, Fri & Sat 9.30 pm; closed Sun D; no Amex.*

BIGBURY-ON-SEA, DEVON 1–4C

Burgh Island Hotel **£91** 4|4|5
TQ7 4BG (01548) 810514
Ladies "can't be overdressed" for the black-tie dinners on offer at this Agatha Christie-style '20s hotel, located on its own "picturesque" small island; for "fantastic food in a fantastic setting", there's "no place like it!" / **Details:** *www.burghisland.com; 8.30 pm; D only, ex Sun open L & D; no Amex; jacket & tie; children: 12+ at D.* **Accommodation:** *25 rooms, from £400.*

The Oyster Shack **£51** 4|4|5
Millburn Orchard Farm, Stakes Hills TQ7 4BE
(01548) 810876
"It's a shack, it serves spanking fresh oysters (and other seafood), and it's proper brilliant!" – not much to add about this "lovely relaxed" haunt which, with its plastic tables and chairs, "rather resembles a Greek taverna".
/ **Details:** *www.oystershack.co.uk; @theoystershack; 9 pm.*

BILDESTON, SUFFOLK 3–1C

The Bildeston Crown
The Crown Hotel **£64** 4|2|3
104 High St IP7 7EB (01449) 740510
New head chef Zack Deakins creates some "outstanding" dishes at this out-of-the-way 15th-century coaching inn; it elicits very positive reports in the main, but... "if only the service were just a tiny bit sharper!"
/ **Details:** *www.thebildestoncrown.com; from the A14, take the B115 to Bildeston; 9.45 pm, Sun 9 pm.*
Accommodation: *12 rooms, from £100.*

BILLERICAY, ESSEX 3–2C

The Magic Mushroom **£50** 4|3|2
Barleyland Rd CM11 2UD (01268) 289963
"An unlikely oasis, but an impressive one"; Darren Bennet's "highly recommended" bistro is not just "a nice change from the endless chains" – it offers "quality ingredients, well cooked".
/ **Details:** *www.magicmushroomrestaurant.co.uk; next to "Barleylands Farm"; midnight; closed Mon & Sun D.*

BIRCHANGER, ESSEX 3–2B

The Three Willows £40 T
Birchanger Ln CM23 5QR (01279) 815913
*Top tip "handy for Stansted Airport" – an unpretentious village inn, just off the M11. / **Details:** www.thethreewillowsbirchanger.co.uk; one mile from Birchanger Green service station on M11; 9 pm; closed Sun D; no Amex.*

BIRCHINGTON, KENT 3–3D

The Minnis £46 332
The Parade CT7 9QP (01843) 841844
*"Nicely situated by a sandy beach", and occupying a building "that looks like a 1950s ice-cream parlour", this Minnis Bay spot attracts praise for its "interesting English cuisine"; the new upstairs Mediterranean-style tapas restaurant "is proving a big hit" too. / **Details:** www.theminnis.co.uk; 9 pm, Sun 8 pm.*

Quex Barn Farmer's Market and Restaurant £32 T
CT7 0BH (01843) 846103
*"Adjoining the owner's farm shop" and "utilising much of its produce", this new venture is particularly tipped for its "lovely" breakfasts; upstairs tables have "great views of the cathedral". / **Details:** www.quexpark.co.uk.*

BIRMINGHAM, WEST MIDLANDS 5–4C

Adam's £49 554
21a Bennetts Hill B2 5QP (01216) 433745
*"Adam's flavours are bold" and his "breathtaking cooking combinations" – from a range of "exquisite" tasting menus – and his wife's "keen" service are helping this "cosy" city-centre yearling go "from strength to strength". / **Details:** www.adamsrestaurant.co.uk; @RestaurantAdams; 9.30 pm; closed Mon & Sun; children: 8+ at D.*

Asha's Indian Bar and Restaurant £46 333
12-22 Newhall St B3 3LX (0121) 200 2767
*It's the "excellent-value lunchtime menu" which attracts particular praise for this "authentic" city-centre Indian (the only English branch of a Gulf States chain); fans still praise the cuisine's "complexity and depth of flavour", but – from a high base – "standards have dropped somewhat" in recent times. / **Details:** www.ashasuk.co.uk; @ashasbirmingham; 10.30 pm, Thu-Sun 11 pm; closed Sat L & Sun L.*

Carters £63 353
20 Wake Green Rd B13 9EZ (0121) 449 8885
*"A delight!"; this "lovely" little Moseley spot offers "imaginative and very well-executed" cuisine from a "fixed(ish) menu" based around "local ingredients"; service is "top notch and friendly" too – "far better than lots of supposedly brilliant other places". / **Details:** www.cartersofmoseley.co.uk; @cartersmoseley; 9.30 pm; closed Mon & Tue; children: 8+.*

Cielo £53 T
6 Oozells Sq B1 2JB (0121) 632 6882
*Looking for a "very useful pre-entertainment venue in the centre of Birmingham", and with a very reasonable fixed-price menu too? – this Brindleyplace Italian is consistently tipped as destination that's both "useful" and "enjoyable". / **Details:** www.cielobirmingham.com; @Cielo_Italian; 11 pm, Sun 10 pm; no Amex; booking: max 20, Sat & Sun D.*

Edmunds £68 443
6 Central Sq B1 2JB (0121) 633 4944
*It may be "surrounded by boring office blocks", but all reports confirm that this "smart" and "business-like" Brindleyplace spot "deserves support" – the "food is well above the local average, and the service is very good too". / **Details:** www.edmundsrestaurant.co.uk; @edmundschefs; 10 pm; closed Mon, Sat L & Sun; no Amex.*

Fiesta Del Asado £42 433
B16 9RP (0121) 4559331
*The party lives up to its name at this "authentic" open-kitchen Argentinian spot, in Edgbaston, where "perfect" steaks are the menu highlight you would hope. / **Details:** www.fiestadelasado.co.uk.*

Hotel du Vin et Bistro £50 334
25 Church St B3 2NR (0121) 200 0600
*"Comfortable", "enjoyable", "consistently dependable"... – this always better-than-average outpost of the hotel/bistro chain has been on pretty good form of late. / **Details:** www.hotelduvin.com; @HdV_Birmingham; 10 pm, Fri & Sat 10.30 pm; booking: max 12. **Accommodation:** 66 rooms, from £160.*

Itihaas £42 T
18 Fleet St B3 1JL (0121) 212 3383
*"A cut above nearly all other Indians in town"; this smart city-centre spot is tipped for offering a "really good experience from start to finish". / **Details:** www.itihaas.co.uk; @itihaasindian; 10 pm; closed Sat L & Sun L.*

Jyoti £23 542
105 Stratford Rd B28 8AS (0121) 77855501
*"With food this good you don't miss the ambience, or the meat either!" – the food at this Formica-topped Gujarati restaurant, in Hall Green, is just "fabulous". / **Details:** www.jyotis.co.uk; 10 pm; closed Mon, Tue-Thu D only; no Amex.*

Il Pirata

Ox

The Merchant Hotel

Lasan **£68** 432
3-4 Dakota Buildings, James St B3 1SD
(0121) 212 3664
"In an otherwise dull road in the Jewellery Quarter", this "welcoming" (but "noisy") modern space is Brum's pre-eminent Indian, serving "very innovative" dishes with "a superb level of attention to ingredients, cooking and presentation"; it also has a "balti belt" offshoot, in Hall Green. / ***Details:*** *www.lasan.co.uk; 11 pm; closed Sat L; no trainers.*

Loves The Glasshouse **£66** 542
B16 8FL (0121) 454 5151
It may be "very difficult to find" ("looks like it is the entrance to a car park"), but Steve Love's canalside venture offers "first-class" cuisine that's "inventive without being faddish"; "from UK-centric bubbles to local liqueurs", the list of drinks is also "outstanding". / ***Details:*** *www.loves-restaurant.co.uk; @lovesrestaurant; 9 pm, Fri-Sat 9.30 pm; closed Mon, Tue, Wed L, Thu L & Sun; no Amex; children: 8+.*

Opus Restaurant **£60** 443
54 Cornwall St B3 2DE (0121) 200 2323
Expansive and woody, this "consistent" city-centre venue feels like "a bit of a barn, but the space does allow you to have a table not on top of the next one"; particularly handy at lunch, when this is a staple of the business set.
/ ***Details:*** *www.opusrestaurant.co.uk; @opuscornwallst; 9.30 pm; closed Sun D; no Amex.*

Purnells **£77** 553
55 Cornwall St B3 2DH (0121) 212 9799
Glynn Purnell's cuisine at this "accomplished" city-centre restaurant is often simply "sublime", and the service is "brilliant" too; the decor? – a fraction "cold" perhaps, but hardly ever mentioned… perhaps a statement in itself?
/ ***Details:*** *www.purnellsrestaurant.com; 9.15 pm; closed Mon, Sat L & Sun; children: 6+.*

San Carlo **£51** 222
4 Temple St B2 5BN (0121) 633 0251
An "always-buzzing" city-centre Italian (part of a chain), which offers "perfectly decent" food, and with "an amazing specials board if you're partial to fish"; critics, though, think it a "noisy" and "pricey" sort of place, with "indifferent" service and cooking "that falls short of aspirations".
/ ***Details:*** *www.sancarlo.co.uk; @SanCarlo_Group; 11 pm.*

Simpsons **£81** 333
20 Highfield Rd B15 3DU (0121) 454 3434
"Birmingham's classiest night out" is to be found at this gracious Edwardian villa in Edgbaston, still acclaimed for its "impeccable" service and "beautifully presented" food; concerns over "exorbitant" bills sapped ratings this year though – "good, but not as exceptional as I would expect at this price".
/ ***Details:*** *www.simpsonsrestaurant.co.uk; @simpsons_rest; 9 pm, Fri & Sat 9.30 pm; closed Sun D.* ***Accommodation:*** *4 rooms, from £160.*

Turners **£83** 322
69 High St B17 9NS (0121) 426 4440
It may be blessed by the tyre men, but Richard Turner's "pricey" Harborne "oasis" attracts only moderate survey feedback; everyone agrees the cuisine is of a "high standard", but critics find the style "pretentious", and service in particular can be a let down.
/ ***Details:*** *www.turnersrestaurantbirmingham.co.uk; @TurnersRestBrum; 9.30 pm; closed Mon, Tue L, Wed L, Thu L & Sun; no Amex.*

BISHOP'S STORTFORD, HERTFORDSHIRE 3–2B

Baan Thitiya **£37** 453
102 London Rd CM23 3DS (01279) 658575
Hearty Thai dishes are served by "an inexhaustible supply of cheerful and efficient" staff at this contemporary-styled suburban restaurant, formerly a 1930s pub, which has a canal-side garden attached; its older Hartford sibling attracts equal praise. / ***Details:*** *www.baan-thitiya.com; 10.30 pm, Sun 9.30 pm.*

BISHOPS TACHBROOK, WARWICKSHIRE 5–4C

Mallory Court **£67** 355
Harbury Ln CV33 9QB (01926) 330214
The "romantic" dining room of this splendid Luyens-style country house hotel (a Relais & Châteaux property) helps make it an "all time favourite" for some reporters; after something of "a bad patch", feedback on its ambitious cooking was generally "excellent" this year. / ***Details:*** *www.mallory.co.uk; @mallorycourt; 2m S of Leamington Spa, off B4087; 8.30 pm; closed Sat L; no trainers.*
Accommodation: *31 rooms, from £159.*

BLAIRGOWRIE, PERTH AND KINROSS 9–3C

Kinloch House **£81** 443
PH10 6SG (01250) 884237
"Nothing fancy, but what they do they do very well" – for those in search of "classic" style, this "beautifully-located" country house hotel "continues to deliver"; "it's worth staying, so you can enjoy the breakfast!"
/ ***Details:*** *www.kinlochhouse.com; past the Cottage Hospital, turn L, procede 3m along A923, (signposted Dunkeld Road); 8.30 pm; no Amex; jacket required; children: 6 for dinner.* ***Accommodation:*** *15 rooms, from £230.*

BLAKENEY, NORFOLK 6–3C

The Moorings £39 444
High St NR25 7NA (01263) 740054
"A great little bistro-style restaurant where fish, in particular, is always cooked to perfection"; the standard has "gone up a notch" in recent times, and all reporters agree that this is "a gem". / **Details:** *www.blakeney-moorings.co.uk.*

The White Horse Hotel £45 223
4 High St NR25 7AL (01263) 740574
"Competent, consistent and busy" – the pretty much invariable theme of commentary on this old coaching inn; befitting the "nice seafront location", it makes "a good choice for fresh fish". / **Details:** *www.blakeneywhitehorse.co.uk; off the A149; 9 pm, Fri & Sat 9.30 pm; no Amex.* **Accommodation:** *9 rooms, from £70.*

BLYTH, NORTHUMBERLAND 8–2B

Sambuca £29 432
NE24 1DG (01670) 365 369
"A super restaurant on a fishing quay, which makes full use of the local catch to create some varied Italian dishes"; it offers "amazing value" too, especially from the daytime menu; there is an offshoot – "stick to the original!" / **Details:** *www.sambucarestaurants.co.uk.*

BODIAM, EAST SUSSEX 3–4C

The Curlew £56 332
Junction Rd TN32 5UY (01580) 861 394
An "old weatherboard coaching inn", with a "quirky" interior, which fans say is "not to be missed if you're in the area", thanks not least to its "first-class" cooking; for doubters, though, "too many changes of chef" in recent times, have led to a number of disappointing meals. / **Details:** *www.thecurlewrestaurant.co.uk; @thecurlewbodiam; 9.30 pm, Sun 9 pm.*

BODSHAM, KENT 3–3C

Froggies at The Timber Batts £52 ⓣ
School Ln TN25 5JQ (01233) 750237
An "isolated" 15th-century inn, tipped for its "good-quality Gallic cuisine" and "great-value" wines too (especially from the Loire). / **Details:** *www.thetimberbatts.co.uk; 9 pm; closed Mon, Tue L & Sun D; no Amex.*

BOLLINGTON, CHESHIRE 5–2B

The Lime Tree £32 444
SK10 5PH (01625) 578182
"Just as good as the Didsbury original"; the "more spacious" semi-rural counterpart to the legendary Manchester bistro is a similarly impressive all-rounder – "it's always on form".

Lord Clyde £44 342
Kerridge SK10 5AH (01625) 562123
"Ambitious, maybe too ambitious dishes… some very good, others a bit weird", typifies the somewhat ambiguous feedback on Ernst van Zyl's conversion of "a small rural pub"; "if he stopped taking bloggers' pics as his inspiration and started cooking from his own imagination, this could be quite a special place!" / **Details:** *www.thelordclyde.co.uk; 9 pm; closed Mon & Sun D.*

BOLNHURST, BEDFORDSHIRE 3–1A

The Plough at Bolnhurst £49 544
MK44 2EX (01234) 376274
Martin Lee's gastroboozer is a real all-rounder, scoring high praise for its "very accomplished cooking", "immaculate" service and "lovely" atmosphere …though avoid sitting in the new extension if you can. / **Details:** *www.bolnhurst.com; 9.30 pm; closed Mon & Sun D; no Amex.*

BOLTON ABBEY, NORTH YORKSHIRE 5–1B

Burlington The Devonshire Arms £90 343
BD23 6AJ (01756) 718 111
The Duke of Devonshire's grand country hotel undoubtedly offers "very good" standards, with "excellent" views contributing to a "delightful" experience all-round; even fans can find prices in the main dining room "grossly OTT", though, and the whole style is too "stuffy" for some tastes. / **Details:** *www.thedevonshirearms.co.uk; 9.30 pm, Sat & Sun 10 pm; closed Mon; jacket at D; children: 7+.* **Accommodation:** *40 rooms, from £250.*

BOUGHTON MONCHELSEA, KENT 3–3C

The Mulberry Tree £50 ⓣ
Hermitage Ln ME17 4DA (01622) 749082
"A surprise, tucked-away in deep countryside, but not far from Maidstone" – this ambitious bar-restaurant is a top local tip for "a good meal in a great setting". / **Details:** *www.themulberrytreekent.co.uk; 9 pm, Fri & Sat 9.30 pm; closed Mon & Sun D; no Amex.*

BOURNE END, BUCKINGHAMSHIRE 3–3A

Darlings Restaurant £40 ⓣ
SL8 5SY (01628) 533000
Offering classic brasserie fare with a twist, this "small and cosy" dining room is tipped as "a great place for a special meal"; it's "best to book".

BOURNEMOUTH, DORSET 2–4C

Chez Fred £26 442
10 Seamoor Rd BH4 9AN (01202) 761023
Fred Capel's well-established and quite upmarket chippy is still serving "beautiful fish 'n' chips",

and still "needs bigger premises"; "you usually need to be in around noon to avoid big queues".
/ **Details:** *www.chezfred.co.uk; 9.45 pm, Sun 9 pm; closed Sun L; no Amex; no booking.*

Edge **£57** Ⓣ
2 Studland Rd BH4 8JA (01202) 757 007
It's really the setting – "unusual modern decor and fantastic views" – that make this top-floor seaside restaurant worthy of a 'tip'; the food can appear to "try a bit too hard".
/ **Details:** *www.edgerestaurant.co.uk; 9.30 pm.*

WestBeach **£51** 3 2 4
Pier Approach BH2 5AA (01202) 587785
A "lovely beachside restaurant", near the pier, that offers "excellent fresh fish and wines at a reasonable mark-up"; it's "getting very popular, so book". / **Details:** *www.west-beach.co.uk; 10 pm.*

BOURTON ON HILL, GLOUCESTERSHIRE 2–1C

Horse & Groom **£42** 4 4 4
GL56 9AQ (01386) 700413
"Excellent food and service at this welcoming pub" – the invariable theme of all of the many reports on this "consistently reliable" and "comfortable" gastroboozer, which devotees proclaim "the best in the Cotswolds".
/ **Details:** *www.horseandgroom.info; 9 pm, Fri & Sat 9.30 pm; closed Sun D; no Amex.*
Accommodation: *5 rooms, from £120.*

BOWNESS-ON-WINDERMERE, CUMBRIA 7–3D

Miller Howe Restaurant & Hotel **£70** 3 2 3
Rayrigg Rd LA23 1EY (01539) 442536
"If you want to impress someone with a view, come here" – that's the raison d'être of this once-famous Lakeland country house hotel; while it can still produce some "very good" food, there are "off days" too, but usually "the ambience makes up for any occasional failings!"
/ **Details:** *www.millerhowe.com; on A592 between Windermere & Bowness; 8.45 pm; no Amex.*
Accommodation: *15 rooms, from £125.*

BRADFORD, WEST YORKSHIRE 5–1C

Akbar's **£34** 4 3 3
1276 Leeds Rd BD3 8LF (01274) 773311
"The original of a popular local chain, and still the best in terms of quality and consistency"; this large subcontinental restaurant is "always busy".
/ **Details:** *www.akbars.co.uk; midnight, Sun 11.30 pm; D only.*

Karachi **£25** 5 4 2
15-17 Neal St BD5 0BX (01274) 732015
"Very simple, incredibly cheap, and wonderful" – this perennial favourite continues to impress all-round (so "ignore anyone who tells you it's gone off of late, as it's still as good as ever"); "knives and forks are looked down on – use your chapati".
/ **Details:** *1 am, Fri & Sat 2 am; no credit cards.*

Mumtaz **£27** 4 3 3
Great Horton Rd BD7 3HS (01274) 571861
"Any curry aficionado should come here at least once"; thanks to its "delicious" food, this "fun" and "lively" landmark remains at the head of the pack; don't forget to BYO.
/ **Details:** *www.mumtaz.com; midnight.*

Zouk **£34** 4 3 3
1312 Leeds Rd BD3 8LF (01274) 258 025
"Big, brash and buzzy", a restaurant that's "directly comparable to the more famous Akbar's" and whose food ("elegant fish dishes and curried quail") is "a step above the usual curry houses".
/ **Details:** *www.zoukteabar.co.uk; 10.30 pm; no Amex; no shorts.*

BRAMPTON, DERBYSHIRE 5–2C

Nonsolovino **£54** 4 4 3
417 Chatsworth Rd S40 3AD (01246) 276760
"A fabulous and unusual Italian" in a small town "on the outskirts of Chesterfield", praised for its "top class food (whether à la carte, or from the tasting menu"). / **Details:** *www.nonsolovino.co.uk; @Nonsolovino1; 9 pm; closed Mon.*

BRANCASTER STAITHE, NORFOLK 6–3B

The White Horse **£50** 2 2 3
Main Rd PE31 8BY (01485) 210262
A great location by the salt marshes ensures the high popularity of this busy local, which has a lovely conservatory dining room; its fish-biased cuisine is variable, though – it can be "superb" but is often quite "ordinary" too.
/ **Details:** *www.whitehorsebrancaster.co.uk; @whitehorsebranc; 9 pm; no Amex.*
Accommodation: *15 rooms, from £94.*

BRAY, BERKSHIRE 3–3A

Caldesi in Campagna **£68** 5 5 4
Old Mill Ln SL6 2BG (01628) 788500
"Better than Italy!" (well almost); Giancarlo Caldesi's "very friendly" Thames-side operation provides "just the right level of informality amongst all that white linen", alongside some "fine" cooking and "superb" wine. / **Details:** *www.caldesi.com; @CaldesiCampagna / @KatieCaldesi ; 9.30 pm; closed Mon & Sun D.*

Crown Inn **£53** 3 2 2
High St SL6 2AH (01628) 621936
"Improved" of late, Heston's 'other' Bray pub investment is your typical village boozer – although it makes a handy-enough fall-back, the realisation of the "short" menu gives no hint of culinary

wizardry. / **Details:** *www.crownatbray.com; @thecrownatbray; 9.30 pm, Fri & Sat 10 pm.*

The Fat Duck **£242** 4 5 4
High St SL6 2AQ (01628) 580333
"The gastronomic equivalent of Cirque du Soleil" – this world-famous pub-conversion offers a "fun experiment on your tastebuds" most reporters find "everything it's billed to be"; prices are "absurd", though, and sceptics say "this may have been cutting edge 10 years ago, but every other restaurant does it nowadays". / **Details:** *www.thefatduck.co.uk; 9 pm; closed Mon & Sun.*

The Hind's Head **£60** 4 3 3
High St SL6 2AB (01628) 626151
"Being next door to the Fact Duck it should be good, and it is!"; Heston's "casual" yet "efficient" operation "may be on the pricey side" but it remains one of the UK's most popular gastropubs thanks to the "modern take on traditional dishes", realised with "flair". / **Details:** *www.hindsheadbray.com; 9.30 pm; closed Sun D.*

Waterside Inn **£200** 5 5 4
Ferry Rd SL6 2AT (01628) 620691
"Champagne and canapés by the Thames can't fail to seduce" – the Roux family's "magical" haven is at its romantic zenith on a sunny day; "it may not be at the culinary cutting edge", but a meal here offers a "divine" combination of "sumptuous" classic cuisine and "seemless" service; the bill? – "heart-stopping". / **Details:** *www.waterside-inn.co.uk; @rouxwaterside; off A308 between Windsor & Maidenhead; 10 pm; closed Mon & Tue; no jeans or trainers; booking: max 10; children: 9+.* **Accommodation:** *11 rooms, from £240.*

BRECON, POWYS 2–1A

The Felin Fach Griffin **£45** 2 4 3
Felin Fach LD3 0UB (01874) 620111
This "quintessential British pub" is a "charming" spot at the foot of the Brecon Beacons; it inspires lots of praise for "good and satisfying meals", but sentiment was undercut by a couple of "awful" reports this year. / **Details:** *www.eatdrinksleep.ltd.uk; @felifachgriff; 20 mins NW of Abergavenny on A470; 9 pm, Fri & Sat 9.30 pm; no Amex.* **Accommodation:** *7 rooms, from £115.*

BRENTWOOD, ESSEX 3–2B

Alec's **£66** 4 3 3
Navestock Side CM14 5SD (01277) 375 696
"The TOWIE styling doesn't detract from the very good food", at this London-style pub conversion – a type of operation of which there is "such a dearth in these parts"; critics find it "too expensive", though, and the acoustics can be "very tinny". / **Details:** *www.alecsrestaurant.co.uk; @Alecsrestaurant; 10 pm, Sun 4.30 pm; closed Mon, Tue L, Wed L & Sun D; no Amex; children: 12+.*

BRIDPORT, DORSET 2–4B

The Bull Hotel **£47** Ⓣ
34 East St DT6 3LF (01308) 422878
"Restaurant, bar and pizza-loft" — there are three eating areas at this family-friendly gastropub, tipped for food that's "tempting" and "consistently good". / **Details:** *www.thebullhotel.co.uk; 9.30 pm.* **Accommodation:** *19 rooms, from £85.*

Hive Beach Cafe **£45** 4 2 4
Beach Rd DT6 4RF (01308) 897070
It may look rather like "a tent on the beach", but this "very popular" and "relaxed" café offers some "superb" locally-sourced seafood, and the views are "wonderful" too; it "gets very busy in good weather so go early". / **Details:** *www.hivebeachcafe.co.uk; @HiveBeachCafe; 8 pm July & August only; L only; no bookings.* **Accommodation:** *2 rooms, from £95.*

Riverside **£52** 5 4 3
West Bay DT6 4EZ (01308) 422011
Arthur Watson "has maintained high standards for straight-from-the-sea fish, simply presented, for over thirty years", at this "lovely" spot, which benefits from a "wonderful" harbourside location; "great-value set lunches" are a highlight. / **Details:** *www.thefishrestaurant-westbay.co.uk; 9 pm; closed Mon & Sun D.*

The Stable **£34** 4 3 4
34 East St DT6 3LF (01308) 422878
"Tasty pizzas and pies" and a "dizzying array of draught ciders" ("try the Pigswill – it tastes far better than the name might suggest!") make this "reinvigorated stable" a real hit with all the family; it's part of a fast-growing seven-strong chain which recently added a Falmouth branch. / **Details:** *www.thestabledorset.co.uk.*

Watch House Cafe **£19** Ⓣ
DT6 4EN (01308) 459330
Tipped for "excellent seafood and very good pizzas, all at fair prices", a beachside café that's "simple but fun". / **Details:** *www.watchhousecafe.co.uk.*

BRIGHTON, EAST SUSSEX 3–4B

64 Degrees **£46** 3 4 3
53 Meeting House Ln BN1 1HB
(01273) 770115
Largely positive feedback so far on this "trendy" Lanes newcomer with an "open kitchen and stool-type seating", which offers some "exciting and innovative" small plates (including a "slightly cooked house egg"); the odd critic, though, simply "can't understand the fuss". / **Details:** *www.64degrees.co.uk.*

Basketmakers Arms **£40** 4 4 4
12 Gloucester Rd BN1 4AD (01273) 689006
"Still the best-value pub in Brighton"; this "proper" North Laine booze offers "traditional" fare that almost invariably satisfies; unsurprisingly it it gets very "busy".
*/ **Details:** www.basketmakersarms.co.uk; 8.30 pm; no booking.*

Bill's at the Depot **£41** 3 2 4
100 North Rd, The Depot BN1 1YE
(01273) 692894
Despite its acquisition by restaurant mogul Richard Caring, the chain's "reliable" North Laine diner continues to please with its "good-sized helpings"; as the queues indicate, it's "best for brunch".
*/ **Details:** www.bills-website.co.uk; 10 pm; no Amex.*

Burger Brothers **£13** Ⓣ
BN1 1YE (01273) 706980
"Don't be put off by the look of the place!" – this tiny late-night joint is in fact a top tip for "superb gourmet burgers", with "funky and fun" service added into the mix; "lovely fresh shakes and smoothies too".

Casa Don Carlos **£32** 3 5 4
5 Union St BN1 1HA (01273) 327177
*A "no-frills" but "cosy" tapas joint in the Lanes, offering "excellent home cooking" and "lovely wines and sherries"; "it must be approaching 'institution' status" by now, says one fan, but it's still "pleasantly inexpensive". / **Details:** 11 pm, Thu 9 pm, Fri-Sun 10 pm; closed Thu L.*

The Chilli Pickle **£42** 5 3 3
17 Jubilee St BN1 1GE (01273) 900 383
*"Delicate, clever little chutneys and pickles" are typical of the "exciting" Indian cuisine at this excellent venture, which is "ahead of the game" compared to others locally; the "superb Thali lunch" is great value. / **Details:** www.thechillipickle.com; 10.30 pm, Sun 10.15 pm; closed Tue.*

La Choza **£23** Ⓣ
BN1 4AQ (01273) 945 926
*A "frenetic" burrito bar in North Laine, tipped for its "great Mexican street food", "fascinating decor" and "fun atmosphere". / **Details:** www.lachoza.co.uk.*

The Coal Shed **£51** 3 2 2
8 Boyces St BN1 1AN (01273) 322998
"Great burgers and steak" are the winning formula behind this "well-run" city-centre grillhouse newcomer; the odd sceptic feels that it's a "poor attempt to do a Hawksmoor"… but they already seem to have got the "pricey" bit of the formula right!
*/ **Details:** www.coalshed-restaurant.co.uk; @thecoalshed1; 10 pm, Fri & Sat 10.30 pm.*

Curry Leaf Cafe **£37** Ⓣ
BN1 1AE (01273) 207070
"A lovely new place near the seafront", tipped for its "proper and authentic Indian street food" (including the "best vegetable pakora ever").
*/ **Details:** www.curryleafcafe.com.*

Donatello **£31** 3 4 3
1-3 Brighton Pl BN1 1HJ (01273) 775477
*With its "very good food" (from a "large menu") and "friendly service" too, this long established Lanes Italian is a great all-purpose standby; the al fresco tables are "a good place to watch the world go by". / **Details:** www.donatello.co.uk; 11.30 pm.*

The Restaurant at Drakes
Drakes Hotel **£63** 4 5 3
44 Marine Pde BN2 1PE (01273) 696934
"A real find", below a Kemp Town boutique hotel – a small (and perhaps "slightly disjointed") basement dining room offering some "perfectly judged" dishes, and "excellent" service too.
*/ **Details:** www.therestaurantatdrakes.co.uk; @drakeshotel; 9.30 pm. **Accommodation:** 20 rooms, from £115.*

English's **£51** 3 4 3
29-31 East St BN1 1HL (01273) 327980
Well into its second century, this "old-fashioned" Lanes seafood restaurant, with its "lovely" outside tables, has tourist-trap potential par excellence; of late, however, it has notably bucked up its standards, offering a lunch menu, in particular, which is "very good value".
*/ **Details:** www.englishs.co.uk; @englishsoB; 10 pm, Sun 9.30 pm.*

Fishy Fishy **£49** 4 2 3
36 East St BN1 1HL (01273) 723750
A "rather cramped" Lanes "staple", offering food of a "surprisingly strong standard", including a "terrific choice of fish".
*/ **Details:** www.fishyfishy.co.uk; @fishybrasserie; 9.30 pm, Fri & Sat 10 pm.*

Food for Friends **£42** 4 3 3
17-18 Prince Albert St BN1 1HF
(01273) 202310
*There is "innovation aplenty" in the "lovely veggie food" served up at this Lanes institution; after a recent make-over, it now has quite a "high-end" interior too. / **Details:** www.foodforfriends.com; 10 pm, Fri & Sat 10.30 pm; no booking, Sat L & Sun L.*

Giggling Squid **£26** 3 3 3
129 Church Rd BN3 2AE (01273) 771991
"Where it all began" – the Hove home of a generally creditable chain of Thai restaurants; the small branch in the Lanes is also consistently hailed for its "full-of-flavour" food – for top value, seek out the lunch menu.
*/ **Details:** www.gigglingsquid.com; Mon-Sat 10.45 pm Sun 9.45 pm.*

Terre a Terre

64 Degrees

The Ginger Dog £46 443
12 College Pl BN2 1HN (01273) 620 990
*Rather limited feedback of late on this cosy Kemp Town gastropub, part of a pre-eminent local restaurant empire; one fan claims it always makes for an "enjoyable evening", however, thanks to seasonal dishes with "exceptionally good flavour". / **Details:** www.gingermanrestaurants.com; @GingerDogDish / @TheGingerChef; off Eastern Road near Brighton College; 10 pm.*

The Ginger Pig £51 433
3 Hove St BN3 2TR (01273) 736123
*This "welcoming" and "lively" Hove gastropub outpost of the Gingerman empire continues to impress most reporters with "delicious and unusual" cuisine of "consistently high quality"; it's "not cheap", though, and can seem "overpriced, given the portions". / **Details:** www.thegingermanrestaurants.com; @gingerpigdish; 10 pm, Sun 9 pm; no trainers.*

Gingerman £50 553
21a Norfolk Sq BN1 2PD (01273) 326688
*With its "well-judged, utterly reliable cooking", this "tiny side street restaurant" – the original member of the Gingerman chain – "is still tops", says one of the many fans of "Brighton's best place to eat, by a country mile". / **Details:** www.gingermanrestaurant.com; @thegingerchef; 9.45 pm; closed Mon.*

Indian Summer £44 544
69 East St BN1 1HQ (01273) 711001
*With its "modern" and "well-balanced" cuisine, this Lanes fixture offers a "totally different" curry house experience, and attracts not only "discerning" locals but also "gastro-tourists down for a racy weekend!" / **Details:** www.indian-summer.org.uk; @indiansummer108; 10.30 pm, Sun 10 pm; closed Mon L.*

Iydea £19 T
17 Kensington Gdns BN1 4AL
(01273) 667 992
*"My favourite cafe ever, not just my favourite vegetarian cafe!" – this North Laine (also Hove) spot is tipped for "great food at fair prices, quick service and lovely staff". / **Details:** www.iydea.co.uk; 5 pm; no Amex or Maestro.*

The Lion & Lobster £32 T
BN1 2PS (01273) 327299
*In a Hove backstreet, a pub tipped as much for its atmosphere ("full of hidden rooms and terraces"), as for its "varied" menu (which is "unsurprisingly strong on fish"). / **Details:** www.thelionandlobster.co.uk.*

Little Fish Market £66 543
10 Upper Market St BN3 1AS
(01273) 722213
*A "great addition to the local food scene"; this tiny two-year-old, in a former fishmonger, is making waves with its "exquisite and refined food – mainly fish, of course" from Duncan Ray (ex-Fat Duck); cash only! / **Details:** www.thelittlefishmarket.co.uk.*

Pizza 500 £26 541
BN1 4QG (01273) 911933
*It's not just the "genuinely Italian feel" which distinguishes this "chaotic" spot, near London Road station – it also offers "amazing" pizzas in "authentic" Neapolitan style. / **Details:** www.pizza500.co.uk.*

Pizzaface £30 43–
BN3 5AB (01273) 965651
*"Take-away only, but excellent and inventive pizzas"; this "fabulous" Hove spot (which also delivers) inspires only very positive feedback; "special diets are well catered for" too. / **Details:** www.pizzafacepizza.co.uk.*

Plateau £44 444
1 Bartholomews BN1 1HG (01273) 733085
*"Somewhat in the style of London's Terroirs and siblings", this wine bar near the Town Hall offers "excellent small plates and sharing platters" alongside "interesting" natural wines (and cocktails too). / **Details:** www.plateaubrighton.co.uk.*

The Regency £31 344
131 Kings Rd BN1 2HH (01273) 325014
*On the seafront, a family-run seafood stalwart with "old-school charm"; its "locally sourced fresh fish, great chips and good old-fashioned puds make it a not-to-be-missed destination for a tasty but low-cost evening out". / **Details:** www.theregencyrestaurant.co.uk; 10 pm. **Accommodation:** 30 rooms, from £50.*

Riddle & Finns £48 434
12a Meeting House Ln BN1 1HB
(01273) 323008
*These "jumping" joints have many fans for their "fresh seafood, well and simply treated"; in addition to the candlelit Lanes original, there's now a beachside offshoot, where the al fresco tables are best – if you must sit inside, make sure you sit at the front. / **Details:** www.riddleandfinns.co.uk; @RiddleandFinns1; 10 pm, Fri & Sat 11 pm; no bookings.*

Small Batch Coffee £15 254
17 Jubilee St BN1 1GE (01273) 697597
*"Lovely Fairtrade coffee" is the foundation of this rapidly growing bean-to-cup venture, with eight outposts across the city; "great staff" too. / **Details:** smallbatchcoffee.co.uk; 7 pm, Sun 6 pm.*

St George's £48 443
BN2 1ED (01273) 626 060
"Fun, engaging and well-conceived" – the food at this Kemp Town spot, which includes some "excellent veggie options", invariably impresses

reporters; in fact, the only real criticism, is that the interior is a little "bare" for some tastes. / **Details:** *www.24stgeorges.co.uk.*

Terre à Terre **£54** 5 4 2
71 East St BN1 1HQ (01273) 729051
"A veggie gastronomic delight" – this "buzzy" meat-free mecca in the Lanes is "the best in the UK", and inspires a hymn of praise for its "passionate" yet "unpretentious" staff and "beautiful" food, with "amazing textures and flavours".
/ **Details:** *www.terreaterre.co.uk; @TerreaTerre; 10.30 pm, Sat 11 pm; booking: max 8-10 fri & sat.*

Warung Tujuh **£36** Ⓣ
7 Pool Valley BN1 1NJ (01273) 720 784
Looking for "creative cooking that's not too pricey"? – some locals tip this small Indonesian venture, somewhat insalubriously located near the bus station. / **Details:** *www.warungtujuh.com; 11 pm.*

BRIGHTWELL BALDWIN, OXFORDSHIRE 2–2D

Lord Nelson **£47** 4 4 4
OX49 5NP (01491) 612497
"Standing out in an area well provided with good pubs", this "idyllic" village inn is hailed in all reports for its "lovely" food "from a regularly-changing menu that makes good use of local produce".
/ **Details:** *www.lordnelson-inn.co.uk; Mon-Sat 10 pm, Sun 9.30 pm; no Amex.*

BRISTOL, CITY OF BRISTOL 2–2B

The Albion **£47** Ⓣ
Boyces Ave BS8 4AA (0117) 973 3522
"Not a bad place for a quick bite and a pint" – a "pleasant rustic dining room above a lively Clifton bar". / **Details:** *www.thealbionclifton.co.uk; 10 pm; closed Mon L & Sun D.*

Bakers & Co **£18** Ⓣ
Gloucester Rd BS7 8BG no tel
Kieran & Imogen Waite's follow-up to Cotham Hill tapas joint Bravas is already gaining the same raves as its elder sibling; it offers Australian-style brunch fare (perhaps huevos rancheros with sweet potato bubble and squeak) in an attractive white-walled setting. / **Details:** *www.bakersbristol.co.uk.*

Bell's Diner And Bar Rooms **£54** 2 2 2
1 York Rd BS6 5QB (0117) 924 0357
"How the mighty have fallen!"; in its new tapas-led format, the out-of-the-way Montpelier bistro that "once had the best food in Bristol" is now "nowhere near as good", and – though it does still have its fans – the few reports the new incarnation has inspired are notably mixed.
/ **Details:** *www.bellsdiner.com; 9.30 pm, Fri & Sat 10 pm; closed Mon, Sat L & Sun.*

Bordeaux Quay **£54** 3 3 3
Canons Way BS1 5UH (0117) 943 1200
With a "great harbourside location", this eco-friendly venue and cookery school makes "a wonderful place for a leisurely lunch", particularly the "attractive" brasserie; beware, though – weekends can be "too busy".
/ **Details:** *www.bordeaux-quay.co.uk; @bordeauxquay; Mon-Sat 10.30 pm, Sun 9.30 pm.*

Bristol Folk House **£27** Ⓣ
BS1 5JG (0117) 908 5035
Linked to an adult education centre, this ethical café-bar is tipped for its "relaxed and informal" setting and "lovely" garden, not to mention pizzas and burgers which are a "legend" locally.

Casamia **£93** 5 5 4
38 High St BS9 3DZ (0117) 959 2884
"Wonderful food from two brothers who are really pushing the boundaries", and with "superb" service too – the Sanchez-Iglesias family's Westbury-on-Trym restaurant is an "amazing" destination.
/ **Details:** *www.casamiarestaurant.co.uk; @casamia_; 9.45 pm; closed Mon & Sun; no Amex.*

The Cowshed **£46** 3 2 2
46 Whiteladies Rd BS8 2NH (0117) 973 3550
"Fantastic for meat, as the name would suggest", this "busy" restaurant attached to a butcher's shop attracts universal praise for its "exceptional-value" lunch menu; somewhat paradoxically, though, it can otherwise seem a touch "overpriced"!
/ **Details:** *www.thecowshedbristol.com; @Cowshedbristol; 11.30 pm.*

eVo **£42** Ⓣ
96 Whiteladies Rd BS8 2QX (01179) 730005
Expect not just the usual pizzas and pastas but also more sophisticated modern Italian fare at this new Whiteladies Road restaurant and cicchetti bar; it's undeniably high-end – all spotlights, marble tables and heavy gold mirrors – and the all-Italian wine list is well above average too.
/ **Details:** *www.evorestaurant.co.uk; @eVoRistorante.*

Fishers **£43** 3 4 2
35 Princess Victoria St BS8 4BX
(0117) 974 7044
"Good, inexpensive and reliable" – all reports on this heart-of-Clifton "gem" confirm this is a "polite" and "friendly" venue, where "good fresh fish" is "simply presented"; a "great place for lunch", in particular.
/ **Details:** *www.fishers-restaurant.com; 10.30 pm, Sun 10 pm.*

Flinty Red **£43** 5 4 2
34 Cotham HIll BS6 6LA (0117) 923 8755
An "unpretentious Cotham bistro serving interesting food" ("especially small plates") and an "outstanding" wine list – perhaps what you'd expect from an operation "owned by a top local

*wine merchant". / **Details:** www.flintyred.co.uk; @flintyred; 10 pm; closed Mon L & Sun.*

Hotel du Vin et Bistro **£55** 2 3 4
Sugar Hs, Narrow Lewins Mead BS1 2NU
(0117) 925 5577
A "very lovely" city-centre dining room makes this outpost of the hotel-bistro chain of more-than-usual note; shame the food, if "well presented", sometimes tends to the "uninspired".
*/ **Details:** www.hotelduvin.com; @HdV_Bristol; 10.30 pm; booking: max 10. **Accommodation:** 40 rooms, from £119.*

Juniper **£39** 4 5 3
21 Cotham Road South BS6 5TZ
(0117) 9421744
A small-scale bistro, in Cotham, offering "innovative" cooking and "the warmest of welcomes from staff who go the extra mile".
*/ **Details:** www.juniperrestaurant.co.uk.*

Lido **£51** 3 3 5
Oakfield Pl BS8 2BJ (0117) 933 9533
"Watch the swimmers while you dine", at this Clifton café-restaurant, in an "amazing restored building overlooking the old pool"; the ex-Moro chef's tapas-style cuisine "never disappoints and is sometimes very good indeed" – "divine" ice-creams are a highlight.
*/ **Details:** www.lidobristol.com; @lidobristol; 10 pm; closed Sun D; no Amex.*

Maitreya Social **£39** 4 4 4
89 St Marks Rd BS5 6HY (0117) 951 0100
"The tastebud party just keeps rocking!", says one of the fans of this "favourite" Bristol veggie – an Easton institution which "never disappoints".
*/ **Details:** www.maitreyasocial.co.uk; 9.45 pm; closed Mon, Tue L, Wed L, Thu L & Sun D; no Amex.*

No Man's Grace **£32** ⓣ
BS6 6PE (07436) 588273
*On foodie hub Chandos Road, and replacing Moreish (RIP), a trendy new dessert bar and tapas den which we tip because it is co-run by John Watson, formerly of the admirable Casamia; it combines slick Anglo-French small plates with interesting bottles and mismatched vintage furniture. / **Details:** www.nomansgrace.com.*

Primrose Café **£46** 4 4 4
1 Clifton Arcade, 6 Boyces Ave BS8 4AA
(0117) 946 6577
*"Don't be fooled by the name or the furniture" – this Clifton Village café offers some "imaginative and excellent" food (a "slightly Mediterranean take on Modern British") and "very cheery" service to boot; "on a nice evening, sit outside and enjoy the good life". / **Details:** www.primrosecafe.co.uk; @theprimrosecafe; 10 pm; Sun D; no booking at L.*

Prosecco **£39** ⓣ
25 The Mall BS8 4JG (0117) 973 4499
Hidden away in Clifton, a small Italian tipped for food "of excellent quality", and extending a "nice welcome" too.
*/ **Details:** www.proseccoclifton.com; 11 pm; closed Mon & Sun, Tue-Thu L ; no Amex.*

River Cottage Canteen **£40** 3 3 4
St Johns Ct, Whiteladies Rd BS8 2QY
(0117) 973 2458
It can seem "pricey", but Hugh Fearnley-Whittingstall's "popular newcomer in an attractively converted church" mostly wins praise for its "healthy" and "tasty" food and its "rustic" and "interesting" setting.

riverstation **£48** 3 4 5
The Grove BS1 4RB (0117) 914 4434
*It's the situation – a striking former river police station on the water's edge – that particularly wins high popularity for this "lively" venue (downstairs bar, first floor restaurant); foodwise, it's "a safe choice with cooking that's good, but not exceptional". / **Details:** www.riverstation.co.uk; @riverstation_; 10.30 pm, Fri & Sat 11 pm; closed Sun D; no Amex.*

Rockfish **£54** 3 3 2
128-130 Whiteladies Road BS8 2RS
(0117) 9737384
"Great fish, great wine, great staff, great times" – fans of Mitch Tonks's fishmonger-cum-restaurant remain very upbeat about its standards all-round; not everyone likes the setting, though, and critics can find the formula "expensive for what you get".
*/ **Details:** www.rockfishgrill.co.uk; 10 pm, Fri & Sat 10.30 pm; closed Mon & Sun.*

San Carlo **£40** 3 3 4
44 Corn St BS1 1HQ (0117) 922 6586
Not the most famous, but arguably the best, of the outlets of this glitzy Italian brand – a "bustling" and "vibrant" venue, whose "very enjoyable" style make its it one of Bristol's most consistent performers; seafood is a speciality.
*/ **Details:** www.sancarlo.co.uk; 11 pm.*

The Thali Café **£31** 3 2 3
12 York Rd BS6 5QE (0117) 942 6687
"Cheap and wholesome Indian dishes" and a "great selection of vegetarian food" (with "take-aways in re-useable tiffin tins") define this five-strong chain; this listing is for the Montpelier HQ, but the new Southville branch is "ideal for a meal before you go to the (on-site) Tobacco Factory".
*/ **Details:** www.thethalicafe.co.uk; 10.30 pm; closed weekday L; no Amex.*

Wallfish Bistro **£42** 5 5 4
BS8 4DB (01179) 735435
"The new place to eat in Bristol"; "on the site of the first Keith Floyd restaurant" apparently,

The Albion Clifton

The Ox

The River Cottage

this "unpretentious" bistro offers an "inventive and constantly changing menu", on which "superb" fish is a stand out; BYO on Wednesdays.
/ **Details:** www.wallfishbistro.co.uk.

Wilks **£61** 5 5 2
1 Chandos Rd BS6 6PG (0117) 9737 999
"A worthy successor to Stephen Markwick and Culinaria"; James Wilkins's "unpretentious"-looking Redland bistro is "deserving of all its awards"; it is clearly now "the best place in Bristol", thanks to his "amazing" cuisine, and the "superb" service.
/ **Details:** www.wilksrestaurant.co.uk/; @wilksrestaurant; 10 pm, sun 9 pm; closed Mon & Tue; no Amex.

BRITWELL SALOME, OXFORDSHIRE 2–2D

The Red Lion **£40** 5 5 4
OX49 5LG (01491) 613140
It may be "hidden away down dark, twisty, narrow roads", but the inn once known as the Goose is again ranked in all reports as "well worth seeking out" for its "wonderful top-notch pub food, served with real passion".
/ **Details:** www.theredlionbritwellsalome.co.uk.

BRIXHAM, DEVON 1–3D

Poopdeck **£47** T
14 The Quay TQ5 8AW (01803) 858 681
Overlooking Brixham harbour, a small fish restaurant again tipped as a good all-rounder.
/ **Details:** www.poopdeckrestaurant.com.

BROAD HAVEN, PEMBROKESHIRE 4–4B

Druidstone Hotel **£45** T
SA62 3NE (01437) 781221
"Still a perennial favourite, despite the sad death of the founder" (in 2012) – this clifftop hotel is a "relaxing" destination known for its family-friendliness ("in an adult way!"), and tipped for its "very good food". / **Details:** www.druidstone.co.uk; from B4341 at Broad Haven turn right, then left after 1.5m; 9.30 pm. **Accommodation:** 11 rooms, from £80.

BROADSTAIRS, KENT 3–3D

Albarino **£34** 5 4 4
CT10 1LX (01843) 600991
"These could be the best tapas in the UK, and all from one (English)-man in the kitchen!" – you can see why "booking is essential" for this small bar-restaurant, where the dishes are invariably "interesting and tasty".
/ **Details:** www.albarinorestaurant.co.uk.

Wyatt & Jones **£40** T
CT10 1EU (01843) 865126
This seaside operation is a "delightful restaurant at any time of day, but breakfast is so good you have to book a table".
/ **Details:** www.wyattandjones.co.uk.

BROADWAY, WORCESTERSHIRE 2–1C

Russell's **£50** 3 2 2
20 High St WR12 7DT (01386) 853555
An "enjoyable" restaurant-with-rooms, in the heart of an idyllic Cotswolds village; it's perhaps especially worth seeking out for its "great-value set lunch".
/ **Details:** www.russellsofbroadway.co.uk; @russelsRandR; 9.30 pm; closed Sun D.
Accommodation: 7 rooms, from £110.

BROCKENHURST, HAMPSHIRE 2–4D

The Pig **£60** 3 4 4
Beaulieu Rd SO42 7QL (01590) 622354
"A little out of the way, but worth the effort to visit", this New Forest country house dining room wins particular acclaim for its "very chilled" style and "enthusiastic" staff, although the "impeccably sourced" food (with pork dishes a speciality) is good too. / **Details:** www.thepighotel.com; @The_Pig_Hotel; 9.30 pm. **Accommodation:** 26 rooms, from £139.

BROCKHAM, SURREY 3–3A

The Grumpy Mole **£43** 3 3 3
RH3 7JS (01737) 845 101
"Better for food, service and ambience than anywhere within a 10-mile radius" – this "popular" bistro-pub is part of a small chain, and wins praise for a "good menu variety" and "very friendly" staff too. / **Details:** www.thegrumpymole.co.uk; 9.30 pm; no Amex.

BROMESWELL, SUFFOLK 3–1D

British Larder **£52** 3 3 4
Oxford Rd, Offord Rd IP12 2PU (01394) 460 310
"Local sourcing" and "correct" cooking ("not seeking to be trendy") win much praise for this former inn; it generates a high volume of reports, most (if not quite all) of which find it "much better than average". / **Details:** www.britishlardersuffolk.co.uk; @britishlarder; 9 pm, Fri-Sat 9.30 pm; closed Mon & Sun D; no Amex.

BROMLEY, GREATER LONDON 3–3B

Cinnamon Culture **£59** 4 3 2
46 Plaistow Ln BR1 3PA (020) 8289 0322
"A rare treat"; even "the normal dishes are special", at this "superb local", which is praised for its "unusual and well-prepared" cooking and "relaxed" service. / **Details:** www.cinnamonculture.com; 10.30 pm, weekends 11 pm; closed Mon.

Tamasha **£50** 4 5 4
131 Widmore Rd BR1 3AX (020) 8460 3240
*"Reliably serving up the best Indian food hereabouts" – a suburban Indian in mock-colonial style, which inspires impressively consistent feedback. / **Details:** www.tamasha.co.uk; 10.30 pm; no shorts. **Accommodation:** 7 rooms, from £75.*

BROOM, WARWICKSHIRE 2–1C

The Broom Tavern **£37** Ⓣ
B50 4HL (01789) 778199
*"A great find"; this "wonderful 16th-century inn" is tipped for food that's "rather good, though this is definitely still a pub"; highlight? – "the best chips in Warwickshire!" / **Details:** www.broomtavern.co.uk.*

BROUGHTON GIFFORD, WILTSHIRE 2–2B

Fox **£45** 4 4 4
The St SN12 8PN (01225) 782949
*"A lovely pub-restaurant with a menu that makes it too hard to choose!"; "imaginative" food and "interesting" wines make it quite a crowd-pleaser – indeed, the main complaint is that it can sometimes be rather "noisy".
/ **Details:** www.thefox-broughtongifford.co.uk; @thefoxbroughton; 9.30 pm; closed Mon L.*

BROUGHTON, NORTH YORKSHIRE 8–4B

Bull at Broughton **£41** 4 4 4
BD23 3AE (01756) 792065
*This "cheerful and relaxed" old coaching inn, the Yorkshire outpost of the Ribble Valley Inns chain, is known for its "well-sourced local produce" (helping make it an ideal location for "one of the best Sunday roasts in the area").
/ **Details:** www.thebullatbroughton.com; 8.30 pm, Fri & Sat 9 pm.*

BRUNDALL, NORFOLK 6–4D

Lavender House **£65** 5 4 3
39 The St NR13 5AA (01603) 712215
*Sometimes proclaimed "the best place to eat round Norwich", Richard Hughes's very "competent" fixture (and cookery school) continues to dish up accomplished locally-sourced food; the only criticism, as ever, is that tables are "too close together". / **Details:** www.thelavenderhouse.co.uk; 9 pm; D only, closed Sun & Mon; no Amex.*

BRUTON, SOMERSET 2–3B

At the Chapel **£48** 3 2 5
28 High St BA10 0AE (01749) 814070
*"Like walking through a door in deepest Somerset and being transported to Hoxton!"; this "very cosmopolitan" former chapel is "refined and relaxed, grand and informal", all at the same time, and offers a menu catering for "all price brackets" – pizzas from the wood-fired oven are the stand-out. / **Details:** www.atthechapel.co.uk; @at_the_chapel; 9.30 pm, Sun 8 pm. **Accommodation:** 8 rooms, from £100.*

Roth Bar & Grill **£37** Ⓣ
Durslade Farm, Dropping Ln BA10 0NL
(01749) 814060
*A tip for art-lovers; Catherine Butler (of local hotspot At The Chapel) is – successfully, on press reports – organising the farm-to-table food at this salvage-clad gallery dining room, which is part of a new rural outpost of the mega-metropolitan Hauser & Wirth gallery empire.
/ **Details:** www.hauserwirthsomerset.com.*

BUCKFASTLEIGH, DEVON 1–3D

Riverford Field Kitchen **£42** 5 4 3
Wash Barn, Buckfast Leigh TQ11 0JU
(01803) 762074
*"Substantial portions of excellent local produce" (much of it grown on-site) is the winning modus operandi of this "informal" communal-tables venue; it also offers "enough colouring books and crayons to keep kids entertained, and space outside for them to run and burn off excess energy".
/ **Details:** www.riverford.co.uk; 8 pm; closed Sun D; no Amex.*

BUCKHORN WESTON, DORSET 2–3B

The Stapleton Arms **£41** Ⓣ
Church Hill SP8 5HS (01963) 370396
*"Deep in the countryside", a "friendly" and "laid-back" gastropub tipped for some "very good" dishes (although even fans can find the food "variable").
/ **Details:** www.thestapletonarms.com; 10 pm.
Accommodation: 4 rooms, from £100.*

BUCKLAND MARSH, OXFORDSHIRE 2–2C

The Trout Inn **£47** 3 2 4
Tadpole Bridge SN7 8RF (01367) 870382
*"Straightforward but well cooked" food in a "magical setting by the Thames" – the reason to seek out this "excellent" pub, which has "a lovely garden for a good day".
/ **Details:** www.trout-inn.co.uk; @TroutInn; 11 pm, sun 10.30 pm; no Amex. **Accommodation:** 6 rooms, from £130.*

BUNBURY, CHESHIRE 5–3B

The Dysart Arms **£43** 3 3 4
Bowes Gate Rd CW6 9PH (01829) 260183
*This "lovely", "traditional-style" pub – part of the Brunning & Price empire – has an attractive village setting near the church, and wins plenty of plaudits for its "above-average pub grub".
/ **Details:** www.dysartarms-bunbury.co.uk; 9.30 pm, Sun 9 pm.*

BUNNY, NOTTINGHAMSHIRE 5–3D

Rancliffe Arms **£41** Ⓣ
139 Loughborough Rd NG11 6QT
(0115) 98447276
"A traditional carvery but the quality of the food far exceeds what you'd generally expect"; it's tipped for "nicely cooked meat in big portions", a "wide variety of vegetables" and "attentive service" too.
*/ **Details:** www.rancliffearms.co.uk; 9 pm; no Amex.*

BURNHAM MARKET, NORFOLK 6–3B

Hoste Arms **£58** 332
The Grn PE31 8HD (01328) 738777
*The new management at this famous, and potentially "lovely", inn divides opinion; while fans claim that "standards are always high and improving", critics find the ambience, in particular, distinctly below par. / **Details:** www.thehoste.com; @thehoste; 6m W of Wells; 9.15 pm.*
***Accommodation:** 62 rooms, from £115.*

BURY ST EDMUNDS, SUFFOLK 3–1C

Benson Blakes **£21** 422
88-89 St. Johns St IP33 1SQ (01284) 755188
"Awesome" burgers and "friendly" staff win praise for this "friendly" bar/diner, which fans insist is "worthy of higher recognition!"
*/ **Details:** www.bensonblakes.co.uk; @BensonBlakes; 9 pm, Fri & Sat 9.30 pm.*

Maison Bleue **£54** 554
30-31 Churchgate St IP33 1RG
(01284) 760623
*"I'm thinking of moving house so I could eat here every day!"; the Crépy family's "provincial French restaurant", near the cathedral, is "one of the best regional restaurants in the country", thanks to its "spot-on" service and "perfect" Gallic fish dishes. / **Details:** www.maisonbleue.co.uk; @Maison_Bleue; 9 pm, Sat 9.30 pm; closed Mon & Sun.*

Pea Porridge **£50** 544
28-29 Cannon St IP33 1JR (01284) 700200
Justin Sharp's "refreshing adventurous" cooking with "exciting combinations of seldom-seen cuts of meat and offal" delivers a "not-to-be-missed" experience at this "rustic" former bakery, in a backstreet near the town centre; "charming and enthusiastic" service from wife Jurga too.
*/ **Details:** www.peaporridge.co.uk; 10 pm; closed Mon, Tue L & Sun; no Amex.*

BUSHEY HEATH, HERTFORDSHIRE 3–2A

The Alpine **£50** 332
135 High Rd WD23 1JA (020) 8950 2024
Established in 1969, this "friendly" and "professional" Italian nonetheless "maintains high standards of cooking", if from a rather "static" menu; it is rumoured that it may relocate in the near future.
*/ **Details:** www.thealpinerestaurant.co.uk; @The_Alpine; 10.30 pm; closed Mon.*

BUSHEY, HERTFORDSHIRE 3–2A

St James **£45** 342
30 High St WD23 3HL (020) 8950 2480
"In the culinary desert that is the Herts borderlands", this "longstanding stalwart" is the "best restaurant for miles around"; indeed, fans say that the cooking has undergone a "sustained and noticeable" improvement of late, as witnessed by "the fact that it's packed nightly".
*/ **Details:** www.stjamesrestaurant.co.uk; opp St James Church; 9.30 pm; closed Sun D.*

CAERNARFON, GWYNEDD 4–2C

Blas **£46** 443
23-25 Hole in the Wall St LL55 1RF
(01286) 677707
"The only time I'd seen foam in Caernarvon before was on the shoreline!" – if you're looking for "great food with imagination", this small establishment near the Royal Welch Fusiliers Museum is well worth seeking out.
*/ **Details:** www.blascaernarfon.co.uk; 9 pm; closed Mon & Sun D.*

CAMBRIDGE, CAMBRIDGESHIRE 3–1B

Alimentum **£75** 221
152-154 Hills Rd CB2 8PB (01223) 413000
"Serious" cuisine with "flashes of brilliance" has earned a huge reputation for Mark Pynton's "stark" foodie hotspot; it's an "awkward" and "soulless" space though, with sometimes unempathetic service, and sceptics report "strange" dishes that are "very creative… not always in a good way".
*/ **Details:** www.restaurantalimentum.co.uk; @alimentum1; Mon-Thu 9.30 pm, Sat 10 pm, Sun 9 pm.*

Bill's **£41** 223
34-35 Green St CB2 3JX (01223) 329638
Still above average for this (deteriorating) chain, an "enjoyable" and "lively" branch, less prominently located than you might expect, where the food in general is usually "decent", and where brunch has a particular following.
*/ **Details:** www.bills-website.co.uk; 11 pm, Sun 10.30 pm.*

The Cambridge Chop House **£46** 222
1 Kings Pde CB2 1SJ (01223) 359506
Handily-located opposite King's, this "reliable" operation isn't at all inspired, but it offers "good, solid British fare" (much of it "meat-focused"); "the ground floor is best".

/ **Details:** *www.cambridgechophouse.co.uk; @cambscuisine; 10.30 pm, Sat 11 pm, Sun 9.30 pm.*

Coast Fish & Chip **£24** ⓣ
CB2 1TB (01223) 351344
One of the best features of this "enjoyable" new chippy, near Trinity? – actually, it's "the best full English breakfast in town"!
/ **Details:** *www.coastrestaurants.co.uk.*

Cotto **£75** 433
183 East Rd CB1 1BG (01223) 302010
"An oasis"; the setting may be on the "quirky" side (entered via a café), but the cuisine at this "unobtrusively experimental" dining room can be "fantastic" – it may help that "the menu is designed to offer something for both safe and more adventurous diners".
/ **Details:** *www.cottocambridge.co.uk; 9.15 pm; D only, Wed-Sat; no Amex.*

d'Arry's **£46** 233
2-4 King St CB1 1LN (01223) 505015
Some excellent meals are still reported at this gastropub behind Christ's – burgers are a "real strength", and there's an above-average wine list too – but standards have been a touch variable of late, and critics feel this is "just a standby" nowadays. / **Details:** *www.darrys.co.uk; 9.30 pm, Sun 8.30 pm; no Amex; need 8+ to book.*

Fitzbillies **£37** 212
52 Trumpington St CB2 1RG (01223) 352500
"Robust" and "imaginative" dishes – plus "wonderful cakes", of course – draw fans to this famous bakery-institution; critics find the dining space "weird", though, and those who encounter "chaotic" service can just find a visit "very disappointing". / **Details:** *www.fitzbillies.com; 8 pm, Fri & Sat 9.45 pm; closed Sun D.*

Midsummer House **£138** 543
Midsummer Common CB4 1HA
(01223) 369299
Daniel Clifford's "sheer innovation" has won a gigantic reputation for this "slightly formal" Cam-side destination, and the results are "terrific"; "ask your bank manager before you open the wine list" though, as the prices are "crazy".
/ **Details:** *www.midsummerhouse.co.uk; @Midsummerhouse; 9.30 pm; closed Mon, Tue L & Sun.*

Oak Bistro **£45** 342
6 Lensfield Rd CB2 1EG (01223) 323361
A "reliable and very pleasant" bistro, between the station and the city-centre; reporters lament the fact that "it should have encouraged the creation of many rivals in restaurant-deprived Cambridge… but alas it hasn't!"
/ **Details:** *www.theoakbistro.co.uk; 10 pm; closed Sun.*

Pint Shop **£40** 233
CB2 3PN (01223) 352293
"A new and welcome addition to the city's pub scene"; its food is "traditional" and "honest", but the "fantastic real ales" and "wonderful gin list" are arguably greater attractions.
/ **Details:** *www.pintshop.co.uk.*

Pipasha Restaurant **£33** ⓣ
529c, Newmarket Rd CB5 8PA
(01223) 577786
"On the outskirts of the town, but always busy and unsurprisingly so" – this Bangladeshi restaurant is tipped for some "new" and "inventive" dishes, and its "consistently excellent" standards too.
/ **Details:** *www.pipasha-restaurant.co.uk; 11 pm; D only.*

Ristorante Il Piccolo Mondo **£44** 444
CB25 9BA (01223) 811434
A "remarkably good" new Italian (formerly in Saffron Walden), in a converted chapel in a village outside Cambridge, combining "outstanding" dishes with "excellent" wine; opened in 2013, it's already "so popular you need to book a month ahead at peak times".
/ **Details:** *www.ristoranteilpiccolomondo.co.uk.*

Sea Tree **£32** ⓣ
13 The Broadway CB1 3AH (01223) 414349
"Yes it's a chippy, but the inventiveness of the menu and the enthusiasm of the owners and staff are praiseworthy"; it is also tipped for its "awesome" fish stew. / **Details:** *www.theseatree.co.uk; 10 pm, Sun 9 pm; closed Mon L & Sun L.*

The St John's Chop House **£49** ⓣ
21-24 Northampton St CB3 0AD
(01223) 353 110
A sibling to the Cambridge Chophouse, tipped for its "good solid British food" (in "enormous portions"); interesting wine list too (concentrating on Languedoc-Roussillon).
/ **Details:** *www.cambscuisine.com; @cambscuisine; 10.30 pm, Sun 9 pm.*

Steak & Honour **£11** 44–
(07766) 568430
"Really great burgers from a van!"; in this still under-served city, it's worth seeking out these "faultless" patties, which twin "obviously well sourced beef" with toppings that are "more interesting than usual".
/ **Details:** *www.steakandhonour.co.uk.*

Yippee Noodle Bar **£32** 444
CB1 1LH (01223) 518111
With its "great flavours" and a "wide range of dishes" too, this "brilliant" and "reasonably-priced" city-centre spot inspires only the most positive reports.
/ **Details:** *www.yippeenoodlebar.co.uk.*

CANTERBURY, KENT 3–3D

The Ambrette £35 T
14-15 Beer Cart Ln CT1 2NY
(01227) 200 777
*In a former pub near the Heritage Museum, the latest and largest outpost of Dev Biswal's innovative Indian restaurant; if it's anything like the Margate and Rye branches, it will soon be making big waves locally. / **Details:** www.theambrette.co.uk.*

Café des Amis £41 434
95 St Dunstan's St CT2 8AD (01227) 464390
*"Consistently good, and always buzzing" – all commentary on this long-established Mexican, by the Westgate, is to pretty much the same effect; service at peak times, though, "can be slow". / **Details:** www.cafedez.com; 10 pm, Fri & Sat 10.30 pm, Sun 9.30 pm; booking: max 6 at D Fri-Sat.*

Cafe du Soleil £41 T
4-5 Pound Lane CT1 2BZ (01227) 479999
*The "buzzing" sibling to the Café des Amis, situated by the river and built into the city wall, is tipped for its "really good pizzas" (from the wood-burning oven), but an "eclectic" range of other dishes is also available. / **Details:** www.cafedusoleil.co.uk; 10 pm.*

Cafe Mauresque £39 444
8 Butchery Ln CT1 2JR (01227) 464300
*Conveniently located just off the main street, a "perfect lunch location" – an "intimate", "friendly" and "efficient" operation where the Spanish and Moroccan dishes are often "excellent"; there's a "small but clever" wine list too. / **Details:** www.cafemauresque.com; 10 pm, Fri & Sat 10.30 pm.*

The Compasses Inn £36 T
CT4 7ES (01227) 700 300
*In the village of Crundale (on the way to Ashford), a "quiet little country pub", under new management in recent times, and tipped for its "fantastic, freshly-prepared food using local ingredients", and a "gorgeous" atmosphere too. / **Details:** www.thecompassescrundale.co.uk.*

Deeson's British Restaurant £50 333
25-27 Sun St CT1 2HX (01227) 767854
*Near the cathedral, this extremely popular haunt wins praise for its "British food in hearty portions"; "at its best it's very good, but it is not completely consistent". / **Details:** www.deesonsrestaurant.co.uk; @DeesonsBritish; 10 pm; booking: max 12.*

Goods Shed £49 434
Station Road West CT2 8AN (01227) 459153
*"On the pricey side, but generally good cooking"; above the permanent farmers' market near Canterbury West station, an "interesting" venue where local produce is often "cooked to perfection"; "great freshly-cooked breakfasts" a highlight. / **Details:** www.thegoodsshed.co.uk; 9.30 pm; closed Mon & Sun D.*

Salt £32 T
CT1 2DZ (01227) 788595
*Already making waves in the city-centre, a small-plates specialist tipped – perhaps paradoxically – for its "hearty" approach, "with a focus on seasonal and local produce". / **Details:** www.saltcanterbury.co.uk.*

La Trappiste £40 T
1-2 Sun St CT1 2HX (01227) 479111
*A quirky outfit in former gents' outfitters, by the cathedral's main gate, serving good coffee, cakes and more substantial fare (plus a big range of beers); service is not the quickest, but "if you've time to kill and a laid-back attitude, you'll love sitting upstairs on the terrace, watching the world go by". / **Details:** www.latrappiste.com; 10.30 pm; no Amex.*

CARDIFF, CARDIFF 2–2A

Casanova £40 432
13 Quay St CF10 1EA (029) 2034 4044
*"The best Italian in Cardiff"; thanks not least to its "good and friendly" service, this is an outfit which rises far above the lacklustre local norm. / **Details:** www.casanovacardiff.com; 10 pm; closed Sun.*

Fish at 85 £25 422
85 Pontcanna St CF11 9HS (02920) 020212
*"The best fish restaurant in Wales, well, practically the only one…" – this fishmonger-cum-restaurant offers some "lovely fresh fish, beautifully cooked", although "in the confined space the pong is sometimes a bit overpowering!" / **Details:** www.fishat85.co.uk; @Fishat85; 9 pm; closed Mon & Sun; no Amex.*

Happy Gathering £33 443
233 Cowbridge Road East CF11 9AL
(029) 2039 7531
*"Strike Cantonese gold", at this "very good-value" quarter-centenarian, aptly located in Canton; its "vast menu" includes "steaming cauldrons" of Won Ton noodle soup – "best I've tasted outside HK!" / **Details:** www.happygatheringcardiff.co.uk; 10.30 pm, Sun 9 pm.*

Mint and Mustard £42 433
134 Whitchurch Rd CF14 3LZ
(02920) 620333
*"In a city full of Bangladeshi baji-likes, a place offering an interesting range of piquant 'nouvelle' Indian dishes"; "very different from the average, and with great flavours" too. / **Details:** www.mintandmustard.com; 11 pm; D only; no shorts.*

The Potted Pig £54 [3][4][3]
27 High St CF10 1PU (029) 2022 4817
"Ideal for visitors"; these former bank vaults offer "an abundance of atmosphere, friendly service and a menu that's quite original by local standards"; "the lunchtime set menu offers amazing value, too… till you're tempted to blow your savings on one of their interesting cocktails!"
*/ **Details:** www.thepottedpig.com; 9 pm; closed Mon & Sun D.*

Purple Poppadom £34 [4][4][3]
185a, Cowbridge Road East CF11 9AJ
(029) 2022 0026
*Despite an "inauspicious" Canton location ("rubbing shoulders with an ever-expanding number of charity shops"), this classy three-year-old offers some "exceptional" Indian cuisine; fans claim that it has now "sprinted past Mint and Mustard", the chef's former platform. / **Details:** purplepoppadom.com; Purple_Poppadom; Mon-Sat 11 pm Sun 9 pm.*

Vegetarian Food Studio £26 [4][3][2]
115-117 Penarth Rd CF11 6JU
(029) 2023 8222
"The decor has improved of late", but the "good-quality" cooking – with an Indian twist – at this fixture, near the Taff, is "just the same as ever"; reports all remain very positive.
*/ **Details:** www.vegetarianfoodstudio.co.uk; 9.30 pm; closed Mon; no Amex.*

CARLISLE, CUMBRIA 7–2D

Alexandros £41 [4][4][3]
68 Warwick Rd CA1 1DR (01228) 592227
"In the gastronomic wasteland of Carlisle, this stands out" – a "hidden gem" offering "good homemade food" ("with the Greek menu now supplemented with weekly specials"); Aris the owner "insists on properly marinating his meats for grilling, which makes all the difference".
*/ **Details:** www.thegreek.co.uk; 9.30 pm; closed Mon L & Sun.*

CARTMEL FELL, CUMBRIA 7–4D

The Masons Arms £43 [3][4][4]
Strawberry Bank LA11 6NW (01539) 568486
*It's not hard to see why fans of this "out-of-the-way" inn regard it as "the ultimate 'safe' Lakeland destination", given its "great value for money, fantastic location, excellent beer, and cosy interior too!" / **Details:** www.strawberrybank.com; W from Bowland Bridge, off A5074; 9 pm.*
***Accommodation:** 7 rooms, from £75.*

CARTMEL, CUMBRIA 7–4D

L'Enclume £122 [5][5][4]
Cavendish St LA11 6PZ (01539) 536362
"In the shadow of the ancient Cartmel Priory", Simon Rogan's "stunning" former smithy provides the setting for "an unforgettable and superlative experience", but not a formal one; "the staff notice everything", and the "adventurous but ungimmicky" cuisine is "constantly improving".
*/ **Details:** www.lenclume.co.uk; @lenclume; J36 from M6, down A590 towards Cartmel; 9 pm; closed Mon L & Tue L. **Accommodation:** 16 rooms, from £119.*

Pig & Whistle £40 [3][3][2]
LA11 6PL (015395) 36482
A "small but noteworthy addition" to Simon Rogan's empire; with its ambitious (if "not exceptional") gastro-grub menu, this revamped village boozer makes "a decent alternative to the fine dining at his other restaurants" (most famously, of course, L'Enclume).
*/ **Details:** www.pigandwhistlecartmel.co.uk.*

Rogan & Co £58 [5][5][3]
Devonshire Sq LA11 6QD (01539) 535917
"An opportunity to taste Rogan's dishes at a more reasonable price than L'Enclume"; the food is perhaps "more similar" than you might expect, though service and, especially, the ambience don't measure up to the flagship.
*/ **Details:** www.roganandcompany.co.uk; @simon_rogan; 9 pm; closed Mon L & Sun; no Amex.*

CASTEL, CHANNEL ISLANDS

Cobo Tearoom £21 (T)
GY5 7HB (01481) 253366
By Cobo Bay, a "fabulous" venue tipped for its "wonderful" view, "fantastic" crab sandwiches and "amazing" home-made cakes; rather sounds as if you could spend a whole holiday there!
*/ **Details:** www.cobotearoom.com.*

CASTLE COMBE, WILTSHIRE 2–2B

Bybrook Restaurant Manor House Hotel £87 [4][4][3]
Manor House Hotel and Golf Course SN14 7HR (01249) 782206
"Refined cooking in a very picturesque Cotswold village" – that's the package that inspires uniformly upbeat feedback on this grand medieval house; "its style seems to be in transition to something more relaxed, but they're not quite there yet".
*/ **Details:** www.exclusivehotels.co.uk; @themanorhouse; 9.30 pm; closed Mon L & Tue L; no jeans or trainers; children: 11+.*
***Accommodation:** 48 rooms, from £205.*

CAVENDISH, SUFFOLK 3–1C

The George £46 [3][4][3]
The Green CO1 8BA (01787) 280248
In a 16th-century building, a restaurant-with-rooms offering "well cooked food from an unpretentious menu"; its "reliable" charms inspire all who comment on it.

/ **Details:** *www.thecavendishgeorge.co.uk; @TheGeorgeCav; 9.30 pm; closed Sun D.* **Accommodation:** *5 rooms, from £75.*

CHADDESLEY CORBETT, WORCESTERSHIRE 5–4B

Brockencote Hall **£63** 4 4 4
DY10 4PY (01562) 777876
"THE place to go for a romantic meal to feel pampered and special" – a Victorian country house hotel that's thriving under corporate ownership; its "superb" cooking is "supplemented by top-drawer service", and the setting is "lovely" too.
/ **Details:** *www.brockencotehall.com; on A448, outside village; 9 pm; no trainers.* **Accommodation:** *21 rooms, from £135.*

CHAGFORD, DEVON 1–3C

Gidleigh Park **£139** 5 5 4
TQ13 8HH (01647) 432367
It's very hard to fault any facet of this "luxurious yet understated" Tudorbethan manor, "beautifully situated" down "a magical mystery tour" of windy lanes on the edge of Dartmoor; despite his many commitments, Michael Caines's cuisine is absolutely "terrific", and service is "flawless" too.
/ **Details:** *www.gidleigh.com; @Gidleighhotel; from village, right at Lloyds TSB, take right fork to end of lane; no jeans or trainers; children: 8+.* **Accommodation:** *24 rooms, from £350.*

CHALFORD, GLOUCESTERSHIRE 2–2B

Lavender Bakehouse **£28** Ⓣ
GL6 8NW (01453) 889239
"Becoming a legend locally", a venue that feels "like the conservatory of your favourite children's bookshop", and tipped as "really excellent for brunch, lunch and cakes".
/ **Details:** *www.lavenderbakehouse.co.uk.*

CHANDLER'S CROSS, HERTFORDSHIRE 3–2A

Colette's
The Grove **£103** 2 3 3
WD17 3NL (01923) 296015
The "intimate" main dining room of this luxurious contemporary-style country house hotel does win recommendations for "subtle" service and ambitious tasting menus; as ever, though, the food can seem "average, at the prices".
/ **Details:** *www.thegrove.co.uk; @TheGroveHotel; 9.30 pm; D only, closed Mon & Sun; children: 16+.* **Accommodation:** *227 rooms, from £310.*

The Glasshouse
The Grove **£64** 3 2 2
WD3 4TG (01923) 296015
"You'll never go hungry" in the "picturesque" surroundings of the "unbeatable" buffet dining room of this glossy country house hotel, acclaimed for its "fabulous variety and quality"… even if you'll "pay a premium price" for the pleasure.
/ **Details:** *www.thegrove.co.uk; @thegrovehotel; 9.30 pm, Sat 10 pm; Fri-Sun booking max 8, Mon-Thu max 12.* **Accommodation:** *227 rooms, from £.*

CHEAM, SURREY 3–3B

Regional Thai Taste **£29** 4 4 2
SM3 8BH (0208) 642 7938 or 643 9919
In the middle of the village, this "tiny" Thai dishes up "unusual" fare with "lots of spice"; "it's always busy, so you have to book".
/ **Details:** *www.regionalthai.co.uk.*

CHELTENHAM, GLOUCESTERSHIRE 2–1C

L'Artisan **£49** Ⓣ
GL50 3NX (01242) 571257
They may be "fairly new in town", but husband-and-wife team Yves and Elisabeth Ogrodzki "really deliver", at this casual neighbourhood yearling – a top tip for "an excellent evening with authentic French trimmings".
/ **Details:** *www.lartisan-restaurant.com.*

Le Champignon Sauvage **£78** 5 5 3
24-28 Suffolk Rd GL50 2AQ (01242) 573449
"Unpretentious but perfect"; "disarmingly humble yet utterly driven" chef David Everitt-Matthias "continues to amaze" at this acclaimed dining room, where his "magically intense" cuisine is served by wife Helen's "brilliant and personable" staff; as ever, though, the decor can seem "a less certain attraction".
/ **Details:** *www.lechampignonsauvage.co.uk; @lechampsauvage; 8.30 pm; closed Mon & Sun.*

The Curry Corner **£46** 4 3 3
133 Fairview Rd GL52 2EX (01242) 528449
"THE best Bangladeshi restaurant"; locals say this is a curry house where "the locally-sourced ingredients, the delicate spice combinations... in fact everything" is just "fabulous"… even the bill!
/ **Details:** *www.thecurrycorner.com; @thecurrycorner; 11 pm; closed Mon & Fri L.*

The Daffodil **£56** 2 2 3
18-20 Suffolk Pde GL50 2AE (01242) 700055
"Go for the ambience, not the food"; the cooking may be "pretty good", but it's the "cheerful" ambience at this former Art Deco cinema which is the particular reason to seek it out.
/ **Details:** *www.thedaffodil.com; @thedaffodil; 10 pm, Sat 10.30 pm; closed Sun.*

Ellenborough Park **£74** 3 2 4
Southam Road GL52 3NH (01242) 808918
On the outskirts of the town, this large country house hotel – "recently upgraded at considerable cost" in "magnificent and lavish Tudorbethan style" – is tipped for its "improving" cuisine; service, though, still needs work.

Lumière £71 442
Clarence Pde GL50 3PA (01242) 222200
*Jon Howe & Helen Aubrey's "excellent-value" venture offers "fabulous" food that's "innovative without being tricksy", and "beautifully presented" too; the location is "unprepossessing", though, and the "modern-bland" decor is no particular compensation. / **Details:** www.lumiere.cc; @LumiereChelt ; 8.45 pm; closed Mon & Sun, Tue L; children: 8+ at D.*

Prithvi £45 554
37 Bath Rd GL53 7HG (01242) 226229
*It may be the "new kid on the Cheltenham block", but this two-year-old gastronomic destination already elicits rave reviews for its "very well-executed twist on modern Indian" cuisine; "book well in advance".
/ **Details:** www.prithvirestaurant.com; @37Prithvi; 10.30 pm; closed Mon & Tue L; no Amex.*

Purslane £49 T
16 Rodney Rd GL50 1JJ (01242) 321639
*A restaurant of recent vintage, tipped for some "outstanding" cooking (including "lots of delicious fish dishes"); the setting is a little "cramped", though, and service can be "indifferent".
/ **Details:** www.purslane-restaurant.co.uk; 9.30 pm; closed Mon & Sun.*

Tavern £38 T
GL50 3DN (01242) 221212
*Tipped as a "really useful, casual and fun place" in the city-centre, this "buzzy" bar/bistro – with its "burgers and spam fritters served in quirky style" – is "doing the dude food thing very well".
/ **Details:** www.thetaverncheltenham.com.*

CHESTER, CHESHIRE 5–2A

Architect £43 333
54 Nicholas St CH1 2NX (01244) 353070
*"Booking advised, even on non-race days!"; this "buzzy" venue (the bar in particular is "throbbing"), overlooking England's oldest racecourse, is a "popular" recent addition to the Brunning & Price chain, serving "light and modern dishes and with a great wine and beer selection".
/ **Details:** www.brunningandprice.co.uk/architect; 10 pm, Sun 9.30 pm; no Amex.*

**La Brasserie
Chester Grosvenor** £58 334
Eastgate CH1 1LT (01244) 324024
*"Pricey but dependable", this "glamorous" and "lively" Gallic-style brasserie, in the shadow of the city's iconic clock, is acclaimed by all reporters for its "decent" standards.
/ **Details:** www.chestergrosvenor.com; 10 pm, Sun 9 pm. **Accommodation:** 80 rooms, from £230.*

Cafe Fude £18 T
CH2 5UG (01244) 313 522
*A mile or so from the city centre, in Boughton, a popular café, particularly tipped as a "great brunch place" – it offers "its own interpretation of the classics, as well as your usual Full English"; tapas nights (BYO) are also worth seeking out.
/ **Details:** www.cafefude.co.uk.*

Joseph Benjamin £44 453
140 Northgate St CH1 2HT (01244) 344295
*Ably manned by a "very hands-on" owner, a "relaxed" and "friendly" deli-restaurant offering a "short menu" of "delicious uncomplicated dishes"; Porta, its newer tapas offshoot, also attracts praise.
/ **Details:** www.josephbenjamin.co.uk; @Joseph_Benjamin; 9.30 pm; closed Mon, Tue D, Wed D & Sun D.*

**Michael Caines
ABode Hotels** £73 444
Grosvener Rd CH1 2DJ (01244) 347 000
*With sweeping views over the racecourse and River Dee, the top-floor restaurant of this modern hotel offers a "smallish" menu of "excellently prepared" food; sceptics feel it's a case of "style over substance", but for fans this is "without doubt the best eating place in town".
/ **Details:** www.michaelcaines.com; @michaelcaines; 9.30 pm; closed Sun D; no jeans or trainers. **Accommodation:** 85 rooms, from £100.*

Moules A Go Go £41 T
39 Watergate Row CH1 2LE (01244) 348818
*A "perennial favourite" mussels parlour, up on the city's unique medieval 'rows', tipped as "a great lunch venue, always busy and good value".
/ **Details:** www.moulesagogo.co.uk; @MoulesaGoGo; 10 pm, Sun 9 pm.*

The Old Harkers Arms £46 324
Russell St CH3 5AL (01244) 344525
*"A very popular establishment for food, drink and conversation", this Brunning & Price gastropub, by the canal, is consistently tipped for its "good, simple cooking" ("especially burgers").
/ **Details:** www.brunningandprice.co.uk; 9.30 pm; no Amex.*

**Simon Radley
The Chester Grosvenor** £98 554
Eastgate CH1 1LT (01244) 324024
*"Chester is SO lucky to have a genuinely smart hotel", and its flagship dining room "has the formality you'd expect, but still manages to be friendly and (relatively) relaxed"; Simon Radley fully lives up to the occasion, offering "wonderful classic cooking" that "features luxury ingredients but avoids cliché". / **Details:** www.chestergrosvenor.com; @TheGrosvenor; 9 pm; D only, closed Mon & Sun; no trainers; children: 12+. **Accommodation:** 80 rooms, from £230.*

Sticky Walnut £46 443
11 Charles St CH2 3AZ (01244) 400400
An "excellent" Hoole bistro which has "gained a lot of publicity recently" and "justifiably so"; Garry Usher serves up "fantastic, locally sourced dishes" (which "major on long, slow cooking"), twinned with a "very approachable" wine list.
/ **Details:** *www.stickywalnut.com; @stickywalnut; 10 pm, Sun 3 pm; closed Sun D; no Amex.*

Upstairs at the Grill £50 442
70 Watergate St CH1 2LA (01244) 344883
Steaks "to die for" make this "intimate" steakhouse worth seeking out; "good cocktails and wines" too.
/ **Details:** *www.upstairsatthegrill.co.uk; @UpstairsatGrill; 10.30 pm, Sun 9.30 pm; closed Mon L, Tue L & Wed L.*

CHEW MAGNA, BRISTOL 2–2B

The Pony & Trap £46 432
Newtown BS40 8TQ (01275) 332 627
"Imaginative cooking" and "great countryside views" win consistent praise for Josh Eggleton's "popular", if "slightly cramped", inn.
/ **Details:** *www.theponyandtrap.co.uk; @theponyandtrap; 9.30 pm; closed Mon; no Amex.*

CHICHESTER, WEST SUSSEX 3–4A

Field & Fork
Pallant House Gallery £50 433
9 North Pallant PO19 1TJ (01243) 770 827
"Good all year round, but especially nice when you can sit out under the trees in summer", this "pleasant" dining room (and conservatory) – removed from its former gallery premises – provides "a suitable base for Sam Mahoney's inventive cooking". / **Details:** *www.fieldandfork.co.uk; 8.45 pm; closed Mon, Tue D, Wed D, Thu D, Fri D, Sat D & Sun D.*

The Kennels £63 T
Goodwood Hs PO18 0PX (01243) 755000
On the Goodwood Estate, a smart contemporary restaurant, tipped for its "sublime" setting; the food is generally rated pretty "reliable" too.
/ **Details:** *www.goodwood.co.uk/thekennels; Tue-Fri 9.15 pm, Sun 3pm; closed Mon & Sun D.*

Marco £40 T
PO19 1AR (01243) 774204
"A good addition to the chain restaurants in Chichester, priced much the same, but offering better choice and quality"; this "uncomplicated" newcomer is tipped for its proximity to the Festival Theatre; "good-value happy hour" too!
/ **Details:** *www.marco-no1.co.uk.*

The Richmond Arms £49 444
The Richmond Arms, The Goodwood Hotel PO18 0QB (01243) 775537
"A new kid on the block, offering an interesting and varied menu that's well prepared and presented" – all reports on this "very professionally-run" country pub, next to a large duck pond, are notably positive.

CHIDDINGFOLD, SURREY 3–3A

The Swan Inn £49 T
Petworth Rd GU8 4TY (01428) 684 688
Run by the former proprietors of Swag 'n' Tails (Knightsbridge), a boutique hotel-cum-gastropub, tipped for its "inventive" menus ("especially puddings") and its "family-friendly" style.
/ **Details:** *www.theswaninnchiddingfold.com; 10 pm, Sun 9 pm.* **Accommodation:** *10 rooms, from £100.*

CHINNOR, OXFORDSHIRE 2–2D

The Sir Charles Napier £58 445
Spriggs Alley OX39 4BX (01494) 483011
"A unique and special place in the countryside" with a "beautiful garden" – Julie Griffiths's "out-of-the-way" Chilterns pub-conversion famously offers ambitious cuisine that's "not cheap but top-notch", and in a "lovely" atmosphere too.
/ **Details:** *www.sircharlesnapier.co.uk; Tue-Fri 9.30 pm, Sat 10 pm; closed Mon & Sun D.*

CHIPPING CAMPDEN, GLOUCESTERSHIRE 2–1C

The Ebrington Arms £45 245
GL55 6NH (01386) 593 223
"A picture-perfect Cotswold boozer, with its own brewery and a homely atmosphere" – "an excellent backdrop" for some generally dependable cooking.
/ **Details:** *www.theebringtonarms.co.uk; @theebrington; 9 pm.*

CHIPPING NORTON, OXFORDSHIRE 2–1C

Wild Thyme £50 543
10 New St OX7 5LJ (01608) 645060
"Now is the time to catch this gem of a restaurant before it becomes too popular!"; all reports concur that – with its "fantastic food and wine, reasonably priced" – this is an establishment "well worth a visit, if you're in the Cotswolds".
/ **Details:** *www.wildthymerestaurant.co.uk; @wtrestaurant; 9 pm; closed Mon & Sun.* **Accommodation:** *3 rooms, from £75.*

CHIPSTEAD, KENT 3–3B

The George & Dragon £43 333
39 High St TN13 2RW (01732) 779 019
A gourmet pub "with a good-sized garden for al freso dining"; it serves "wonderful" grub "from a versatile menu", and makes a "perfect lunchtime venue" in particular.
/ **Details:** *www.georgeanddragonchipstead.com; @georgechipstead; 9.30 pm, Sun 8.30 pm; no Amex.*

CHOBHAM, SURREY 3–3A

Stovell's £56 444
125 Windsor Rd GU24 8QS (01276) 858000
"A very good attempt at fine-ish dining" – Fernando & Kristy Stovell's ambitious two-year-old in a "lovely" contemporary conversion of a 16th-century farmhouse is "a gem in an area needing good restaurants", serving "creative" cuisine and "with 10/10 for presentation" too.
*/ **Details:** www.stovells.com; 9.30 pm; closed Mon, Sat L & Sun D.*

CHRISTCHURCH, DORSET 2–4C

The Jetty £54 545
95 Mudeford BH23 3NT (01202) 400950
*"In a stunning location overlooking the sea", Alex Aitken's contemporary-style venture continues to win praise for its "really good choice of super-fresh fish straight from the quay"; "superb puddings" too. / **Details:** www.thejetty.co.uk; @alexatthejetty; 9.45 pm, Sun 7.45 pm; SRA-71%.*

CHURCHILL, OXFORDSHIRE 2–1C

Chequers £48 444
Church Ln OX7 6NJ (01608) 659393
"In an area already "pretty well-served with good pubs", fans of this cosy classic hail it as "the hippest and most switched-on"; others feel it "suffers from its 'Chippy Set' reputation", however, or note "a slip in standards" of late.
*/ **Details:** www.thechequerschurchill.com; @TheChequersC; 10 pm; closed Sun D.*

CIRENCESTER, GLOUCESTERSHIRE 2–2C

Jesses Bistro £60 Ⓣ
14 Black Jack St GL7 2AA (01285) 641497
"Hidden away behind a butcher's shop", this "cosy" and "enthusiastic" town-centre bistro is tipped as much for its "good fish" as for its meat – "the simpler dishes are best".
*/ **Details:** www.jessesbistro.co.uk; @jessesbistro; 9.15 pm; closed Mon D & Sun.*

Made By Bob £45 432
The Cornhall 26 Market Pl GL7 2NY
(01285) 641818
This "fantastic deli" and restaurant is particularly rated for lunch, when it has a "great party atmosphere" – it's "not for the quiet shy recluse!"; "grab a seat at the kitchen bar to watch Bob prepare your meal".
*/ **Details:** www.foodmadebybob.com; 9.30 pm; closed Mon D, Tue D, Wed D, Sat D & Sun D.*

Soushi £34 Ⓣ
GL7 QA (01285) 641414
"An excellent Japanese restaurant", tipped not just for its food, but also for its "friendly" service; some al fresco tables too.
*/ **Details:** www.soushi.co.uk.*

CLACHAN, ARGYLL AND BUTE 9–3B

Loch Fyne Oyster Bar £49 334
PA26 8BL (01499) 600236
*"A great place to break a journey"; this "well-run" seafood destination and deli on a remote lochside – which inspired the national chain to which it is no longer related – pleases all who comment on it; the menu, though, is "less extensive than it used to be". / **Details:** www.lochfyne.com; 10m E of Inveraray on A83; 8 pm.*

CLAVERING, ESSEX 3–2B

The Cricketers £44 324
Wicken Rd CB11 4QT (01799) 550442
This "good, old-fashioned" north Essex pub (proprietor Jamie Oliver's dad) is "well known internationally thanks to the family name"... and "well known locally for the quality of the food".
*/ **Details:** www.thecricketers.co.uk; @CricketersThe; on B1038 between Newport & Buntingford; 9.30 pm; no Amex. **Accommodation:** 14 rooms, from £95.*

CLIFTON, CUMBRIA 8–3A

George & Dragon £47 333
CA10 2ER (01768) 865381
"Reliable, if a bit pricey" – this "above-average" gastroboozer is a "relaxing" sort of place, praised for its "friendly, youthful staff" and a "good basic menu supplemented daily with very interesting specials".
*/ **Details:** www.georgeanddragonclifton.co.uk; on the A6 in the village of Clifton; 9 pm.*
***Accommodation:** 12 rooms, from £95.*

CLIPSHAM, RUTLAND 6–4A

The Olive Branch £52 434
Main St LE15 7SH (01780) 410355
The stellar reputation of this "delightful old pub" precedes it, and most reports are indeed of "excellent" meals that are "always a treat"; perhaps unfairly, though, "slippage" from past best standards is something of a refrain.
*/ **Details:** www.theolivebranchpub.com; @theolivebranch; 2m E from A1 on B664; 9.30 pm, Sun 9 pm; no Amex. **Accommodation:** 6 rooms, from £135.*

CLITHEROE, LANCASHIRE 5–1B

The Assheton Arms £42 424
BB7 4BJ (01200) 441227
This newly refurbished pub in a "picturesque" village offers "excellent fish and seafood dishes" ("including a superb prawn cocktail"); service can be "a little slow", but this matters little if you are "sitting outside, savouring the view of Pendle Hill".
*/ **Details:** seafoodpubcompany.com/the-assheton-arms/.*

Inn at Whitewell **£52** 4 2 5
Forest of Bowland BB7 3AT (01200) 448222
"A stunning location in the Forest of Bowland" underpins the huge appeal of this "wonderfully romantic" inn; it also draws plenty of plaudits for its "good consistent fresh food", but service still has scope to "sharpen up its act".
*/ **Details:** www.innatwhitewell.com; 9.30 pm; bar open L & D, restaurant D only; no Amex.*
***Accommodation:** 23 rooms, from £120.*

CLYST HYDON, DEVON 1–3D

The Five Bells Inn **£46**
EX15 2NT (01844) 277288
The sort of place that's "brilliant for a Sunday lunch", this 16th-century village inn is tipped as "the best place in the area"; don't miss the "perfect" Scotch eggs!
*/ **Details:** www.fivebells.uk.com.*

CLYTHA, MONMOUTHSHIRE 2–1A

Clytha Arms **£49** 4 3 2
NP7 9BW (01873) 840206
"Wonderful" food (with mixed shellfish a highlight) makes this rural inn, long in the ownership of the same family, well worth seeking out.
*/ **Details:** www.clytha-arms.com; on Old Abergavenny to Raglan road; 9.30 pm; closed Mon L & Sun D.*
***Accommodation:** 4 rooms, from £80.*

COBHAM, SURREY 3–3A

La Capanna **£60** 4 3 4
48 High St KT11 3EF (01932) 862121
The menu ("not really Italian") may be a bit of a supporting attraction, but this "friendly" restaurant is still quite a crowd-pleaser, and its charming setting in a medieval building helps make it a top venue locally for a celebration.
*/ **Details:** www.lacapanna.co.uk; 9.30 pm; closed Mon & Sun D.*

COGGESHALL, ESSEX 3–2C

Baumann's Brasserie **£54** 3 2 4
4-6 Stoneham St CO6 1TT (01376) 561453
"Single-handedly keeping Coggeshall house prices at a premium!" – this veteran brasserie continues to please most reporters most of the time.
*/ **Details:** www.baumannsbrasserie.co.uk; @baumannsbrasserie; 9.30 pm, Fri & Sat 10 pm, Sun 9 pm; closed Mon & Tue.*

COLCHESTER, ESSEX 3–2C

The Lion **£41**
CO6 2PA (01787) 226823
"In an area where gastropubs are all serving the same thing", this "perfect local" stands out from the crowd; it's tipped for "fresh" pizza and a good atmosphere too.
*/ **Details:** www.theioncolchester.com.*

COLERNE, WILTSHIRE 2–2B

Lucknam Park
Luckham Park Hotel **£105** 3 3 2
SN14 8AZ (01225) 742777
In an "idyllic" park setting, this Palladian country house hotel impresses most (if not quite all) reporters with an all-round experience of the "highest quality", not least Hywel Jones's "outstanding" cuisine, and the "magnificent", "old-fashioned" surroundings.
*/ **Details:** www.lucknampark.co.uk; @LucknamPark; 6m NE of Bath; 10 pm; closed Mon, Tue–Sat D only, closed Sun D; jacket and/or tie; children: 5+ D & Sun L.*
***Accommodation:** 42 rooms, from £360.*

COLNE, LANCASHIRE 5–1B

Banny's Restaurant **£30** 4 5 2
1 Vivary Way BB8 9NW (01282) 856220
Part of the Boundary Mill Outlet, this "smart" modern venture is a "real family restaurant" with "genuinely friendly staff" who serve up "excellent" fish and chips "with alacrity!"
*/ **Details:** www.bannys.co.uk; 8.45 pm; no Amex.*

CONGLETON, CHESHIRE 5–2B

Pecks **£55** 3 3 3
Newcastle Rd CW12 4SB (01260) 275161
*"Still at the very top of their game after 25 years"; despite the somewhat "theatrical" presentation and "limited" evening menu (the 7-course "Dinner at 8"), this family-run fixture continues to impress – and "you can't fail to be enticed by the wonderful range of puddings". / **Details:** www.pecksrest.co.uk; @pecksrest; off A34; 8 pm; closed Mon & Sun D; booking essential.*

COOKHAM, BERKSHIRE 3–3A

Bel & The Dragon **£51**
High St SL6 9SQ (01628) 521263
It's the "fantastic" ambience of this large and lavishly furnished gastroboozer (part of a small chain) which makes it a tip worth knowing about; the food, though, is generally "tasty" and "well-prepared".
*/ **Details:** www.belandthedragon-cookham.co.uk; @BelDragon_R; 10 pm, Sun 9.30 pm.*

Maliks **£41** 5 2 3
High St SL6 9SF (01628) 520085
*The "area's top Indian" offers "original" dishes with a "real range of flavour", in a "cosy" beamed cottage that seems "even better after a recent interior revamp"; the Sunday buffet is "a winner" too. / **Details:** www.maliks.co.uk; from the M4, Junction 7 for A4 for Maidenhead; 11.30 pm, Sun 10.30 pm.*

The White Oak £41 333
The Pound SL6 9QE (01628) 523043
A "pleasantly decorated" village gastropub with a "lovely garden"; it remains "a little variable" on the food front, but its cuisine is never less than "good", and occasionally it's "excellent".
/ **Details:** *www.thewhiteoak.co.uk; 9.30 pm, Sun 8.30 pm.*

COPSTER GREEN, LANCASHIRE 5–1B

Yu And You £44 545
500 Longsight Rd BB1 9EU (01254) 247111
In the Ribble Valley, this former 'Ramsay's Best Restaurant' winner continues to draw plaudits for its "fantastic" Cantonese cuisine and "great" ambience; it "might be slightly on the expensive side", but everyone agrees that it is well worth it.
/ **Details:** *www.yuandyou.com; @yuandyou; off the A59 7 miles towards Clitheroe; 11 pm, Fri & Sat 2 am; D only, closed Mon; no Amex.*

CORSE LAWN, GLOUCESTERSHIRE 2–1B

Corse Lawn Hotel £51 433
GL19 4LZ (01452) 780771
"Never fails to please, like an old and trusted friend"; the "menu hasn't changed much over the years", but the Hine family's restaurant-with-rooms still offers some very good traditional fare (especially game); opt for the more atmospheric bistro or "better still, eat outside overlooking the pond".
/ **Details:** *www.corselawnhotel.com; @corselawn; 5m SW of Tewkesbury on B4211; 9.30 pm.* **Accommodation:** *18 rooms, from £120.*

CORSHAM, WILTSHIRE 2–2B

Methuen Arms £52 T
2 High St SN13 0HB (01249) 717060
Tipped as "one of the few places round here worth a return visit", a town-centre inn offering "consistent" cooking in "generous" portions.
/ **Details:** *www.themethuenarms.com; @MethuenArms; 10 pm.* **Accommodation:** *14 rooms, from £140.*

COWBRIDGE, VALE OF GLAMORGAN 1–1D

Bar 44 £13 444
44c High St CF71 7AG (01446) 776488
A "casual" tapas joint which makes "a brilliant place for 'spur-of-the-moment' dining"; it "continues to impress, evolve, and constantly change its offering" – "this year, the sherry and wine list seems to have gone up a considerable notch".
/ **Details:** *www.bar44.co.uk; @Bar44tapas; 9 pm, Fri-Sun 10 pm; closed Mon D; no Amex.*

COWER, ISLE OF WIGHT

Murrays £42 T
PO31 7AT (01983) 296233
Tipped as a good all-rounder, a "cosy" seafood restaurant which makes good use of "oysters from the Exe and lobsters from Bembridge"; perhaps unsurprisingly, it gets "very busy during Cowes Week"! / **Details:** *www.murrays.co.uk.*

CRANBROOK, KENT 3–4C

Apicius £57 542
23 Stone St TN17 3HF (01580) 714666
"A gem!"; "don't be put off by the spartan room" – Faith Hawkins & Timothy Johnson's remote village-restaurant offers "highly imaginative but not overworked" British cuisine that "delivers on taste and style". / **Details:** *www.restaurant-apicius.co.uk; 9 pm; closed Mon, Tue, Sat L & Sun D; no Amex; children: 8+.*

CRASTER, NORTHUMBERLAND 8–1B

Jolly Fisherman £38 334
NE66 3TR (01665) 576461
A seaside inn with "fantastic views", where the "kipper pate from the smokehouse opposite is great, and the crab sandwiches are legendary"; "new owners and a refurbishment", though, seem to "have led to a hike in prices".
/ **Details:** *www.thejollyfishermancraster.co.uk; near Dunstanburgh Castle; 9 pm; no Amex; no booking.*

CRAYKE, NORTH YORKSHIRE 5–1D

Durham Ox £48 433
Westway YO61 4TE (01347) 821506
"Always pleasant and relaxed", this famous inn attracts only positive reports, not least for a menu from which "all the dishes reach the same high standard". / **Details:** *www.thedurhamox.com; @thedurhamox; 9.30 pm, Sun 8.30 pm.*
Accommodation: *5 + 1 studio suite rooms, from £100.*

CREIGIAU, CARDIFF 2–2A

Caesars Arms £49 223
Cardiff Rd CF15 9NN (029) 2089 0486
This "popular pub-restaurant" is "still going strong", and it remains a "firm favourite" for most reporters, thanks to its "simple formula, well executed" (you pick out a piece of meat or fish, and how it's to be cooked); critics, though, can just find the whole experience "unremarkable".
/ **Details:** *www.caesarsarms.co.uk; beyond Creigiau, past the golf club; 10 pm; closed Sun D.*

CROMER, NORFOLK 6–3C

No1 £33 T
NR27 9HP (01263) 512316
"A quality new fish and chips restaurant from Galton Blackiston" (of Morston Hall fame), tipped for its "tasty" and "honest" food; now, if he could just get the "erratic" service under control...
/ **Details:** *www.no1cromer.com.*

Rocket House Cafe £40 444
NR27 9ET (01263) 519126
"A must-visit when in the area", and not just for its "fantastic" views – this bright all-day café is hailed in all reports for its "beautifully-cooked, simple food". / **Details:** *www.rockethousecafe.co.uk.*

CROSTHWAITE, LYTH VALLEY, CUMBRIA 7–4D

The Punch Bowl £50 455
LA8 8HR (01539) 568237
An "absolute gem"; it's not just the "idyllic" setting which has won renown for this "cosy" rural inn, but also its "friendly and attentive" service and "moreish" menu of "country fare"; if you decide to stay, bedrooms are "attractively furnished" too. / **Details:** *www.the-punchbowl.co.uk; @PunchbowlInn; off A5074 towards Bowness, turn right after Lyth Hotel; 9 pm.* **Accommodation:** *9 rooms, from £105.*

CROYDON, SURREY 3–3B

Albert's Table £53 434
49c South End CR0 1BF (020) 8680 2010
The "perhaps surprising" environs of South Croydon are the location for this "innovative" venture where "everything hits the spot"; "you might wonder if your car will survive unscathed, but the cooking is worth the anxiety!" / **Details:** *www.albertstable.co.uk; @albertstable; 10.30 pm; closed Mon & Sun D.*

McDermotts Fish & Chips £28 543
5-7 The Forestdale Shopping Centre Featherbed Ln CR0 9AS (020) 8651 1440
"Better fish 'n' chips than you'll ever find at the seaside" again win raves for Tony McDermott's "very welcoming" suburban chippy. / **Details:** *www.mcdermottsfishandchips.co.uk; 9.30 pm, Sat 9 pm; closed Mon & Sun.*

CRUDWELL, WILTSHIRE 2–2C

The Potting Shed £45 344
The St SN16 9EW (01666) 577833
"In an area with lots of competition", this "lovely country pub" still stands out, thanks to its "delicious food" and "great environment". / **Details:** *www.thepottingshedpub.com; @pottingshedpub; 9.30 pm, Sun 9 pm; no Amex.* **Accommodation:** *12 rooms, from £95.*

CUCKFIELD, WEST SUSSEX 3–4B

Ockenden Manor £81 222
Ockenden Ln RH17 5LD (01444) 416111
No one doubts this is a "pleasant" country house hotel, and it is consistently decently rated; prices aren't cheap however and the food is "good… but no more" – "how they got a Michelin star I don't know!" / **Details:** *www.hshotels.co.uk; 8.30 pm; no jeans or trainers.* **Accommodation:** *28 rooms, from £190.*

CUPAR, FIFE 9–3D

Ostlers Close £50 444
25 Bonnygate KY15 4BU (01334) 655574
"A gem in the wilderness"; this "intimate" and "friendly" town-centre veteran offers "delicious fare, with quite an emphasis on local sourcing"; it has quite a name locally – "even in August, most of the visitors seemed to be locals!" / **Details:** *www.ostlersclose.co.uk; centrally situated in the Howe of Fife; 9.30 pm; closed Sun & Mon, Tue-Fri D only, Sat L & D; children: 5+.*

The Peat Inn £86 442
KY15 5LH (01334) 840206
Geoffrey & Katherine Smeddles' famous country inn offers "first-class" but "unpretentious" cooking from ingredients sourced "as close to home as possible", plus some "interesting and knowledgeably-served" wines. / **Details:** *www.thepeatinn.co.uk; @thepeatinn; at junction of B940 & B941, SW of St Andrews; 9 pm; closed Mon & Sun.* **Accommodation:** *8 rooms, from £180.*

DALRY, NORTH AYRSHIRE 9–4B

Braidwoods £66 554
Drumastle Mill Cottage KA24 4LN (01294) 833544
"A real gem"; Keith & Nicola Braidwood "have been delivering an exceptionally consistent experience for more than a decade now", at this cosily converted croft; "whilst others come and go, they continue to deliver, but the menu is always being enlivened by innovations from their winter holiday!" / **Details:** *www.braidwoods.co.uk; 9 pm; closed Mon, Tue L & Sun; children: 12+ at D.*

DANEHILL, EAST SUSSEX 3–4B

Coach And Horses £50 343
School Ln RH17 7JF (01825) 740369
A rural boozer that combines a "great wine list and excellent bin offers" with a locally-sourced menu never short of "interesting specials"; "great that it's still run like a proper pub!". / **Details:** *www.coachandhorses.co; off A275; 9 pm, Fri-Sat 9.30 pm, Sun 3 pm; closed Sun D.*

DARSHAM, SUFFOLK 6–4D

Darsham Nurseries £31 443
IP17 3PW (01728) 667022
"A renovated nursery which serves really imaginative sharing plates in a tastefully shabby-chic space"; its reputation "has soared", thanks to its "great fresh approach to ingredients" – "you have to book". / **Details:** *www.darshamnurseries.co.uk.*

DARTMOUTH, DEVON 1–4D

RockFish
Seafood & Chips **£35** 4 2 3
8 South Embankment TQ6 9BH
(01803) 832800
"Massive queues but sit outside with a pint next door and that view of the harbour – bliss!"; this "extremely good" riverside chippy remains quite a crowd-pleaser.
*/ **Details:** www.rockfishdevon.co.uk/index.php; 9.30 pm.*

The Seahorse **£63** 5 4 4
5 South Embankment TQ6 9BH
(01803) 835147
Fans say "you'll not find a more perfect place to eat fish" than Mitch Tonks's "lovely and light" dining room, where "everything is done beautifully but without fuss" – not least "lovely fish, straight out of the sea", cooked "with great flair".
*/ **Details:** www.seahorserestaurant.co.uk; @SeahorseDevon; 9.30 pm; closed Mon & Sun.*

DATCHWORTH, HERTFORDSHIRE 3–2B

The Tilbury **£49** 4 3 4
Watton Rd SG3 6TB (01438) 815 550
*"A highly enjoyable country gastropub where Paul Bloxham's food is always a delight" – the consistency of upbeat reports this place inspires is truly impressive; "sumptuous Sunday lunches" a highlight. / **Details:** www.thetilbury.co.uk; 9 pm, Fri & Sat 9.30 pm; closed Mon & Sun D.*

DEAL, KENT 3–3D

Deal Hoy **£26**
CT14 6DU (01304) 363 972
A "friendly" nautical-style pub tipped for its "excellent, locally produced" patties from Kent coast chain The Burger Brothers.
*/ **Details:** www.shepherdneame.co.uk/pubs/deal/deal-hoy.*

Victuals & Company **£42** 4 4 3
CT14 6TA (01304) 374389
*This "very friendly" newcomer, in pedestrianised St George's Passage, has brought "London quality and prices" to this seaside town; it offers "inventive" menus (with daily specials), and is "really very good for lunch". / **Details:** www.victualsandco.com.*

DEDHAM, ESSEX 3–2C

Milsoms **£42** 2 3 4
Stratford Rd CO7 6HW (01206) 322795
"Yes, it's now part of Loch Fyne", but this Constable Country brasserie remains a decent choice for trippers, and with "attentive" service too; for overnighters, there is a "good hotel" attached.
*/ **Details:** www.milsomhotels.com; 9.30 pm, Fri & Sat 10 pm; no booking. **Accommodation:** 15 rooms, from £120.*

The Sun Inn **£45** 2 2 4
High St CO7 6DF (01206) 323351
*Reports on this Constable Country inn remain somewhat mixed, but were slightly more positive of late; as ever, the cooking and service can be a "trifle hit-and-miss", but the venue "usually pleases", and its "excellent" atmosphere and "delightful" surroundings can make for a "fun" experience overall. / **Details:** www.thesuninndedham.com; Fri & Sat 10 pm, 9.30 pm; no Amex. **Accommodation:** 7 rooms, from £110.*

Le Talbooth **£68** 4 4 5
Gun Hill CO7 6HP (01206) 323150
This classic Constable Country spot, recently refurbished for its 60th anniversary, enjoys a "picture-postcard setting" (especially "if you can get a table by the river"); all reports, say the food being turned out by new chef Andrew Hirst is "wonderful".
*/ **Details:** www.milsomhotels.com; @milsomhotels; 5m N of Colchester on A12, take B1029; 9 pm; closed Sun D; no jeans or trainers.*

DENHAM, BUCKINGHAMSHIRE 3–3A

Swan Inn **£47** 3 4 4
Village Rd UB9 5BH (01895) 832085
A "great pub in a beautiful little village", which inspires only positive reports for its "varied" menu (with "many vegetarian options") and "good, if pricey, wine list"; "lovely large beer garden" too.
*/ **Details:** www.swaninndenham.co.uk; 9.30 pm, Fri & Sat 10 pm.*

DERBY, DERBYSHIRE 5–3C

Anoki **£43** 4 3 3
First Floor, 129 London Rd DE1 2QN
(01332) 292888
A "very broad range of excellent dishes" is served "in spectacular style" at this city-centre Indian, the main dining room of which occupies a former Art Deco cinema; "the new downstairs bar area is much less stylish than the main room".
*/ **Details:** www.anokiderby.co.uk; 11.30 pm, Sun 9.30; D only.*

Cardamom Club **£49**
DE21 6DA (01332) 867 840
Near the cricket club, an "imposing" subcontinental restaurant tipped for its "carefully spiced" and "very nicely presented" dishes; atmosphere can be a bit elusive at quieter times.
*/ **Details:** www.cardamom-club.com.*

Darleys **£56** 4 5 4
Darley Abbey Mill DE22 1DZ (01332) 364987
"The best restaurant in Derby by far" – a "longtime favourite", part of an old mill, whose "lovely riverside

setting" is ideal "for a special occasion"; superlatives abound for its "beautiful presentation of quality food", and the "separate vegetarian menu is a big plus" too. / **Details:** www.darleys.com; 9 pm; closed Sun D; no Amex; children: 10+ Sat eve.

Ebi Sushi **£38** 5 4 2
Abbey St DE22 3SJ (01332) 265656
"Best sushi I have had in the UK!"; is it really so implausible you should find "great and authentic" Japanese food in a "not-so-beautiful part of Derby"? – not if you know there's a Toyota factory just down the road! / **Details:** 10.30 pm; D only, closed Mon & Sun; no Amex.

The Wonky Table **£45** 4 4 4
DE1 3NR (01332) 295000
"A nice intimate restaurant, offering a small but well executed menu" – all reports confirm that this city-centre 'café-bar-restaurant' is a "gem".
/ **Details:** www.wonkytable.co.uk.

DINTON, BUCKINGHAMSHIRE 2–3C

La Chouette **£50** 4 3 2
Westlington Grn HP17 8UW (01296) 747422
The "unique combination of cooking and insults" certainly makes it an experience to visit Freddie the "charismatic and opinionated" Belgian chef's "oddball" institution; delicious "classic meat and fish dishes are the order of the day" – "veggies look elsewhere". / **Details:** www.lachouette.co.uk; off A418 between Aylesbury & Thame; 9 pm; closed Sat L & Sun; no Amex.

DISLEY, CHESHIRE 5–2B

Sasso **£30** T
SK12 2AA (01663) 765 400
"Much improved under its new Italian ownership", the site formerly known as Conti's is tipped for "a good mix of traditional pasta and pizza dishes alongside some more interesting fish and meat options". / **Details:** www.sassorestaurant.com.

DITTISHAM, DEVON 1–4D

Anchor Stone Cafe **£25** T
TQ6 0EX (01803) 722 365
In a scenic village, this "cramped" former tea room is a top tip locally, thanks to its "exceptional location on the River Dart" and its "amazing" fish dishes; get a table on the terrace if you can.
/ **Details:** www.anchorstonecafe.co.uk.

DODDISCOMBSLEIGH, DEVON 1–3D

The NoBody Inn **£48** 3 3 4
EX6 7PS (01647) 252394
It's the extensive wine list – offering "seriously good value-for-money" – which is the "real star" of this country boozer; fans insist, though, that it also offers "the best pub food in Devon"!
/ **Details:** www.nobodyinn.co.uk; off A38 at Haldon Hill (signed Dunchidrock); 9 pm, Fri & Sat 9.30 pm; no Amex. **Accommodation:** 5 rooms, from £60.

DONHEAD ST ANDREW, WILTSHIRE 2–3C

The Forester **£43** 4 3 3
Lower St SP7 9EE (01747) 828038
"The best in the area"; this village gastroboozer continues to attract plaudits for its "very high standard of cuisine"; "nice people too".
/ **Details:** www.theforesterdonheadstandrew.co.uk; off A30; 9 pm; closed Sun D.

DORCHESTER, DORSET 2–4B

Sienna **£65** 5 5 4
36 High West St DT1 1UP (01305) 250022
Russell & Elena Brown's town-centre fixture remains "head and shoulders above the competition"; it's rather "snug", though... in fact, "with only around twenty covers it must be one of the smallest top-class restaurants in the country".
/ **Details:** www.siennarestaurant.co.uk; @siennadorset; 9 pm; closed Mon, Tue L & Sun; no Amex; children: 12+.

DORKING, SURREY 3–3A

The Pilgrim **£35** 3 3 3
Station Rd RH4 1HF (01306) 889951
This "hospitable" boozer defies its "poor location, near the railway station" to offer "super" food at "reasonable" prices; "well-kept ales" too.

Restaurant Two To Four **£54** 4 4 3
2-4 West St RH4 1BL (01306) 889923
"The perfect local"; with its "consistently lovely" food (and "interesting flavour combinations"), this "friendly" beamed venture, on the edge of the town, is an all-round hit. / **Details:** www.2to4.co.uk; @Two_FourDorking; 10 pm; closed Mon & Sun D.

DOUGLAS, ISLE OF MAN 7–4B

Tanroagan **£54** 4 4 3
9 Ridgeway St IM1 1EW (01624) 612 355
"The best restaurant on the Isle of Man", acclaimed in all reports for its "fabulous" fish and seafood in "generous" portions, and its "cheerful" service too; the Boatyard at Peel, same owners, is an "airier" destination with "the same great standards".
/ **Details:** www.tanroagan.co.uk; @Tanroagan_Rest; 9.30 pm; closed Sat L & Sun; no Amex.

DREWSTEIGNTON, DEVON 1–3C

The Old Inn **£66** 5 4 4
EX6 6QR (01647) 281 276
"The food is out of this world"; the inn presided over by ex-22 Mill Street chef Duncan Walker may offer a "slightly off-beat" menu, but his "always-excellent" standards seduce all who comment on it; "very good breakfasts" too. / **Details:** www.old-inn.co.uk; 9 pm;

closed Sun-Tue, Wed L, Thu L.; no Amex; children: 12+. **Accommodation:** *3 rooms, from £90.*

DUNDEE, CITY OF DUNDEE 9–3D

Rama Thai £34 T
DD1 3DR (01382) 223366
"Heavy wood carved furniture and low lighting" sets an "old school Thai" tone at this venue in the docklands area of the city; tipped for its "delicious" grub, it's also "a useful source of enjoyable veggie fare in a city – or is it country? – which doesn't cater too well for them".
/ **Details:** *www.rama-thai.co.uk.*

DUNVEGAN, HIGHLAND 9–2A

The Three Chimneys £79 445
Colbost IV55 8ZT (01470) 511258
Eddie and Shirley Spears' "secluded" and "very romantic" venture, in a former crofter's cottage by Loch Dunvegan, offers some "sublime" cuisine – not least "very fresh" seafood; there's admittedly the occasional critic, but most reporters feel it's "well worth the (very, very long) trip".
/ **Details:** *www.threechimneys.co.uk; 5m from Dunvegan Castle on B884 to Glendale; 9.45 pm; children: 8+.* **Accommodation:** *6 rooms, from £345.*

DURHAM, COUNTY DURHAM 8–3B

Bistro 21 £50 344
Aykley Heads Hs DH1 5TS (0191) 384 4354
"A lovely house", complete with courtyard, shelters this well-established "old favourite", just outside the city centre (part of Terry Laybourne's Newcastle-based empire); the seasonal cooking is "consistently good", and "you are always made to feel welcome".
/ **Details:** *www.bistrotwentyone.co.uk; @bistro_21; 10 pm; closed Sun D.*

The Crown at Mickleton £38 334
DL12 0JZ (01833) 640 381
A "picturesque" and "comfortable" country pub, attracting plaudits for its "very solid" food and "good" wines; get one of the right seats, and "the open kitchen adds theatre to the experience" too.
/ **Details:** *www.thecrownatmickleton.co.uk.*

Finbarr's £47 443
Flass Vale DH1 4BG (0191) 370 9999
"The best restaurant in Durham" – thanks to its "reliably good" food ("with contemporary touches") and "friendly and helpful staff", this smart but "tucked away" venture "has now thoroughly established itself".
/ **Details:** *www.finbarrsrestaurant.co.uk; 9.30 pm, Sun 9 pm.*

DUSTON, NORTHAMPTONSHIRE 2–1D

The Hopping Hare £42 T
NN5 6PF (01604) 580090
This small inn, on the city outskirts, is tipped for "substantial portions" of "good-quality" food that's "far better and more interesting than average pub grub"; "super vegetarian options" too.
/ **Details:** *www.hoppinghare.com.*

DYFED, PEMBROKESHIRE 4–4B

The Grove - Narberth £72 323
Molleston, Narberth SA67 8BX
(01834) 860915
This "impressive" country house hotel enjoys a "wonderful, secluded location"; most reports applaud the "excellence of its cooking" from "mainly local" sources, but service is a weak link, and "do people really want the whole fine dining thing on hols in Pembrokeshire?"
/ **Details:** *www.thegrove-narberth.co.uk/; 9 pm.*

EAST CHILTINGTON, EAST SUSSEX 3–4B

Jolly Sportsman £49 322
Chapel Ln BN7 3BA (01273) 890400
"Tricky to locate but worth the effort" – Bruce Wass's "very rural" inn offers a "tranquil" setting in which to enjoy "lots of local produce on the excellent menu, plus some interesting English wines"; one regular, though, complains of "portions getting smaller, prices higher!"
/ **Details:** *www.thejollysportsman.com; @JollySportsman1; NW of Lewes; 10 pm; closed Mon & Sun D; no Amex.*

EAST CHISENBURY, WILTSHIRE 2–3C

Red Lion £53 453
SN9 6AQ (01980) 671124
An ex-Chez Bruce team produce some "fantastic" food at this "tucked away village pub", which has "all the key elements that make dining out enjoyable"; important safety tip – "watch out for tanks on the surrounding roads"!
/ **Details:** *www.redlionfreehouse.com; @redlionfreehse; 8.45 pm mon-sat, 7.45 pm sun; no Amex.* **Accommodation:** *5 rooms, from £130.*

EAST CLANDON, SURREY 3–3A

Queen's Head £42 334
The Street GU4 7RY (01483) 222332
"A superb local"; this modernised village inn, in the Surrey Hills, is tipped for its "solid" British dishes, consistently realised to an "above-average" standard.
/ **Details:** *www.queensheadeastclandon.co.uk; @TheQueensPub; Mon-Thu 9 pm, Fri & Sat 9.30 pm, Sun 8 pm.*

EAST GRINSTEAD, WEST SUSSEX 3–4B

Gravetye Manor £95 225
Vowels Ln RH19 4LJ (01342) 810567
"Gardens to die for" provide a "beautiful" setting for this "wonderfully atmospheric" Elizabethan country house hotel of long standing; it came into new management in recent history and nowadays the food is "acceptable, but not stunning".
/ **Details:** *www.gravetyemanor.co.uk; @GravetyeManor; 2m outside Turner's Hill; 9.30 pm, Sun 9 pm; booking: max 8; children: 7+.*
Accommodation: *17 rooms, from £250.*

EAST HENDRED, OXFORDSHIRE 2–2D

The Eyston Arms £49 334
High St OX12 8JY (01235) 833320
"In a picture-perfect Oxfordshire village between Didcot and Wantage", a small pub offering a "wonderful creative menu" – "quite expensive, but what isn't in this part of the world?"
/ **Details:** *www.eystons.co.uk; 9 pm; closed Sun D.*

EAST LOOE, CORNWALL 1–4C

Trawlers £48 T
On The Quay PL13 1AH (01503) 263593
Tipped for its "fantastic" standards, a fish restaurant pre-eminent among many locally; "your fish probably came from the boat moored outside the restaurant window"… and many of the wines don't have to travel too far either.
/ **Details:** *www.trawlersrestaurant.co.uk; 9 pm; closed Sun D.*

EAST MOLESEY, SURREY 3–3A

Mezzet £33 554
43 Bridge Rd KT8 9ER (020) 89794088
"What a wonderful little neighbourhood spot" – this "fantastic" Lebanese offers "so much more than the usual shawarma and hummus", at "prices which are too low for the quality and presentation of the food!"; "the perfect complement to a trip to Hampton Court"! / **Details:** *www.mezzet.co.uk; 10 pm; closed Sun D.*

EAST WITTON, NORTH YORKSHIRE 8–4B

Blue Lion £46 223
DL8 4SN (01969) 624273
"Luxurious" but "authentic", this grand coaching inn is just the sort of place to enjoy, for example, "some of the best grouse around"; of late, however, the occasional reporter has found standards not quite being maintained.
/ **Details:** *www.thebluelion.co.uk; @bluelioninn; between Masham & Leyburn on A6108; 9.15 pm; no Amex.* **Accommodation:** *15 rooms, from £94.*

EASTBOURNE, EAST SUSSEX 3–4B

The Mirabelle
The Grand Hotel £63 454
King Edwards Pde BN21 4EQ (01323) 412345
"Service so good it's like Claridge's 30 years ago" helps make the restaurant of this "continental-style grand hotel" a rare – perhaps unique – venue to find by the English seaside; it offers "true fine dining" in "a wonderful anachronistic setting – like a G Bernard Shaw play, and all the better for it!"
/ **Details:** *www.grandeastbourne.com; 9.45 pm; closed Mon & Sun; jacket or tie required at D.*
Accommodation: *152 rooms, from £199.*

EASTON GREY, WILTSHIRE 2–2C

The Dining Room
Whatley Manor £104 443
SN16 0RB (01666) 822888
This "quintessentially English" country house hotel is a "special occasion place" par excellence, and Martin Bruge's dishes are "fabulous" – "the dining room is rather on the plain side, but the food more than makes up for it!"
/ **Details:** *www.whatleymanor.com; 8 miles from J17 on the M4, follow A429 towards Cirencester to Malmesbury on the B4040; 9.30 pm; D only, closed Mon-Tue; no jeans or trainers; children: 12+.*
Accommodation: *23 rooms, from £305.*

EDINBURGH, CITY OF EDINBURGH 9–4C

Angels With Bagpipes £52 T
343 High St, Royal Mile EH1 1PW
(0131) 2201111
Tipped as a handy lunchspot in the heart of Edinburgh, this "very busy" Royal Mile outpost of the Valvona & Crolla empire offers "interesting" Scottish dishes that can sometimes seem a touch pricey for what they are.
/ **Details:** *www.angelswithbagpipes.co.uk; @angelsfood; 9.45 pm.*

Bell's Diner £30 332
7 St Stephen St EH3 5EN (0131) 225 8116
"Great burgers" (plus the usual sides and old-style American desserts) continue to please the crowds at this fun and "good-value" retro haunt.
/ **Details:** *10 pm; closed weekday L & Sun L; no Amex.*

Bia Bistrot £36 T
EH10 5DP (0131) 452 8453
A top tip as a "great-value" destination – a Morningside bistro that's well worth seeking out.
/ **Details:** *www.biabistrot.co.uk.*

Café Marlayne £42 323
1 Thistle St EH2 1EN (0131) 226 2230
Thanks to its "solid and reliable cooking", this small New Town bistro (which looks rather like a "'70s tearoom") is "usually very busy"; there

Kitchin

Old Bakehouse

Timberyard

is also a well-reviewed outpost in Antigua Street.
/ ***Details:*** *www.cafemarlayne.com; 10 pm; no Amex.*

Le Café St-Honoré **£48** **334**
34 NW Thistle Street Ln EH2 1EA
(0131) 226 2211
"This Gallic charmer never waivers!"; this "secret gem" of a New Town bistro is "a perfect place for older romancing", and the "refined" cuisine it offers is realised to generally "reliable" standards too.
/ ***Details:*** *www.cafesthonore.com; @CafeStHonore; 10 pm.*

Calistoga Central **£43** Ⓣ
70 Rose St EH2 3DX (01312) 251233
Surprisingly "difficult to find" for somewhere so central, this "friendly" establishment serves "excellent-value" wines ("try a tasting if you can") which somewhat eclipse the diverse range of dishes.
/ ***Details:*** *www.calistoga.co.uk; 10 pm.*

The Castle Terrace **£77** **554**
33/35 Castle Ter EH1 2EL (0131) 229 1222
"A favourite with Scots and with tourists", and no wonder! – Tom Kitchin's "fantastic" dining room, by the Castle, hardly ever hits even the slightest duff note; the worst any reporter could come up with is that the interior is a touch "unimaginative".
/ ***Details:*** *www.castleterracerestaurant.com; 10 pm; closed Mon & Sun.*

Centotre **£48** Ⓣ
103 George St EH2 3ES (0131) 225 1550
In one of the New Town's most fashionable streets, an "impressive" former banking hall tipped as a useful (and always "busy") lunchtime rendezvous; fans hail the Italian cuisine as "authentic" whereas, to critics, it is just "hit-and-miss".
/ ***Details:*** *www.centotre.com; @centotre; 10 pm, Fri & Sat 11 pm, Sun 8 pm.*

Chaophraya **£50** Ⓣ
33 Castle St EH2 3DN (01312) 267614
Tipped for its "excellent" castle-view location (once the site of Oloroso, RIP), a Thai restaurant where the food is always "decent" or better.
/ ***Details:*** *www.chaophraya.co.uk; @ChaophrayaThai; On the 4th Floor; 10 pm.*

David Bann **£41** **233**
56-58 St Marys St EH1 1SX (0131) 556 5888
A veteran Old Town spot still hailed by loyal fans as a "great veggie", thanks to David Bann's "robust and well-flavoured" cuisine; the performance can be uneven though ("great starters, mains were a let-down") and critics say the food is "decent rather than top-end".
/ ***Details:*** *www.davidbann.com; 10 pm, Fri & Sat 10.30 pm.*

The Dogs **£39** **323**
110 Hanover St EH2 1DR (0131) 220 1208
"Quirky, fun and good value", this shabby-chic gastroboozer is a handy sort of place to know about, just off Princess Street.
/ ***Details:*** *www.thedogsonline.co.uk; 10 pm.*

The Dome **£47** **345**
14 George St EH2 2PF (0131) 624 8624
"The obvious place to meet for a meal in Edinburgh!" – a "timeless" former banking hall provides the "dramatic" and "uplifting" setting for this New Town rendezvous, and the cooking is often surprisingly "imaginative" too.
/ ***Details:*** *www.thedomeedinburgh.com; 10 pm.*

Enzo **£48** Ⓣ
8 Lister Sq EH3 9GL (0131) 229 4634
In the new Quartermile development, the Scottish capital's most ambitious (and probably most expensive) Italian to have opened for some time; is it worth it? – we look forward to the verdict of next year's survey.
/ ***Details:*** *www.enzo-edinburgh.co.uk.*

L' Escargot Blanc **£36** **344**
17 Queensferry St EH2 4QW (0131) 226 1890
"A gem… as long as you can make it up the steep steps!"; this "basic" Gallic bistro, in the New Town, is an "authentic" spot, and "reasonably priced" too, especially at lunch.
/ ***Details:*** *www.lescargotblanc.co.uk; 10 pm, Fri & Sat 10.30 pm; closed Sun.*

L'Escargot Bleu **£42** **344**
56 Broughton St EH1 3SA (0131) 557 1600
"A bourgeois bistro transported from France to the New Town"; its "consistent" cooking and notably "charming" service contribute much to its "authentic" appeal.
/ ***Details:*** *www.lescargotblanc.co.uk; 10 pm, Fri & Sat 10.30 pm; closed Sun; no Amex.*

Favorita **£45** **443**
325 Leith Walk EH6 8SA (0131) 554 2430
The Crolla family's "friendly and fun" Leith Walk venture offers top Italian fare including "superb (wood-fired) pizza"; with four home delivery outlets, it's "now branching out all through the city" too.
/ ***Details:*** *www.la-favorita.com; 11 pm.*

Field **£35** **343**
41 West Nicolson St EH8 9DB
(01316) 677010
"A great find"; opened in January 2013, this "cosy" little Southside restaurant is "rather cramped" for some tastes (the "poorly designed tables" don't help), "but the choice and quality of food is first-class", and it's "very well priced" to boot.
/ ***Details:*** *www.fieldrestaurant.co.uk; @Field_Edinburgh.*

Fishers in the City **£55** **333**
58 Thistle St EH2 1EN (0131) 225 5109
"A good variety of honest seafood" is the highlight

of the menu at this "reliable" New Town bistro, where a "very good-value lunch menu" is the top tip. / **Details:** *www.fishersbistros.co.uk; 10.30 pm.*

Galvin Brasserie de Luxe The Caledonian **£48** 222
Princes St EH1 2AB (0131) 222 8988
Still surprisingly mixed feedback on the Galvin brothers' Parisian-style brasserie in this famous hotel; fans say it's "less expensive and less ambitious than the (fine dining) Pompadour upstairs, but what it does it does very well"; critics, though, just find a "poor relation" to Baker Street – "very disappointing".
/ **Details:** *www.galvinbrasserie.com; @galvinbrasserie; 10 pm; booking: max 8 a la carte.*
Accommodation: *245 rooms, from £325.*

Gardener's Cottage **£42** 344
1 Royal Terrace Gdns, London Rd EH7 5DX (0131) 558 1221
This "extraordinary" spot, near the A1, has made quite a splash with its "unique" formula – "a beautifully crafted menu of fresh and seasonal produce", served in a "tiny but authentic" space; service is at communal tables, so the ambience "can rather depend on who you sit next to!"
/ **Details:** *www.thegardenerscottage.co; @gardenersctg; 10 pm; closed Tue & Wed.*

La Garrigue **£47** 333
31 Jeffrey St EH1 1DH (0131) 557 3032
"Everything you might hope to encounter in a relaxed but classy French bistro" – this Old Town favourite has "improved over the years", say its many fans, and offers rustic, family-style cooking alongside a "superb wine list, with wonderful Languedoc delights".
/ **Details:** *www.lagarrigue.co.uk; @lagarrigue; 9.30 pm.*

Henderson's **£34** 234
94 Hanover St EH2 1DR (0131) 225 2131
"No visit to Edinburgh is complete without eating at Henderson's!"; this "great veggie venue", located in the crypt of a New Town church, is "still as good as it was thirty years ago", say fans, thanks to its "attractive setting outside and in", and its "plentiful" self-service fare too.
/ **Details:** *www.hendersonsofedinburgh.co.uk; 10 pm; closed Sun D; no Amex.*

The Honours **£58** 454
58a, North Castle St EH2 3LU
(0131) 220 2513
"Five star food at four-star prices"; Martin Wishart's brassserie-style operation in the New Town is, on most accounts, a "superb" destination across the board – "fantastic for a business lunch or for impressing visitors".
/ **Details:** *www.thehonours.co.uk; @TheHonours; 10 pm; closed Mon & Sun.*

Karen's Unicorn **£32** 443
8b Aberecomby Pl EH3 6LB (01315) 566333
"Top Chinese!"; they inspire surprisingly few reports, but these New Town and Stockbridge spots attract consistent survey feedback for "smashing" food and "tip-top" service. / **Details:** *www.karensunicorn.com; 11 pm.*

The Kitchin **£69** 554
78 Commercial Quay EH6 6LX (0131) 555 1755
"Tom & Michaela Kitchin are still very hands-on and their restaurant is a credit to them!"; this "efficient" Leith operation provides "real fireworks" – "wow-factor cooking of the highest level, using the best of local ingredients, beautifully presented".
/ **Details:** *www.thekitchin.com; @TomKitchin; 9.30 pm; closed Mon & Sun; children: 5+.*

Mithas **£58** 543
7 Dock Pl EH6 6LU (0131) 554 0008
"A cut above the rest" – this smart Leith Indian, from the Khushi family, is acclaimed in all reports as a "quality" destination, where the menu offers "some wonderful surprises for the more adventurous diner". / **Details:** *www.mithas.co.uk; @mithasedinburgh; 10 pm; closed Mon; children: 8+.*

Mother India's Cafe **£33** 444
3-5 Infirmary St EH1 1LT (0131) 524 9801
"Does what it says on the tiffin tin!"; this "Indian tapas" joint was one of the pioneers of that concept long before it was trendy, and it still offers some "brilliant" and "subtle" dishes.
/ **Details:** *www.motherindiaglasgow.co.uk; Sun 10 pm, 10.30 pm, Fri & Sat 11 pm; no Amex.*

Mussel Inn **£43** 443
61-65 Rose St EH2 2NH (0131) 225 5979
"Noisy, great-value, good fun, and right in the heart of the city!" – this "basic" but "efficient" and "bustling" New Town stalwart has quite a fan club for its "great" seafood ("including, of course, mussels"). / **Details:** *www.mussel-inn.com; 9.50 pm.*

Number One Balmoral Hotel **£75** 544
1 Princes St EH2 2EQ (0131) 557 6727
"Consistently the best in Edinburgh", say fans – Jeff Bland's perhaps "unexpectedly fabulous" cuisine makes a visit to the basement dining room of the grandest hotel in town a "not-to-be-missed" experience; the wine-pairing menu attracts particular raves.
/ **Details:** *www.thebalmoralhotel.com; 10 pm; D only; no jeans or trainers.* **Accommodation:** *188 rooms, from £360.*

Ondine **£63** 433
2 George IV Bridge EH1 1AD (0131) 2261888
The setting within an office block off the Royal Mile may be "rather clinical", but on most accounts the

seafood dishes on offer are "worth saving up for"; that said, there were occasions this year when the cooking seemed "more competent than inspired". / **Details:** www.ondinerestaurant.co.uk; @OndineEdin; 10 pm; closed Sun; booking: max 8.

The Outsider **£43** 3 2 4
15-16 George IV Bridge EH1 1EE (0131) 226 3131
"Bright" and "busy", this Old Town brasserie (with Castle views) is tipped as a "popular lunch spot" with an "unusual and varied" menu; it also has its fans as a pre-theatre destination.
/ **Details:** 11 pm; no Amex; booking: max 12.

The Pompadour by Galvin The Caledonian **£82** 3 4 4
Princes St EH1 2AB (0131) 222 8975
The Galvin brothers' "lovely" Gallic dining room offers "fantastic views" and some "excellent food and wine", with the midweek set dinner menu "one of the top bargains" in the city; for the odd critic, though, standards are no more than "average-to-good". / **Details:** www.galvinrestaurants.com; @Galvin_Brothers; 10 pm; closed Mon & Sun.

Restaurant Mark Greenaway **£70** 4 2 3
67 North Castle St EH2 3LJ (0131) 557 0952
"A great new venue in a good location"; this New Town townhouse-restaurant impresses almost all reporters with its "innovative" and "cleverly presented" cuisine and "fabulous" wine list; service doesn't always quite measure up.
/ **Details:** markgreenaway.com.

Restaurant Martin Wishart **£92** 5 5 4
54 The Shore EH6 6RA (0131) 553 3557
"Consistently near perfection"; with its "wonderful" dishes and its "first-class" but "unobtrusive" service, this Leith fixture is, say fans, "the best restaurant in Scotland"; if there is a criticism, it is that the style can sometimes seem a little "stiff".
/ **Details:** www.martin-wishart.co.uk; @RMWLeith; 9.30 pm; closed Mon & Sun; no trainers.

Rhubarb Prestonfield Hotel **£76** 3 4 4
Priestfield Rd EH16 5UT (0131) 225 1333
There's no denying the "wonderful setting" of this "unique" and opulent country house dining room near the city; while it's not immune to the odd critique of "style over substance", fans say it's "one of the best", and the wine list "shows that the whole team truly understands food".
/ **Details:** www.prestonfield.com; 10 pm, Fri & Sat 11 pm; children: 12+ at D, none after 7pm.
Accommodation: 23 rooms, from £295.

Scran & Scallie **£41** 5 5 4
1 Comely Bank Rd EH4 1DT
(0131) 332 6281
"The best addition to the Edinburgh pub scene"; with its "fantastic" food and "friendly" and "efficient" service, Tom Kitchin's "buzzing" Stockbridge boozer is "certainly not your normal pub". / **Details:** scranandscallie.com/; @ScranandScallie; 10 pm.

The Stockbridge **£52** 5 5 4
54 St Stephen's St EH3 5AL (0131) 226 6766
With its "hearty yet imaginative" menu and "cosy" ambience, this picture-lined city-centre venture is, by all accounts, a "great little gem".
/ **Details:** www.thestockbridgerestaurant.co.uk; 9.30 pm; D only, closed Mon; children: 18+ after 8 pm.

Three Birds **£37** 4 5 4
EH10 4JD (0131) 229 3252
A "lovely" and "cheerful" small restaurant, in Bruntsfield, offering a menu that's "limited, in the positive sense", complemented by a good list of wines (many available by the glass).
/ **Details:** www.threebirds.co.uk.

Timberyard **£57** 4 4 5
10 Lady Lawson St EH3 9DS (01312) 211222
With its "postmodern industrial setting", this former costume store, near the Traverse Theatre, is now the "coolest" venue in town; sample its "imaginative" menu (strong on "unusual locally-foraged vegetables"), and then "relax with a post-prandial drink by the wood-burning stove".
/ **Details:** www.timberyard.co; @timberyard10; 9.30 pm; closed Mon & Sun.

Twenty Princes Street **£48** Ⓣ
EH2 2AN (0131) 652 7370
"An upstairs grill and smokehouse at the smart end of Princes Street"; tipped for its "lovely sunny location" and "quiet booths" – "a good place for business or a proper conversation".
/ **Details:** www.twnetyprincesstreet.co.uk.

21212 **£93** 4 4 4
3 Royal Ter EH7 5AB (0845) 222 1212
Critics may find the menu a trifle "weird" and "fussy", but the general verdict on Paul Kitching's cuisine is that "he deserves every award he is winning" for his Calton Hill townhouse – "prepare to be surprised and enjoy!".
/ **Details:** www.21212restaurant.co.uk; @paulk21212; 9.30 pm; closed Mon & Sun; children: 5+. **Accommodation:** 4 rooms, from £95.

Valvona & Crolla **£38** 2 2 3
19 Elm Row EH7 4AA (0131) 556 6066
Once Edinburgh's go-to foodie hang out, this café annex to the famous Italian deli and wine importer, on the way to Leith, attracts relatively little commentary nowadays; it can seem pricey, but fans praise its great simple fare, and "friendly" style.

/ **Details:** *www.valvonacrolla.com; 11.30 pm, Sun 6 pm.*

Wedgwood **£57** **553**
267 Canongate EH8 8BQ (0131) 558 8737
"A little gem, just off the tourist trap which is the Royal Mile"; thanks to the "unusual combinations of ingredients" and "ridiculously good-value lunch menus", Paul Wedgwood's cuisine attracts nothing but praise, even if it is slightly "let down by being served in a cramped and slightly sterile basement".
/ **Details:** *www.wedgwoodtherestaurant.co.uk; 10 pm.*

The Witchery by the Castle **£74** **125**
Castlehill, The Royal Mile EH1 2NF
(0131) 225 5613
Notwithstanding the "so sexy" Gothic setting, and "one of the best wine lists around", this famous landmark, by the Castle, has too often seemed to rest heavily "on its laurels" of late – for some reporters it's now just a "tourist trap".
/ **Details:** *www.thewitchery.com; @thewitchery; 11.30 pm.* **Accommodation:** *8 rooms, from £325.*

EGHAM, SURREY 3–3A

The Estate Grill Great Fosters Hotel **£61** Ⓣ
Stroude Rd TW20 9UR (01784) 433822
An impressive Elizabethan country house hotel, tipped for its "excellent" tasting menus, and an impressive all-round experience too.
/ **Details:** *www.greatfosters.co.uk; no jeans or trainers; booking: max 12.* **Accommodation:** *43 rooms, from £155.*

ELDERSFIELD, GLOUCESTERSHIRE 2–1B

The Butcher's Arms **£64** **554**
Lime St GL19 4NX (01452) 840 381
Despite being lauded by the tyre men, James & Elizabeth Winter's "idyllic and remote village pub" remains an "unaffected and charming" spot (complete with "locals at the bar with their dogs"), but there's no mistaking the "skilful and unusual" cooking coming from the kitchen; NB limited service hours, no under-10s.
/ **Details:** *www.thebutchersarms.net; 9 pm; closed Mon, Tue L, Wed L, Thu L & Sun D; children: 10+.*

ELLAND, WEST YORKSHIRE 5–1C

La Cachette **£49** **444**
31 Huddersfield Rd HX5 9AH
(01422) 378833
"For a special occasion, or an everyday visit", Jonathan Nichols's Gallic fixture remains well worth seeking out (not least for its "unusual and good-value wines and beers"); "the earlybird menu offers a good selection at a much reduced cost".
/ **Details:** *www.lacachette-elland.com; 9.30 pm, Fri & Sat 10 pm; closed Sun; no Amex.*

ELLEL, LANCASHIRE 5–1A

The Bay Horse **£45** Ⓣ
Bay Horse Ln LA2 0HR (01524) 791204
Close to the university, a top gastropub tip that's "popular with parents, students and staff"; for business discussions, there are some "slightly tucked away" tables too.
/ **Details:** *www.bayhorseinn.com; 9 pm, Sun 8 pm; closed Mon; no Amex.*

ELLON, ABERDEENSHIRE 9–2D

Eat on the Green **£64** Ⓣ
AB41 7RS (01651) 842337
Tipped for "marvellous" food that's "always reliable" – the well-established restaurant of Craig Wilkinson ('the kilted chef'), in a former inn.
/ **Details:** *www.eatonthegreen.co.uk.*

ELSLACK, NORTH YORKSHIRE 5–1B

The Tempest Arms **£42** **334**
BD23 3AY (01282) 842 450
"Our favourite place to eat, when we go back to our Yorkshire roots"... this "relaxing" inn offers a "good choice" of dishes, and in portions sufficient "to leave you comfortably replete".
/ **Details:** *www.tempestarms.co.uk; 9 pm, Fri & Sat 9.30 pm, Sun 7.30 pm.* **Accommodation:** *21 rooms, from £89.95.*

ELY, CAMBRIDGESHIRE 3–1B

Old Fire Engine House **£43** **354**
25 St Mary's St CB7 4ER (01353) 662582
The "traditional" and "home-cooked" cuisine may seem "on the simple side" nowadays, but that's how fans of this "delightful" city-centre institution (est 1968) seem to like it – "still the best place in Ely", they insist!
/ **Details:** *www.theoldfireenginehouse.co.uk; 9 pm; closed Sun D; no Amex.*

EMSWORTH, HAMPSHIRE 2–4D

Fat Olives **£49** **454**
30 South St PO10 7EH (01243) 377914
"Undeniably small" but "very civilised", the Murphy family's "friendly" venture, in an old house on the street leading down to the harbour, wins almost invariable praise for its "wonderfully prepared" and "beautifully presented" dishes, making "good use of local ingredients".
/ **Details:** *www.fatolives.co.uk; @fat_olives; 9.15 pm; closed Mon & Sun; no Amex; children: 8+, except Sat L.*

36 on the Quay **£81** **313**
47 South St PO10 7EG (01243) 375592
Ramon Farthing's harbour-side restaurant is pretty much defined by its long-held Michelin star, and some dishes (especially seafood) are indeed "exceptional"; critics feel you "pay through the

nose", though, and service is sometimes surprisingly "off-hand". / **Details:** www.36onthequay.co.uk; off A27 between Portsmouth & Chichester; 9 pm; closed Mon & Sun; no Amex. **Accommodation:** 5 (plus cottage) rooms, from £100.

EPPING, ESSEX 3–2B

Haywards Restaurant £55 543
CM16 4DZ (01992) 577350
"A new restaurant trying very hard to bring fine dining to this part of Essex" – run by a "talented husband-and-wife team", it's already hailed as offering "the best food for miles around"; "attentive" service too.
/ **Details:** www.haywardsrestaurant.co.uk.

EPWORTH, LINCOLNSHIRE 5–2D

Hatty's Tea Room £12 Ⓣ
DN9 1ET (01427) 875507
A "welcoming" café of recent vintage, which makes a "pleasant location for a cup of coffee and something to eat"; it's already tipped for food "of a very high standard", and supporters say it's going "from strength to strength".
/ **Details:** www.hattystearoom.co.uk.

ESHER, SURREY 3–3A

Good Earth £58 443
14-18 High St KT10 9RT (01372) 462489
"Still the best in the area"; this "fine dining Chinese" stalwart may be "a bit pricey", but few reporters seem to mind, given the "stunning" food.
/ **Details:** www.goodearthgroup.co.uk; 11.15 pm, Sun 10.45 pm; booking: max 12, Fri & Sat.

ETON, BERKSHIRE 3–3A

Gilbey's £43 244
82-83 High St SL4 6AF (01753) 854921
"Nicely situated" near the College, and with an "attractive" conservatory at the rear, this long-established restaurant is tipped as a "reliable" option with good wine; critics, though, say "the food looks good on the plate, but it's a bit bland".
/ **Details:** www.gilbeygroup.com; 5 min walk from Windsor Castle; 9.45 pm, Fri & Sat 10 pm.

EVERSHOT, DORSET 2–4B

Summer Lodge £68 333
DT2 0JR (01935) 482000
Ignore the slightly "stuffy" ambience, and there's an "entirely enjoyable" experience to be had at this cosy and very "pleasantly-located" country house hotel; gastronomic high point? – the "brilliant wine list", mixing "old classics with well-researched new finds". / **Details:** www.summerlodgehotel.co.uk; 12m NW of Dorchester on A37; 9.30 pm; no jeans or trainers. **Accommodation:** 24 rooms, from £235.

EXETER, DEVON 1–3D

The Digger's Rest £40 Ⓣ
EX5 1PQ (01395) 232375
In Woodbury Salterton, a few miles to the south east of the city, a "popular" country pub where "delicious" steaks are a top tip on a menu that brings some "imaginative" touches to an essentially "traditional" formula.
/ **Details:** www.diggersrest.co.uk.

The Lazy Toad £43 Ⓣ
EX5 5DP (01392) 841591
A "popular" but "unassuming" pub-restaurant, tipped for its "good local food"; highlights? – "puddings, and fresh cordials made from berries from the inn's own garden".
/ **Details:** www.thelazytoad.co.uk.

Michael Caines Royal Clarence Hotel £73 532
Cathedral Yd EX1 1HD (01392) 223 638
By all accounts, MC's central dining room with cathedral views has upped its game of late, to offer "food of Gidleigh Park-standard for a quarter of the price" – "I enjoyed it so much I returned the next day!"; lunch and early-bird menus offer top value.
/ **Details:** www.michaelcaines.com; @michaelcaines; 9.45 pm; closed Sun. **Accommodation:** 53 rooms, from £79.

Rendezvous £39 Ⓣ
EX1 1PE (01392) 270 222
Worth seeking out in Southernhay, a "lovely" wine bar, tipped not just for its "really first-class selection of wines", but also its "varied, good-quality and reasonably-priced" cooking.
/ **Details:** www.winebar10.co.uk.

EXTON, HAMPSHIRE 2–3D

Shoe Inn £41 Ⓣ
Shoe Ln SO32 3NT (01489) 877526
A top tip for "tasty food in an idyllic setting" in the Meon Valley – a "great small village pub", offering "real food, freshly prepared"; quiet garden too.
/ **Details:** www.theshoeinn.moonfruit.com.

EXTON, RUTLAND 5–3D

The Fox And Hounds £40 434
19 The Grn LE15 8AP (01572) 812403
"Worth it, if you can get a table…" – this ivy-clad coaching inn makes a "wonderful destination on a sunny day"; the pizzas and the "locally-sourced Rutland fare" are all very good too.
/ **Details:** www.foxandhoundsrutland.co.uk; 9 pm; closed Mon & Sun D; no Amex. **Accommodation:** 4 rooms, from £70.

FALMOUTH, CORNWALL 1–4B

The Cove Restaurant & Bar **£48** 5 4 4
Maenporth Beach TR11 5HN (01326) 251136
"Top-quality food, service and location" – all reports on this smart restaurant-with-terrace, overlooking Maenporth Beach, confirm that a visit here is a "delightful" experience.
/ **Details:** www.thecovemaenporth.co.uk.

Rick Stein's Fish & Chips **£37** ⓣ
Discovery Quay TR11 3XA (01841) 532700
By the National Maritime Museum (so "with easy parking!"), the TV chef's "posh" chippy is tipped for its "well cooked and tasty" fare ("including scallops"); "it's a lot cheaper to take out".
/ **Details:** www.rickstein.com; @TheSeafood; 9 pm; no Amex; no booking.

Wheelhouse **£38** 4 5 5
Upton Slip TR11 3DQ (01326) 318050
"A hard to find gem with limited opening hours, and a menu depending on what is landed by the fishermen each morning"; reports aren't numerous, but they do agree on one thing – "if only there were more places like this!" / **Details:** 9 pm; D only, closed Sun-Tue; no credit cards.

FARNBOROUGH, HAMPSHIRE 3–3A

Aviator **£45** 4 2 4
55 Farnborough Rd GU14 6EL
(01252) 555890
This smart hotel is still "Farnborough's best place to eat", with cooking, much of it "locally sourced", offering some lovely marriages of flavours; service, though, can be lacklustre.
/ **Details:** www.aviatorbytag.com.

FAVERSHAM, KENT 3–3C

Read's **£79** 5 5 4
Macknade Manor, Canterbury Rd ME13 8XE
(01795) 535344
David and Rona Pitchford have presided over this "very genteel" restaurant, now housed in a Georgian rectory, for over 35 years – "a perfect setting" for this "slightly 'old school' Kent" experience; service is "genuine", and the "excellent" cooking "takes old favourites and adds a hint of innovation".
/ **Details:** www.reads.com; 9.30 pm; closed Mon & Sun. **Accommodation:** 6 rooms, from £165.

FENCE, LANCASHIRE 5–1B

Fence Gate Inn **£43** ⓣ
Wheatley Lane Rd BB12 9EE (01282) 618101
Tipped for its "always reliably good food" – an old-fashioned inn that's especially worth knowing about in a rather thinly-provided for part of the world.
/ **Details:** www.fencegate.co.uk; @fencegateinn; 9 pm, Fri 9.30 pm, Sat 10 pm, Sun 8 pm; no Amex.

White Swan at Fence **£37** 5 4 4
BB12 9QA (01282) 611773
"Recently reopened, with a Northcote-trained chef at the helm", this rural inn is acclaimed as a "fantastic find" thanks to its "absolutely superb" seasonal cuisine, and a "lovely relaxed atmosphere" too. / **Details:** www.whiteswanatfence.co.uk.

FERRENSBY, NORTH YORKSHIRE 8–4B

General Tarleton **£49** 3 2 2
Boroughbridge Rd HG5 0PZ (01423) 340284
Just off the A1, this "smart" gastropub-with-rooms offers "new angles on traditional dishes" ("my rabbit came in half a dozen different forms"); for the odd critic, though, it's "nowhere near as good as the Angel at Hetton", chef-patron John Topham's former home. / **Details:** www.generaltarleton.co.uk; @generaltarleton; 2m from A1, J48 towards Knaresborough; 9.15 pm. **Accommodation:** 14 rooms, from £129.

FLAUNDEN, HERTFORDSHIRE 3–2A

The Bricklayers Arms **£51** 3 4 3
Hogpits Bottom HP3 0PH (01442) 833322
It may be "very difficult to find", but this "charming" country pub is "well worth the trip", thanks to its often "excellent" food (from the classics to "more cheffy dishes") and "exhaustive" wine list.
/ **Details:** www.bricklayersarms.com; @bricklayerspub; J18 off the M25, past Chorleywood; 9.30 pm, Sun 8.30 pm.

FLETCHING, EAST SUSSEX 3–4B

The Griffin Inn **£48** 2 2 4
TN22 3SS (01825) 722890
In its "pretty" village location, and with an "attractive" garden too, this "lovely" pub has many fans for its "high-quality" food and its "interesting" wine list too; reporters who insist it's "going downhill", though, are really becoming quite vociferous. / **Details:** www.thegriffininn.co.uk; off A272; 9.30 pm, Sun 9 pm. **Accommodation:** 13 rooms, from £85.

FOLKESTONE, KENT 3–4D

Rocksalt **£46** 2 3 5
4-5 Fishmarket CT19 6AA (01303) 212 070
"A panoramic view of Folkestone beach, plus a balcony for those who wish to dine outside" – the highpoint at Mark Sergeant's "entertaining" two-year-old; the cooking achieves an OK rating despite numerous gripes about "high-end London prices", and quite a few reporters "expected more, given the reputation".
/ **Details:** www.rocksaltfolkestone.co.uk; @rocksalt_kent; 10 pm; closed Sun D; no Amex. **Accommodation:** 4 rooms, from £85.

FONTHILL GIFFORD, WILTSHIRE 2–3C

Beckford Arms **£44** 3 4 4
SP3 6PX (01747) 870 385
A "posh country pub", which is "peaceful midweek, and invaded by Londoners at the weekend" – "if you have children and/or dogs and enjoy good food, you can't do better than this!"
/ **Details:** www.thebeckfordarms.co.uk; @beckfordarms; 9.30 pm, Sun 9 pm; no Amex.
Accommodation: 10 rooms, from £95.

FOREST GREEN, SURREY 3–3A

The Parrot Inn **£42** 3 3 4
RH5 5RZ (01306) 621339
The Gotto family's "picturesque inn on the green" is "well worth seeking out" for its "very good" (if "not particularly experimental") cooking; "pork and lamb comes from the owners' farm", and they also run a "great butcher and deli" next door. / **Details:** www.theparrot.co.uk; 10 pm; closed Sun D; no Amex.

FORMBY, MERSEYSIDE 5–2A

The Sparrowhawk **£40** 3 4 5
L37 0AB (01704) 882 350
A "new kid on the block", set in five acres of grounds, that's made a spectacular debut; "repeating the successful Brunning & Price gastropub formula", it's "as handy a destination for a snack as it is for a three-course meal".
/ **Details:** www.brunningandprice.co.uk/sparrowhawk/.

FORT WILLIAM, HIGHLAND 9–3B

Crannog **£57** 5 3 4
Town Pier PH33 6DB (01397) 705589
"Right at the top of Loch Linhe", an "outstanding" fish restaurant, on a pier over the water (they also run cruises) – not just "the freshest" seafood, but "fantastic" puddings too!
/ **Details:** www.crannog.net; @CrannogHighland; 0; no Amex.

FOWEY, CORNWALL 1–4B

The Q Restaurant
The Old Quay House **£56** ⓣ
28 Fore St PL23 1AQ (01726) 833302
It's not just the "lovely" setting, with views of the River Fowey, which make this boutique hotel dining room a top tip locally – the food is "interesting" and of "excellent quality".
/ **Details:** www.theoldquayhouse.com; @theoldquayhouse; 9 pm; children: 8+ at D. **Accommodation:** 11 rooms, from £190.

FRANKWELL, SHROPSHIRE 5–4A

The Glutton Club **£49** 4 3 3
166-167 SY3 8LG (01743) 361672
By the Welsh Bridge, a former pop-up that's "opening more frequently in response to demand", where a "talented young chef" dishes up many "inventive" and "delicious" dishes.
/ **Details:** www.gluttonclubrestaurant.com/.

FRESSINGFIELD, SUFFOLK 3–1D

The Fox & Goose **£47** 3 4 4
Church Rd IP21 5PB (01379) 586247
A large country pub whose reputation for "reasonably-priced fine dining" ensures it's "always pretty full"; reports, though, are a little up-and-down, and even fans may note the place as being "at its best when the owner is doing the cooking".
/ **Details:** www.foxandgoose.net; off A143; 8.45 pm, Fri & Sat 9 pm, Sun 8.15 pm; closed Mon; no Amex; children: 9+ at D.

FRILSHAM, BERKSHIRE 2–2D

The Pot Kiln **£51** 4 4 4
RG18 0XX (01635) 201366
"You'd be pushed to find an equal array of game elsewhere" (most notably "superb" venison) – highlight of this "really rural" and "beautifully-located" pub; good snacks in the huge garden, and pizza nights too. / **Details:** www.potkiln.org; between J12 and J13 of the M4; 9 pm, Sun 8.30 pm; closed Tue.

FRITHSDEN, HERTFORDSHIRE 3–2A

The Alford Arms **£48** 3 3 4
HP1 3DD (01442) 864480
A reputation as "a great country pub" precedes this "perfect local gastroboozer", which generates many reports; indeed, there's some feeling that "it'a bit too well-known nowadays", and perhaps "not quite as good as they think it is".
/ **Details:** www.alfordarmsfrithsden.co.uk; @alfordarmshp1; near Ashridge College and vineyard; 9.30 pm, Fri & Sat 10 pm; booking: max 12.

FROXFIELD, WILTSHIRE 2–2C

The Palm **£37** 5 4 4
Bath Rd SN8 3HT (01672) 871 818
"Worth travelling to the middle of nowhere for!" – this "glass oasis on the A4" attracts the most positive reviews for its "really interesting and excellent" menu, on which South Indian (and especially seafood) dishes are the highlight; it's a "smart" place too, with "great" service.
/ **Details:** www.thepalmindian.com.

GATESHEAD, TYNE AND WEAR 8–2B

Raval **£46** ⓣ
Church St, Gateshead Quays NE8 2AT
(0191) 4771700
"A hint of luxury and a definite effort to make this dining experience something special" – it's not just the "exceptionally good food" which makes this

Gamba

Stravaigin

Two Fat Ladies Buttery

popular Indian a top local tip; good views too.
*/ **Details:** www.ravalrestaurant.com; @ravalrestaurant; 11 pm; D only, closed Sun; no shorts.*

GERRARDS CROSS, BUCKINGHAMSHIRE 3–3A

Maliks **£43** 4 2 2
14 Oak End Way SL9 8BR (01753) 880888
*"Dependable, and a great curry!" – the spin-off of the celebrated Cookham tandoori offers "mostly standard dishes, but at a level above your usual curry house"; "I often bump into Heston on the way in…" / **Details:** www.maliks.co.uk; 10.45 pm.*

Three Oaks **£47** 4 4 4
Austenwood Ln SL9 8NL (01753) 899 016
A "top-notch gastropub serving the local market and beyond"; it has "stepped up a level" in the last year or two.
*/ **Details:** www.thethreeoaksgx.co.uk; 9.15 pm.*

GLASGOW, CITY OF GLASGOW 9–4C

Black Sheep Bistro **£42** Ⓣ
G20 7QD (0141) 333 1435
"A likeable local in a run-down area" – this "quirky" destination, near St George's Cross Subway station, is strongly tipped "for a relaxed and reasonably-priced meal".

Café Gandolfi **£44** 3 3 4
64 Albion St G1 1NY (0141) 552 6813
"The first place I head upon arrival in town!"; this characterful all-day Merchant City institution – a bright L-shaped room clad in wooden panelling – is a very "relaxed" sort of place, offering dependable food and quality wines "at a reasonable cost".
*/ **Details:** www.cafegandolfi.com; 11 pm; no booking, Sat.*

Cail Bruich **£49** Ⓣ
725 Great Western Road G12 8QX (01413) 346265
"Fast becoming a destination, and deservedly so", Chris Charalambous's ambitious West End restaurant continues to inspire only positive reports… but not as many as we would like.
*/ **Details:** www.cailbruichreatruants.co.uk; 9 pm; closed Mon.*

Crabshakk **£48** 5 4 4
Finnestone G3 8TD (0141) 334 6127
"THE place to eat fish in the West End"; this "buzzing" joint dishes up "sensational" produce that's "simply served to let its true quality shine through"; "good luck getting a seat without booking… and it's a tight squeeze even if you do!"
*/ **Details:** www.crabshakk.com; @CRABSHAKK; 10 pm; closed Mon; no Amex; booking: max 12.*

The Fish People Cafe **£46** 4 3 3
G5 8QF (0141) 429 8787
"Wonderful", "sensational", "amazing"… – reporters express only the highest satisfaction with the cooking at this "lively" and "welcoming" spot; "the only problem is the out-of-the-way location" – by Shields Road subway station.
*/ **Details:** www.thefishpeoplecafe.co.uk/.*

Gamba **£62** Ⓣ
225a West George St G2 2ND (0141) 572 0899
Fewer reports of late on a city-centre basement that has had quite a name for its fish and seafood in recent years; it's still tipped for its "competent" cooking, albeit "at a price", but there has been the odd gripe about "unexciting" fare of late.
*/ **Details:** www.gamba.co.uk; @Gamba_Glasgow; 10 pm; closed Sun L.*

Gandolfi Fish **£49** 5 4 3
84-86 Albion St G1 1NY (0141) 552 6813
*"An excellent fish restaurant in the heart of the Merchant City" – this "friendly" and "lively" spot, near to Café Gandolfi, is a creditable all-rounder, with "knowledgeable" service and "well-priced" wines. / **Details:** www.cafegandolfi.com; @cafegandolfi; 11.30 pm,.*

The Gannet **£41** 4 4 4
G3 8TB (0141) 2042081
"Great buzz, great food, great decor" – this new venture from chefs who perviously worked at the prestigious ABode hotel is already hailed for its well-realised flavours and presentation.
*/ **Details:** www.thegannetgla.com/.*

Malaga Tapas **£30** 4 4 3
G41 1PD (0141) 429 4604
*"Tucked away in Glasgow's Southside", this "authentic" tapas joint offers "a real taste of Spain"; it's a "cheap and cheerful" sort of place, where the lunchtime deals offer particularly "excellent value". / **Details:** www.malagatapas.co.uk.*

Mother India **£37** 4 4 3
28 Westminster Ter G3 7RU (0141) 221 1663
"Still the best in Glasgow" according to its fans, this "very special Indian" is a West End fixture known for its eclectic tapas-style dishes; "avoid the basement, and you'll enjoy the whole experience".
*/ **Details:** www.motherindiaglasgow.co.uk; 10.30 pm, Fri & Sat 11 pm, Sun 10 pm; Mon-Thu D only, Fri-Sun open L & D.*

La Parmigiana **£63** 4 4 4
447 Great Western Rd G12 8HH (0141) 334 0686
"Sometimes, old-fashioned is excellent!"; well into its fourth decade, this "tiny traditional Italian", on the borders of the West End, is a "real haven of tranquility", where "wonderful handmade pastas"

*are a highlight. / **Details:** www.laparmigiana.co.uk; 10 pm, Sun 6 pm.*

Piece **£11** Ⓣ
G4 9SS (0141) 2217975
"Easily the best sandwich joints in town"; one of a small chain tipped for "consistently excellent" sarnies, and in a "wide variety of options" too.

Rogano **£61** 4 4 4
11 Exchange Pl G1 3AN (0141) 248 4055
"Simply another world" – this "treasure" of an "Art Deco institution", in the city centre, continues to please all reporters with its splendid interior (by the people who did the Queen Mary) and "seafood platters to die for"; "a good cocktail menu helps reinforce the historic vibe".
*/ **Details:** www.roganoglasgow.com; @roganoglagow; 10.30 pm.*

Shandon Belles **£32** Ⓣ
G3 8UF (0141) 221 8188
The bistro-basement of the Two Fat Ladies at the Buttery (see also), tipped in its own right as a "reliable" destination offering "great food at reasonable prices".
*/ **Details:** www.twofatladiesrestaurant.com/shandonbelles.*

Shish Mahal **£40** 4 4 4
66-68 Park Rd G4 9JF (0141) 334 7899
A "longstanding favourite", near Kelvinbridge Underground, this "extremely friendly and helpful" establishment is a "legend" – it was here, it is claimed, that chicken tikka masala first came into being nearly 50 years ago!
*/ **Details:** www.shishmahal.co.uk; 11 pm; closed Sun L.*

Stravaigin **£50** 4 2 4
28 Gibson St G12 8NX (0141) 334 2665
"If you want to experience the best of Glasgow's West End, and be in an atmosphere of great humour, bonhomie and conviviality, this is the place to go" – Colin Clydesdale's bar (upstairs)/restaurant (downstairs) continues to please, not least with dishes displaying a "unique Scottish twist".
*/ **Details:** www.stravaigin.co.uk; @straivaiging12; 11 pm; closed weekday L; no Amex.*

Two Fat Ladies at The Buttery **£60** 3 4 4
652 Argyle St G3 8UF (0141) 221 8188
This "very pleasant" outpost of the popular local seafood mini-chain is housed in a characterful Victorian building near the SECC that's long been one of the city's plusher destinations; a typical food report? – "all to a high standard, although nothing stood out".
*/ **Details:** www.twofatladiesrestaurant.com; 10 pm, Sun 9 pm.*

Ubiquitous Chip **£60** 4 5 5
12 Ashton Ln G12 8SJ (0141) 334 5007
"A great Glasgow institution"; this "buzzing" West End venue, established in 1971, has inspired very consistent feedback of late – even a reporter who notes that the Scottish cuisine "doesn't really move with the times" concedes it's "always solid", and the list of wines and whiskies is "biblical".
*/ **Details:** www.ubiquitouschip.co.uk; 11 pm.*

Wee Lochan **£39** Ⓣ
G11 7HT (0141) 338 6606
Tipped especially for its "good fresh fish dishes", a "very reliable" all-day operation in Broomhill, where "everything is cooked to order".
*/ **Details:** www.an-lochan.com.*

GODALMING, SURREY 3–3A

La Luna **£55** 4 5 2
10-14 Wharf St GU7 1NN (01483) 414155
You get "a marvellous welcome" at this "wonderful" and "creative" commuter belt favourite, which offers "a modern angle on Italian cooking", ably supported by a "wide and interesting" wine list.
*/ **Details:** www.lalunarestaurant.co.uk; 10 pm; no Amex.*

GODSHILL, ISLE OF WIGHT 2–4D

The Taverners **£38** 4 4 3
High St PO38 3HZ (01983) 840 707
"A 'pub and eating house', in a bustling village in the middle of the Isle of Wight"; it's "justifiably popular with locals and visitors", thanks to the good use its menu make of "fantastically fresh" produce, and the "first-rate" service too; "book well ahead".
*/ **Details:** www.thetavernersgodshill.co.uk; 9 pm, Fri & Sat 9.30 pm; closed Sun D.*

GOLDSBOROUGH, NORTH YORKSHIRE 8–3D

The Fox And Hounds Inn **£59** Ⓣ
YO21 3RX (01947) 893372
Again a dearth of reports on chef Jason Davies's hidden-away country inn, but it is again tipped for its very high standards overall.
*/ **Details:** www.foxandhoundsgoldsborough.co.uk; 8.30 pm; D only, closed Sun-Tue; no Amex.*

GORING-ON-THAMES, BERKSHIRE 2–2D

Leatherne Bottel (Rossini at) **£61** 3 2 5
Bridleway RG8 0HS (01491) 872667
*"Nothing beats the Thames-side alfresco lunches" at this riverside venture, whose outside tables are heaven when the sun shines; after numerous incarnations, the culinary style is nowadays Italian, with weekday set menus coming especially recommended. / **Details:** www.leathernebottel.co.uk; 9 pm; closed Sun D; children: 10+ for D.*

GRASMERE, CUMBRIA 7–3D

The Jumble Room £47 334
Langdale Rd LA22 9SU (01539) 435188
"Small", "quirky" and "idiosyncratic", this is a restaurant which has long pleased reporters with its "out-of-the-ordinary" approach; have prices crept up a little though? – it seems more "pricey".
*/ **Details:** www.thejumbleroom.co.uk; 9.30 pm; closed Mon, Tue, Wed L & Thu L. **Accommodation:** 3 rooms, from £180.*

GRASSINGTON, NORTH YORKSHIRE 8–4B

The Grassington House Hotel £42 544
5 The Sq BD23 5AQ (01756) 752406
"Great food in a lovely Dales village"; the Rudden family's "friendly" dining room is the sort of place where the food "pleases the eye as much as the palate" – in short, quite a "gem".
*/ **Details:** www.grassingtonhousehotel.co.uk; 9.30 pm, Sun 7.30 pm. **Accommodation:** 9 rooms, from £110.*

GREAT GONERBY, LINCOLNSHIRE 5–3D

Harry's Place £82 552
17 High St NG31 8JS (01476) 561780
*"It should be on everyone's bucket list!"; Harry & Caroline Hallam's "unique" 10-seat venture "never fails to delight", thanks to his "exquisite French-based cooking" and her "exceptional attention to detail"; of necessity though, the atmosphere is "rather dependent on who else is dining that day". / **Details:** on B1174 1m N of Grantham; 8.30 pm; closed Mon & Sun; no Amex; booking essential; children: 5+.*

GREAT MILTON, OXFORDSHIRE 2–2D

Le Manoir aux Quat' Saisons £190 554
Church Rd OX44 7PD (01844) 278881
"Worth the 300 mile round trip!"; for "spectacular" food in a "stunning" setting, Raymond Blanc's "impeccable" country house hotel and dining room offers "a sublime experience" that's "worth pushing the boat out for"; "make sure you leave time to explore the gardens before dinner!"
*/ **Details:** www.manoir.com; @lemanoir; from M40, J7 take A329 towards Wallingford; 9.15 pm; booking: max 12. **Accommodation:** 32 rooms, from £555.*

GREAT MISSENDEN, BUCKINGHAMSHIRE 3–2A

The Nags Head £53 324
London Rd HP16 0DG (01494) 862200
"A welcoming country pub, doing very good food" – this is the sort of 'plain vanilla' gastroboozer that makes a "nice Sunday lunch venue".
*/ **Details:** www.nagsheadbucks.com; @nagsheadhotel; off the A413; 9.30 pm, Sun 8.30 pm.*
***Accommodation:** 5 rooms, from £95.*

GREETHAM, RUTLAND 5–3D

The Wheatsheaf £40 444
Stretton Rd LE15 7NP (01572) 812325
*"Carol is a fine chef, and wine enthusiast Scott a natural host" – no wonder this village gastroboozer is proclaimed "a gem and a joy", or that it gets "very busy" either. / **Details:** 9 pm; closed Sun D.*

GRESFORD, WREXHAM 5–3A

Pant-yr-Ochain £46 344
Old Wrexham Rd LL12 8TY (01978) 853525
This "club-like" manor house (part of the Brunning & Price gastropub chain) comes complete with its own small lake! – its "comfortable" and "friendly" charms win praise from all who comment on it.
*/ **Details:** www.brunningandprice.co.uk/pantyrochain; 1m N of Wrexham; 9.30 pm, Sun 9 pm.*

GRINDLETON, LANCASHIRE 5–1B

The Duke Of York Inn £47 443
Clitheroe BB7 4QR (01200) 441266
*"Yet another well-established Ribble Valley star" – a gastropub offering "solid, reliable, high-quality cooking at reasonable prices", and "lovely views" too. / **Details:** www.dukeofyorkgrindleton.com; 9 pm, Sun 7.30 pm; closed Mon; no Amex.*

GUERNSEY, CHANNEL ISLANDS

Da Nello £46 443
46 Lower Pollet St GY1 1WF (01481) 721552
"Still a classic after all these years"; this St Peter Port trattoria hides sizeable premises behind a small shopfront, and continues to please with "delicious" food; it's "great for larger parties".
*/ **Details:** www.danello.gg; 10 pm.*

Le Petit Bistro £52 Ⓣ
56 Le Pollet GY1 1WF (01481) 725055
For a "great menu of Gallic classics", you're unlikely to do much better than this "typique" St Peter Port bistro, tipped for its "always-excellent" food; "the café does perfect breakfasts" too.
*/ **Details:** www.petitbistro.co.uk; @PetitBistroGsy; 10 pm, 10.30 pm Fri & Sat; closed Sun.*

GUILDFORD, SURREY 3–3A

Britten's £49 443
GU1 3RT (01483) 302888
Opened by former MasterChef competitor Dan Britten in November 2013, this "great new independent", in the city-centre, is already attracting plaudits for its "interesting" modern British cuisine and "great ambience".
*/ **Details:** www.brittensrestaurant.com.*

Cau £48 [4][4][4]
274 High St GU1 3JL (01483) 459777
"On a good day, the steaks are to die for", at this "fun and vibrant" ("noisy and bustling") Argentinian steakhouse; "good chips and wine" too.
/ **Details:** *www.caurestaurants.com; @CAUrestaurants; 11 pm, Sun 10.30 pm.*

Rumwong £38 [3][3][2]
18-20 London Rd GU1 2AF (01483) 536092
A Thai veteran (est 1978) which is "still the best in Guildford", say fans, thanks to its "consistently delicious" food and "traditional surroundings"; "book ahead as it's always crowded".
/ **Details:** *www.rumwong.co.uk; 10.30 pm; closed Mon; no Amex.*

The Thai Terrace £41 [4][4][4]
Castle Car Pk, Sydenham Rd GU1 3RW
(01483) 503350
Implausibly located on top of a multi-storey car park, this lively oriental restaurant (with large terrace for drinks) offers "great views of Guildford"; perhaps even more surprisingly, both food and service are consistently very highly rated!
/ **Details:** *10.30 pm; closed Sun; no Amex.*

GULLANE, EAST LOTHIAN 9–4D

Chez Roux
Greywalls Hotel £59 [4][5][4]
EH31 2EG (01620) 842144
An outpost of the Roux empire in a Lutyens house – a marriage that makes this "a classy place to eat high-quality food in beautiful surroundings"; highlights include "the perfect weekend lunch".
/ **Details:** *www.greywalls.co.uk; 10 pm; jacket at D.*
Accommodation: *23 rooms, from £260.*

La Potinière £53 (T)
Main St EH31 2AA (01620) 843214
A continuing dearth of reports on Keith Marley & Mary Runciman's small outfit which, we suspect, may deserve more prominent billing; perhaps the reason is that the same reporter who tips the place for cuisine that's "better than good" also notes "a certain lack of atmosphere".
/ **Details:** *www.lapotiniere.co.uk; 20m SE of Edinburgh, off A198; 8.30 pm; closed Mon, Tue & Sun D; no Amex; no jeans or trainers.*

GWITHIAN TOWANS, CORNWALL 1–4A

Godrevy Beach Cafe £25 (T)
TR27 5ED (01736) 757999
An award-winning modern building whose balcony offers "one of the best views in Cornwall"; it is tipped for its "breakfast, teas, coffees and full meals", all "freshly cooked in huge portions".
/ **Details:** *www.godrevycafe.co.uk.*

HALE, CHESHIRE 5–2B

Earle £49 [2][2][2]
4 Cecil Rd WA15 9PA (0161) 929 8869
"A local favourite" that attracts mixed reports for its cooking; on the plus side, it's "reliable and friendly", and "good for friends and family", but there's a general feeling that the "menu needs revamping" – indeed, for a Simon Rimmer venture, sceptics feel it's "no great shakes".
/ **Details:** *earlebysimonrimmer.com; @EarleHale; 9.30 pm, Sun 8 pm; closed Mon L.*

HALIFAX, WEST YORKSHIRE 5–1C

Design House £41 [3][2][2]
Dean Clough HX3 5AX (01422) 383242
A "brilliant" tasting menu wins particular praise for these dining facilities of a former mill (and it does "excellent" early-bird menus too); it can, though, suffer from "a few inconsistencies".
/ **Details:** *www.designhouserestaurant.co.uk; from Halifax follow signs to Dean Clough Mills; 9.30 pm; closed Sat L & Sun.*

Ricci's Place £33 [4][4][3]
4 Crossley Hs, Crossley St HX1 1UG
(01422) 410203
"A trendy tapas bar with excellent wine and a wide choice of dishes, including top desserts" – this grandly housed all-day operation continues to please all who comment on it.
/ **Details:** *www.riccis-place.co.uk; @riccisplaceltd; 9 pm; closed Sun; no Amex.*

Shibden Mill Inn £53 [4][4][4]
Shibden Mill Fold HX3 7UL (01422) 365840
"Dark and cluttered", and with log fires in winter, this "friendly" inn makes a "cosy" destination to enjoy some "imaginative" dishes made from local produce; for the summer, there's a large terrace.
/ **Details:** *www.shibdenmillinn.com; @ShibdenMill; off the A58, Leeds/Bradford road; 9 pm, Fri & Sat 9.30 pm, Sun 7.30 pm.* **Accommodation:** *11 rooms, from £117.*

HAMBLETON, RUTLAND 5–4D

Finch's Arms £44 [3][2][4]
Oakham Rd LE15 8TL (01572) 756575
The "beautiful" location, overlooking Rutland Water, makes this rustic inn a "great choice for a romantic meal"; the food can be pretty good too, but it's not inexpensive, and commentary on all aspects of the operation is a little up-and-down.
/ **Details:** *www.finchsarms.co.uk; 9.30 pm, Sun 8 pm.*
Accommodation: *10 rooms, from £100.*

Hambleton Hall £79 [5][4][5]
LE15 8TH (01572) 756991
The complete country house dining package doesn't come much better than at Tim Hart's "truly unforgettable" house, with its "lovely situation

overlooking Rutland Water"; Aaron Patterson's "solidly classical" cooking is "extraordinarily consistent" and matched by "terrific" wines, "perfectly pitched" service and "beautiful" decor.
*/ **Details:** www.hambletonhall.com; @hambleton_hall; near Rutland Water; 9.30 pm; children: 5+.*
***Accommodation:** 17 rooms, from £265.*

HARDWICK, CAMBRIDGESHIRE 3–1B

The Blue Lion £52 Ⓣ
74 Main St CB23 7QU (01954) 210328
A charming olde-worlde inn, tipped not just for its "well-executed and imaginative" dishes, but also for its "cheaper pub classics" too.
*/ **Details:** www.bluelionhardwick.co.uk; @bluelionhardwic; 9 pm, Fri & Sat 9.30, Sun 8 pm; no Amex.*

HAROME, NORTH YORKSHIRE 8–4C

The Pheasant Hotel £59 454
YO62 5JG (01439) 771241
Expect a "typical Yorkshire welcome" at this "well-organised but laid-back hotel", full of "log fires, beams and deep sofas"; it offers "beautifully presented" cuisine, and is arguably (even) "better and more comfortable" than its famous nearby parent, the Star Inn.
*/ **Details:** www.thepheasanthotel.com; 9 pm; no Amex. **Accommodation:** 15 rooms, from £155.*

The Star Inn £62 445
YO62 5JE (01439) 770397
Andrew Pern's cooking – "very hearty" and "seasonal", and using many foraged ingredients – is "on top form", according to the many fans of this "storybook" country pub, in the North Yorks moors; there are refuseniks, though, who find it "hyped" and too "expensive".
*/ **Details:** www.thestaratharome.co.uk; 3m SE of Helmsley off A170; 9.30 pm, Sun 6 pm; closed Mon L & Sun D; no Amex. **Accommodation:** 8 rooms, from £150.*

HARROGATE, NORTH YORKSHIRE 5–1C

Baltzersens £30 Ⓣ
HG1 1PU (01423) 202363
*A sleek and woody Scandi café, tipped for its "superb" lunch plates and "delicious" bakes; by night, after a quick turnaround, it re-opens as Norse, serving more ambitious Noma-inspired fare. / **Details:** www.baltzersens.co.uk.*

Bettys £46 345
1 Parliament St HG1 2QU (01423) 814070
"THE quintessential tearoom" is "a throwback worth queuing for" and definitely "not to be missed"; go for coffee or afternoon tea, though – lunches can be "slightly disappointing".
*/ **Details:** www.bettysandtaylors.co.uk; 9 pm; no Amex; no booking.*

Drum & Monkey £45 444
5 Montpellier Gdns HG1 2TF (01423) 502650
"Back to best past standards under new ownership", this long-established seafood specialist wins consistent praise for its "varied and innovative" menu, and its "consistent quality"; "especially good at lunch".
*/ **Details:** www.drumandmonkey.co.uk; 10 pm; closed Sun; no Amex; booking: max 10.*

Graveley's Fish & Chip Restaurant £40 542
8-12 Cheltenham Pde HG1 1DB (01423) 507093
*"Like stepping back to the '50s" – a "longstanding favourite", offering some of the "best fish in the county", and proper "Yorkshire service" too; their other chippy on Elland Road is also "well worth the queue". / **Details:** www.graveleysofharrogate.com; 9 pm, Fri & Sat 10 pm, Sun 8 pm.*

Mirabelle £48 454
28a, Swan Rd HG1 2SE (01423) 565551
"An excellent dining experience in a town with so many good restaurants" – Lionel Strub's comfortable basement venture garners consistent praise for its "authentic French cooking" (and not least its "very generous" tasting menu).
*/ **Details:** www.mirabellerestaurant.co.uk; @mirabellesHG1; 9.30 pm; closed Mon L & Sun.*

Orchid £43 554
28 Swan Rd HG1 2SE (01423) 560425
"The best food in town" – with "culinary delights from China, Indonesia, Japan, Korea, Malaysia…" – win adulatory reviews for this "deservedly always-packed" dining room; "the superb all-you-can-eat lunch is the stuff of local legend".
*/ **Details:** www.orchidrestaurant.co.uk; 10 pm; closed Sat L. **Accommodation:** 28 rooms, from £115.*

Quantro £46 334
3 Royal Pde HG1 2SZ (01423) 503034
"A Harrogate stalwart now back to its best" – this "civilised", "small" town-centre operation offers "superb value in a town where competition is keen" – lunch in particular is "the best deal ever".
*/ **Details:** www.quantro.co.uk; @quantroHG1; 10 pm, Sat 10 pm; closed Sun; children: 4+ at D.*

Sasso £44 333
8-10 Princes Sq HG1 1LX (01423) 508 838
"One of the few non-chain Italians hereabouts", this popular spot inspires surprisingly divergent views, which balance out somewhere round "reliable" all-round.
*/ **Details:** www.sassorestaurant.co.uk.*

Van Zeller £73 431
8 Montpellier St HG1 2TQ (01423) 508762
Tom Van Zeller serves up some "outstanding" modern cuisine at this "consistently good" venture in the 'Montpellier Quarter'; it's a shame, however,

that his "innovative" food is "let down by the room". / **Details:** www.vanzellerrestaurants.co.uk; 9.30 pm; closed Mon & Sun.

HARROW, GREATER LONDON 3–3A

Incanto
The Old Post Office £50 443
41 High St, Harrow On The Hill HA1 3HT
(020) 8426 6767
"Worth a detour", this is a "great local Italian" which transcends the genre, offering "ambitious" and "interesting" cooking (albeit at "West End prices"), plus an "interesting" wine list which includes some "really good organics".
/ **Details:** www.incanto.co.uk; @incantoharrow; 10.30 pm; closed Mon & Sun D.

HARTSHEAD, WEST YORKSHIRE 5–1C

The Gray Ox Inn £43 Ⓣ
15 Hartshead Ln WF15 8AL (01274) 872845
"A lovely country pub", tipped for "really first-rate food"; get there in time for an early-bird menu, and the value is "excellent" too.
/ **Details:** www.grayoxinn.co.uk; Mon-Fri 8.45 pm, Sat 9.15 pm, Sun 6.45 pm; closed Sun D.

HARWICH, ESSEX 3–2D

The Pier at Harwich £54 Ⓣ
The Quay CO12 3HH (01255) 241212
A good tip for those heading for the ferry, the Milsom family hotel's ground-floor Ha'Penny Bistro attracts praise for its "well executed" dishes; even fans, though, can find it "on the expensive side" – there's also a pricier Harbourside Restaurant. / **Details:** www.milsomhotels.com; @pierhotel; 9.30 pm, Sat 10 pm; closed Mon & Tue; no jeans. **Accommodation:** 14 rooms, from £117.

HASSOP, DERBYSHIRE 5–2C

Hassop Hall £60 444
DE45 1NS (01629) 640488
The Chapman family's "stately" country house hotel offers "good food in a very beautiful setting", and "tremendous" service too; a bit more menu variety, though, might not go amiss?
/ **Details:** www.hassophall.co.uk; on the B6001 Bakewell - Hathersage Road, Junction 29 of M1; 9 pm; closed Mon L, Sat L & Sun D. **Accommodation:** 13 rooms, from £100.

HASTINGS, EAST SUSSEX 3–4C

Boulevard Bookshop £28 Ⓣ
TN34 3EA (01424) 436521
"A real hoot, with culinary pleasure to boot!"; this "amazing little restaurant in a secondhand book shop" has a big name for its "outstanding", "freshly cooked", "Thai home-style" cuisine… and "they positively encourage you to bring your own wine". / **Details:** www.thaicafeandbookshop.com.

Maggie's £21 453
Rock-a-Nore Rd TN34 3DW
(01424) 430 205
"Crispy-battered moist fish and triple-cooked chips" have made the name of this "unassuming café above the fishmarket" (and right by the beach); it now offers late-night opening on weekends, "so if you miss out at lunch you might make dinner instead!" / **Details:** 1.45 pm; L only, closed Sun; no credit cards.

The Pelican Diner £15 444
TN34 3AL (01424) 421555
A former seafront rock shop now houses this "tiny but very friendly" American-owned diner, praised for its "enthusiastic" service of quality "US comfort food" – "top-quality burgers, ethically sourced hot dogs, pulled pork, and home made fries".

Webbe's Rock-a-Nore £48 324
1 Rock-a-Nore Rd TN34 3DW
(01424) 721650
"A cut above your average seafront seafood restaurant", this "posh" branch of Paul Webbe's local chain remains, for most reporters, the "best place in the area for well-cooked fish"; at times, though, the "charming" service can seem "a little uncertain".
/ **Details:** www.webbesrestaurants.co.uk; 9.30 pm.

HATFIELD PEVEREL, ESSEX 3–2C

The Blue Strawberry £48 344
The St CM3 2DW (01245) 381333
"Beats other local brasseries"; in an "attractive old building", this well-established village staple is "worth the drive for a lovely meal out", and is particularly rated as a "favourite place to celebrate".
/ **Details:** www.bluestrawberrybistro.co.uk; @thebluestrawb; 3m E of Chelmsford; 10 pm; closed Sun D.

HAUGHTON MOSS, CHESHIRE 5–3B

The Nag's Head £42 Ⓣ
Long Ln CW6 9RN (01829) 260265
The latest gastropub outpost of Lancashire's celebrated Ribble Valley Inns chain is already tipped as a "charming" destination; the ultimate "cross between a locals' watering hole and a destination restaurant", its menu packs "plenty of flavour into each dish". / **Details:** www.nagsheadhaughton.co.uk.

HAWKHURST, KENT 3–4C

The Great House £46 333
Gills Grn TN18 5EJ (01580) 753119
In an old Wealden house that's "stylish without being over-styled" (and has a "nice garden area too"), a "very reliable" local gastropub which features some "unusual menu choices".

/ **Details:** *www.elitepubs.com/the_greathouse; 9.30 pm; no Amex.*

HAYWARDS HEATH, WEST SUSSEX 3–4B

Jeremy's at Borde Hill £50 544
Balcombe Rd RH16 1XP (01444) 441102
Jeremy Ashpool's "outstanding and inventive" cuisine must be the main reason to seek out this "lovely" venture of long standing, the terrace of which overlooks a Victorian walled garden, but service from the "long-standing" team is "quite exceptional", too.
/ **Details:** *www.jeremysrestaurant.com; Exit 10A from the A23; 10 pm; closed Mon & Sun D.*

HEBDEN BRIDGE, WEST YORKSHIRE 5–1B

The Olive Branch £33 Ⓣ
HX7 8UQ (0142) 284 22 99
"Very popular with the locals", a small Turkish restaurant tipped for its "superb" lamb dishes (stews and kebabs), and its 'pide' (pizzas) too.
/ **Details:** *www.theolivebranchrestaurant.co.uk.*

HEDLEY ON THE HILL, NORTHUMBERLAND 8–2B

The Feathers Inn £43 542
Hedley-on-the-Hill NE43 7SW
(01661) 843607
An "inspiring menu that doesn't disappoint" underpins the massive popularity of this "village pub on top of a hill", which – though "off the beaten track" – is "well situated not far from Durham/Gateshead/Hexham/Newcastle"; it is, however, rather "cramped".
/ **Details:** *www.thefeathers.net; @thefeathersinn; 8.30 pm; closed Mon & Sun D; no Amex.*

HELMSLEY, NORTH YORKSHIRE 8–4C

Black Swan £62 444
Market Pl YO62 5BJ (01439) 770466
"A hidden gem in a gorgeous town"; this trendified inn offers Paul Peters's ambitious tasting menus (with paired wines) which almost invariably seem to please; tea, coffee and bar snack options are also praised. / **Details:** *www.blackswan-helmsley.co.uk; 9.30 pm.* **Accommodation:** *45 rooms, from £130.*

Feversham Arms £73 Ⓣ
1-8 High St Y062 5AG (01439) 770766
A very grand inn, complete with open-air swimming pool; it's tipped for its "interesting" food, although there is some question about whether prices are a little ahead of themselves.
/ **Details:** *www.fevershamarmshotel.com; 9.30 pm; no trainers; children: 12+ after 8 pm.*
Accommodation: *33 rooms, from £260.*

HEMINGFORD GREY, CAMBRIDGESHIRE 3–1B

The Cock £48 334
47 High St PE28 9BJ (01480) 463609
"Good food and an interesting wine list" – two of the attractions which make this "charming" small pub, "a stone's throw from the River Ouse", a hit with all who comment on it; "great beer" too!
/ **Details:** *www.thecockhemingford.co.uk; @cambscuisine; off the A14; follow signs to the river; 9 pm, Fri & Sat 9.30 pm, Sun 8.30 pm; children: 5+ at D.*

HENLEY, WEST SUSSEX 3–4A

The Duke Of Cumberland £48 434
GU27 3HQ (01428) 652280
A "top-class pub-restaurant in an idyllic setting", with a "fantastic garden" and some "lovely" views; the word is out about its "elegantly simple" cooking, which uses "excellent" produce – "booking is essential".
/ **Details:** *www.thedukeofcumberland.com; @theduke_Henley; 9 pm; closed Mon D & Sun D.*

HENLEY-ON-THAMES, OXFORDSHIRE 3–3A

Giggling Squid £26 423
40 Hart St RG9 2AU (01491) 411044
"Top-quality Thai food that won't break the bank" – the majority verdict on this south-eastern chain's crowd-pleasing new branch; the lunchtime set menu, "catering for hoards of yummy mummies", offers particularly good value.
/ **Details:** *www.gigglingsquid.com; @GigglingSquid; 10 pm.*

Hotel du Vin et Bistro Hotel du Vin £55 344
New St RG9 2BP (01491) 848400
One of the better outlets of the wine-led bistro/hotel chain; housed in a former brewery, near the river, it's a "relaxed" sort of place, where the food is often "very good"; Sunday brunch is a highlight.
/ **Details:** *www.hotelduvin.com; 10 pm, Sat 10.30 pm, Sun 9.30 pm.* **Accommodation:** *43 rooms, from £110.*

Luscombes at the Golden Ball £56 Ⓣ
Lower Assendon RG9 6AH (01491) 574157
A "restaurant-cum-bar", tipped for its "beautiful" and "rustic" setting, and its "very good" food.
/ **Details:** *www.luscombes.co.uk; no Amex.*

Shaun Dickens at The Boathouse £55 444
RG9 1AZ (01491) 577937
A 2013 opening, this riverside venue is a "welcome addition" to a town that is "surprisingly lacking in distinctive dining"; it attracts praise for its "imaginative and very tasty" cuisine (though

"portion sizes are gourmet rather than gourmand!") and "attentive but not fussy" service.
/ **Details:** www.shaundickens.co.uk.

Spice Merchant **£41** 5 5 4
Thameside RG9 2LJ (01491) 636118
"In an area well served by good Indian restaurants", this large riverside venture "still stands out as the best", thanks to its "delicious" cooking and "excellent service".
/ **Details:** www.spicemerchantgroup.com; 11 pm; no Amex.

The Three Tuns **£44** T
RG9 2AA (01491) 410 138
Handily located in the heart of the town, a pub tipped for its "very high quality food" – "great for a family Sunday lunch".
/ **Details:** www.threetunshenley.co.uk.

Villa Marina **£39** 3 4 4
18 Thameside RG9 1BH (01491) 575262
"Sister to the Villa D'Este in Marlow and quite similar in approach" – this well-established venture is a "good Italian all-rounder", with a "lovely setting" and offering a "warm welcome" too.
/ **Details:** www.villamarina-henley.com; opp Angel pub, nr Bridge; 10.30 pm.

HEREFORD, HEREFORDSHIRE 2–1B

Castle House Restaurant
Castle House Hotel **£53** 3 4 3
Castle St HR1 2NW (01432) 356321
Regularly hailed as "probably the best place to eat in Herefordshire", the dining room of this central townhouse hotel has "excellent" service and serves "reasonably-priced" cooking with an emphasis on local sourcing – the owner also farms locally.
/ **Details:** www.castlehse.co.uk; @castlehsehotel; 9.30 pm, Sun 9 pm. **Accommodation:** 24 rooms, from £150.

HERNE BAY, KENT 3–3D

Le Petit Poisson **£41** 4 4 3
Pier Approach, Central Parade CT6 5JN
(01227) 361199
"Worth visiting Herne Bay for!" – it can seem "bizarre" to find such a "talented kitchen" just a few feet from the waves, but this "friendly" spot offers "classic seafood cookery and some delicious puddings too".
/ **Details:** www.lepetitpoisson.co.uk; 9.30 pm, Sun 15.30 pm; closed Mon & Sun D; no Amex.

HETHE, OXFORDSHIRE 2–1D

The Muddy Duck **£44** 3 4 3
Main St OX27 8ES (01869) 278099
An "immensely popular" gastropub (cum-deli) of quite recent vintage, in a pretty rural setting; it's hailed by reporters for its "innovative", "good-value" grub and "lovely friendly atmosphere".
/ **Details:** www.themuddyduckpub.co.uk; 9 pm.

HETTON, NORTH YORKSHIRE 5–1B

The Angel Inn **£52** 4 4 4
BD23 6LT (01756) 730263
"The original, one of the best, and still going strong!" – this "cosy and characterful" Dales inn was a culinary hotspot long before the coining of the term 'gastropub'; the food is "not trying for any stars" but it's "gorgeous", and backed up by "a brilliant wine list overseen by a knowledgeable sommelier". / **Details:** www.angelhetton.co.uk; 5m N of Skipton off B6265 at Rylstone; 9 pm; D only, ex Sun open L only. **Accommodation:** 9 rooms, from £150.

HEXHAM, NORTHUMBERLAND 8–2A

Bouchon Bistrot **£45** T
4-6 Gilesgate NE46 3NJ (01434) 609943
"The nearest we have to a real bistro in this neck of the woods"; this "well-established" Gallic venture is tipped for its "consistently good" and "reasonably-priced" fare. / **Details:** www.bouchonbistrot.co.uk; @bouchonhexham; 9 pm; closed Sun; no Amex.

Diwan E Am **£29** 4 3 3
NE46 1PH (01434) 606575
After more than three decades in business, what's propelling this moody Indian back to local stardom? – "the original family are now back in charge and the food has hit its historic best again".
/ **Details:** diwaneam.com.

The Rat Inn **£40** 4 3 3
Anick NE46 4LN (014) 3460 2814
"A delightful place altogether"; in a small hamlet overlooking the village green, with the River Tyne in the distance, this "cracking" ivy-clad pub is certainly "off the beaten track", but it's "well worth searching out", thanks to its "reliably good" grub, and at "honest prices" too.
/ **Details:** www.theratinn.com.

HINTLESHAM, SUFFOLK 3–1D

Hintlesham Hall **£68** T
Duke St IP8 3NS (01473) 652334
Mixed reports of late on this imposing country house hotel; it's undoubtedly set in "beautifully countryside", but there's a feeling that – aside from the "good-value" set lunch – there's a mismatch between the ("reasonable") cooking and the sky-high prices. / **Details:** www.hintleshamhall.com; 4m W of Ipswich on A1071; 9.30 pm; jacket at D; children: 12+. **Accommodation:** 33 rooms, from £99.

HINTON ST GEORGE, SOMERSET 2–3A

Lord Poulett Arms **£45** 4 3 4
TA17 8SE (01460) 73149
"A real gem, a bit tucked away but well worth the

effort"; this gastropub-with-rooms in a "lovely village location" is a "very welcoming" sort of place with "wonderful" food; it is particularly of note for its "amazing atmosphere" – "like a private house". / **Details:** *www.lordpoulettarms.com; 9 pm; no Amex.* **Accommodation:** *4 rooms, from £85.*

HOLT, NORFOLK 6–3C

The Pigs **£44** 343
Norwich Rd NR24 2RL (01263) 587634
"Worth seeking out for better than average pub food", this rural boozer is also of note for its famous 'Pudding Club'; good play area for the kids too. / **Details:** *www.thepigs.org.uk; @PigsPubNorfolk; 9 pm.* **Accommodation:** *10 rooms, from £145.*

Wiveton Hall Cafe **£32** 434
NR25 7TE (01263) 740525
"A wonderful discovery at a fruit farm, offering amazing sea views and and seriously delicious food at reasonable prices" – this "brightly-decorated" dining room inspires only the most positive reports, so "book ahead". / **Details:** *www.wivetonhall.co.uk/thecafe.*

HONITON, DEVON 2–4A

Combe House **£61** 233
Gittisham EX14 3AD (01404) 540400
In a romantic rural setting, this Elizabethan country house hotel offers "consistently wonderful" cuisine – the private kitchen tables come particularly "highly recommended"; there's the odd dissenter, however, not convinced that "London prices" are quite justified. / **Details:** *www.combehousedevon.com; @CombeHouseDevon; on the outskirts of Honiton; not far from the A30, A375, 303; 9.30 pm; no Amex.* **Accommodation:** *15, cottage for 2 ppl, thatched house for 8 ppl rooms, from £215.*

The Holt **£43** 342
178 High St EX14 1LA (01404) 47707
Run by a local brewery, this is a pub fans praise not only for its "imaginative menu" but also for offering "the best beer in England"; when it's busy, though, it can get "far too noisy". / **Details:** *www.theholt-honiton.com; 11 pm; closed Mon & Sun.*

HOOK, HAMPSHIRE 2–3D

Old House at Home **£48** Ⓣ
Newham Grn RG27 9AH (01256) 762222
Modest but very upbeat feedback of late on this "homely" old boozer; for a "lovely" lunch, though, it's still tipped as "really worth a visit". / **Details:** *www.oldhousenewnham.co.uk; @oldhousenewnham; 9 pm; closed Sun D.*

HORNDON ON THE HILL, ESSEX 3–3C

The Bell Inn **£49** 444
High Rd SS17 8LD (01375) 642463
"Much more than a gastropub" – for over 40 years, John & Christine Vereker have run an "impeccable" inn where the food is of "fine-dining standard" (and which has "fabulous" rooms too); "eating in the bar is as good as in the restaurant" and, while you're there, don't miss "the collection of historic hot cross buns"! / **Details:** *www.bell-inn.co.uk; signposted off B1007, off A13; 9.45 pm; booking: max 12.* **Accommodation:** *15 rooms, from £50.*

HORSHAM, WEST SUSSEX 3–4A

Camellia Restaurant South Lodge Hotel **£66** 332
Brighton Rd RH13 6PS (01403) 891711
Chef Steven Edwards's victory on Masterchef The Professionals has raised the profile of the dining room of this "beautiful" country house hotel; his "conservative" dishes are almost invariably "well executed". / **Details:** *www.southlodgehotel.co.uk; @SouthLodgeHotel; 9.30 pm.* **Accommodation:** *85 rooms, from £195.*

The Pass Restaurant South Lodge Hotel **£90** 554
Brighton Rd RH13 6PS (01403) 891711
You get a "very different" dining experience – "you sit in the kitchen and are served by the chefs" from an "indulgent and joyous" 7-course menu – at this country house hotel; "excellent" wines, too – "take the opportunity to visit the cellar and try a selection before dining!" / **Details:** *www.southlodgehotel.co.uk; @southlodgehotel; 8.30 pm; closed Mon & Tue; children: 12+.* **Accommodation:** *89 rooms, from £235.*

Restaurant Tristan **£57** 533
3 Stans Way, East St RH12 1HU
(01403) 255688
"Very consistent quality" – the invariable theme of commentary on the "amazing", "melt-in-the-mouth" dishes on offer at Tristan Mason's town-centre restaurant, housed in an attractive 16th-century building. / **Details:** *www.restauranttristan.co.uk; 9.30 pm; closed Mon & Sun.*

HORSTED KEYNES, WEST SUSSEX 3–4B

The Crown Inn **£40** 443
RH17 7AW (01825) 791609
With a former chef-proprietor of Gravetye Manor at the helm, it's perhaps no great surprise that this new gastropub offers "imaginative" cooking that's already being hailed as "the best in the area". / **Details:** *www.thecrown-horstedkeynes.co.uk.*

HOUGH ON THE HILL, LINCOLNSHIRE 6–3A

Brownlow Arms £49 T
NG32 2AZ (01400) 250234
A prettily-located village gastropub, consistently tipped by reporters for its all-round good standards; is it maybe "a bit pricey", though, for what it is?
/ **Details:** www.brownlowarms.com; on the Grantham Road; 9.15 pm; closed Mon, Tue–Sat D only, closed Sun D; no Amex; children: 10+. **Accommodation:** 5 rooms, from £98.

HUDDERSFIELD, WEST YORKSHIRE 5–1C

Bradley's £46 T
84 Fitzwilliam St HD1 5BB (01484) 516773
As ever, this bistro of over two decades' standing is tipped as an "always-reliable" destination, particularly worth seeking out for its "great-value" lunch and earlybird menus.
/ **Details:** www.bradleyscatering.co.uk; 10 pm; closed Mon, Sat L & Sun; no Amex.

Eric's £54 223
73-75 Lidget St HD3 3JP (01484) 646416
"Adventurous cooking and generous portions" make this Lindley restaurant "a welcome venue in an area where good food is very hard to track down" (and one that's particularly "lovely for lunch"); several reporters find the service "much improved" of late. / **Details:** www.ericsrestaurant.co.uk; @ericrestaurant; 10 pm; closed Mon, Sat L & Sun D; no Amex.

Med One £41 T
10-12 West Gate HD1 1NN (01484) 511100
"Well worth a visit", this town-centre spot is tipped for its "marvellous" Lebanese food ("breads to die for"), and "efficient" service; it even offers "reasonably-priced Château Musar"!
/ **Details:** www.med-one.co.uk.

HUNSDON, HERTFORDSHIRE 3–2B

The Fox And Hounds £43 444
2 High St SG12 8NH (01279) 843999
"The best and most welcoming restaurant for miles around" – a family-run gastroboozer which "never disappoints".
/ **Details:** www.foxandhounds-hunsdon.co.uk; @thefoxhunsdon; off the A414, 10 min from Hertford; 10 pm; no Amex.

HUNTINGDON, CAMBRIDGESHIRE 3–1B

The Abbot's Elm £44 443
PE28 2PA (01487) 773773
Reports find nothing to fault at this "excellent" thatched inn, where dishes both savoury and sweet are "interesting and well-cooked", and complemented by a "small but good" selection of wines; "impeccable" service too.
/ **Details:** www.theabbotselm.co.uk.

Old Bridge Hotel £50 344
1 High St PE29 3TQ (01480) 424300
The hotel's "stunning" adjacent wine shop advertises the prime reason to seek out the dining room of this ivy-clad townhouse; even if the food plays second fiddle, its quality can come as a "pleasant surprise" too. / **Details:** www.huntsbridge.com; @oldbridgehotel; off A1, off A14; 10 pm. **Accommodation:** 24 rooms, from £160.

HURWORTH, COUNTY DURHAM 8–3B

The Bay Horse £50 434
45 The Grn DL2 2AA (01325) 720 663
"Well worth a considerable detour", this "beautiful pub-restaurant" is touted as a "super" all-rounder, thanks not least for its "tempting" menus, and at "incredible-value" prices too.
/ **Details:** www.thebayhorsehurworth.com; @thebayhorse_; 9.30 pm, Sun 8 pm.

HYTHE, KENT 3–4D

Hythe Bay £45 332
Marine Pde CT21 6AW (01303) 267024
"Not a large restaurant but the standards are high, and the fish and seafood are fresh and full of flavour" – this Channel-view dining room inspires consistently positive reports.
/ **Details:** www.thehythebay.co.uk; 9.30 pm.

The Hythe Brasserie £43 T
CT21 5JT (01303) 267912
"The owners are so modest, but they produce food of a very high standard" – this husband-and-wife operation is very strongly tipped as an "excellent find"; more reports please.
/ **Details:** www.hythebrasserie.com.

ILKLEY, WEST YORKSHIRE 5–1C

The Box Tree £68 553
35-37 Church St LS29 9DR (01943) 608484
This landmark fine dining destination (since 1962) can seem "a little stuffy" by contemporary standards, but the "faultless" food offered by new head chef Laurence Yates is decidedly "21st century"; "not cheap… but then for a restaurant with this heritage, producing food of this quality, it shouldn't be!"
/ **Details:** www.theboxtree.co.uk; on A65 near town centre; 9.30 pm; closed Mon, Tue L, Wed L, Thu L & Sun D; no jeans or trainers; children: 10+.

INVERNESS, HIGHLAND 9–2C

Chez Roux Rocpool Reserve £55 554
Culduthel Rd IV2 4AG (01463) 240089
"Always a great experience"; a number of reporters express "surprise" at the "very high standard

of traditional French cuisine" on offer at this riverside outpost of the Roux empire; puddings are "particularly superb" – "don't bother to count the calories!" / **Details:** *www.rocpool.com; @ICMI_UK; 10 pm.* **Accommodation:** *11 rooms, from £210.*

The Mustard Seed £44 [T]
16 Fraser St IV1 1DW (01463) 220220
On the banks of the River Ness, an "atmospheric" former Georgian church, tipped for its "interesting" food; noise levels can be high, though, making this "not the place for a relaxing evening". / **Details:** *www.themustardseedrestaurant.co.uk; 10 pm.*

IPSWICH, SUFFOLK 3–1D

Baipo £37 [5][3][1]
63 Upper Orwell St IP4 1HP (01473) 218402
"Still a favourite after all these years"; this "authentic" Thai restaurant continues to transcend its "rather run-down" location ("which at least makes it easy to drive to, and park free in the evenings!"). / **Details:** *www.baipo.co.uk; 10.45 pm; closed Mon L & Sun; no Amex.*

Mariners at Il Punto £43 [4][3][5]
Neptune Quay IP4 1AX (01473) 289748
"Lovely food, romantic setting, fabulous service"; the Crépy family's restaurant aboard a restored naval vessel offers "a little bit of France", in an up-and-coming location on the waterfront. / **Details:** *www.marinersipswich.co.uk; 9.30 pm; closed Mon & Sun; no Amex.*

Trongs £35 [4][5][3]
23 St Nicholas St IP1 1TW (01473) 256833
"An oasis in a desert"; there have been "so many awards" over the years, but this small Vietnamese-run Chinese restaurant somehow "maintains its standards", which are "exemplary"; "always book, as it's very popular". / **Details:** *10.30 pm; closed Sun.*

The Waterfront Bar & Bistro £42 [4][3][4]
IP4 1FH (01473) 226 082
"There are many restaurants alongside the Ipswich marinas, but this place stands out" (and "it's the first one you come to too!") – service can sometimes be "scatty", but the only real complaint seems to be that the dining room "can be noisy". / **Details:** *www.waterfrontbistroipswich.co.uk.*

IRBY, MERSEYSIDE 5–2A

Da Piero £52 [4][4][2]
5-7 Mill Hill Rd CH61 4UB (0151) 648 7373
Look beyond its "anonymous exterior" and "rather sparse decor" (even "the menu descriptions are understated") and there's some "delicious Sicilian food" on offer at this "friendly" family-run venture; "if this place was in London it would be impossible to get in!" / **Details:** *www.dapiero.co.uk; 9 pm; D only, closed Mon & Sun; no Amex.*

ISLE OF SKYE, HIGHLAND 9–2A

Red Roof Cafe £20 [T]
IV55 8WS (01470) 511 766
Expect a long journey to this out-of-the-way café, tipped for food that's not only "delicious" but surprisingly "decorative" too. / **Details:** *www.redroofskye.co.uk.*

JERSEY, CHANNEL ISLANDS

Bohemia The Club Hotel & Spa £82 [4][4][2]
Green St, St Helier JE2 4UH (01534) 876500
Oddly mixed feedback of late from this celebrated St Helier dining room; most reports do support the view that Stephen Smith's cuisine is "the best on the island", but it's pricey, and the experience can be tainted by staff who are "too impressed with themselves", or "zero ambience". / **Details:** *www.bohemiajersey.com; 10 pm; closed Sun; no trainers.* **Accommodation:** *46 rooms, from £185.*

Chateau La Chaire £45 [T]
JE3 6AJ (01534) 863354
In a "great location" in St Martin, a small yet grand hotel, in quite traditional style, tipped for its "wonderful seafood and service"; the lunch menu is especially worth seeking out. / **Details:** *chateau-la-chaire.co.uk.*

Green Island Restaurant £54 [4][3][3]
St Clement JE2 6LS (01534) 857787
"Still one of the best on the island, but not a cheap evening"; two decades in business, the most southerly restaurant in the British Isles is a "friendly" place, with a pleasant terrace – a good place to enjoy a menu strong in "locally caught fish and seafood". / **Details:** *www.greenisland.je; 9.30 pm; closed Mon & Sun D; no Amex.*

Longueville Manor £70 [4][4][4]
Longueville Rd, St Saviour JE2 7WF (01534) 725501
"Back to its best", this luxurious but "friendly" country house hotel, on the outskirts of St Helier, is now hailed by all who report on it as offering "a good experience… for breakfast, lunch or dinner". / **Details:** *www.longuevillemanor.com; @longuevillemanor; head from St. Helier on the A3 towards Gorey; less than 1 mile from St. Helier; 10 pm; no jeans or trainers.* **Accommodation:** *31 rooms, from £170.*

Mark Jordan at the Beach £50 [3][4][4]
La Plage, La Route de la Haule, St Peter JE3 7YD (01534) 780180
"Fantastic sea views" are one undoubted reason to seek out this "friendly" and "relaxed" St Aubin's

Bay spot; most, but not quite all, reporters would say the simple food is "delicious" too ("especially fish"). / **Details:** *www.markjordanatthebeach.com; 9.30 pm; closed Mon.*

Ocean Restaurant Atlantic Hotel **£82** 554
Le Mont de la Pulente, St Brelade JE3 8HE (01534) 744101
A "lovely, light" ocean liner-style dining room offering not just "great views" of the bay but "amazing seafood, as you'd expect"; the "wonderfully charming" restaurant manager and "excellent" sommelier also garner praise.
/ **Details:** *www.theatlantichotel.com; 10 pm; no jeans or trainers.* **Accommodation:** *50 rooms, from £150 - 250.*

Ormer **£74** 543
7-11 Don St, St Helier JE2 4TQ (015) 3472 5100
"An altogether outstanding experience"; Shaun Rankin, formerly of Bohemia, wows almost all reporters with the "very interesting" cuisine on offer at his St Helier yearling; perhaps no surprise that it's "expensive", but it can occasionally seem unduly "formal" too. / **Details:** *www.ormerjersey.com; 10 pm; closed Sun.*

The Oyster Box **£58** 545
St Brelade's Bay JE3 8EF (01534) 743311
A "delightful" beachside bistro, which twins "quality seafood" with an "unmatchable outlook" – "what could be better than sitting on the terrace drinking wine and eating fabulous food in the sun?"
/ **Details:** *www.oysterbox.co.uk; @jerzypottery; 9 pm; closed Mon L & Sun D; no Amex.*

KENILWORTH, WARWICKSHIRE 5–4C

Bosquet **£55** 552
97a Warwick Rd CV8 1HP (01926) 852463
"The best cooking in the area"; Bernard and Mary Lignier may have been in business for over 30 years, but his "authentic" SW France cuisine and her "charming" and "efficient" service make this the sort of "old-fashioned" establishment that's still very hard to beat; "good wine selection" too.
/ **Details:** *www.restaurantbosquet.co.uk; 9.15 pm; closed Mon, Sat L & Sun; closed 2 weeks in Aug.*

The Cross at Kenilworth **£63** 432
16 New St CV8 2EZ (01926) 853840
"A great new venture that deserves to do well", say fans of Andreas Antona's (of Simpson's, Birmingham) "interesting and original" former pub; it's also "very expensive", though, and service can be on the slow side.
/ **Details:** *www.thecrossatkenilworth.co.uk.*

KESWICK, CUMBRIA 7–3D

Lyzzick Hall Country House Hotel **£52** Ⓣ
Underskiddaw CA12 4PY (017687) 72277
Looking for "a Spanish retreat in the Lakes"? - look no further than this family-run country house hotel, tipped especially for a wine list that's "a real treat for Iberian fans". / **Details:** *www.lyzzickhall.co.uk; 9 pm; no Amex.* **Accommodation:** *30 rooms, from £148.*

KETTLESHULME, CHESHIRE 5–2B

The Swan Inn **£46** 433
Macclesfield Rd SK23 7QU (01663) 732943
"Very popular locally", this attractive inn is particularly tipped for its "excellent seafood"; its location makes it a "great base for a summer walk" too – "booking at weekends is essential".
/ **Details:** *www.verynicepubs.co.uk/swankettleshulme/; 8.30 pm, Thu-Fri 7 pm, Sat 9 pm, Sun 4 pm; closed Mon; no Amex.*

KEYSTON, CAMBRIDGESHIRE 3–1A

The Pheasant at Keyston **£50** 433
Loop Rd PE28 0RE (01832) 710241
"Reliable quality" is the gist of pretty much all feedback on this "capable" and "good-value" village inn – sibling to the better-known Old Bridge in Huntingdon; Sunday lunch is a highlight.
/ **Details:** *www.thepheasant-keyston.co.uk; 1m S of A14 between Huntingdon & Kettering, J15; 9.30 pm; closed Mon & Sun D; no Amex.*

KIBWORTH BEAUCHAMP, LEICESTERSHIRE 5–4D

The Lighthouse **£47** 454
9 Station St LE8 0LN (0116) 279 6260
"The only fish restaurant for miles, offering fantastically fresh food", say fans of the Bobolis' "friendly" and "good-value" venture (which replaced their popular Italian restaurant, Firenze); "there's a little bit of turf for the diehards, but refreshing to have so much choice from the surf!".
/ **Details:** *www.lighthousekibworth.co.uk; @ourlighthouse; 9.30 pm; D only, closed Mon & Sun; no Amex.*

KINGHAM, GLOUCESTERSHIRE 2–1C

Daylesford Café **£43** 314
GL56 0YG (01608) 731700
Beloved of a well-heeled crowd, this farmshop and café has a "gorgeous setting" and offers "tasty and appealing (but "pricey") food"; service is on the up of late, but can still be frustratingly "slow"; best to "go there on a summer's day for a wood-fired pizza in the garden".
/ **Details:** *www.daylesfordorganic.com; Mon-Wed 5 pm, Thu-Sat 6 pm, Sun 4pm; L only.*

KINGHAM, OXFORDSHIRE 2–1C

The Kingham Plough £52 4 3 3

The Green OX7 6YD (01608) 658327
"In a wonderful Cotswold village setting", Emily Watkins's "fancy" inn – famously a stomping ground of the 'Chipping Norton set' – offers sometimes "astonishingly good" food; "excellent local ales from the Cotswolds and Hook Norton Breweries" too.
/ **Details:** *www.thekinghamplough.co.uk; 8.30 pm, Fri & Sat 8.45 pm, Sun 8 pm; no Amex.*
Accommodation: *7 rooms, from £95.*

The Wild Rabbit £49 2 2 3

Church St OX7 6YA (01608) 658 389
"No expense has been spared" on Lady ('JCB') Bamford's latest 'Daylesford' venture; supporters say it offers "beautiful food in a gorgeous environment", but there are almost as many critics who find the whole performance "pompous" and "overpriced" – that this is Michelin's 'pub of the year' is beyond parody! / **Details:** *www.thewildrabbit.co.uk.*

KINGSDOWN, KENT 3–3D

Zetland Arms £30 T

CT14 8AF (01304) 370114
A handy tip for "a pint of Shepherd Neame, contemplating Calais, across the Straits of Dover" – it also offers "good food in a friendly atmosphere".
/ **Details:** *www.shepherdneame.co.uk.*

KINGSTON BAGPUIZE, OXFORDSHIRE 2–2C

Fallowfields £79 4 4 3

Faringdon Rd OX13 5BH (01865) 820416
Our own visit did not wow us, but this "lovely" hotel dining room put in a very impressive performance in the survey, and fans say standards "have reached a new high since the arrival of Matt Weedon".
/ **Details:** *www.fallowfields.com; just off A420 at junction with A415; 9.30 pm; children: 8+.*
Accommodation: *10 rooms, from £123.*

KINGSTON UPON THAMES, SURREY 3–3A

The Canbury Arms £44 3 3 3

49 Canbury Park Rd KT2 6LQ
(020) 8255 9129
"A really good gastropub without the pretentions", where culinary highlights range from "fantastic-value" tapas-style dishes to highly recommended Sunday roasts. / **Details:** *www.thecanburyarms.com; @thecanburyarms; 10 pm, Sun 9 pm.*

fish! Kitchen £47 4 3 1

56-58 Coombe Rd KT2 7AF (020) 8546 2886
A "good variety" of "splendid" fish and seafood is the main – OK, sole (geddit!) – reason to seek out this unadorned dining room.
/ **Details:** *www.fishkitchen.com; 10 pm; closed Mon & Sun.*

Jin Go Gae £43 T

KT3 4NL (020) 8949 2506
"A great Korean restaurant populated by the local Korean community", tipped for "interesting" food of a consistently high quality.

Roz ana £46 4 3 2

4-8 Kingston Hill KT2 7NH (020) 8546 6388
"Really good fusion cuisine" and "monthly regional specials" – all part of the formula that makes this Norbiton Indian quite a crowd-pleaser.
/ **Details:** *www.roz-ana.com; @Rozana; 10.30 pm, Fri & Sat 11 pm, Sun 10 pm; no Amex.*

KINGUSSIE, HIGHLAND 9–2C

The Cross £75 4 4 4

Tweed Mill Brae, Ardbroilach Rd PH21 1LB
(01540) 661166
"Tasty and imaginatively presented", the food at this "fabulously-located" restaurant-with-rooms "is generating a growing reputation"; puddings are a highlight – "the soufflé was so good I had it again the next evening!" / **Details:** *www.thecross.co.uk; @CrossRelax; 8.30 pm; children: 9+.*
Accommodation: *8 rooms, from £100.*

KIRKBURTON, WEST YORKSHIRE 5–2C

The Dye Works £35 T

HD8 0RH (01484) 602891
Looking for "really solid" French cooking? – this all-day café-bistro, run by the erstwhile owners of the Kaye Arms at Grange Moor, is tipped as the "sort of place people would rave about if they found it in the Dordogne"! / **Details:** *www.thedyeworks.co.uk.*

KIRKBY LONSDALE, CUMBRIA 7–4D

Hipping Hall £74 5 5 4

Cowan Bridge LA6 2JJ (01524) 271187
"A delightful experience from beginning to end"; a "romantic" historically-housed hotel whose 15th-century hall makes a "beautiful" setting in which to dine; the food is usually "superb" too.
/ **Details:** *www.hippinghall.com; 8.45 pm; closed weekday L; no Amex; no trainers; children: 12+.*
Accommodation: *10 rooms, from £239.*

KNOWSTONE, DEVON 1–2D

The Mason's Arms £61 5 4 4

EX36 4RY (01398) 341231
In a "picturesque village on the edge of Exmoor", a "terrific" gastropub where chef Mark Dodson (ex-Waterside Inn) produces many "terrific" dishes which at their best "approach perfection".
/ **Details:** *www.masonsarmsdevon.co.uk; 9 pm; closed Mon & Sun D; children: 5+ after 6pm.*

KNUTSFORD, CHESHIRE 5–2B

Belle Époque **£53** 3 3 4
60 King St WA16 6DT (01565) 633060
Of particular note for its eye-catching Art Nouveau building, a town-centre restaurant with "good" standards overall, even if its modern British cuisine can seem "a bit expensive for what you get".
/ **Details:** *www.thebelleepoque.com; @TheBelleEpoque; 1.5m from M6, J19; 9.30 pm; closed Mon & Sun D.* **Accommodation:** *7 rooms, from £110.*

KYLESKU, HIGHLAND 9–1B

Kylesku Hotel **£43** 4 5 4
IV27 4HW (01971) 502231
"The tempura batter would grace any restaurant anywhere let alone one as remote as this!"; this "welcoming" small hotel, offers "innovative" seafood dishes in a dining room whose loch-side setting enjoys "what must be one of the best views you'll see from any restaurant".
/ **Details:** *www.kyleskuhotel.co.uk; on A894, S of Scourie, N of loch inver; 9 pm; no Amex.*
Accommodation: *8 rooms, from £55.*

LAMPETER, CEREDIGION 4–4C

Falcondale Hotel **£50** 3 4 3
Falcondale Drive SA48 7RX (01570) 422910
"Once a country house then a care home"… and now a "very good hotel restaurant deep in the countryside"; "improved greatly in recent years", it now offers "great-quality" fare, served by "welcoming and well-trained" staff.
/ **Details:** *www.thefalcondale.co.uk; 8.30 pm.*
Accommodation: *19 rooms, from £149.*

LANGAR, NOTTINGHAMSHIRE 5–3D

Langar Hall **£49** 4 4 5
Church Ln NG13 9HG (01949) 860559
This "quirky and fun" hotel "really feels like a country house" – a romantic place with an "enchanting" location and "very warm" service; the "unpretentious" cooking is "everything you'd hope for" too. / **Details:** *www.langarhall.com; off A52 between Nottingham & Grantham; 9.30 pm; no Amex; no trainers.* **Accommodation:** *12 rooms, from £100.*

LANGHO, LANCASHIRE 5–1B

Northcote **£80** 5 5 4
Northcote Rd BB6 8BE (01254) 240555
"Improved , even if it is flashier!" – after some "terrific renovations", including a new kitchen, the North West's most prominent restaurant-with-rooms "has moved up a gear" (and it was no slouch before); Lisa Allen's cooking is "truly gorgeous", and the "brilliantly compiled" wine list a major attraction in its own right.
/ **Details:** *www.northcote.com; M6, J31 then A59; 9 pm; no trainers.* **Accommodation:** *18 rooms, from £280.*

LANGSHOTT, SURREY 3–3B

Langshott Manor **£78** Ⓣ
Ladbroke Rd RH6 8PB (01293) 786680
Top tip near Gatwick, this "wonderful" country house hotel enjoys a particularly "beautiful setting", and fans say the food is "delicious" too.
/ **Details:** *www.langshottmanor.com; just off the A23, in Horley; 9.30 pm; no trainers.*
Accommodation: *22 rooms, from £190.*

LAPWORTH, WARWICKSHIRE 5–4C

The Boot **£43** Ⓣ
Old Warwick Rd B94 6JU (01564) 782464
With its large beer garden, this sizeable modernised inn is tipped as a "welcoming" sort of place, with good standards all-round.
/ **Details:** *www.lovelypubs.co.uk; 10 pm, Sun 9 pm; no Amex.*

LAVENHAM, SUFFOLK 3–1C

Great House **£54** 5 5 4
Market Pl CO10 9QZ (01787) 247431
"It's so good I have now moved to the village to be close by!"; the Crépy family's "extraordinary" venture is "top drawer in every respect"… from the "beautiful" setting in an ancient house on the market square, to the "lovely" service and "excellent Gallic cooking". / **Details:** *www.greathouse.co.uk; @GreatHouseHotel; follow directions to Guildhall; 9.30 pm; closed Mon & Sun D; closed Jan; no Amex.*
Accommodation: *5 rooms, from £95.*

Number Ten **£35** Ⓣ
CO10 9RA (01787) 249438
This "friendly" wine bar is mainly tipped for "good-quality, moderately priced" bottles from the owner's South African vineyard, but its "excellent" casual eats also contribute to the "buzzy" vibe.

Swan Hotel **£56** 3 3 4
High St CO10 9QA (01787) 247477
"If all you want is dramatic surroundings", you won't be disappointed by this venture in a "stunning" half-timbered hotel; both the brasserie and restaurant offer some "tasty" dishes, and an "excellent" wine list too. / **Details:** *www.theswanatlavenham.co.uk; @SwanLavenham; 9.30 pm; no jeans or trainers; children: 12+ at D.* **Accommodation:** *45 rooms, from £195.*

LEAMINGTON SPA, WARWICKSHIRE 5–4C

La Coppola **£51** 4 4 4
86 Regent St CV32 4NS (01926) 888 873
Still rated as "the best Italian" in town, an upmarket venture that's "extremely good for seafood"; it's "a good idea to book", though – "there are

no offers or cheap lunch menus, and yet I have never been when it's not very full". / **Details:** www.lacoppola.co.uk; 10 pm, Sun 9 pm; no Amex.

Kayal **£34** Ⓣ
CV32 5EG
This outpost of a popular four-strong chain offers "light and delicious" Keralan cuisine, and is particularly tipped for its "great selection of vegan and vegetarian" dishes; the "Thali-type" business lunch offers "excellent value for money" too.
/ **Details:** www.kayalrestaurant.com.

Oscars French Bistro **£44** Ⓣ
39 Chandos St CV32 4RL (01926) 452807
"Sometimes, nothing can beat good old-fashioned French bistro cooking!" – this "genuine" (and "slightly eccentric") spot is strongly tipped for its "nostalgic" appeal, occasional "inconsistency" notwithstanding.
/ **Details:** www.oscarsfrenchbistro.co.uk; 9.30 pm; closed Mon & Sun.

Queans Restaurant **£53** 344
15 Dormer Pl CV32 5AA (01926) 315522
"Great British food at its best" – chef-patronne Laura Hamilton's "intimate" basement restaurant, in a Georgian townhouse, is "a wonderful treat for a special occasion"; highlights include "ice creams to die for". / **Details:** www.queans-restaurant.co.uk; 9.30 pm; closed Mon, Tue L, Sat L & Sun.

Restaurant 23 **£63** 444
34 Hamilton Ter CV32 4LY (01926) 422422
"Friendly" staff and "tasty" food make an almost invariably positive impression on visitors to this "cheerful" restaurant, relocated in recent times to a "nicely refurbished" Victorian house; it has a "great cocktail bar" upstairs, and is rated a convenient venue for romance too.
/ **Details:** www.restaurant23.com; @Restaurant23; 9.30 pm; closed Mon & Sun; children: 12+.

LECHLADE, GLOUCESTERSHIRE 2–2C

The Five Alls **£42** 434
Filkins GL7 3JQ (01367) 860875
Fans are very up indeed on Sebastian Snow's "highly recommended" village gastroboozer, which is proclaimed a great example of "a fine restaurant and a proper drinking pub, peacefully co-existing"; there's no denying, though, that the service can sometimes grate.
/ **Details:** www.thefiveallsfilkins.co.uk; 9.30 pm, Fri & Sat 10 pm; closed Sun D; no Amex.

LEEDS, WEST YORKSHIRE 5–1C

Aagrah **£38** 433
Aberford Rd LS25 2HF (0113) 287 6606
"Still the sector leader", this "very consistent" city-centre branch of a well-established Yorkshire chain continues to win praise for Kashmiri cuisine of "unrivalled quality", and "very friendly service".
/ **Details:** www.aagrah.com; from A1 take A642 Aberford Rd to Garforth; 11.30 pm, Sun 10.30 pm; D only.

Akbar's **£32** 323
16 Greek St LS1 5RU (0113) 242 5426
Part of a ten-strong South Asian chain, this "busy and noisy" venue "churns out great Pakistani curries relentlessly" (including some "fabulous" Balti dishes).
/ **Details:** www.akbars.co.uk; midnight; D only.

Art's **£42** 422
42 Call Ln LS1 6DT (0113) 243 8243
Difficult to believe that it was a dozen years ago that this, the city's original trendy restaurant, was launched near the Corn Exchange; it remains ever-"popular", and the food is "still good"; lunch plates, served till 5pm, offer "particularly good value". / **Details:** www.artscafebar.com; 10 pm.

The Bird And Beast **£30** Ⓣ
Central Rd LS1 6DX (0113) 245 3348
It opened too late for significant survey commentary, but given its pedigree (the man behind Gato Negro in Ripponden) it would be a surprise if this city-centre rôtisserie weren't quite a hit… and the local reviews suggest it already is!
/ **Details:** http://thebirdandbeast.co.uk/.

El Bareto **£33** Ⓣ
LS17 6LX (0113) 2666946
In the "leafy suburb" of Chapel Allerton, this "cramped" cellar tapas bar is tipped not just for its "fine" ambience, but for "consistently decent" food too. / **Details:** www.elbareto.co.uk.

Flying Pizza **£38** 344
60 Street Ln LS8 2DQ (0113) 266 6501
Now part of the San Carlo empire, a Headingley pizzeria long celebrated locally as a see-and-be-seen destination; reporters generally – if not invariably – regard it as a "fun" destination which "deserves its accolades". / **Details:** www.theflyingpizza.co.uk; 11 pm, Sun 10 pm; no shorts.

Fuji Hiro **£25** 542
45 Wade Ln LS2 8NJ (0113) 243 9184
"Not tasted better noodles in the UK!"; this is a city-centre stand-by that "never fails to satisfy".
/ **Details:** 10 pm, Fri & Sat 11 pm; need 5+ to book.

Hansa's **£31** 543
72-74 North St LS2 7PN (0113) 244 4408
"Still perfect every time" – Mrs Hansa Dabhi's "excellent" city-centre Gujarati stalwart continues to elicit raves from all who comment on it; the food, "lovingly served" by the lady herself, is so good that "even non-veggies will love it!"
/ **Details:** www.hansasrestaurant.com; 10 pm, Fri & Sat 11 pm; D only, ex Sun L only.

Kendells Bistro £44 444
St Peters square LS9 8AH (0113) 243 6553
With its "well-executed French classics" and "exceptionally friendly staff", this seriously "buzzy" city-centre bistro is becoming "something of a Leeds institution"; "candles everywhere and binoculars for the regularly changing blackboard add to the great ambience". / ***Details:*** *www.kendellsbistro.co.uk; @KendellsBistro; 9 pm, Fri & Sat 10 pm; D only, closed Mon & Sun; no Amex.*

The Man Behind The Curtain £32 Ⓣ
LS1 7JH (0113) 2432376
"New, and very 'different'", this "refreshing" city-centre venue, the creation of an ex-Noma chef, specialises in tasting menus tipped for "great combination of unusual ingredients that really excite the taste buds"; we suspect we're going to hear more of this one!
/ ***Details:*** *www.themanbehindthecurtain.co.uk.*

Prashad £37 544
137 Whitehall Rd BD11 1AT (0113) 285 2037
"Moving to bigger and better (Drighlington) premises has, if anything, only improved the great food" at this well-established and "extremely friendly" Gujarati veggie, whose "amazing" cuisine is "worth travelling a long way for"; it now offers "wine and cocktails too".
/ ***Details:*** *www.prashad.co.uk; closed Mon; no Amex.*

Red Chilli £40 333
6 Great George St LS1 3DW (01132) 429688
"Ignore the standard Cantonese fare", say fans of this city-centre basement, and dive into what they hail as "outrageously good" Sichuanese dishes; even a reporter who acknowledges this may be "the best Chinese in Leeds", however, slyly add that "that doesn't say much!"
/ ***Details:*** *www.redchillirestaurant.co.uk; 10.30 pm, Fri & Sat 11.30 pm.*

Reds True Barbecue £38 Ⓣ
LS1 2HD (0113) 834 5834
On all reports, the city's "first real attempt to ride the barbecue bandwagon" does "a pretty decent job"; it's tipped for "hugely tasty Texan-style" ribs and "as good a burger as you can get" locally... and, you "can't beat dinner being served on a dustbin lid!" / ***Details:*** *www.truebarbecue.com.*

The Reliance £38 344
76-78 North St LS2 7PN (0113) 295 6060
Despite its seeming "neo-hippie casualness", this "unusual and unexpected" boozer offers some "first-class" food (including "truly epic burgers"); "one of the few pubs where the coffee is as good as the locally-sourced craft beers".
/ ***Details:*** *www.the-reliance.co.uk; 10 pm, Thu-Sat 10.30 pm, Sun 9.30 pm; no booking.*

Roast + Conch £41 Ⓣ
LS1 5EL (01132) 442 421
"Different from your usual dining experience!" – this "industrial-style" but "comfortable" outpost of the Hotel Chocolat empire "brings a cocoa influence to most dishes".
/ ***Details:*** *www.hotelchocolat.com.*

Salvo's £47 443
115 Otley Rd LS6 3PX (0113) 275 5017
"Continually reinventing itself, and getting even better", this Headingley Italian fixture is a "friendly and helpful" sort of place, "worth a 15-minute cab journey from the city centre for the food and value-for-money". / ***Details:*** *www.salvos.co.uk; @salvosleeds; 10.30 pm, Fri & Sat 11 pm, Sun 9 pm; no booking at D.*

Sous le Nez en Ville £45 433
Quebec Hs, Quebec St LS1 2HA
(0113) 244 0108
"A very pleasant and reasonably priced place to have lunch in the business district" – this "bustling" cellar stalwart dishes up some "gorgeous" Gallic fare, with an "extensive" wine selection too; the early-evening prix-fixe is something of a local legend. / ***Details:*** *www.souslenez.com; @SousLeNezLeeds; 9.45 pm, Sat 10.30 pm; closed Sun.*

Sukhothai £41 554
8 Regent St LS7 4PE (0113) 237 0141
"Still the trendsetter for Thai food"; the Chapel Allerton HQ of a four-strong local chain offers "a wonderful all-round experience, but special mention has to go to the wonderful service", with customers "treated like family".
/ ***Details:*** *www.sukhothai.co.uk; 11 pm; Mon-Thu D only, Fri-Sun open L & D; no Amex.*

Tharavadu £30 Ⓣ
LS1 5DQ (0113) 244 0500
Tipped for its "excellent" curries, and service that's "so friendly and efficient" too – a new outfit near the railway station, which bills itself as the city's 'First Authentic Kerala restaurant'.
/ ***Details:*** *www.tharavadurestaurants.com.*

LEICESTER, LEICESTERSHIRE 5–4D

Hotel Maiyango £46 444
13-21 St Nicholas Pl LE1 4LD
(0116) 251 8898
Encouraging feedback of late for this "interesting" and "comfortable" town-centre boutique hotel and restaurant (with nearby deli); it now offers "imaginative cooking" with "a great Asian influence", courtesy of new head chef Nick Wilson, a protégé of Jean-Christophe Novelli.
/ ***Details:*** *www.maiyango.com; 9 pm; closed Mon L, Tue L & Sun L.* ***Accommodation:*** *14 rooms, from £90.*

Kayal £36 424
153 Granby St LE1 6FE (0116) 255 4667
"Slightly different" from the general run, but "one of Leicester's favourites" – this modest-looking outfit, near the railway station, offers "fresh South Indian cooking with particularly good fish dishes, reflecting the coastal origin of the family who own it".
*/ **Details:** www.kayalrestaurant.com; 11 pm, Sun 10 pm.*

LEIGH-ON-SEA, ESSEX 3–3C

Sandbank £39 Ⓣ
1470 London Rd SS9 2UR (01702) 719 000
A well-established restaurant tipped for its "fabulous food and theme nights", and "high standards of service" too.
*/ **Details:** www.sandbankrestaurant.co.uk; @sandbankdining; 10.30 pm; closed Mon, Sat L & Sun D.*

LEIGHTON BUZZARD, BEDFORDSHIRE 3–2A

The Kings Head £54 532
Ivinghoe LU7 9EB (01296) 668388
"THE place for duck!"; the owner of this ancient inn trained at Paris's legendary Tour d'Argent, and it shows through in the quality of the Aylesburys served here; all this, plus service "with an amusing hint of Fawlty Towers about it".
*/ **Details:** www.kingsheadivinghoe.co.uk; 3m N of Tring on B489 to Dunstable; 9.15 pm; closed Sun D; jacket & tie required at D.*

LEINTWARDINE, SHROPSHIRE 5–4A

Jolly Frog £48 444
The Todden SY7 0LX (01547) 540298
"Jolly indeed!"; this "excellent fish-pub", near Ludlow Castle, is making real waves with its "honest", "tasty" and "sensibly-priced" dishes.
*/ **Details:** www.jollyfrogpub.co.uk; 9.30 pm; closed Mon; no Amex.*

LEWES, EAST SUSSEX 3–4B

Bill's Produce Store £41 333
56 Cliffe High St BN7 2AN (01273) 476918
*Bill Collison's produce-packed HQ, a noted breakfast spot, is praised for "imaginative food and lots of it"; there's the odd quibble about "homogenisation" since it expanded nationwide, but the general opinion is that it's "still the best in the chain". / **Details:** www.bills-website.co.uk; 10.30 pm, Fri-Sat 11.30 pm; no Amex.*

Pelham House £42 333
BN7 1UW (01273) 488600
"A peaceful oasis just a few steps away from the busy High Street"; with its "beautiful period interior" and "sunny terrace", this hotel restaurant gives "a feeling of gracious living at its best"; the food's "always good" too – the "only reservation is that portions are too generous"!
*/ **Details:** www.pelhamhouse.com; @pelhamlewes; off the High Street in Lewes; 9 pm, Sun 8.30 pm.*
***Accommodation:** 31 rooms, from £130.*

LINCOLN, LINCOLNSHIRE 6–3A

Browns Pie Shop £45 Ⓣ
33 Steep Hill LN2 1LU (01522) 527330
Tipped for its "very unusual" setting in an ancient building (beware stairs!), a "friendly" and "efficient" local institution, particularly tipped for its "interesting selection of pies".
*/ **Details:** www.brownspieshop.co.uk; 9.30 pm, Sun 8 pm; no Amex.*

Jew's House Restaurant £49 544
15 The Strait LN2 1JD (01522) 524851
"Always nice to eat in a 12th-century house… but the food is good too!"; this "welcoming" establishment in one of this historic town's most ancient buildings may offer a relatively "short" menu, but results can be "excellent"; lunch is particularly "competitively priced".
*/ **Details:** www.jewshouserestaurant.co.uk; 9.30 pm; closed Mon, Tue L & Sun; no Amex.*

The Old Bakery £49 444
26-28 Burton Rd LN1 3LB (01522) 576057
The odd reporter considers it "over-rated", but this olde-worlde restaurant with rooms (with an airy conservatory at the back) is for most reporters a "firm favourite" – a "special" place, offering a "good mix of Italianate and English dishes".
*/ **Details:** www.theold-bakery.co.uk; @theoldbakeryrestaurant; 9 pm; closed Mon; no jeans.*
***Accommodation:** 4 rooms, from £65.*

LINLITHGOW, WEST LOTHIAN 9–4C

Champany Inn £77 Ⓣ
EH49 7LU (01506) 834532
"A spectacular wine list, and steaks as they should be" – the twin attractions for which this famous (and not inexpensive) inn has long been a destination of some renown.
*/ **Details:** www.champany.com; 2m NE of Linlithgow on junction of A904 & A803; 10 pm; closed Sat L & Sun; no jeans or trainers; children: 8+.*
***Accommodation:** 16 rooms, from £125.*

LINTON IN CRAVEN, NORTH YORKSHIRE 8–4B

The Fountaine Inn £40 Ⓣ
BD23 5HJ (01756) 752210
An "attractive pub in a lovely village", tipped for its "interesting ever-changing menu" (with "an emphasis on game or fish") plus "good" real ales; "it is also a lovely place to stay".
*/ **Details:** www.fountaineinnatlinton.co.uk/.*

LISS, HAMPSHIRE 2–3D

Madhubon **£31** Ⓣ
94 Station Rd GU33 7AQ (01730) 893363
*"Still maintaining very high standards" – a village tandoori tipped for the quality of its Bangladeshi cuisine. / **Details:** www.madhubanrestaurant.co.uk; 10 pm; closed Fri L.*

LITTLE ECCLESTON, LANCASHIRE 5–1A

The Cartford Inn **£42** 422
Cartford Ln PR3 0YP (01995) 670 166
*This Gallic riverside restaurant-with-rooms, "a modernised ancient country inn by the side of a working toll bridge", is a "buzzy and popular" spot; ignore the sometimes "dim" service and "almost trippy décor", and focus on the "jolly good food" – best sampled from a table "by the picture windows overlooking the River Wyre". / **Details:** www.thecartfordinn.co.uk; 9 pm, Fri & Sat 10 pm, Sun 8.30 pm; closed Mon L.*

LITTLE WILBRAHAM, CAMBRIDGESHIRE 3–1B

The Hole In The Wall **£47** 233
2 High St CB21 5JY (01223) 812282
*Former MasterChef winner Alex Rushmer's inn continues to divide opinion – while fans praise its "innovative and flavourful" cuisine (and at "reasonable" prices too), there's a vociferous band of critics who have "no idea why the place is so talked up". / **Details:** www.holeinthewallcambridge.com; @hitwcambridge; 9 pm; closed Mon & Sun D; no Amex.*

LITTLEHAMPTON, WEST SUSSEX 3–4A

East Beach Cafe **£43** 224
Sea Rd, The Promenade BN17 5GB
(01903) 731903
*"Wonderful fresh fish dishes" and "lovely" views are among the virtues which make this seafront "gem" a hit with all who report on it; it's "even better in winter, when the crowds have subsided!" / **Details:** www.eastbeachcafe.co.uk; @EastBeachCafe; 8.30 pm; closed Mon D, Tue D, Wed D & Sun D.*

LIVERPOOL, MERSEYSIDE 5–2A

Delifonseca **£41** 342
12 Stanley St L1 6AF (0151) 255 0808
*"A deli that's more of a wine bar nowadays"; it has earned quite a local reputation for its "imaginative" food, and "really good service" too. / **Details:** www.delifonseca.co.uk; 9 pm, Fri & Sat 9.30 pm; closed Sun D.*

Fazenda **£46** Ⓣ
L2 3YL (0151) 227 2733
*This "great" Brazilian steakhouse is tipped for its "wonderful" meat ("cut and carved at your table"), "brilliant" wine list and "superb" salad bar, and all in "an ambience ideal for business". / **Details:** www.fazenda.co.uk/liverpool.*

Host **£39** 443
31 Hope St L1 9XH (0151) 708 5831
*Near the Phil, a minimalist spin off from 60 Hope Street, offering "good-quality", "consistent" and "imaginative" Asian fusion fare; "good value" too. / **Details:** www.ho-st.co.uk; 11 pm, Sun 10 pm.*

The Italian Club Fish **£45** 432
128 Bold St L1 4JA (0151) 707 2110
*"Superb fish and oysters" (with, and without, chips) are on offer at this "casual" Italo-Scottish bistro, near Central Station. / **Details:** www.theitalianclubfish.co.uk; @italianclubnews; 10 pm, Sun 9 pm; no Amex.*

The London Carriage Works Hope Street Hotel **£54** 222
40 Hope St L1 9DA (0151) 705 2222
*The dining room of the city's pioneering design hotel has its fans, who praise its "lovely" food with "unusual" touches; the "style-over-substance" lobby, however, was again quite vocal this year. / **Details:** www.thelondoncarriageworks.co.uk; 10 pm, Sun 9 pm; no shorts. **Accommodation:** 89 rooms, from £150.*

Lunya **£45** 433
18-20 College Ln L1 3DS (0151) 706 9770
*"Liverpool's answer to London's Brindisa"; "you wouldn't expect to find a really very good tapas restaurant in the middle of the spanking-new regenerated shopping district", but this clubby fixture is a real hit with all who comment on it; "good deli too!" / **Details:** www.lunya.co.uk; @Lunya; 11 pm, Sun 10 pm.*

The Monro **£42** 344
92-94 Duke St L1 5AG (0151) 707 9933
*A "great gastropub" whose real ales, Sunday roasts and so on are "very popular"; by local standards, though, it can seem "a wee bit expensive". / **Details:** www.themonro.com; 9.30 pm, Sun 7.30 pm; no Amex; no trainers.*

Puschka **£50** 444
16 Rodney St L1 2TE (0151) 708 8698
*"Intimate fine dining at its best"; situated in the city's Georgian quarter, a "small and friendly" restaurant praised for its "very interesting" cooking – "look out for the blackboard specials!". / **Details:** www.puschka.co.uk; 10 pm, Sun 9 pm; D only.*

Salt House **£33** 3 4 4
Hanover Sq L1 3DW (0151) 706 0092
"Very good tapas dished up by a friendly team in a convivial atmosphere" – all reports on this "noisy" central stand-by are to pretty much the same effect.
/ **Details:** *www.salthousetapas.co.uk; 10.30 pm.*

San Carlo **£42** 3 4 5
41 Castle St L2 9SH (0151) 236 0073
This "dressed-to-the-nines" Italian, the city-centre branch of a "glossy" national chain, offers food of a "surprisingly high" standard, with fish "always the best option"; tables, though, "might be too close for some". / **Details:** *www.sancarlo.co.uk; @SanCarlo_Group; 11 pm.*

The Side Door **£40** T
29a, Hope St L1 9BQ (0151) 7077888
Some reporters regard this restaurant in a Georgian house as an "old favourite", and it's undoubtedly "good for pre-theatre"; overall, however, feedback is a little up-and-down.
/ **Details:** *www.thesidedoor.co.uk; 10 pm, Sun 4 pm; closed Sun D.*

60 Hope Street **£57** 4 4 4
60 Hope St L1 9BZ (0151) 707 6060
This townhouse near the Anglican cathedral was the first modern British restaurant of any repute in the city, and fans claim it's "still head and shoulders above the rest"; perhaps that's over-egging it nowadays, but all reports acclaim its "very good" food and "helpful" and "informative" service.
/ **Details:** *www.60hopestreet.com; @60HopeSt; 10.30 pm, Sun 8 pm.*

Spire **£46** 4 4 2
1 Church Rd L15 9EA (0151) 734 5040
"Very busy" this "cramped" Wavertree restaurant may be, but fans insist that's because the food it offers is "the best in town"; critics, though, do feel it "could do with a bit more panache".
/ **Details:** *www.spirerestaurant.co.uk; @spirerestaurant; Mon-Thu 9 pm, Fri & Sat 9.30 pm; closed Mon L, Sat L & Sun.*

Tai Pan **£36** T
WH Lung Bdg, Great Howard St L5 9TZ
(0151) 207 3888
"Excellent dim sum on a Sunday lunchtime, and at very reasonable prices" – this hangar-sized Cantonese, above an oriental supermarket, is a top tip "for all the family… whatever its size!"
/ **Details:** *11.30 pm, Sun 9.30 pm.*

Yukti **£36** 3 4 3
L13 3BS (0151) 228 2225
In a striking new building in Old Swan, an Indian restaurant that's "a bit different from the norm" – especially useful in a city with a weak subcontinental scene; it's praised for its "fantastic range of Indian and fusion dishes", and its "prompt" and "friendly" service too.
/ **Details:** *www.yukti.co.uk.*

LLANARMON DC, DENBIGHSHIRE 5–3A

The Hand at Llanarmonn **£45** T
Ceiriog Valley LL20 7LD (01691) 600666
"Well worth a journey from the NW for Sunday lunch" – a cheerful pub-cum-restaurant recommended for its all-round standards.
/ **Details:** *www.thehandhotel.co.uk; 8.45 pm; no Amex.* **Accommodation:** *13 rooms, from £105.*

The West Arms Hotel **£47** T
LL20 7LD (01691) 600665
Not much choice in this "remote" area, so all the more worth knowing about this "dated but charming" hotel, tipped for its "very good food".
/ **Details:** *www.thewestarms.co.uk; 9 pm; no Amex.*
Accommodation: *15 rooms, from £65.*

LLANDENNY, MONMOUTHSHIRE 2–2A

Raglan Arms **£46** T
NP15 1DL (01291) 690800
In a thinly provided area, a smart rural gastropub, tipped not just for its "consistently good" food, but also for its "lovely atmosphere" ("especially in winter, when you can sink into the sofa by the fire"). / **Details:** *www.raglanarms.com; 9 pm; closed Mon & Sun D.*

LLANDEWI SKIRRID, MONMOUTHSHIRE 2–1A

The Walnut Tree **£62** 5 4 3
NP7 8AW (01873) 852797
"Eschewing any ostentatious novelty, Shaun Hill just cooks fantastic dishes with every flavour-note perfectly pitched", at this famous rural restaurant, which is currently on something of a 'high'; the occasional critic, though, can find the setting rather "dull". / **Details:** *www.thewalnuttreeinn.com; @lovewalnuttree; 3m NE of Abergavenny on B4521; 9.30 pm; closed Mon & Sun.* **Accommodation:** *5 rooms, from £300 (2 bed cottage).*

LLANDRILLO, DENBIGHSHIRE 4–2D

Tyddyn Llan **£76** 5 5 4
LL21 0ST (01490) 440264
"A great destination"; Bryan & Susan Webb's "special" country house hotel has a "lovely" and "remote" rural location, and won Wales's highest rating for cuisine this year – "top-class" food (and "not just in token portions either!"), and "complemented by a superb wine list".
/ **Details:** *www.tyddynllan.co.uk; @bryanwweb; on B4401 between Corwen and Bala; 9 pm; (Mon-Thu L by prior arrangement only); no Amex.*
Accommodation: *12 rooms, from £180.*

LLANDUDNO, CONWY 4–1D

Dining Room
Bodysgallen Hall £69 335
The Royal Welsh Way LL30 1RS
(01492) 584466
*A "marvellous setting" (just outside the town, with beautiful gardens) makes this long-established Elizabethan manor house hotel (owned by the National Trust) a major local destination; though one long term fan would like to see "more menu variation", its "silver service" style generally pleases. / **Details:** www.bodysgallen.com; @BodysgallenHall; 2m off A55 on A470; 9.15 pm, Fri & Sat 9.30 pm; closed Mon; no tracksuits, trainers or sportswear; children: 6+. **Accommodation:** 31 rooms, from £179.*

Jaya £37 433
36 Church Walks LL30 2HN (01492) 818 198
*"Smart and well-presented", the Indian cuisine at this restaurant-with-rooms often comes with an African twist – of interest anywhere, but especially in N Wales!; occasional diners, though, may feel that they "don't get nearly as much attention as the residents". / **Details:** www.jayarestaurant.co.uk; 9.15 pm; closed Mon, Tue, Wed L, Thu L, Fri L, Sat L & Sun L; no Amex.*

Terrace Restaurant
St Tudno Hotel £49 342
Promenade LL30 2LP (01492) 874411
*This "very traditional seaside hotel", on the front, has made quite a name for itself with its "imaginative" cuisine (and a "comprehensive", if "pricey", wine list); "despite the odd flaw, the food is good". / **Details:** www.st-tudno.co.uk; @sttudnohotel; 9.30 pm; no shorts; children: 6+ after 6.30 pm. **Accommodation:** 18 rooms, from £100.*

LLANGYBI, MONMOUTHSHIRE 2–2A

The White Hart
Village Inn £39 ⓣ
NP15 1NP (01633) 450258
*"Set in the relaxed setting of a village pub", this is tipped as an "amazing place to visit", "whether it's a full tasting menu you're after, or just a steak sandwich" – "this place does it all and does it well". / **Details:** www.thewhitehartvillageinn.com.*

LLANWRTYD WELLS, POWYS 4–4D

Carlton Riverside £53 443
Irfon Cr LD5 4SP (01591) 610248
*"What a delightful find in a foodie desert" – TV chef Mary Ann Gilchrist "has not lost her touch" at this "reliable" mid-Wales inn, commended for its "beautifully judged" food and "warm" atmosphere; menus have got "more varied" in recent times too. / **Details:** www.carltonriverside.com; 8.30 pm; D only, closed Sun; no Amex. **Accommodation:** 4 rooms, from £60.*

LLYSWEN, POWYS 2–1A

Llangoed Hall £93 324
LD3 0YP (01874) 754525
*"Wonderful" food and a "real sense of occasion" reward many of the reporters who seek out this "romantic" country house hotel; "very ambitious pricing", though, undercuts support on a number of fronts. / **Details:** www.llangoedhall.com; @TheLlangoedHall; 11m NW of Brecon on A470; 8.45 pm; no Amex; jacket required at D. **Accommodation:** 23 rooms, from £210.*

LOCH LOMOND, DUNBARTONSHIRE 9–4B

Martin Wishart
Cameron House £94 554
G83 8QZ (01389) 722504
*"Lovely views of Loch Lomond" are undoubtedly a major draw to Martin Wishart's "light" and "bright" country house hotel dining room, but by all accounts the food is "amazing" too. / **Details:** www.martinwishartlochlomond.co.uk; @RMWLeith; over Erskine Bridge to A82, follow signs to Loch Lomond; 9.45 pm. **Accommodation:** 134 rooms, from £215.*

LOCHINVER, HIGHLAND 9–1B

The Albannach £66 544
IV27 4LP (01571) 844407
*"A brilliant dining experience"; this luxurious restaurant-with-rooms, in a remote and beautiful corner of the Highlands, offers not just a fixed menu "to die for", but a "great wine list" and "very well-trained staff" – "worth the long trip". / **Details:** www.thealbannach.co.uk; closed Mon, Tue, Wed L, Thu L, Fri L, Sat L & Sun L; no Amex; children: 12+. **Accommodation:** 5 rooms, from £295.*

LOCKSBOTTOM, KENT 3–3B

Chapter One £56 544
Farnborough Common BR6 8NF
(01689) 854848
*"Always a firm favourite" – this well-known destination in a small village outside Bromley maintains an impressive following, thanks to Andrew McLeish's "unfailingly good" cuisine; it offers "amazing bang for the buck" too, especially the "conspicuous bargain" of a weekday lunch. / **Details:** www.chaptersrestaurants.com; @chapter1kent; Mon-Thu 9.30 pm, Fri & Sat 10.30 pm; no trainers; booking: max 12.*

LONG CRENDON, BUCKINGHAMSHIRE 2–2D

The Angel £49 322
47 Bicester Rd HP18 9EE (01844) 208268
Generally good feedback of late for this restaurant-with-rooms, which combines "above-average pub

food", a "lovely country location" and "friendly and efficient service"; some regulars feel, though, that "it's just not as good as it used to be". / **Details:** www.angelrestaurant.co.uk; @theangeluk; 2m NW of Thames, off B4011; 9.30 pm; closed Sun D. **Accommodation:** 4 rooms, from £110.

The Mole & Chicken £50 344
Easington HP18 9EY (01844) 208387
"The scene is set for romance", at this "cosy, informal country restaurant-with-rooms", which benefits from a garden and a "pleasant terrace with views"; fans also praise its "lovely" and "imaginative" food.
/ **Details:** www.themoleandchicken.co.uk; @moleandchicken; follow signs from B4011 at Long Crendon; 9.30 pm, Sun 9 pm. **Accommodation:** 5 rooms, from £110.

LONG MELFORD, SUFFOLK 3–1C

Melford Valley Tandoori £27 454
Hall St CO10 9JT (01787) 311 518
"The best Indian we've found in many years of searching" – this smartly modern subcontinental continues to deserve its local pre-eminence.
/ **Details:** www.melfordvalley.com; 11.30 pm.

Swan £48 455
Hall St CO10 9JQ (01787) 464545
"So much more than a gastropub", the Macmillan family's fine-dining venture has "real aspirations"; the "creative menu" is "the best it has ever been", showcasing food that "excites the palate" – and "they are adding rooms this year so there'll be even more reason to visit".
/ **Details:** www.longmelfordswan.co.uk; Mon-Thu 9 pm, Fri-Sat 10 pm; closed Sun D.

LONG WHITTENHAM, OXFORDSHIRE 2–2D

The Vine and Spice £42 434
High St OX14 4QH (01865) 409 900
With its "offbeat and delicious" Indian dishes and "friendly and charming" service too, this "cosy, converted village pub" is a hit with all who comment on it. / **Details:** www.thevineandspice.co.uk; 10.30 pm.

LOUGHBOROUGH, LEICESTERSHIRE 5–3D

The Hammer & Pincers £48 332
5 East Rd LE12 6ST (01509) 880735
"Great food, good-value set menu, best Sunday lunch in the area…" – such are the plusses fans see in the family-run beamed restaurant, in the village of Wymeswold, which almost invariably inspires positive reports.
/ **Details:** www.hammerandpincers.co.uk; 9.30 pm, Sun 6 pm; closed Mon & Sun D; no Amex.

LOWER BOCKHAMPTON, DORSET 2–4B

Yalbury Cottage £53 554
DT2 8PZ (01305) 262382
"Truly wow", "the best meal we've eaten in a long time"… there's no let-up in superlatives for Ariane & Jamie Jones's "wonderful" (and remote) restaurant-with-rooms; only problem? – "you wants to eat everything", so "pace yourself to leave room for the wonderful puds!"
/ **Details:** www.yalburycottage.com; @YalburyDorset; 9 pm; Tues to Sat L - booking only; no Amex. **Accommodation:** 8 rooms, from £120.

LOWER FROYLE, HAMPSHIRE 2–3D

The Anchor Inn £48 424
GU34 4NA (01420) 23261
A "ridiculously pretty" and "well-established" pub, with a "wonderful location in the middle of the Hampshire countryside"; it offers a "sophisticated menu" (including good game), so it's perhaps no surprise that it can seem "a bit pricey".
/ **Details:** www.anchorinnatlowerfroyle.co.uk; 9.30 pm, Sun 9 pm. **Accommodation:** 5 rooms, from £120.

LOWER HARDRES, KENT 3–3D

The Granville £44 T
Street End CT4 7AL (01227) 700402
"Superior-quality food for a pub", and "good value" too – this country pub is consistently tipped in the survey… but, judging by the very modest volume of reports, you'd never guess it was under the same ownership as the fabled Sportsman at Seasalter.
/ **Details:** 9 pm; closed Mon & Sun D.

LOWER ODDINGTON, GLOUCESTERSHIRE 2–1C

The Fox Inn £47 334
GL56 0UR (01451) 870555
This "classic Cotswold gastropub" offers "superior" grub in a "wonderful location" (with "lots of lovely eating areas"); there's a feeling among some regulars that it's "more expensive" and has "lost some of its buzz", though, since being taken over by The Old Butchers in Stow.
/ **Details:** www.foxinn.net; @foxinn; on A436 near Stow-on-the-Wold; 9.30 pm, Sun 9.30 pm; no Amex. **Accommodation:** 3 rooms, from £85.

LOWER SLAUGHTER, GLOUCESTERSHIRE 2–1C

Lower Slaughter Manor Von Essen £50 343
GL54 2HP (01451) 820456
Part of the same empire as Gidleigh Park, this Cotswolds country house hotel offers "top-notch food in lovely surroundings"; lunches offer particularly "great value".
/ **Details:** www.lowerslaughter.co.uk; 2m from

Burton-on-the-Water on A429; 9 pm; no jeans or trainers. ***Accommodation:*** *19 rooms, from £310.*

LUDLOW, SHROPSHIRE 5–4A

La Bécasse **£89** 222
17 Corve St SY8 1DA (01584) 872325
Perhaps as a result of the recent trials and tribulations of the vainglorious parent '10-in-8' empire, this destination restaurant appears "rather to have lost the plot"; fans do still hail an "excellent gourmet experience with fabulous wines", but the overall experience seems "unremarkable" or "pretentious" too often for comfort.
/ ***Details:*** *www.labecasse.co.uk; 9 pm, Sat 9.30 pm; closed Mon, Tue L & Sun D; no Amex; no trainers.*

The Fish House **£25** 543
SY8 1AB (01584) 879790
"Just four tables within a fish shop... but the best seafood platter ever" – that's the whole story on a tiny establishment which "lives up to the rave reviews".

The French Pantry **£48** 433
SY8 1RL (01584) 879133
"A good second to Mr Underhill's!"; the consistency of feedback on this "genuinely French-feeling" bistro is impressive – "good ingredients, well presented and with intense flavours", plus a "great wine list" too. / ***Details:*** *www.thefrenchpantry.co.uk/.*

Green Café
Ludlow Mill On The Green **£36** 554
Dinham Millennium Grn SY8 1EG
(01584) 879872
"Simple and sublime", this riverside café ("with a fantastic view of the weir") is "pretty much perfect on a sunny day"; the food may be "uncomplicated", but it is "glorious" – "as good as, if not better than, the local Michelin-starred jobs"; "I've eaten here 100 times, and only been disappointed once!"
/ ***Details:*** *www.thegreencafe.co.uk; closed Mon, L only Tue-Sun; no Amex.*

Mr Underhill's **£90** 554
Dinham Weir SY8 1EH (01584) 874431
"The Bradleys are consummate hosts" and their "gorgeous" riverside restaurant-with-rooms "does everything incredibly well, but in a confident, relaxed and low-key kind of way", not least cuisine that's "creative without being silly or pretentious".
/ ***Details:*** *www.mr-underhills.co.uk; 8.15 pm; D only, closed Mon & Tue; no Amex; children: 8+.*
Accommodation: *6 rooms, from £140.*

LUPTON, CUMBRIA 7–4D

The Plough Inn **£44** 333
Cow Brow LA6 1PJ (01539) 567 700
Sibling to the Punch Bowl in Crossthwaite, this recently refurbished inn enjoys a "stunning location" (close to the M6 too) and has a "lovely airy dining area"; fans praise its "delicious menu" and child-friendly service, but the occasional sceptic can find standards merely "ordinary".
/ ***Details:*** *www.theploughatlupton.co.uk; @ThePloughLupton; 9 pm.* ***Accommodation:*** *6 rooms, from £115.*

LUTON, BEDFORDSHIRE 3–2A

Luton Hoo
Luton Hoo Hotel **£48** 345
LU1 3TQ (01582) 734437
There's not much doubt that sheer grandeur makes this country house hotel dining room "a stunning place to dine", and the "very jolly" staff are impressive too; the food has traditionally been a weakness, but reports overall suggest it has "stepped up a notch" in recent times.
/ ***Details:*** *www.lutonhoo.co.uk; 4.45 pm; L only.*

LYDFORD, DEVON 1–3C

The Dartmoor Inn **£50** 343
Moorside EX20 4AY (01822) 820221
"Simple but surprisingly good" – the "seasonal" and "sensibly-priced" fare at this old coaching inn, within the National Park, impresses all who report on it, and service is notably "attentive" too; "a great place for lunch and a moorland walk".
/ ***Details:*** *www.dartmoorinn.com; on the A386 Tavistock to Okehampton road; 9.30 pm; closed Mon L & Sun D.* ***Accommodation:*** *3 rooms, from £95.*

LYME REGIS, DORSET 2–4A

Hix Oyster
& Fish House **£55** 435
Cobb Rd DT7 3JP (01297) 446910
The "sensational view" of Lyme Bay isn't the only draw to Mark Hix's glass-fronted building on top of the cliffs – it serves "divine tasting and uniformly superbly presented fish".
/ ***Details:*** *www.restaurantsetcltd.co.uk; @hixlymeregis; 10 pm.*

LYMINGTON, HAMPSHIRE 2–4C

Egan's **£51** 432
24 Gosport St SO41 9BE (01590) 676165
As ever, "consistently high standards" are the hallmark of John and Debbie Egan's bistro, which fans continue to hail for its "amazing value-for-money". / ***Details:*** *10 pm; closed Mon & Sun; no Amex.*

LYMM, CHESHIRE 5–2B

La Boheme **£42** 343
3 Mill Ln WA13 9SD (01925) 753657
"Very popular with the locals in this bit of leafy Cheshire", a "comfortable" dining room where "complex, very French dishes" are often "extremely well done"... and "the quality is continually

*improving". / **Details:** laboheme.co.uk; Mon-Sat 10 pm; Sun 9 pm; closed Mon L & Sat L.*

LYNDHURST, HAMPSHIRE 2–4C

Hartnett Holder & Co Lime Wood Hotel £42 234
Beaulieu Rd SO43 7FZ (02380) 287177
*Ratings have slipped at Angela Hartnett's "delightfully tranquil" and "luxurious" country house yearling, in the New Forest; few reports say the food is terrible, but even some fans "can't help thinking this beautiful spot deserves better", and others just find it "horribly disappointing", given the pedigree. / **Details:** www.limewoodhotel.co.uk; @limewoodhotel; 11 pm.*

MADINGLEY, CAMBRIDGESHIRE 3–1B

Three Horseshoes £49 213
High St CB23 8AB (01954) 210221
*Long a staple for undergrads and their parents, this "lovely" pub with "good interiors" (especially the conservatory) wins praise for its "ambitious" food; as ever, though, the positive feedback vies with protests over "exorbitant" prices and "scatty" service.
/ **Details:** www.threehorseshoesmadingley.co.uk; @3hs_restaurant; 2m W of Cambridge, off A14 or M11; 9.30 pm, Sun 8.30 pm.*

MAIDENHEAD, BERKSHIRE 3–3A

Boulters Riverside Brasserie £52 Ⓣ
Boulters Lock Island SL6 8PE (01628) 621291
*The clue is in the name; it's not really the food ("fair value") which is the attraction of this waterside venue, perched over the Thames, but it's a "lovely setting on a sunny day" – "ask for a window table".
/ **Details:** www.boultersrestaurant.co.uk; @boultersuk; 9.30 pm; closed Sun D.*

The Royal Oak £67 333
Paley St SL6 3JN (01628) 620541
*Parkie's "down-to-earth" (by local standards) pub is something of a "culinary destination" hereabouts, thanks to its "consistent high standards" and "lovely setting" – "sitting in the garden on a sunny day with your pudding and coffee just can't be beaten".
/ **Details:** www.theroyaloakpaleystreet.com; @royaloakpaleystreet; 9.30 pm, Fri & Sat 10 pm; closed Sun D; children: 3+ .*

MAIDSTONE, KENT 3–3C

Frederic Bistro £38 Ⓣ
ME14 1HO (01622) 297414
*"Great French home-cooking at very reasonable prices" makes this "cheerful" bistro a top tip locally.
/ **Details:** www.fredericbistro.com.*

MALMESBURY, WILTSHIRE 2–2C

The Old Bell Hotel £56 Ⓣ
Abbey Row SN16 0BW (01666) 822344
*Many centuries in the hospitality business seem to have taught them something, at this ancient inn in the shadow of the Abbey, which is tipped as a "friendly", "professional" and "relaxed" dining destination; star attraction? – "the best breakfast ever", obviously.
/ **Details:** www.oldbellhotel.com; @oldesthotel; 9 pm, Fri & Sat 9.30 pm. **Accommodation:** 33 rooms, from £115.*

MALVERN, WORCESTERSHIRE 2–1B

The Fig Tree £39 Ⓣ
WR14 2AE (01684) 569909
*A Mediterranean café near the theatre, tipped for its "varied" menu, and its "simple but tasty" cooking; look out for "interesting specials".
/ **Details:** www.figtreemalvern.co.uk.*

MANCHESTER, GREATER MANCHESTER 5–2B

Akbar's £32 434
73-83 Liverpool Rd M3 4NQ (0161) 834 8444
*Thanks to its "excellent authentic curries" at "amazingly reasonable prices", this big and "fancy" Pakistani venture "always seems to be rammed"; "the family-sized naans add to the convivial atmosphere". / **Details:** www.akbars.co.uk; 11 pm, Fri & Sat 11.30 pm; D only; need 10+ to book.*

Albert Square Chop House £46 323
The Memorial Hall, Albert Sq M2 5PF
(0161) 834 1866
*"A new mainstay of the Manchester landscape", which fans say is "just as good as its siblings Sam's and Mr Thomas's"; an 80-seater operation in a Victorian warehouse, it offers a "pleasing mix" of "traditional English dishes" and "more modern variants".
/ **Details:** www.albertsquarechophouse.com; @chophouseAlbert; 9.45 pm, Sun 8.30 pm.*

Albert's Shed £47 344
20 Castle St M3 4LZ (0161) 839 9818
*A canal-side Castlefield fixture which "needs to work on its consistency"; it's a "lovely" sort of place, though, and on a good day "unbelievable value for money" ("especially the two- or three-course lunch menu"). / **Details:** www.albertsshed.com; 10 pm, Fri 10.30 pm, Sat 11 pm, Sun 9.30 pm; no Amex.*

Albert's Worsley £43 Ⓣ
M27 0AA (0161) 794 1234
*In Swinton, a "crowded" and "hectic" offshoot of Albert's Shed, already tipped for its "generally very good" food; lunchtime menus offer particularly "excellent" value. / **Details:** www.albertsworsley.com.*

Almost Famous **£16** 332
100-102 High St M4 1HP () no tel
A "high-octane" hangout, consistently highly rated for its "inventive" burgers; staff can seem irritatingly "busy taking selfies of themselves", though, and 30+s may decry the formula as "slop with loud music"; there is another branch in the Great Northern Warehouse (as well as Liverpool and Leeds).

Armenian Taverna **£37** 433
3-5 Princess St M2 4DF (0161) 834 9025
Heading for half a century in business, this hidden-away city-centre stalwart is still a real "find"; "gusty" mezze stand out on a menu which offers "generous portions of tasty Armenian fare".
*/ **Details:** www.armeniantaverna.co.uk; 11 pm; closed Mon, Sat L & Sun L.*

Aumbry **£79** 332
2 Church Ln M25 1AJ (0161) 7985841
The "weird and wonderful" combinations at this "bright and simple" Prestwich venture divides reporters; to most, this is "a star of the north", offering "exquisite" dishes, but there are those who "are disappointed after the raves", feeling "it tries too hard" (and, in particular, "over-uses sous-vide").
*/ **Details:** www.aumbryrestaurant.co.uk; @_aumbry; 9.30 pm; closed Mon, Tue L, Wed L, Thu L & Sun D; SRA-67%.*

Australasia **£62** 335
1 The Avenue Spinningfields M3 3AP
(0161) 831 0288
*"Enjoy the vibe!"; this "cool but unpretentious" basement, just off Deansgate, has a "fabulous" interior, and most reports say the Pacific Rim fusion fare is "fantastic" too; critics do find the place "flashy" and "deafening", though, not to mention "too expensive". / **Details:** www.australasia.uk.com; @AustralasiaMcr; 10.45 pm.*

Bar San Juan **£30** Ⓣ
M21 9EG (0161) 881 9259
*A top tip for those seeking a "really authentic Spanish experience", this "tiny" Chorlton tapas bar serves "great, good-value" food in a "relaxed" yet "buzzy" environment. / **Details:** barsanjuan.com.*

Chaophraya, **£47** 333
Chapel Walks M2 1HN (0161) 832 8342
*"Always very good", this "top-drawer Thai" remains quite a crowd-pleaser; doubters can find it on the "pricey" side, though, or feel the cooking needs more "pizzazz". / **Details:** www.chaophraya.co.uk; @ChaophrayaThai; 10.30 pm.*

Croma **£35** 344
1-3 Clarence St M2 4DE (0161) 237 9799
"Still the easiest choice in the city-centre", this "buzzy" spot, near the Town Hall, remains "very popular" for its "well-prepared" pizzas and "charming" service; it's "so much better than the big chains" (including PizzaExpress, for whom the proprietors used to work).
*/ **Details:** www.cromapizza.co.uk; 10 pm, Fri & Sat 11 pm.*

Dimitri's **£46** 334
1 Campfield Arc M3 4FN (0161) 839 3319
"Always worth a visit", especially for "really good fresh mezze'" – this Greek establishment, adjoining a Victorian arcade off Deansgate, maintains its position as a general crowd-pleaser.
*/ **Details:** www.dimitris.co.uk; 11.30 pm.*

Evuna **£43** 334
Deansgate M3 4EW (0161) 819 2752
*"The genuine Spanish experience"; this city-centre bar offers "great tapas and fantastic wines" (including "some interesting and good-value marques from small producers"), in a brick interior that's "full of character". / **Details:** www.evuna.com; @evunamanchester; 11 pm, Sun 9 pm.*

The French Restaurant
Midland Hotel **£99** 343
Peter St M60 2DS (0161) 236 3333
"This is the food Manchester was waiting for!", says one of the many fans of Simon Rogan's "stunning" modernistic relaunch of what, back in the '70s, was the grandest dining room in town; even fans, though can note dishes varying "from exceptional to ordinary", and the decor is "stark" for some tastes.
*/ **Details:** www.qhotels.co.uk; 8.45 pm; closed Mon, Tue L & Sun; no jeans or trainers; children: 9+.*
***Accommodation:** 312 rooms, from £145.*

Glamorous **£39** 433
Wing Yip Bus' Centre, Oldham Rd M4 5HU
(0161) 839 3312
"Dim sum well worth the hike" are the particular draw to the "HK-style" restaurant above the Ancoats branch of the Wing Yip supermarket empire; "good-value banquets" too.
*/ **Details:** www.glamorous-restaurant.co.uk.*

Great Kathmandu **£37** 533
140 Burton Rd M20 1JQ (0161) 434 6413
"Forget the Curry Mile, and head to West Didsbury for the best curry in town"; this "always-busy" spot is "much expanded in recent years, but has not suffered any decline in quality".
*/ **Details:** www.greatkathmandu.com; midnight.*

Green's **£43** 343
43 Lapwing Ln M20 2NT (0161) 434 4259
"Best veggie in Manchester…" – this crammed West Didsbury spot has many admirers for the "yummy loveliness" of its no-meat cuisine.
*/ **Details:** www.greensdidsbury.co.uk; Sun-Wed 9.30 pm, Thu-Sat 10 pm; closed Mon L; no Amex.*

Grill on the Alley £51 343
5 Ridgefield M2 6EG (0161) 833 3465
An "intimate" and "atmospheric" spot, in the heart of the city; culinary attractions – "top-notch" steaks and "good-value lunch specials".
*/ **Details:** www.blackhouse.uk.com; @GrillManc; 11 pm.*

Hawksmoor £64 T
184-186 Deansgate M3 3WB awaiting tel
This acclaimed steakhouse group finally makes its move outside the capital, having snapped up a space in a former courthouse building on Deansgate, just a stone's throw from the city's new Spinningfields development; opening early-2015.

James Martin £52 T
M3 4LP (0161) 828 0345
In a warehouse, and above a casino, this city-centre restaurant has an odd but, on most reports, "tasteful" setting; reports are all good and some rate the place "excellent".
*/ **Details:** www.jamesmartinmanchester.co.uk.*

Jem & I £43 432
1c School Ln M20 6RD (0161) 445 3996
"Good food at reasonable prices" – the invariable theme of commentary on this "warm" and "professional" Didsbury bistro, which continues to flourish in the shade of the Lime Tree (where the boss once worked).
*/ **Details:** www.jemandirestaurant.co.uk; 10 pm, Fri & Sat 10.30 pm; no Amex.*

Katsouris Deli £14 432
113 Deansgate M3 2BQ (0161) 819 1260
*"The mezze plates are great value" at this affordable city-centre feature; you may have to queue. / **Details:** www.karsourisdeli.co.uk; L only; no Amex.*

The Lime Tree £50 454
8 Lapwing Ln M20 2WS (0161) 445 1217
*This "superb" Didsbury brasserie is for its many fans "the best and most consistent restaurant in Manchester" – a "second home" that "never puts a foot wrong", offering "excellent" cooking, and "most welcoming" service that's "never rushed". / **Details:** www.thelimetreerestaurant.co.uk; @thelimetreeres; 10 pm; closed Mon L & Sat L.*

Manchester House £81 544
M3 3BZ (0161) 835 2557
"At last, the decent restaurant Manchester has been waiting for!"; with its "clever, innovative and fun" menu, and its "cool and relaxed" style, Aiden Byrnes's new venture has – on most (if not quite all) accounts – made a simply "stunning" début.
*/ **Details:** www.manchesterhouse.uk.com.*

Michael Caines ABode Hotel £67 553
107 Piccadilly M1 2DB (0161) 200 5678
"No one would rate it in the top three in Manchester… but the cooking is actually fabulous!"; the basement setting may be a bit "dour", but this well-established dining room, by Piccadilly Station, actually inspires much more consistent feedback than those which have recently been hogging the headlines!
*/ **Details:** www.michaelcaines.com; 10 pm; closed Mon & Sun; no shorts or football colours; to book 8+ to go through Events. **Accommodation:** 61 rooms, from £79.*

Mr Cooper's House & Garden The Midland Hotel £50 443
Peter St M60 2DS (0161) 236 3333
"The less posh part of Simon Rogan's empire" – this "massively high-ceilinged" brasserie offers an opportunity for the ever more celebrated chef to "stretch his legs beyond the narrow focus of British ingredients", to create some "vibrant and delicious" dishes.
*/ **Details:** www.mrcoopershouseandgarden.co.uk.*

Mr Thomas's Chop House £41 322
52 Cross St M2 7AR (0161) 832 2245
"Consistently good enough!"; the solidly English fare on offer at this Victorian boozer, in the city centre, may be "unexciting"… but that's just how the big business crowd the place attracts seem to like it!
*/ **Details:** www.tomschophouse.com; @chophouseToms; 9.30 pm, Sun 8 pm.*

Piccolino £48 343
8 Clarence St M2 4DW (0161) 835 9860
"Still a little gem in the city-centre"; this Italian brasserie, near the Town Hall, is a "lively" and "reliable" operation which, though part of a chain, retains a surprisingly "individual" appeal.
*/ **Details:** www.piccolinorestaurants.co.uk/manchester; 11 pm, Sun 10 pm.*

Red Chilli £25 443
70-72 Portland St M1 4GU (0161) 236 2888
It's not just "the best set lunch in Chinatown" (or Oxford Road) that makes this "nicely decorated" spot "simply the best Chinese" for some reporters – all reports confirm that the food is "fantastic", and diehard fans, inevitably, insist that it "puts the Yang Sing in the shade".
*/ **Details:** www.redchillirestaurant.co.uk; 11 pm; need 6+ to book.*

Rose Garden £42 543
218 Burton Rd M20 2LW (0161) 478 0747
William Mills's minimalist restaurant offers "beautifully presented modern European fare" alongside "excellent wines" from a local merchant... no wonder it's fast becoming "a favourite amongst the hip south Manchester crowd".

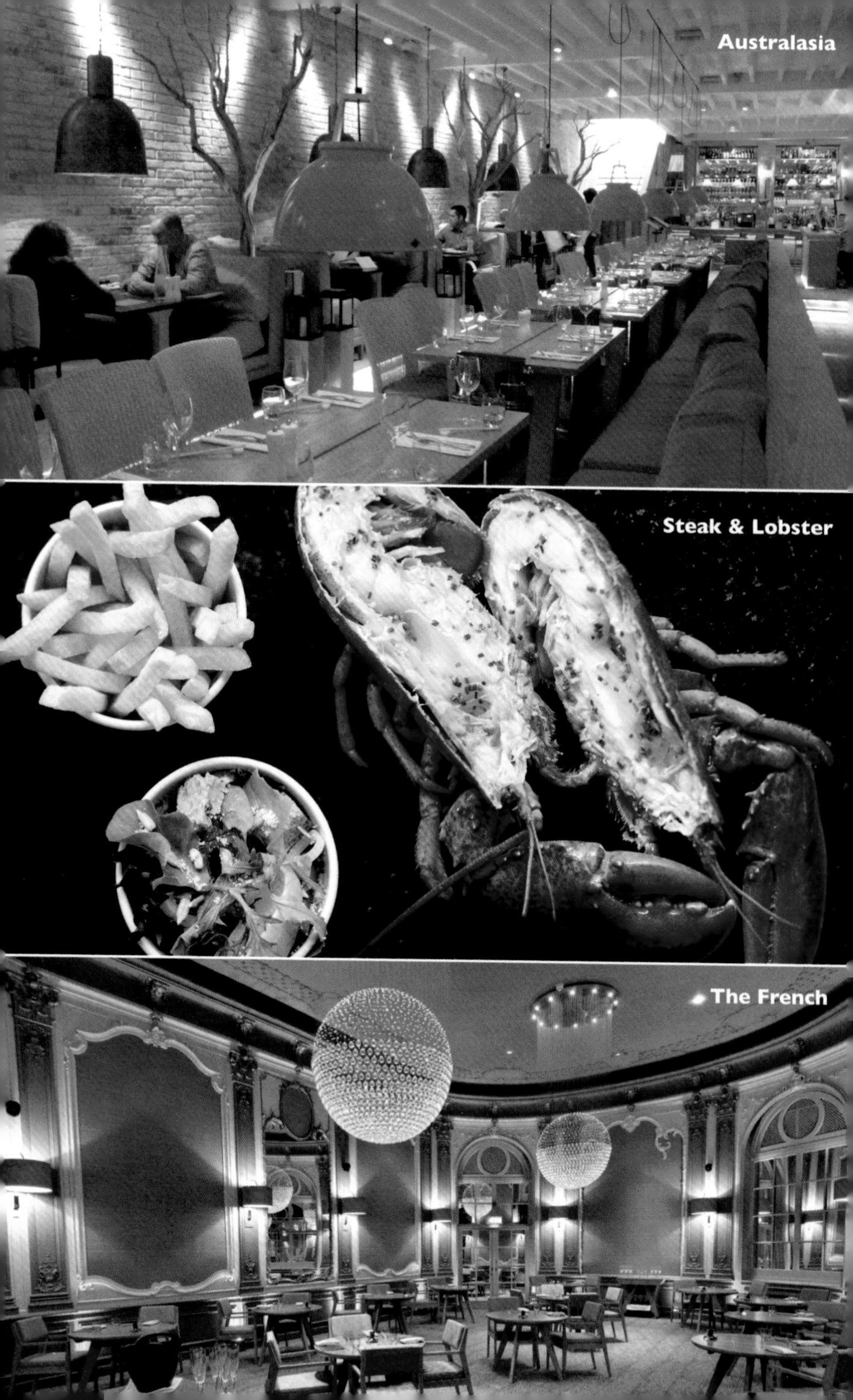
Australasia
Steak & Lobster
The French

Rosso £67 224
43 Spring Gdns M2 2BG (0161) 8321400
Grandly housed in a former bank at the top of a fashionable shopping street, Rio Ferdinand's "blingy" restaurant is a handy venue for a "good-value set lunch" – pay full whack, though, and you may be more inclined to feel that it's just a "bog-standard Italian".
/ **Details:** *www.rossorestaurants.com; @rossorestaurants; 11 pm.*

Sam's Chop House £45 343
Back Pool Fold, Chapel Walks M2 1HN
(0161) 834 3210
"Hard to beat for filling, very traditional British comfort food" ("steak and kidney pud' is the star!") – this pubby city-centre spot is "very appealing to the Mancunian palate".
/ **Details:** *www.samschophouse.com; @chophousesams; 9.30 pm, Sun 8 pm.*

San Carlo £41 214
40 King Street West M3 2WY
(0161) 834 6226
"Love the buzz", say fans of this "always-busy" central Italian, who find it "always busy" and "fun-filled"; the food is "very average", though, and service can be "disinterested" – "if you like paying through the nose to spot the Man U reserves and their orange-skinned WAGS, you'll love this place", sniffs one critic.
/ **Details:** *www.sancarlo.co.uk; 11 pm.*

San Carlo Cicchetti £50 223
42 King Street West M3 2QG
(0161) 839 2233
Implausibly located on the ground-floor of House of Fraser, a "bustling" San Carlo Group offshoot serving Venetian-style small plates "with pizzaz"; while its cuisine is "not always successful", and its waiters can "lay on the smarm", fans say it's "good for a quick pick-me-up during shopping".
/ **Details:** *www.sancarlocicchetti.co.uk; 11 pm.*

Second Floor Restaurant Harvey Nichols £58 232
21 New Cathedral St M1 1AD
(0161) 828 8898
"OK, so it's not cutting edge", but this department store restaurant continues to attract new converts with its "fantastic" flavours and "basic" but "well-executed" cuisine. / **Details:** *www.harveynichols.com; 9.30 pm; closed Mon D & Sun D.*

63 Degrees £60 232
20 Church St M4 1PN (0161) 832 5438
"Well prepared" the Gallic dishes certainly are… so it's a shame reports on the Moreau family's Northern Quarter restaurant almost invariably note that they come in "small portions" and/or "priced above their station".
/ **Details:** *www.63degrees.co.uk; @63DegreesNQ; 10.30 pm, Fri 11 pm; closed Mon & Sun; to book 6+ deposit £15 per head.*

Solita £41 322
37 Turner St M4 1DW (0161) 839 2200
"Top burgers" win almost universal praise for this Northern Quarter adherent to the 'dirty food' movement; the social media marketing, though, does contribute to some reporters' impression that the place is "very up itself".
/ **Details:** *www.solita.co.uk; 10 pm, Fri-Sat 11 pm, Sun 9 pm.*

Tai Pan £36 443
81-97 Upper Brook St M13 9TX (0161) 273 2798
"A great favourite of Chinese students and restaurateurs"; this Longsight Chinese is particularly sought out for dim sum on Sundays, when this is a particularly "family-friendly" destination.
/ **Details:** *11 pm, Sun 9.30 pm.*

Tampopo £31 334
16 Albert Sq M2 5PF (0161) 819 1966
"A Manchester favourite"; this "cheap and cheerful" canteen-style stalwart, the original outpost of a noodle bar mini-chain, is "always a good choice for a tasty Asian meal at a reasonable price".
/ **Details:** *www.tampopo.co.uk; 11 pm, Sun 10 pm; need 7+ to book.*

Teacup On Thomas Street £23 343
53-55 Thomas St M4 1NA (0161) 832 3233
"Epic cakes and lunches that are much better than you'd ever guess, all washed down by artisanal teas and a cool vibe!"… and if you visit this Northern Quarter café "you might see proprietor and local DJ/hero Mr Scruff too!"
/ **Details:** *www.teacupandcakes.com.*

This & That £12 522
3 Soap St M4 1EW (0161) 832 4971
"Don't be fooled by it being cheap, this is quality food!" – this "rough-and-ready" Pakistani café, "down a hidden side street", changes little from year to year, and continues to offer "homestyle curries with huge depth of flavour at peanuts-prices".
/ **Details:** *www.thisandthatcafe.co.uk; 4 pm, Fri & Sat 8 pm; no credit cards.*

Wing's £51 455
1 Lincoln Sq M2 5LN (0161) 834 9000
"A five-star Chinese, right in the heart of the city"; judged as an 'all-rounder', there is no real doubt that this "pricey" spot is "the best Chinese restaurant in Manchester" (and arguably the best of any type) – even hardcore Yang Singers may conceded that "service and ambience here are far superior". / **Details:** *www.wingsrestaurant.co.uk; 10.30 pm; closed Sat L; children: 11+ after 8 pm Mon-Fri.*

Yang Sing £43 5 3 3
34 Princess St M1 4JY (0161) 236 2200
*"Still the best Chinese in town" – "you can eat like a king" at the Yeung family's "vast" Chinatown legend (est 1977), which serves many "ethereal" dishes (and where there's been "a greater emphasis on dim sum of late"); "keep an eye on social media for specials". / **Details:** www.yang-sing.com; @yangsing; 11.30 pm, Sat 12.15 am, Sun 10.30 pm.*

Yuzu £33 5 4 2
M1 4EE (0161) 236 4159
*"A fabulous new Japanese, which avoids sushi and sashimi and concentrates on tempura and yakitori to great effect"; no wonder this Chinatown spot gets "very busy"… "mostly with Japanese people!" / **Details:** www.yuzumanchester.co.uk.*

MANNINGTREE, ESSEX 3–2C

Lucca Enoteca £38 4 3 3
39-43 High St CO11 1AH (01206) 390044
*"Great pizzas at reasonable prices" (with "tasty salads" too) are the highlight attraction at this "busy and bustling Italian", run by the owners of the nearby Mistley Thorn; all the reports it inspires are notable for their enthusiasm. / **Details:** www.luccafoods.co.uk; 9.30 pm, Fri & Sat 10 pm; no Amex.*

MARAZION, CORNWALL 1–4A

Ben's Cornish Kitchen £37 4 5 3
TR17 0EL (01736) 719200
*Plenty of positive feedback for this "friendly" five-year-old family-run bistro, by the sea, where chef Ben Prior produces some "stunning" dishes (mostly fish and seafood, but meat options are also "excellent"); "sit upstairs to catch a glimpse of St Michael's Mount". / **Details:** www.benscornishkitchen.com.*

MARGATE, KENT 3–3D

The Ambrette £40 5 3 2
44 King St CT9 1QE (01843) 231 504
*"Fantastic Anglo-Indian cuisine in this haven in a generally depressing town!" – Dev Biswal "maintains high standards" at this "unremarkable-looking" operation, where the "subtle" cuisine offers "a different taste experience every time". / **Details:** www.theambrette.co.uk; @the_ambrette; 9.30 pm, Fri & Sat 10 pm.*

Bay at Sands £51 Ⓣ
CT9 1DH (01843) 228228
*Tipped for its "beautiful sea views", this new hotel dining room is certainly as "calming" a venue as you'll find; most, but not quite all, early-days reports say this is a "wonderful" all-rounder too. / **Details:** www.sandshotelmargate.co.uk.*

GB Pizza £28 4 4 3
14a Marine Drive CT9 1DH (01843) 297 700
*A "basic" seafront spot with wonderful views, and a single culinary attraction – "superb" pizzas with "extremely thin crusts" and an "unusual" range of "stunning" toppings. / **Details:** www.greatbritishpizzacompany.wordpress.com; 9.30 pm; closed Sun D.*

The Greedy Cow £15 5 4 4
CT9 1ER (01843) 447557
*For an "amazing burger" or "great pulled pork sarnie" this "no-frills" café is hard to beat locally – "wholesome food, served by very pleasant staff, in a relaxed style". / **Details:** www.thegreedycow.com/.*

Yama's Thai Eaterie £30 Ⓣ
CT9 1JT (01843) 229899
A "friendly and unpretentious" high street café that's tipped not only for its English breakfasts but also for "amazing" Thai food at notably "reasonable" prices; okay, so it's "not posh nosh, but it's very good" nonetheless.

MARLBOROUGH, WILTSHIRE 2–2C

The Harrow at Little Bedwyn £76 5 5 4
Little Bedwyn SN8 3JP (01672) 870871
*"A stunning hidden-away restaurant, serving sublime food"; Sue & Roger Jones's "cosy" venue is hailed in pretty much all reports for its "excellent food and ambience"; "splendid" wines too, especially the "superb Australian selection". / **Details:** www.theharrowatlittlebedwyn.co.uk; 9 pm; closed Mon, Tue & Sun; no trainers.*

MARLOW, BUCKINGHAMSHIRE 3–3A

Hand & Flowers £77 4 3 3
West St SL7 2BP (01628) 482277
*"To call it a gastropub is unfair, as it is perhaps THE gastropub"; so say the legions of fans of Tom Kerridge's two-Michelin-star establishment, lauding dishes "packed full of flavour", which turn "the everyday into something extraordinary"; a hard core of refuseniks, though, continues to find it "over-rated". / **Details:** www.thehandandflowers.co.uk; 9.30 pm; closed Sun D. **Accommodation:** 4 rooms, from £140.*

The Royal Oak £43 4 4 4
Frieth Rd, Bovingdon Grn SL7 2JF (01628) 488611
*A "friendly" and "relaxed" Chilterns pub-restaurant whose "consistently good" food – "classics with a twist" – goes down well with all who comment on it. / **Details:** www.royaloakmarlow.co.uk; @royaloakSL7; 9.30 pm, Fri & Sat 10 pm.*

The Vanilla Pod £65 5 4 3
31 West St SL7 2LS (01628) 898101
Michael Macdonald's dining room can feel "a tiny

bit cramped", but its style can also be described as "intimate", and it wins high praise for its "attentive" service and "absolutely top-notch food" (which is at least as good as at the much-ballyhooed Hand & Flowers, nearby).
/ **Details:** *www.thevanillapod.co.uk; 10 pm; closed Mon & Sun.*

MASHAM, NORTH YORKSHIRE 8–4B

Black Sheep Brewery Bistro **£35** 3|4|3
Wellgarth HG4 4EN (01765) 680101
A "busy" and "bustling" café in the heart of the brewery, with hearty food and "cheerful and attentive" service plus, as you might expect, a "wide choice of ales, from Black Sheep Best to Riggwelter"; "sit in the balcony area, where you can view the activity below".
/ **Details:** *www.blacksheep.co.uk; @blacksheepbeer; 9 pm; Sun-Wed L only, Thu-Sat L & D; no Amex.*

Samuel's Swinton Park Hotel & Spa **£76** 4|5|5
HG4 4JH (01765) 680900
A "most memorable experience all-round" – the "magisterial" dining room of this large country house hotel makes a "very romantic" backdrop in which to enjoy Stephen Bulmer's "exquisite" cuisine, matched with a "proper" wine list.
/ **Details:** *www.swintonpark.com; @SwintonPark; 9.30 pm, Fri & Sat 10 pm; closed Mon L; no jeans or trainers; booking: max 8; children: 8+ at D.* **Accommodation:** *31 rooms, from £185.*

MELBOURNE, DERBYSHIRE 5–3C

Bay Tree **£49** ⓣ
4 Potter St DE73 8HW (01332) 863358
A veteran restaurant (recently refurbished) especially tipped for its champagne breakfasts; service can be "hilarious" too.
/ **Details:** *www.baytreerestaurant.co.uk; 9.30 pm; closed Mon, Tue & Sun D.*

MELLS, SOMERSET 2–3B

The Talbot Inn **£44** 3|4|5
Selwood St BA11 3PN (01373) 812254
TV chef James Martin's home-town venture is the "relaxed" dining room of a grand old inn; the food inspires rather mixed reports, but it's almost invariably rated at least "sound", and supporters say that it's "innovative" and "sensibly-priced" too. / **Details:** *www.talbotinn.com; @TheTalbotMells; 9.30 pm.*

MENAI BRIDGE, GWYNEDD 4–1C

Dylan's Restaurant **£41** 4|4|4
LL59 5EY (01248) 716 714
It's not just the "fabulous views over the Menai Straights" which win praise for this "casual but excellent" operation, open all day every day of the week; the "best pizza ever" is a highlight of the wide-ranging menu.
/ **Details:** *www.dylansrestaurant.co.uk.*

MICKLEHAM, SURREY 3–3B

The Running Horses **£55** 2|1|2
Old London Rd RH5 6DU (01372) 372279
As this guide goes to press, word reaches us that this celebrated inn will be relaunched in late-2014; reports please on the new régime!
/ **Details:** *www.therunninghorses.co.uk; @therunnerspub; off A24 near Dorking or Leatherhead; 10.30 pm, Sun 10 pm.*
Accommodation: *5 rooms, from £135.*

MIDDLE HANDLEY, SOUTH YORKSHIRE 5–2C

The Devonshire Arms **£46** ⓣ
S21 5RN (01246) 434 800
"Difficult to find, but well worth the effort", a "great gastropub", tipped for its "something-for-everyone menu", "good wine list" and "friendly service".

MIDDLESBOROUGH, NORTH YORKSHIRE 8–3C

Dosa Houze **£30** ⓣ
TS1 3QD (01642) 242441
An intimate five-year-old South Indian specialising in the eponymous pancakes, but also a handful of daily-changing curries (latterly including meat options too); a move to the old Yorkshire Bank Building was imminent as this guide went to press, so we think 'tip' status is right for the moment.
/ **Details:** *dosahouze.co.uk.*

MILFORD-ON-SEA, HAMPSHIRE 2–4C

La Perle **£47** ⓣ
Lymington SO41 0QD (01590) 643 557
The "friendly French chef/patron" of this informal restaurant apparently "has many years experience in Michelin-starred restaurants" – fans say it's "a venue where he may one day have one of his own!" / **Details:** *www.laperlemilford.co.uk; 9 pm; closed Mon L & Sun.*

Verveine Fishmarket Restaurant **£55** 5|5|3
98 High St SO41 0QE (01590) 642 176
A "must-go place" which "punches far above its weight"; reporters are wowed by this fishmonger-offshoot, which offers "wonderfully inventive" food, based on "fabulously fresh ingredients"; but hurry – it's "a very well-kept secret that won't last long".
/ **Details:** *www.verveine.co.uk; 9.30 pm; closed Mon & Sun; no Amex.*

MILTON KEYNES, BUCKINGHAMSHIRE 3–2A

Jaipur **£35** 4 3 4
599 Grafton Gate East MK9 1AT
(01908) 669796
Surprisingly well worth seeking out near the railway station, a vast purpose-built operation where the food is "always good", and whose lavish interior "doesn't feel like an Indian restaurant".
/ ***Details:*** *www.jaipur.co.uk; 11.30 pm, Sun 10.30 pm; no shorts.*

MISTLEY, ESSEX 3–2D

The Mistley Thorn Hotel **£43** 4 3 3
High St CO11 1HE (01206) 392 821
"Friendly home cooking" (including "a good selection of fish dishes") is the gist of most reports on Sherri Singleton's "enjoyable" gastropub-with-rooms – "a great place for a weekend break".
/ ***Details:*** *www.mistleythorn.com; @mistleythorn; 9.30 pm; no Amex.* ***Accommodation:*** *11 rooms, from £100.*

MOLD, FLINTSHIRE 5–2A

Glasfryn **£42** 2 3 3
Raikes Ln CH7 6LR (01352) 750500
A large gastropub offers the usual Brunning & Price formula – it's not a star performer by the group's standards, but it's a "warm and welcoming" sort of place, offering a "lovely panorama of the town", and handy for the Theatr Clywd too.
/ ***Details:*** *www.glasfryn-mold.co.uk; 9.30 pm, Sun 9 pm.*

MONTGOMERY, POWYS 5–4A

Checkers **£64** 5 5 4
Broad St, Powys SY15 6PN (01686) 669 822
An "outstanding" restaurant-with-rooms that's not just "by far the best place to eat (and stay) for miles around", but of a quality that's "very unexpected" – chef-proprietors "Stéphane Borie & Sarah Francis used to work at the Waterside Inn, and you get very similar quality at a fraction of the price!"
/ ***Details:*** *www.thecheckersmontgomery.co.uk; @checkerschef; 9 pm; closed Mon, Tue L, Wed L, Thu L & Sun; no Amex; children: 8+ at D.* ***Accommodation:*** *5 rooms, from £125.*

MORECAMBE, LANCASHIRE 5–1A

Midland Hotel English Lakes hotels and venues **£52** 3 4 4
Marine Road west LA4 4BU (01524) 424000
"Stunning" architecture and a "wonderful" sea-view from the dining room help make it a festive experience to dine at this Art Deco hotel; the "enjoyable" cooking plays something of a supporting role. / ***Details:*** *www.englishlakes.co.uk; 9.30 pm, Fri & Sat 10 pm.* ***Accommodation:*** *44 rooms, from £94.*

MORSTON, NORFOLK 6–3C

Morston Hall **£88** 4 2 3
Main Coast Rd NR25 7AA (01263) 741041
"Very genteel" and "rather couple-y", Galton Blackiston's country house hotel still offers most reporters a "memorable" dining experience – a "one-sitting, one-choice" format, which pairs "exquisite" food with "well-matched" wines; a little more staff training, though, "would not go amiss".
/ ***Details:*** *www.morstonhall.com; between Blakeney & Wells on A149; 8 pm; D only, ex Sun open L & D.* ***Accommodation:*** *13 rooms, from £330.*

MOULSFORD, OXFORDSHIRE 2–2D

The Beetle & Wedge Boathouse **£46** 2 3 5
Ferry Ln OX10 9JF (01491) 651381
A rôtisserie in an ex-boathouse, whose "beautiful" Thameside location (the inspiration for the "Wind in the Willows") adds much to its appeal; despite its "infrequently changing menu", fans find the "lovely open-flame grill" is "worth going back for over and over again". / ***Details:*** *www.beetleandwedge.co.uk; on A329 between Streatley & Wallingford, take Ferry Lane at crossroads; 9.45 pm.* ***Accommodation:*** *3 rooms, from £90.*

MOULTON, CAMBRIDGESHIRE 3–1C

The Packhorse Inn **£46** 3 3 4
CB8 8SP (01638) 751818
"They've spent a fortune on the fit-out" of this "superb" new restaurant-with-"posh"-rooms, outside Newmarket, which wins many plaudits as a "great local gastropub". / ***Details:*** *www.packhorseinn.com.*

MOUSEHOLE, CORNWALL 1–4A

Old Coastguard Hotel **£38** 4 3 4
TR19 6PR (01736) 731222
"What a difference, since it was taken over by the same people who run the Gurnards Head!" – this "excellent" hotel dining room, with "fantastic sea views", now offers "very good" food – "with fish being a speciality, of course" – and "lovely" accommodation too.
/ ***Details:*** *www.oldcoastguardhotel.co.uk; 9.30 pm.* ***Accommodation:*** *20 rooms, from £170.*

MURCOTT, OXFORDSHIRE 2–1D

The Nut Tree Inn **£55** 4 4 4
Main St OX5 2RE (01865) 331253
"Excellently located in a pretty village", Michael North & Imogen Young's thatched pub has "a lovely fine dining extension", with "passionate" staff and "exciting" cuisine; "has success gone to their heads"

though? – some reports suggest "it's lost its edge lately". / **Details:** *www.nuttreeinn.co.uk; 9 pm, Sun 3 pm.*

NAILSWORTH, GLOUCESTERSHIRE 2–2B

Wild Garlic **£50** 4 3 2
3 Cossacks Sq GL6 0DB (01453) 832615
Reporters are "absolutely delighted" by this small restaurant-with-rooms, where Matthew Beardshall serves "clever" ("but not irritatingly so") dishes, where good use is made of the eponymous ingredient. / **Details:** *www.wild-garlic.co.uk; @TheWildGarlic; 9.30 pm, Sun 2.30 pm; closed Mon, Tue & Sun D; no Amex.* **Accommodation:** *3 rooms, from £90.*

NANT-Y-DERRY, MONMOUTHSHIRE 2–2A

The Foxhunter **£59** 3 3 2
NP7 9DN (01873) 881101
"Worth the detour, if you're looking for inventive cooking off the beaten track" – Matt Tebbutt's village restaurant-with-rooms is recommended by fans for its "different and interesting" menu, and a "very good wine list" too; as ever, however, the occasional critic is unconvinced.
/ **Details:** *www.thefoxhunter.com; 9.30 pm; closed Mon, Tue & Sun D.* **Accommodation:** *2 cottages rooms, from £155.*

NANTGAREDIG, CARMARTHENSHIRE 4–4C

Y Polyn **£43** 4 4 3
SA32 7LH (01267) 290000
"Delicious from start to finish" – a country restaurant, in a "great setting", near the National Botanic Garden of Wales, which "uses locally-sourced produce to create imaginative and tasty menus"; set lunches, in particular, offer "amazing value for money". / **Details:** *www.ypolyn.co.uk; @PolyNation; 9 pm; closed Mon & Sun D.*

NETHER BURROW, CUMBRIA 7–4D

The Highwayman **£43** 3 4 4
LA6 2RJ (01524) 273338
Slightly up-and-down feedback of late on this outpost of the Northcote-based Ribble Valley Inns gastropub chain; most reports, though, suggest that with its "reliable" cuisine, it is a "top-class all-rounder". / **Details:** *www.highwaymaninn.co.uk; @highwayman_inn; 8.30 pm, Fri & Sat 9 pm, Sun 8 pm.*

NETHER WESTCOTE, OXFORDSHIRE 2–1C

The Feathered Nest Inn **£63** 4 4 4
OX7 6SD (01993) 833 030
"Creative, pitch-perfect cooking", a "fabulous environment inside and out" and a "fantastic" selection of wines and champagnes make this Cotswolds gastropub a "winner every time"; if there's a quibble, it's that service can be "slow".
/ **Details:** *www.thefeatherednestinn.co.uk; @FeatheredNestIn; 9.15 pm; closed Mon & Sun D.*
Accommodation: *4 rooms, from £150.*

NEW MILTON, HAMPSHIRE 2–4C

Vetiver
Chewton Glen **£87** 3 3 4
Chewton Glen Rd BH23 5QL (01425) 275341
This "lovely" and luxurious country house hotel wins praise from its large fan club for an "all-round culinary experience"; it's by no means inexpensive however, and there are a disappointing number of reports of a "bad night" – "I felt I'd stepped back 10 years in terms of ambition and execution".
/ **Details:** *www.chewtonglen.com; @chewtonglen; on A337 between New Milton & Highcliffe; 10 pm.*
Accommodation: *70 rooms, from £310.*

NEWARK, NOTTINGHAMSHIRE 5–3D

Farndon Boathouse **£40** ⓣ
NG24 3SX (01636) 676578
A trendily got up riverside bar and restaurant, where fans say the food is "fabulous".
/ **Details:** *www.farndonboathouse.co.uk.*

NEWBURY, BERKSHIRE 2–2D

The Crab at Chieveley **£56** 4 1 2
Wantage Rd RG20 8UE (01635) 247550
This nautical-themed restaurant may be "a long way from the sea", but it still serves up some "gorgeous" fish dishes; indeed, many reporters are delighted by its all-round standards, but there was the occasional incident this year when service was "spectacularly bad".
/ **Details:** *www.crabatchieveley.com; @crabatchieveley; M4 J13 to B4494 – 0.5 mile on right; 9.30 pm.* **Accommodation:** *14 rooms, from £90.*

NEWCASTLE UPON TYNE, TYNE AND WEAR 8–2B

Artisan
The Biscuit Factory **£44** 3 4 3
Shieldfield NE2 1AN (0191) 2605411
FKA David Kennedy's Food Social, this "light" and "airy" art gallery-cum-restaurant has a "slightly revamped" interior to go with its new name; "it's always a pleasure to eat here", says one of the fans of its "consistently high standards" – "meat is particularly good". / **Details:** *www.foodsocial.co.uk; 9.30 pm; closed Sun D.*

Blackfriars Restaurant **£49** 4 3 4
Friars St NE1 4XN (0191) 261 5945
With its "lovely cloistered setting", this city-centre restaurant can genuinely claim to have an "historic" (1239) location, and a "romantic" one too; the menu, which makes good use of "local

produce", is also hailed as "very special"... especially given the relatively "ordinary" prices! / **Details:** www.blackfriarsrestaurant.co.uk; 10 pm; closed Sun D.

Broad Chare **£40** 344
25 Broad Chare NE1 3DQ (019) 1211 2144
"A truly fantastic pub", run by local restaurant mogul Terry Laybourne, uniformly acclaimed for its "fantastic beer list" and "a kitchen on great form" too – "I'm glad I have a son at the Uni, which gives me an excuse to go!"
/ **Details:** www.thebroadchare.co.uk; @_thebroadchare; 10 pm; closed Sun D; no Amex.

Café 21
Fenwick **£39** ⓣ
39 Northumberland St, First Floor NE1 7DE
(0191) 260 3373
An all-day fashion store dining room tipped as a "great meeting place" – "good for what it is" if, for some reporters, "very expensive" too.
/ **Details:** www.cafetwentyone.co.uk; 0; L only.

Café 21 **£47** 554
Trinity Gdns NE1 2HH (0191) 222 0755
"Terry Laybourne forever!" – the cradle of the empire of the North East's leading restaurateur "never fails to impress"; it's not particularly a foodie haunt, but the brasserie fare is "fantastic" and "good value", service is "highly professional", and the setting "buzzy".
/ **Details:** www.cafetwentyone.co.uk; 10.30 pm, Sun 9.30 pm.

Café Royal **£45** 323
8 Nelson St NE1 5AW (0191) 231 3000
"Much improved now it has settled down since the refurbishment", this "cool and comfortable" grand café, by Grainger Market, offers "delicious quiches, sandwiches, and cakes"; "staff cope well" with the crowds. / **Details:** www.sjf.co.uk; @caferoyalsjf; 6 pm; L only; no booking, Sat.

Caffé Vivo **£43** 342
29 Broad Chare NE1 3DQ (0191) 232 1331
"Terry Laybourne's (not very) Italian restaurant" has a "handy" location that's "very convenient for the Quayside"; food standards have varied, but one regular senses "improvement" of late.
/ **Details:** www.caffevivo.co.uk; @caffevivo; 10 pm; closed Mon & Sun.

The Cherry Tree **£54** 323
9 Osborne Rd NE2 2AE (0191) 239 9924
In Jesmond, a restaurant on an ambitious scale, in a former telephone exchange; with its "attentive" service and food of a "very good standard", it's the sort of place that's a natural for "a large family lunch". / **Details:** www.thecherrytreejesmond.co.uk; @CherryTree_NE; 10 pm, Sun 9 pm.

Dabbawal **£36** 445
69-75 High Bridge NE1 6BX (0191) 232 5133
Near the Theatre Royal, this cool, urban-chic Indian serves "highly enjoyable street-food in tapas-style portions"; its sister venue in Jesmond (opened in 2013) is just as popular.
/ **Details:** www.dabbawal.com; 10.30 pm; closed Sun.

Francesca's **£35** 344
Manor House Rd NE2 2NE (0191) 281 6586
This "good-value" Jesmond institution is hailed by all who comment on it as a "real Italian treat" – "don't know if it's down to the food or the prices, but the queues start around 5.30pm!" / **Details:** 9.30 pm; closed Sun; no Amex; no booking.

House of Tides **£58** 534
NE1 3RF (0191) 2303720
"A great addition to Newcastle"; Kenny Atkinson's "absolutely outstanding" new restaurant – offering "multi-course tasting menus at half London prices" – is already being hailed in some quarters as "possibly the best of its kind in the North East".
/ **Details:** www.houseoftides.co.uk.

Jesmond Dene House **£60** 333
Jesmond Dene Rd NE2 2EY (0191) 212 6066
Occupying a "Victorian armaments tycoon's statement house", in a wooded gorge, Terry Laybourne's boutique hotel has an undeniably "beautiful" setting; its food can approach "perfection", but the "sky-high prices" mean that it's "aimed squarely at those on expense accounts".
/ **Details:** www.jesmonddenehouse.co.uk; @Nicky_Sherman; 9.30 pm. **Accommodation:** 40 rooms, from £120.

Osaka **£26** ⓣ
NE1 6EF (0191) 2615300
Who cares if "the chef is, in fact, Chinese"? – this new restaurant, opposite the Theatre Royal, is tipped for its "convincing" Japanese food; "the presence of numerous Asian people attests to the quality". / **Details:** www.osakanewcastle.co.uk.

Pan Haggerty **£54** ⓣ
21 Queen St NE1 3UG (0191) 221 0904
A small restaurant that's tipped for its "vibrant and iconic" location near the quayside; reports on the cooking are decent, if a little more variable.
/ **Details:** www.panhaggerty.com; @panhaggerty; 9.30 pm; closed Sun D.

Pani's **£31** 354
61-65 High Bridge NE1 6BX (0191) 232 4366
"Newcastle's most reliable choice for a cheap night out in a group!" – this "bustling" and "noisy" institution has "the friendliest service ever"; it "steers clear of pizza", serving "proper" Sardinian grub (pastas, fish dishes, cakes, coffee) at "cheap" prices. / **Details:** www.paniscafe.co.uk; 10 pm; closed Sun; no Amex; no booking at L.

Paradiso **£41** 3 4 5
1 Market Ln NE1 6QQ (0191) 221 1240
An Italian café-bar "in the heart of the city", which combines a "warm and happy" atmosphere with "completely reliable" and "great-value" food; "my children feel so at home here and are recognised every time we visit".
/ **Details:** *www.paradiso.co.uk; 10.30 pm, Fri & Sat 10.45 pm; closed Sun.*

Peace & Loaf **£42** 4 4 3
NE2 1LA (0191) 281 5222
"A good new addition to Jesmond", from Masterchef finalist David Coulson, acclaimed for its "accomplished" cooking and "smooth" service; a fan does note, though, that the "clever" culinary style may be "a little nouvelle" for some tastes.
/ **Details:** *www.peaceandloaf.co.uk.*

Sachins **£38** 3 3 4
Forth Banks NE1 3SG (0191) 261 9035
A long-established Punjabi, near Central Station; it impresses all reporters with its sheer "consistency". / **Details:** *www.sachins.co.uk; 11.15 pm; closed Sun.*

Six
Baltic Centre for Contemporary Arts **£58** 3 3 4
Gateshead Quays, South Shore Rd NE8 3BA (0191) 440 4948
"Impressive views of the Tyne and Quayside" ("especially from the Ladies") reward visitors to the sixth-floor restaurant of this Gateshead arts centre; oddly for a room with a view, the "modern bistro-type fare" is generally "reliable" too.
/ **Details:** *www.sixbaltic.com; @six_baltic; 9.30 pm, Fri & Sat 10 pm; closed Sun D.*

A Taste of Persia **£31** 4 4 2
14 Marlborough Cr NE1 4EE (0191) 221 0088
"Perfectly spiced food in an unassuming location on the edge of the city centre" helps establish this "affordable" and "really enjoyable" Persian as quite a local "favourite".
/ **Details:** *www.atasteofpersia.com; 11 pm; closed Sun.*

Tyneside Coffee Rooms
Tyneside Cinema **£25** 2 5 5
10 Pilgrim St NE1 6QG (0191) 227 5520
"A Tyneside legend – many of us remember visits here as children"; this "homely but stylish" venue in an Art Deco cinema offers "comfort food and more", and "is a great place to meet up with friends before a film". / **Details:** *www.tynesidecinema.co.uk; 9 pm; no Amex.*

Vujon **£45** Ⓣ
29 Queen St NE1 3UG (0191) 221 0601
"Head and shoulders above the other Indians locally" – a surprisingly "elegant and upmarket" fixture, offering "rich" subcontinental cooking.
/ **Details:** *www.vujon.com; 11.30 pm; closed Sun L.*

NEWENT, GLOUCESTERSHIRE 2–1B

Three Choirs Vineyards **£49** Ⓣ
GL18 1LS (01531) 890223
In the heart of a famous vineyard, this is a venue perhaps most safely tipped for its charming location; sceptics feel the food only "tries to be sophisticated", but more generally it's rated "good to very good". / **Details:** *www.threechoirs.com; 8.45 pm; no Amex.* **Accommodation:** *8, & 3 lodges rooms, from £120.*

NEWMARKET, SUFFOLK 3–1B

The Pantry **£40** Ⓣ
CB8 8EQ (01638) 661181
Sometimes (but not invariably) tipped as a "hidden gem", a "bustling" café serving "fresh and well-prepared" fare; "given how little choice there is in Newmarket", even critics may concede that the place clearly has a point!
/ **Details:** *www.thepantryfinefoods.com.*

Thai Street Cafe **£39** Ⓣ
26-28 High St CB8 8LB (01638) 674123
A "first-rate" Thai tip, in the town centre, often hailed for its "value for money".
/ **Details:** *www.thaistreetcafe.co.uk; 10 pm; no Amex.*

NEWPORT, PEMBROKESHIRE 4–4B

Llys Meddyg **£50** 3 4 3
East St SA42 0SY (01239) 820008
"A very charming restaurant-with-rooms"; it's almost invariably reported as being "strong in all categories", but it is perhaps the "friendly" and "welcoming" service which particularly stands out.
/ **Details:** *www.llysmeddyg.com; @llysmeddyg; 9 pm; D only in winter, L & D in summer; no Amex.*
Accommodation: *8 rooms, from £100.*

NEWTON-IN-BOWLAND, LANCASHIRE 5–1B

The Parkers Arms **£43** 5 4 4
BB7 3DY (01200) 446236
"The awards keep coming" for Kathy Smith & Stosie Madie's "totally authentic and unaffected" pub, which benefits from a "beautiful" country location; it offers "absolutely top-notch" cooking – "a lot of places may pay lip service to local sourcing, but it really means something here".
/ **Details:** *www.parkersarms.co.uk; @parkersarms; 8.30 pm, Sun 6.30 pm; closed Mon.*
Accommodation: *4 rooms, from £77.*

NOMANSLAND, WILTSHIRE 2–3C

Les Mirabelles **£43** 5 5 4
Forest Edge Rd SP5 2BN (01794) 390205
"An idyllic New Forest bistro overlooking a village

cricket ground"; thanks to its "sophisticated" and "substantial" Gallic cuisine, and "knowledgeable owner" Claude Laage's "interesting" wine list, it inspires a hymn of praise.
/ **Details:** *www.lesmirabelles.co.uk; off A36 between Southampton & Salisbury; 9.30 pm; closed Mon & Sun; no Amex.*

NORDEN, LANCASHIRE 5–1B

Nutter's **£51** 4 4 2
Edenfield Rd OL12 7TT (01706) 650167
"On a hill overlooking Rochdale and Manchester", "local celebrity chef" Andrew Nutter creates some "fabulous" dishes, "strongly featuring local ingredients", at this manor house hotel; it "maintains top standards" across the board… but it's the "excellent" puddings which attract particular praise.
/ **Details:** *www.nuttersrestaurant.com; between Edenfield & Norden on A680; 9 pm; closed Mon.*

NORTH SHIELDS, TYNE AND WEAR 8–2B

Irvins Brasserie **£44** T
NE30 1JH
Tipped as a "decent addition to the North Shields Fish Quay", an operation offering "interesting" and "carefully seasoned" dishes – "plenty of seafood", of course, plus Northumbrian meat dishes.
/ **Details:** *www.irvinsbrasserie.co.uk.*

Staith House **£43** T
NE30 1JA (0191) 270 8441
A new restaurant "on the site of a run down pub", run by Masterchef finalist John Calton; "as you'd expect, fish straight from the boats is a highlight", but the general picture is "great food at good prices, in a warm and friendly atmosphere".
/ **Details:** *www.thestaithhouse.co.uk.*

NORTH UIST, WESTERN ISLES 9–2A

Langass Lodge **£45** T
Loch Eport HS6 5HA (01876) 580285
"Well worth a visit, if you ever find yourself that far north!" – this former hunting lodge is tipped as the sort of place "you can stay for a week, and never get bored, thanks to the ever-evolving menu"; "good bar food" too.
/ **Details:** *www.langasslodge.co.uk; 8.45 pm; D only; no Amex.* **Accommodation:** *11 rooms, from £95.*

NORTHALLERTON, NORTH YORKSHIRE 8–4B

The Cleveland Tontine **£55** 3 3 4
Staddlebridge DL6 3JB (01609) 882 671
"Still good, and the wine list is still very fine"; the "local favourite" formerly known as 'McCoy's at the Tontine' seems to have made a pretty good start under new ownership; overall, it's no bargain but "the start-the-week menu offers especially good value". / **Details:** *www.theclevelandtontine.co.uk; @Tontine_Hotel; near junction of A19 & A172; 9 pm, Fri & Sat 9.30 pm; no Maestro.* **Accommodation:** *7 rooms, from £130.*

NORTHAW, HERTFORDSHIRE 3–2B

The Sun at Northaw **£55** 3 2 2
1 Judges Hill EN6 4NL (01707) 655507
A "very good" but "quite expensive" gastropub, offering "the best pub grub hereabouts"; the menus are "always interesting", and there is a "nice garden", but service can be "a bit hit-and-miss". / **Details:** *www.thesunatnorthaw.co.uk; 10 pm; closed Mon & Sun D; no Amex.*

NORTHLEACH, GLOUCESTERSHIRE 2–1C

Wheatsheaf Inn **£48** 3 4 5
GL54 3EZ (01451) 860244
This popular gastropub-with-rooms offers "exceptional" food and "cocktails you'll want again and again", as well as the more usual wines and real ales; being a "lively" sort of place, it can get "quite noisy" at times.
/ **Details:** *www,cotswoldswheatsheaf.com; @wheatsheafgl54; 9 pm, Sat & Sun 10 pm.*
Accommodation: *14 rooms, from £140.*

NORTHWICH, CHESHIRE 5–3B

The Fishpool Inn **£41** T
Fishpool Rd CW8 2HP (01606) 883277
A lavishly furnished, almost nightclubby gastropub on quite a scale, which earns its 'tip' rating with consistently high ratings from reporters.
/ **Details:** *thefishpoolinn.co.uk.*

NORTON, WILTSHIRE 2–2B

The Vine Tree **£46** T
Foxley Rd SN16 0JP (01666) 837654
A top tip for those in search of a country boozer handy for the M4 – "we'd certainly go back when we are anywhere near!"
/ **Details:** *www.thevinetree.co.uk; @TheVineTree; 9.30 pm, Fri & Sat 10 pm; closed Sun D.*

NORWICH, NORFOLK 6–4C

The Gunton Arms **£47** 5 5 4
Cromer Rd, Thorpe Mkt NR11 8TZ
(01263) 832010
"A gorgeous setting in parkland and the ambience of a hunting lodge" help make this "beautiful" and "quirky" country pub "a perfect out-of-town experience"; appropriately enough, the menu is "game-orientated".
/ **Details:** *www.theguntonarms.co.uk; 8.30 pm.*
Accommodation: *8 rooms, from £95.*

Last Wine Bar **£46** 4 4 4
70-76 St Georges St NR3 1AB
(01603) 626626
"A real Norwich institution"; in a former shoe

factory, this bistro and wine bar offers a "huge selection of wines by the glass" and its food (best sampled in the "buzzy bar") is "more ambitious" of late, too; elsewhere, a newish brasserie sibling is a "welcome addition" to the Golden Triangle. / **Details:** *www.thelastwinebar.co.uk; @LastWineBar; 10.30 pm; closed Sun.*

Roger Hickman's **£67** 432
79 Upper St. Giles St NR2 1AB
(01603) 633522
This "oasis of top-quality food" offers "one of East Anglia's best gastronomic experiences"; Roger Hickman's "inventiveness" and "excellent execution" are not in doubt, but sceptics feel "a less fussy approach would work better", and the ambience can be "a bit of a let down". / **Details:** *www.rogerhickmansrestaurant.com; 10 pm; closed Mon & Sun.*

NOSS MAYO, DEVON 1–4C

The Ship Inn **£43** Ⓣ
PL8 1EW (01752) 872387
Tipped as "a top place to sit outside, especially on a sunny day when the tide is in" – this attractive inn continues to generate only positive reports. / **Details:** *www.nossmayo.com; 9.30 pm, Sun 9 pm.*

NOTTINGHAM, NOTTINGHAMSHIRE 5–3D

Atlas **£27** 443
9 Pelham St NG1 2EH (0115) 950 1295
A Nottingham stalwart that "never lets you down", whether you opt for the "inspired sandwiches", "brilliant coffee" or "very good cakes". / **Details:** *www.atlasdeli.co.uk; 4 pm, Sat 5 pm; L only.*

Cafe Roya **£38** Ⓣ
NG9 2PE (0115) 922 1902
A vegetarian restaurant where the "Middle Eastern-influenced" menu is "so imaginative as to satisfy even the most reluctant carnivore!"; it can be "hard to get a table".

Cast **£35** 223
The Playhouse, Wellington Circus NG1 5AN
(0115) 852 3898
"Part of the Playhouse building – a wonderful spot for al fresco drinks and food in front of Anish Kapoor's sky mirror"; the food is "less spectacular", but "generally well-prepared" (and "obviously ideal for a pre-theatre meal"); alternatively, opt for tapas in the bar. / **Details:** *www.nottinghamplayhouse.co.uk; 10 pm, Sun 6 pm; no Amex.*

Chino Latino
Park Plaza Hotel **£60** 532
41 Maid Marian Way NG1 6GD
(0115) 947 7444
There's some (surprisingly) "exciting and very tasty" food to be had at this "fun" pan-Asian venture in an "unlikely" setting off the foyer of a large modern hotel; by all accounts, though, "the decor needs updating". / **Details:** *www.chinolatino.co.uk; @chinilatinoeu; 10.30 pm; closed Sun.*

The Cumin **£39** 353
62-64 Maid Marian Way NG1 6BQ
(0115) 941 9941
A family-run city-centre venture that attracts plaudits for "real, rather than anglicised, Indian cooking" – "still the best biryani around!" – and a "very friendly" front-of-house; "upstairs is a bit soulless", though. / **Details:** *www.thecumin.co.uk; 10.45 pm; closed Mon L, Tue L, Sat L & Sun.*

4550 Miles From Delhi **£34** 343
Maid Marian Way NG1 6HE (0115) 947 5111
In a "good city-centre location", this spacious Indian offers "modern, fresh, moreish" cuisine and a "wide choice of dishes (many vegetarian)"; it's "a bit noisy", though... must be the "lack of soft furnishings". / **Details:** *www.milesfromdelhi.com; @4550Nottingham; Mon-Thu 10 pm, Fri & Sat 11 pm, Sun 10.30 pm; no Amex.*

French Living **£42** 222
27 King St NG1 2AY (0115) 958 5885
"Still doing what it does as well as ever after 20 years" – namely "proper French food at very reasonable prices" (and especially "excellent pre-theatre deals"). / **Details:** *www.frenchliving.co.uk; 10 pm; closed Sun; no Amex.*

Hart's **£50** 352
Standard Ct, Park Row NG1 6GN
(0115) 988 1900
Few modern city restaurants in Britain have such a track record as this '90s brasserie-style fixture near the castle, where "excellent value" (and business-friendly) lunches and an "exemplary" wine list are particular features; of late, however, culinary consistency has been something of an issue. / **Details:** *www.hartsnottingham.co.uk; 10 pm, Sun 9 pm.* **Accommodation:** *32 rooms, from £125.*

Iberico **£36** 454
The Shire Hall, High Pavement NG1 1HN
(01159) 410410
This "outstanding" tapas bar, in the vaults of an historic building, is a "lively" place, well worth seeking out for its "imaginative" fare; for top value, seek out the "fabulous express lunch deal". / **Details:** *www.ibericotapas.com; 10 pm; closed Sun; no Amex; children: 12+ D.*

Kayal **£35** 443
8 Broad St NG1 3AL (0115) 941 4733
Thanks to its "high-quality" Keralan food, this mini-chain outlet is a "busy" sort of place that attracts only positive reports; "great dosas". / **Details:** *www.kayalrestaurant.com; 11 pm, Sun 10 pm.*

The Larder on Goosegate £45 ⓣ
1st Floor, 16 -22 Goosegate NG1 1FE
(01159) 500 111
*"Above Jesse Boot's original chemist's shop", this "never-disappointing" spot in the Lace Market is tipped for its "interesting" menu which makes "good use of local produce"; fish in particular is done "very well". / **Details:** www.thelarderongoosegate.co.uk; 10 pm; closed Mon & Sun.*

MemSaab £40 443
12-14 Maid Marian Way NG1 6HS
(0115) 957 0009
*"Hard to fault on any level" – this "upmarket" city-centre Indian is perhaps "even better under its new owners"; "the quality of the food is the main strong point, and it offers top bang for your buck". / **Details:** www.mem-saab.co.uk; near Castle, opposite Park Plaza Hotel; 10.30 pm, Fri & Sat 11 pm, Sun 10 pm; D only; no shorts.*

Petit Paris £34 233
2 Kings Walk NG1 2AE (0115) 947 3767
*Critics accuse the food of being a touch "generic", but this "long-standing local favourite" is a "bustling" city-centre rendezvous which is "reliable" and "good value" (especially if you go for the set menus). / **Details:** www.petitparisrestaurant.co.uk; near Theatre Royal; 10 pm; closed Sun.*

Restaurant Sat Bains £111 543
Lenton Ln NG7 2SA (0115) 986 6566
*The "strange" city-fringe location is a bit "Crossroads Motel"… but "once you're inside you can't see the flyover and pylons", from Sat Bains's famous restaurant-with-rooms; "you're here for the kitchen", and the food is indeed "incredible" – just like the prices! / **Details:** www.restaurantsatbains.com; @satbains1; 8.30 pm, Fri & Sat 9.45 pm; closed Mon & Sun; children: 8+. **Accommodation:** 8 rooms, from £129.*

Shanghai Shanghai £30 ⓣ
NG1 1FE (0115) 958 4688
*The Sichuanese cooking can be so "genuinely authentic" that it is "not always to the taste of Western palates", but this "no-frills" venture is nonetheless tipped as "well worth a detour". / **Details:** www.shanghai-shanghai.co.uk.*

Tarn Thai £42 234
9 George St NG1 1BU (0115) 959 9454
*Somewhat mixed feedback of late for this "impressive-looking" Thai establishment, near the Lace Market; for fans it just "keeps getting better", but more than one critic was left bemused by confused service and the occasional "nondescript" dish. / **Details:** www.tarnthai.co.uk; 10.30 pm, Fri & Sat 11 pm.*

Victoria Hotel £34 344
Dovecote Ln NG9 1JG (0115) 925 4049
*"A proper real ale pub", near Beeston station, with an "interesting and diverse chalkboard menu", and offering an "excellent selection for vegetarians"; in summer, the garden makes a "good family destination". / **Details:** www.victoriabeeston.co.uk; 9.30 pm, Sun-Tue 8.45 pm; no Amex; children: 18+ after 8 pm.*

The Wollaton £42 333
Lambourne Drive NG8 1GR (0115) 9288610
*"Going from strength to strength", a "reliably good" gastropub, near Wollaton Park, offering "better-than-average" pub food from a "regularly changing" menu; real ales and a "reasonably-priced" wine list too. / **Details:** www.thewollaton.co.uk; 9 pm, Fri & Sat 10 pm, Sun 8.30 pm.*

World Service £54 333
Newdigate Hs, Castlegate NG1 6AF
(0115) 847 5587
*Preceded locally by a reputation for "very good food with exceptional contemporary twists", this intriguing venue near the castle is a "stylish" sort of place, with a "beautiful courtyard"; it's "pricey", though, and standards have been a touch "variable" of late. / **Details:** www.worldservicerestaurant.com; 10 pm; closed Sun D, except bank holidays; children: 10+ at D.*

OARE, KENT 3–3C

The Three Mariners £41 443
2 Church Rd ME13 0QA (01795) 533633
*With its "tasty" and "very reasonably priced" cuisine, (much of which is fish-based), this "no-nonsense" gastropub is a real crowd-pleaser – "getting a table has become more difficult" of late. / **Details:** www.thethreemarinersoare.co.uk; Mon-Thu 9 pm, Fri-Sat 9.30 pm, Sun 9 pm; no Amex.*

OBAN, ARGYLL AND BUTE 9–3B

Ee-Usk (Seafood Restaurant) £46 434
North Pier PA34 5QD (01631) 565666
*"Not just superb fish but also a superb location looking over the harbour and out to the Isles" – this popular restaurant impresses almost all reporters with its "amazing" food; among the highlights – "the best oysters I have ever had!" / **Details:** www.eeusk.com; @eeuskoban; 9 pm; no Amex; children: 12+ at D .*

Manor House Hotel £57 ⓣ
Gallanach Rd PA34 4LS (01631) 562087
*"My only complaint is that their portions are over generous!" – this Georgian villa, on the harbour, remains a top tip for those looking for a comfortable all-rounder. / **Details:** www.manorhouseoban.com; Follow the signs to the ferry terminal, the hotel is 200 yards past it on*

the right; 8.30 pm; children: 12+.
Accommodation: *11 rooms, from £195.*

Seafood Temple **£45** ⓣ
Dungallan Pk, Gallanach Rd PA34 4LS
(01631) 566000
"You can see the boats where the fish come in from the picture windows and chat to chef while she/he cooks it!" – this family-run restaurant is tipped as a "wonderful" destination.
/ **Details:** *www.obanseafood.com; D only.*

OCKHAM, SURREY 3–3A

The Black Swan **£51** **334**
Old Ln KT11 1NG (01932) 862364
It may be "in the middle of nowhere", but this "lovely country pub" has a big name for its "well-executed and hearty" fare, so it's "best to book ahead"; for the summer, there are "BBQs and a children's play area".
/ **Details:** *www.blackswanockham.com; @blackswancobham; 9.30 pm, Fri & Sat 10 pm, Sun 6.30 pm.*

OCKLEY, SURREY 3–4A

Bryce's at the Old School House **£51** **443**
Stane St RH5 5TH (01306) 627430
This "slightly dated and old-fashioned" former schoolhouse continues to defy its landlocked location to offer the "best fish for miles around"; it's "well worth the odd visit, not least for the excellent wine list". / **Details:** *www.bryces.co.uk; 8m S of Dorking on A29; 9.30 pm; no Amex.*

OLD HUNSTANTON, NORFOLK 6–3B

The Neptune **£79** **554**
85 Old Hunstanton Rd PE36 6HZ
(01485) 532122
"The coastal leader in north Norfolk"; Kevin Magneolle's "very-out-of-the-way" 18th-century coaching inn matches up his well-honed culinary skills with "memorable" locally-sourced ingredients and "charming" service; "simple but comfortable accommodation" too.
/ **Details:** *www.theneptune.co.uk; 9 pm; closed Mon, Tue-Sat D only, Sun open L & D; children: 10+.*
Accommodation: *6 rooms, from £120.*

OLD WOKING, SURREY 3–3A

London House **£52** **543**
GU22 9JN (01483) 750610
Small but "superb", a local restaurant which "has transformed the Woking eating scene", no less; chef Ben Piette, a former MasterChef semi-finalist, attracts praise for his "excellent, competitively-priced" food.
/ **Details:** *www.londonhouseoldwoking.co.uk.*

OLDSTEAD, NORTH YORKSHIRE 5–1D

Black Swan **£70** **443**
YO61 4BL (01347) 868 387
A "friendly and cosy" former boozer, near Byland Abbey, hailed by most reporters for its "fantastic" cuisine and service, and in particular its "highly recommended" tasting menu (though a few meals "not up to expectations" were also reported); "excellent accommodation".
/ **Details:** *www.blackswanoldstead.co.uk; 9 pm; closed Mon L, Tue L & Wed L; no Amex.*
Accommodation: *4 rooms, from £270 (includes dinner).*

ONGAR, ESSEX 3–2B

Smith's Brasserie **£60** **443**
Fyfield Rd CM5 0AL (01277) 365578
A "spacious" venue that's "as good if not better than any fish restaurant in Central London", say fans, and which remains popular with an "exuberant" crowd; "home-made and yummy" puddings attract particular praise.
/ **Details:** *www.smithsbrasserie.com; left off A414 towards Fyfield; Mon-Fri 10 pm, Sat 10.30 pm, Sun 10 pm; closed Mon L; children: 12+.*

ONICH, HIGHLAND 9–3B

Loch Leven Seafood Café **£47** **544**
PH33 6SA (01855) 821048
"Off the beaten track", it may be, but "spanking fresh seafood, beautifully cooked" makes it "well worth the detour" to visit this waterside café; it enjoys a "stunning" location too.
/ **Details:** *www.lochlevenseafoodcafe.co.uk; 9 pm; no Amex.*

ORFORD, SUFFOLK 3–1D

Butley Orford Oysterage **£38** **443**
Market Hill IP12 2LH (01394) 450277
"Unchanging after 50 years, but still without rival" – this "no frills, old-fashioned and quaint" establishment – "basic, but spotlessly clean" – serves "massive, creamy oysters unlike any others", "really special smoked fish" (from their own smokery) and some other "straightforward" fare.
/ **Details:** *www.butleyorfordoysterage.co.uk; on the B1078, off the A12 from Ipswich; 9 pm; no Amex.*

The Crown & Castle **£50** **444**
IP12 2LJ (01394) 450205
"Local ingredients are the rule", at celebrity co-owner Ruth Watson's "great" gastropub-with-rooms, where "fresh and delicious" seafood is the menu highlight. / **Details:** *www.crownandcastle.co.uk; on main road to Orford, near Woodbridge; 9 pm, Sat & Sun 9.15 pm; no Amex; booking: max 10; children: 8+ at D.* **Accommodation:** *21 rooms, from £135.*

ORKNEY ISLANDS, ORKNEY ISLANDS

The Creel £57 543
St Margaret's Hope, South Ronaldsay KW17 2SL
(01856) 831311
"Absolutely top-class cooking using the very best local ingredients" has long won rave reviews for this "down-to-earth" restaurant-with-rooms, which "feels very much in tune with the location".
*/ **Details:** www.thecreel.co.uk; off A961 S of town, across Churchill barriers; 8 pm; D only; closed Jan-Mar; no Amex. **Accommodation:** 3 rooms, from £110.*

ORPINGTON, KENT 3–3B

Cyprianis £33
BR6 8NN (01689) 859 000
*Making a bit of a stir locally, this new 'Mediterranean bar and grill', in a parade of shops, offers "good grilled meat and fish in a lively modern setting". / **Details:** www.cyprianis.com.*

Osteria da Fabrizio £44 433
254 High St BR6 0LZ (01689) 874 488
The style may seem "very traditional", but all reports speak to the great standards on offer at this town-centre Italian – a surprise find behind a deli.
*/ **Details:** www.dafabrizio.co.uk; @DaFabrizio11; 11 pm, Sun 9 pm; closed Mon D.*

Xian £31 433
324 High St BR6 0NG (01689) 871881
*"Jaw-droppingly good" – this unassuming-looking high street Chinese "always surprises the uninitiated" with its "authentic" flavours; brace yourself, though, for a "hectic" atmosphere at busy times. / **Details:** 11 pm; closed Mon & Sun L.*

OSWESTRY, SHROPSHIRE 5–3A

Sebastian's £59 443
45 Willow St SY11 1AQ (01691) 655444
"What a surprise!"; this restaurant-with-rooms – ambience "improved by recent redecoration" – continues to dish up many "excellent" Gallic dishes… and "its desserts, as supplied to the Orient Express, are still the menu highlight".
*/ **Details:** www.sebastians-hotel.co.uk; 9.30 pm; D only, closed Mon & Sun; no Amex.*
***Accommodation:** 5 rooms, from £75.*

OXFORD, OXFORDSHIRE 2–2D

Al-Shami £28 333
25 Walton Cr OX1 2JG (01865) 310066
*"An excellent find"; this "family-friendly" Jericho spot continues to offer "great-value" Lebanese mezze with "subtle spices and flavours"; eat in the intimate front room or enjoy the "luxurious surroundings" out back. / **Details:** www.al-shami.co.uk; 11.30 pm; no Amex. **Accommodation:** 12 rooms, from £60.*

Ashmolean Dining Room £51 114
Beaumont St OX1 2PH (01865) 553 823
"I guess you're paying for the rooftop terrace", at this museum venue – "an amazing location when the sun shines", with "superb views"; even fans may note that the "variable" food is "very expensive", though, and service is no great shakes.
*/ **Details:** www.ashmoleandiningroom.com; 10 pm; closed Mon, Tue D, Thu D & Sun D.*

Atomic Burger £31 443
96 Cowley Rd OX4 1JE (01865) 790 855
*"Awesome burgers" (featuring "succulent meat" in "generous portions") are the main draw to this "quirky" local venture, but the "sci-fi fries are well worth a go" too; the decor – "filled with lots of old toys" – also provides a "nostalgic '80s feast for the senses". / **Details:** www.atomicburger.co.uk; @atomicburgers; 10.30 pm; no Amex.*

Aziz £34 423
228-230 Cowley Rd OX4 1UH
(01865) 794945
"In the swelling sea of Cowley Road restaurants" this staple curry house "continues to hold its own"; service "can be variable", but the "excellent" cooking means it's "always worth a visit".
*/ **Details:** www.aziz.uk.com; 11.30 pm, Sat midnight; closed Fri L.*

Branca £42 333
111 Walton St OX2 6AJ (01865) 556111
Still the "most dependable restaurant in Oxford" say fans, this Jericho staple serves Italian food "of a high standard", and with portions "on the generous side" too; the mixed clientele ("students, schoolgirls, business people, grannies, dons, hen parties…") make it a "fun place, even if one is dining alone".
*/ **Details:** www.branca.co.uk; 11 pm; no Amex.*

Brasserie Blanc £49 223
71-72 Walton St OX2 6AG (01865) 510999
"Good… by Oxford standards!"; the city-centre brasserie from the famous 'Manoir' chef used to be something of a standout, but its performance of late has been very middling.
*/ **Details:** www.brasserieblanc.com; @brasserieblanc; 10 pm, Sat 10.30 pm, Sun 9.30 pm.*

Cherwell Boathouse £45 335
Bardwell Rd OX2 6ST (01865) 552746
*This "lovely" venue has long been of note for its "fantastic" location – "overlooking the river and an entertaining punt-embarkation point" – and its "excellent and inexpensive wine list"; nowadays, though, most reporters find the food "surprisingly good" too. / **Details:** www.cherwellboathouse.co.uk; @cherwellboathouse; 9 pm, Fri & Sat 9.30 pm.*

Chiang Mai £43 335
Kemp Hall Passage OX1 4DH (01865) 202233
"A quirky old building", just off the High, has long hosted this "consistently high-scoring" Thai favourite;

"others in town may have taken pole position", but – with its "fragrant" and "authentic" dishes – it "remains a safe-as-houses choice for superior city-centre food". / **Details:** *www.chiangmaikitchen.co.uk; 10.30 pm.*

Edamame **£32** 4 2 2
15 Holywell St OX1 3SA (01865) 246916
"A much loved beacon of independence in the chain-dominated Oxford food scene" – this "tucked away" Japanese serves "healthy" and "quick" fare that's "hearty" and "full-flavoured"; the menu, though, is "limited", and "you often have to wait and share tables". / **Details:** *www.edamame.co.uk; 8.30 pm; L only, ex Thu-Sat open L & D, closed Mon & Tue; no Amex; no booking.*

The Fishes **£44** 2 1 4
North Hinksey OX2 0NA (01865) 249796
"Decent pub grub" and a "fabulous garden" overlooking the water make this venue a popular choice for those "looking for somewhere near but not in" the city; the "menu needs to change more often", though, and service, though "friendly", can be somewhat "chaotic". / **Details:** *www.fishesoxford.co.uk; @fishesoxford; 9.45 pm.*

The Folly **£46** Ⓣ
OX1 4JU (01865) 201293
Beside the eponymous bridge, a restaurant tipped not just for its "romantic" waterside location, but for food that's sometimes "very good" too. / **Details:** *www.no1-folly-bridge.co.uk/.*

Gee's **£53** 2 1 3
61 Banbury Rd OX2 6PE (01865) 553540
Opinions still divide on this north Oxford venture in a Victorian glasshouse; fans overlook "hit-and-miss" cooking, as it's a "joyful" place with a "lovely" location – to critics "it's not a pleasant experience, as the service is terrible and the food only adequate". / **Details:** *www.gees-restaurant.co.uk; @geesrestaurant; 10 pm, Fri & Sat 10.30 pm.*

The Magdalen Arms **£43** 3 2 3
243 Iffley Rd OX4 1SJ (01865) 243 159
Sibling to London's Hope & Anchor, this estimable gastropub "continues to cook up a storm"; this is a perennially "busy" place, though, and service can seem stretched. / **Details:** *www.magdalenarms.com; 10 pm, Sun 9.30 pm; closed Mon L; no Amex.*

My Sichuan **£39** 5 1 3
The Old School, Gloucester Grn OX1 2DA
(01865) 236 899
"Volcanically authentic", the Sichuan cooking on offer at this centrally-located former schoolhouse makes "no concessions to European tastes"; service is "not brilliant"… but "the fact that the majority of diners are Chinese is always a good sign". / **Details:** *www.mysichuan.co.uk; 11 pm.*

The Nosebag **£28** Ⓣ
6-8 St Michael's St OX1 2DU (01865) 721033
With its "delicious and varied soups and salads", this city-centre spot it tipped as a "great place to go for lunch"; indeed, such is its fame that the best advice is: "try to avoid it at lunchtimes"! / **Details:** *www.nosebagoxford.co.uk; 9.30 pm, Fri & Sat 10 pm, Sun 8.30 pm.*

Oli's Thai **£30** 5 5 4
OX4 1RB (01865) 790223
"Massive taste sensations" have made a big name for this small but "lovely" café, where "the short menu is beautifully cooked", and served by "friendly" staff; "booking is essential".

Pierre Victoire **£42** 3 4 3
Little Clarendon St OX1 2HP (01865) 316616
"Always packed out and buzzing" – this "old-fashioned" French bistro (a survivor of what was once a national chain) remains mightily popular, thanks to its "a wide variety" of "unpretentious and reasonably-priced dishes"; "the value at lunch is extraordinary". / **Details:** *www.pierrevictoire.co.uk; 11 pm, Sun 10 pm; no Amex.*

The Punter **£35** Ⓣ
OX2 0BE (01865) 248832
An Osney Island boozer, tipped for "the best pub food in Oxford" (with a "lemon posset to die for" identified as the stand-out dish); more reports please! / **Details:** *www.thepunteroxford.co.uk.*

Quod
Old Bank Hotel **£45** 2 2 2
92-94 High St OX1 4BJ (01865) 799599
"For a straightforward, no-frills lunch", this city-centre fixture is, say fans, "exactly what the average parent and undergrad want"; its ratings are perennially mediocre though – it may be "competent" but it's also "expensive for what it is". / **Details:** *www.oldbank-hotel.co.uk; @QuodBrasserie; 11 pm, Sun 10.30 pm; no booking at D.* **Accommodation:** *42 rooms, from £140.*

Shanghai 30s **£40** Ⓣ
82 St Aldates OX1 1RA (01865) 242230
An "amazing" old building (one of England's more notable restaurant sites, once the 'Elizabeth', long RIP) now houses a "great" Chinese restaurant, tipped for its "unusual" dishes, "elegantly served"; lunches offer "outstanding" value. / **Details:** *www.shanghai30s.com; 10.30 pm; closed Mon L.*

Sojo **£41** 5 3 2
8-9 Hythe Bridge St OX1 2EW
(01865) 202888
"If the number of Asian customers is a guide, this continues to be the Chinese restaurant of choice"; it serves a rather "different" range of dishes, some of them realised to an "exceptional"

The Folly

Cherwell Boathouse

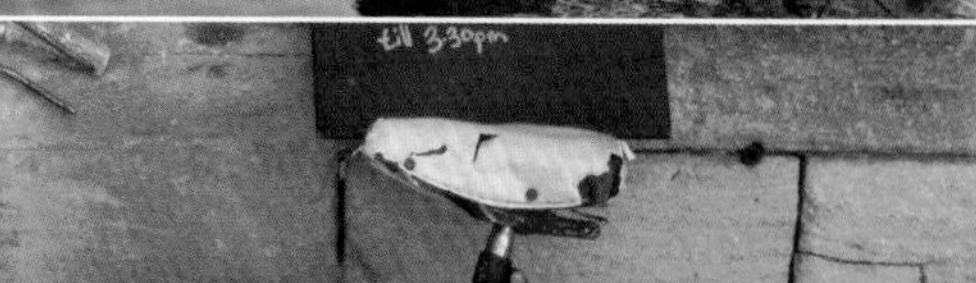

Vaults and Garden Cafe

*standard. / **Details:** www.sojooxford.co.uk; 10.30 pm, Sun 9.30 pm.*

Turl Street Kitchen £31 442
16 Turl St OX1 3DH (01865) 264 171
"Giles Coren was right!" – with its "attractive staff, attractive menu and attractive prices", this "bustling" not-for-profit café is seen by reporters as a worthy antidote to the city's "many chain eateries"; it offers "delicious" organic fare, which comes with a "sustainable edge".
*/ **Details:** www.turlstreetkitchen.co.uk; @turlskitchen; 10 pm.*

The Vaults And Garden Cafe £17 444
University Church of St Mary the Virgin, Radcliffe Sq OX1 4AH (01865) 279112
"In a lovely ex-chapel within a church or, if you wish, the graveyard on a nice day!" – this self-service veggie is a real crowd-pleaser, offering "very tasty and hearty" mains and "sensational salads".
*/ **Details:** www.thevaultsandgarden.com; @VaultsandGarden; 6 pm; L only.*

OXTON, CHESHIRE 5–2A

Fraiche £90 543
11 Rose Mount CH43 5SG (0151) 652 2914
"Mark Wilkinson is a brilliant one-of-a-kind", and his "marvellous", "artful" cuisine made this "serene" but unshowy Wirral dining room this year's UK's No. 1 in the survey; "in Tour de France parlance, «hors catégorie!»".
*/ **Details:** www.restaurantfraiche.com; 8.30 pm, Sun 7 pm; closed Mon, Tue, Wed L, Thu L, Fri L & Sat L; no Amex.*

PADSTOW, CORNWALL 1–3B

Margot's £50 544
11 Duke St PL28 8AB (01841) 533441
It may be "tiny" (19 covers), but Adrian Oliver's bistro "turns out consistently superb food" that's "always a delight" – it "deserves to be famous just as much as Rick Stein's restaurants".
*/ **Details:** www.margotsbistro.co.uk; @adrian_margots; 9 pm; closed Mon & Sun.*

Paul Ainsworth at Number 6 £70 454
6 Middle St PL28 8AP (01841) 532093
"Padstow's best dining experience" is to be had at Paul Ainsworth's backstreet operation, which is "amazing on all counts"; "there's a real passion to ensure you enjoy your meal" and the "original and surprising" cuisine is "superb".
*/ **Details:** www.number6inpadstow.co.uk; @no6padstow / paulainsw6rth; 10 pm; closed Mon & Sun; no Amex; children: 4+.*

Rick Stein's Café £43 544
10 Middle St PL28 8AP (01841) 532700
"A lovely restaurant, where the food is superb and competitively priced too"; this "buzzing" establishment may not be as ambitious as 'The Seafood', but it's been a notably safer bet of late; "busy weekends", though, are best avoided.
*/ **Details:** www.rickstein.com; 9.30 pm; no Amex; no booking at L. **Accommodation:** 3 rooms, from £100.*

Rojanos £45 444
9 Mill Sq PL28 8AE (01841) 532796
*Paul Ainsworth's "first-class Italian" continues to elicit raves for its "very tasty and very good-value" staples; there has been a refurbishment in recent times, and the atmosphere is "enjoyable" too. / **Details:** www.rojanos.co.uk; @rojanos; 10 pm; no Amex.*

St Petroc's Hotel & Bistro £56 443
4 New St PL28 8EA (01841) 532700
"Really good food in a friendly atmosphere"; it has had its ups and downs over the years, but this "buzzy" bistro currently seems to be on quite a high; as you'd hope, "superb fish" is a highlight.
*/ **Details:** www.rickstein.com; 10 pm; no Amex.*
***Accommodation:** 10 rooms, from £150.*

Seafood Restaurant £82 433
Riverside PL28 8BY (01841) 532700
"Rick Stein is an icon who deserves his star status", say the many fans of his harbourside HQ famous for its "always-impressive" fish and seafood; those who say it's become "way too big and commercial", however, found renewed voice this year, damning "average food in a sterile setting".
*/ **Details:** www.rickstein.com; @TheSeafood; 9.45 pm; ; no Amex; booking: max 14; children: 3+.*
***Accommodation:** 16 rooms, from £150.*

Stein's Fish & Chips £35 543
South Quay PL28 8BL (01841) 532700
"The top place to go for fish 'n' chips"; the TV chef's "industrial"-style chippy has put in a much improved performance of late; "you may need to queue", though, and the interior can be "noisy" – "better to find somewhere scenic to eat al fresco".
*/ **Details:** www.rickstein.com; 9 pm; no Amex.*

PARKGATE, CHESHIRE 5–2A

The Boathouse £42 ➊
1 The Pde CH64 6RN (0151) 336 4187
"Beautiful views over the River Dee" make it worth remembering this marshside fixture; other plusses include "well prepared and filling food" and "friendly service".
*/ **Details:** www.theboathouseparkgate.co.uk/.*

PEEBLES, SCOTTISH BORDERS 9–4C

Horseshoe Inn £45 455
Eddleston EH45 8QP (01721) 730225
"A joy"; this "beautiful" inn inspires rapturous reports for its "excellent" service (in particular), as well as its "wide" menu of "well-presented" dishes. / **Details:** *www.horseshoeinn.co.uk; Weds-Thu & Sun 9 pm, Fri & Sat 9.30 pm; closed Mon & Tue; no Amex; children: 5+ for D in eve.* **Accommodation:** *8 rooms, from £120.*

PENALLT, MONMOUTHSHIRE 2–2B

Inn at Penallt £45 443
NP25 4SE (01600) 772765
Beautifully hidden away, in glorious countryside near Monmouth, this "very good" pub is universally hailed by reporters as a "great hide-away", thanks not least to its often-"excellent" food.
/ **Details:** *www.theinnatpenallt.co.uk/; 9 pm; closed Mon, Tue L & Sun D; no Amex.* **Accommodation:** *4 rooms, from £75.*

PENARTH, VALE OF GLAMORGAN 1–1D

Fig Tree £41 ⓣ
The Esplanade CF64 3AU (029) 2070 2512
In a former Victorian beach shelter, this "family-friendly" venture, with a veranda, is a top tip for "very good cuisine by the sea" – "feel perfectly replete after lunch and then stroll along the front by the pier". / **Details:** *www.thefigtreepenarth.co.uk/; 9.30 pm; closed Mon & Sun D; no Amex.*

Restaurant James Sommerin £78 443
The Esplanade CF64 3AU (07722) 216 727
The chef who made his name at the former Crown at Whitebrook is already producing many "excellent" dishes at this new waterside restaurant-with-rooms; service is excellent too.
/ **Details:** *www.jamessommerinrestaurant.co.uk/#welcome.*

PENRITH, CUMBRIA 7–3D

Four & Twenty £41 ⓣ
CA11 7AY (01768) 210231
In a former high street bank, a newly-minted open-kitchen restaurant, tipped for its "excellent-value" fare, with "everything made from scratch".
/ **Details:** *www.fourandtwentypenrith.co.uk.*

PENSFORD, SOMERSET 2–2B

The Pig Hunstrete House £44 545
BS39 4NS (01761) 490490
"If you want to know how to run a great restaurant and hotel, observe closely here"; this outpost of a growing shabby-chic empire has been a "most surprising" find for some reporters – not only is the food "sensational", but the wines are highly approved too. / **Details:** *www.thepighotel.com.*

PENZANCE, CORNWALL 1–4A

The Honey Pot £22 ⓣ
5 Parade St TR18 4BU (01736) 368686
A simple central café that's often very busy, and is a top tip locally for "lovely soups, great dishes, fabulous cakes and an excellent range of coffees, teas and soft drinks" (and nowadays ice cream too).
/ **Details:** *www.thehoneypotpz.co.uk; L only, closed Sun; no credit cards.*

Tolcarne Inn £39 443
TR18 5PR (01736) 363074
"This ancient harbourside inn on the edge of Newlyn" still has the "appearance of a traditional tavern", but acclaimed Cornish chef Ben Tunnicliffe has given the food a "drastic makeover" since taking over in 2012; a location "yards from the fish market" dictates the "superb" daily-changing menu.
/ **Details:** *www.tolcarneinn.co.uk.*

PERSHORE, WORCESTERSHIRE 2–1C

Belle House £53 ⓣ
Bridge St WR10 1AJ (01386) 555055
"What a find"; tipped as the "best place to eat in Worcestershire by far", a town-centre restaurant and traîteur which pleases all reporters with its "solid", if "not particularly innovative", modern British fare, and "great wine list".
/ **Details:** *www.belle-house.co.uk; 9.30 pm; closed Mon & Sun.*

PERTH, PERTH AND KINROSS 9–3C

Cafe Tabou £50 343
4 St John's Pl PH1 5SZ (01738) 446698
"A smile, a good day, and sometimes a bonjour" help set the "welcoming" tone at this "little bit of France" (though actually the family is Polish); it pleases all who comment on it with its "consistently good" standards, and is particularly popular as a lunch destination.
/ **Details:** *www.cafetabou.com; 9.30 pm, Fri & Sat 10 pm; closed Mon D & Sun; no Amex.*

Pig'Halle £59 344
PH2 8PG (01738) 248784
All reports praise the "well-priced" fare on offer at this "genuine" Gallic-owned and family-run spot – "strictly speaking, this is a Breton restaurant, so come and enjoy the slow cooked food, such as pig's trotters, and the rich sauces".
/ **Details:** *www.pighalle.co.uk.*

63 Tay Street £59 433
63 Tay St PH2 8NN (01738) 441451
"A lovely dining experience every time"; Graham Pallister's town-centre dining room doesn't try too hard, but its "well thought-out" menu invariably

seems to please; "keep up the good work!" / **Details:** *www.63taystreet.com; @63TayStreet; on city side of River Tay, 1m from Dundee Rd; 9 pm; D only, closed Mon & Sun; no Amex.*

PETERSFIELD, HAMPSHIRE 2–3D

JSW **£70** 4 3 2
20 Dragon St GU31 4JJ (01730) 262030
"Innovative" and "satisfying", the cuisine (including 7-couse taster menus) at Jake Saul Watkins's former coaching inn almost invariably impresses; staff can seem a little "stiff", though, and critics say the interior has "all the ambience of a doctor's waiting room". / **Details:** *www.jswrestaurant.com; on the old A3; 8 min walk from the railway station; 9 pm; closed Mon, Tue & Sun D; children: 5+ D.* **Accommodation:** *4 rooms, from £95.*

PETTS WOOD, KENT 3–3B

Cyprianis **£33** Ⓣ
BR5 1LY (01689) 896 899
"The kind of place you seek out on holiday", this "modern and lively" venture, on the site of the former Café Plaza, is a top tip locally for "tasty" Italian and Greek food (not least "good grilled meat and fish"). / **Details:** *www.cyprianis.com.*

Indian Essence **£35** 4 5 3
176-178 Petts Wood Rd BR5 1LG (01689) 838 700
"What an amazing local restaurant!"; Atul Kochar has brought a little of his Mayfair (Benares) magic to this "outstanding" Indian, where "fantastic" service is a particular highlight, and there are some "lovely" and "unusual" wines on offer too. / **Details:** *www.indianessence.co.uk; 10.45 pm, fri & sat 11 pm, sun 10.30 pm; closed Mon L.*

Uskudar **£33** 4 3 3
61 Queensway BR5 1DQ (01689) 820055
This "fantastic little Turkish restaurant" has a "lovely interior", and serves "great tapas at prices such that you can dine out on every night"; it's tailormade for carnivores, but offers "good non-meat salads and starters too". / **Details:** *www.uskudar.co.uk/; 11 pm; no Amex.*

PETWORTH, WEST SUSSEX 3–4A

The Noahs Ark Inn **£44** 3 3 4
Lurgashall GU28 9ET (01428) 707346
On a pretty village green, an "excellent village pub and restaurant" – perhaps not a place of culinary pilgrimage but, on almost all reports, "consistently good". / **Details:** *www.noahsarkinn.co.uk; @TheNoahsArkInn; 9.30 pm, Sun 3 pm; closed Sun D.*

PICKERING, NORTH YORKSHIRE 8–4C

The White Swan **£47** 4 4 4
Market Pl YO18 7AA (01751) 472288
An old coaching inn, whose "very pleasant" restaurant benefits from notably "cheerful" service; culinary attractions include "freshly battered scampi that's worth a trip on its own", and some "unusual veggie options" too. / **Details:** *www.white-swan.co.uk; 9 pm.* **Accommodation:** *21 rooms, from £150.*

PINNER, GREATER LONDON 3–3A

Friends **£55** 4 4 4
11 High St HA5 5PJ (020) 8866 0286
The "best restaurant in upmarket Pinner" – Terry Farr's "intimate", "olde-worlde" stalwart continues to elicit favourable reports, thanks to its convivial atmosphere and sometimes "really excellent food". / **Details:** *www.friendsrestaurant.co.uk; 9.30 pm; closed Mon & Sun D.*

PLAXTOL, KENT 3–3B

The Papermaker's Arms **£42** Ⓣ
TN15 0QJ (01732) 810407
"Trading successfully under new ownership", a country pub tipped as "consistently very good on all counts"; for the summer, it boasts a "beautiful" garden too. / **Details:** *www.papermakersarms.org.uk.*

PLEASINGTON, LANCASHIRE 5–1B

Clog & Billycock **£44** 2 3 3
Billinge End Rd BB2 6QB (01254) 201163
"The best of the Ribble Valley Inns" – this "friendly" and "reliable" gastropub offers "good cooking" based on produce from "local suppliers"... in fact, say its many fans, it's the sort of spot that "just gets everything right". / **Details:** *www.theclogandbillycock.com; @CloganBillycock; 8.30 pm Mon-Thu, Fri & Sat 9 pm, Sun 8 pm.*

PLUMTREE, NOTTINGHAMSHIRE 5–3D

Perkins **£49** Ⓣ
Old Railway Station NG12 5NA (0115) 937 3695
"Rural cooking with style!"; this well-established family-run restaurant is tipped for its "dependable" standards, including "good and well-presented" dishes in "generous" portions. / **Details:** *www.perkinsrestaurant.co.uk; @PerkinsNotts; off A606 between Nottingham & Melton Mowbray; 9.30 pm; closed Sun D.*

PLUSH, DORSET 2–4B

Brace of Pheasants **£43** 3 4 4
DT2 7RT (01300) 348357
"A very special beacon of hope for great ingredients and cooking, in a region that's high on the first, but low on the second"; this "fantastic village pub" serves some "hearty" fare but it's location is a little off-piste – "you have to know where it is!" / **Details:** *www.braceofpheasants.co.uk; 9.30 pm.* **Accommodation:** *4 rooms, from £95.*

PLYMOUTH, DEVON 1–3C

Chloe's
Gill Akaster House £59 322
Princess St PL1 2EX (01752) 201523
*"Convenient for the theatre" too – this "small" Gallic-run "bistro-style restaurant" is a "reliable favourite". / **Details:** www.chloesrestaurant.co.uk; 9.30 pm; closed Sun.*

Rhodes at The Dome £41 Ⓣ
Hoe Rd PL1 2NZ (01752) 266600
*"Cannot beat the view, and the food is consistently reliable"; Gary Rhodes's sole remaining UK outlet doesn't inspire much commentary, but it is consistently tipped as an "enjoyable" destination. / **Details:** www.rhodesatthedome.co.uk/; 9.30 pm, Sat & Sun 10 pm.*

River Cottage Canteen £40 444
Royal William Yd PL1 3QQ (01752) 252702
Occupying an "airy" ("noisy at times") warehouse in the "novel environment of an ex-naval yard", Hugh Fearnley-Whittingstall's "friendly" canteen offers "tasty food with just enough finesse to add interest".

Rock Salt £43 454
31 Stonehouse St PL1 3PE (01752) 225522
*"Complex, inventive food combinations served in smart cafe environment" – in a "one-time red light district", this "smart" ("defiantly upmarket") spot strikes all who report on it as "a real find". / **Details:** www.rocksaltcafe.co.uk; rocksaltcafeuk; 11 pm.*

POLKERRIS, CORNWALL 1–3B

Sams on the Beach £47 445
PL24 2TL (01726) 812255
*"Operating precariously in a converted lifeboat station", this "lovely" and "laid-back" diner serves "fine pizzas, but even better fresh fish" – "get there early for lunch and roll onto the beach for your siesta". / **Details:** www.samsfowey.co.uk; 9 pm; no Amex.*

POOLE, DORSET 7–3D

Branksome Beach £53 334
Pinecliff Rd BH13 6LP (01202) 767235
*"Good seaside food", and "reasonably priced" too by Southbanks standards – this sea-view beachside restaurant is an all-round crowd-pleaser. / **Details:** www.branksomebeach.co.uk; 9.30 pm.*

Guildhall Tavern £52 454
15 Market St BH15 1NB (01202) 671717
*"At first glance this looks like any other harbour pub", but probe further and you'll find the "most perfect French bistro", serving "really good" food (not least for fish-lovers); "the recent revamp has made the ambience jolly pleasant too". / **Details:** www.guildhalltavern.co.uk; 10 pm; closed Mon & Sun; no Amex.*

Storm £50 312
16 High St BH15 1BP (01202) 674970
*Pete & Frances Miles's restaurant offers "well cooked" fare, primarily fish, but with "very good desserts" as a bonus; it's deemed "worth the visit" on most accounts… "especially as there's not much else in Poole"! / **Details:** www.stormfish.co.uk; 9.30 pm, Fri & Sat 10 pm; closed Mon L, Tue L & Sun L.*

PORT APPIN, ARGYLL AND BUTE 9–3B

Airds Hotel £75 Ⓣ
PA38 4DF (01631) 730236
*Less feedback than we'd like on this Relais & Châteaux hotel dining room-with-a-view (occupying a converted ferry inn); such as it is, though, again tips its "high-quality" cooking and "impeccable" service, and all in "delightful" surroundings too. / **Details:** www.airds-hotel.com; @AirdsHotel; 20m N of Oban; 9.30 pm; no jeans or trainers; children: 8+ at D. **Accommodation:** 11 rooms, from £290.*

Pierhouse Hotel £56 445
PA38 4DE (01631) 730302
*An "idyllic" spot, by the ferry pier, where "everything is cooked to perfection" (not least the seafood); there's a "stunning" view of Loch Linhe too – no wonder it's so "busy". / **Details:** www.pierhousehotel.co.uk; just off A828, follow signs for Port Appin & Lismore Ferry; 9.30 pm. **Accommodation:** 12 rooms, from £100.*

PORT ISAAC, CORNWALL 1–3B

Outlaw's Fish Kitchen £36 454
1 Middle St PL29 3RH (01208) 881138
*This "tiny" harbourside gem offers "really moreish" fish tapas – as you'd hope with "Nathan Outlaw's name on the door and Paul Ripley in the kitchen"; by almost all accounts, it's a "worthy replacement" for the former Harbour Restaurant, and "very high on the satisfaction scale overall". / **Details:** www.outlaws.co.uk.*

PORTHGAIN, PEMBROKESHIRE 4–4B

The Shed £40 222
SA62 5BN (01348) 831518
*Up-and-down reports of late on this "rustic" harbourside spot; fans still praise its "imaginative" dishes, but critics of "variable" standards don't see much to distinguish it from "a standard fish 'n' chip café". / **Details:** www.theshedporthgain.co.uk; 9 pm; no Amex.*

PORTHLEVEN, CORNWALL 1–4A

Kota **£46** 444
Harbour Head TR13 9JA (01326) 562407
So good it now has an equally good twin (Kota Kai), a picturesquely-located harbourfront restaurant with an interesting menu (on which many dishes have an antipodean twist).
*/ **Details:** www.kotarestaurant.co.uk; 9 pm; D only, closed Sun-Tue; no Amex. **Accommodation:** 2 rooms, from £70.*

PORTMAHOMACK , HIGHLAND 9–2C

The Oystercatcher **£57** 443
Main St IV20 1YB (01862) 871560
*In a "small coastal village north of Inverness", this "welcoming and friendly" bistro offers "excellent fresh seafood" and "very reasonably-priced" wine in a "traditional rather than 'designer' ambience" – "perfect!" / **Details:** www.the-oystercatcher.co.uk; 10 pm; closed Mon, Tue, Wed, Thu L & Sun D. **Accommodation:** 3 rooms, from £82.*

PORTMEIRION, GWYNEDD 4–2C

Portmeirion Hotel **£60** Ⓣ
LL48 6ET (01766) 772440
*"Still a favourite, with fine food and wonderfully caring service"... or "sloppy" all round? – feedback on the dining room of the hotel at the heart of Sir Clough Williams-Ellis's Italianate-fantasy village is thinner and more mixed than once it was; it's always tipped, though, for its "magical" waterside location. / **Details:** www.portmeirion-village.com; off A487 at Minffordd; 9 pm. **Accommodation:** 14 rooms, from £185.*

PORTSMOUTH, HAMPSHIRE 2–4D

abarbistro **£41** 343
58 White Hart Rd PO1 2JA (02392) 811585
"Perfect fish and steaks" win a thumbs up for this Old Portsmouth bistro (which is good with kids too); "look out for 'Fishy Fridays'!"
*/ **Details:** www.abarbistro.co.uk; midnight, Sun 10.30 pm.*

Loch Fyne **£41** 233
Unit 2 Vulcan Buildings PO1 3TY (023) 9277 8060
"I never feel wowed, but it is fairly reliable" – this "very well-located" outpost of the national fish chain inspires a surprising volume of commentary, most of it to the effect that it's "a safe bet".
*/ **Details:** www.lochfyne-restaurants.com; 10.30 pm.*

Relentless Steak & Lobster House **£46** Ⓣ
85 Elm Grove PO5 1JF (02392) 822888
A Southsea surf 'n' turf spot which is tipped for "fantastic steak and local lobster".
*/ **Details:** www.larrythelobster.co.uk; 9.30 pm.*

Restaurant 27 **£59** 444
27a, Southsea Pde PO5 2JF (023) 9287 6272
"Finally puts Southsea on the culinary map!" – this "understated" and "traditional" local continues to "strive for excellence", and its "interesting" and "beautifully presented" cooking is deemed a "real treat" by all who comment on it.
*/ **Details:** www.restaurant27.com; 9.30 pm; closed Mon, Tue, Wed L, Thu L, Fri L, Sat L & Sun D.*

POULTON, GLOUCESTERSHIRE 2–2C

The Falcon Inn **£44** 443
London Rd GL7 5HN (01285) 850878
"Great menu, great food, great service, great value" – reporters rarely stint in their praise for this "friendly" inn; the only possible criticism seem to be that the interior is a little "bland" for some tastes.
*/ **Details:** www.falconinnpoulton.co.uk; on A417 between Cirencester and Fairford; 10 pm; closed Sun D; no Amex.*

PRESTBURY, CHESHIRE 5–2B

Bacchus **£52** 443
The Village SK10 4DG (01625) 820009
"Excellent value" (especially at lunch, of course) – the gist of all feedback on this good all-rounder, run by refugees from Manchester's once-celebrated Moss Nook (RIP).
*/ **Details:** www.bacchusprestbury.co.uk; @bacchusprestbur; 9.30 pm, Fri & Sat 10 pm; closed Mon & Sun D.*

PRESTON BAGOT, WARWICKSHIRE 5–4C

The Crabmill **£45** 334
B95 5EE (01926) 843342
A large and "buzzy" gastropub, handily located for M40 travellers, that's "always well attended at any time of the week", thanks not least to the consistency of its "good-quality" cuisine (and in "generous portions" too).
*/ **Details:** www.thecrabmill.co.uk; @Ivlycrabmill; on main road between Warwick & Henley-in-Arden; 9.30 pm; closed Sun D; no Amex.*

PRESTON CANDOVER, HAMPSHIRE 2–3D

The Purefoy Arms **£41** 434
RG25 2EJ (01256) 389 777
*A "great little pub" that offers some "imaginative Spanish-influenced cooking" – "improved" of late, "now the chef has a bigger brigade"; "it's always busy". / **Details:** www.thepurefoyarms.co.uk; @thepurefoyarms; 10 pm; closed Mon & Sun D.*

PRESTON, LANCASHIRE 5–1A

Bukhara **£32** 433
154 Preston New Rd PR5 0UP
(01772) 877710
"The best Indian in central Lancashire" continues to win plaudits for its "great-tasting food and real

value for money" – a view we can assume is a clear-eyed one, as alcohol is not permitted.
/ **Details:** www.bukharasamlesbury.co.uk; 11 pm; D only; no Maestro.

PWLLHELI, GWYNEDD 4–2C

Plas Bodegroes **£64** 443
Nefyn Rd LL53 5TH (01758) 612363
The Chowns' "serene" and "tastefully-appointed", Georgian restaurant-with-rooms enjoys a "perfect location with lovely garden", and offers up some "superb cooking" in "silver service" style (which the odd critic finds "on the verge of being pretentious").
/ **Details:** www.bodegroes.co.uk; @plasbodegroes; on A497 1m W of Pwllheli; 9.00 pm; closed Mon, Tue-Sat D only, closed Sun D; no Amex; children: 12+ at D. **Accommodation:** 10 rooms, from £130.

QUEENSBURY, MIDDLESEX 3–3A

Regency Club **£31** 433
19-21 Queensbury Station Pde HA8 5NR
(020) 8952 6300
"So unlike a normal high-street Indian" – "when it comes to authentic food", this Edgware destination ("hard to tell if it's a pub or a restaurant") is "the pinnacle"; with its "refurbished bar and big-screen sport", the concept "sounds naff", but fans insist that "it works".
/ **Details:** www.regencyclub.co.uk; @RegencuClubUK; 10.30 pm; closed Mon L; children: 18+.

RADLEY GREEN, ESSEX 3–2B

The Cuckoo **£47** Ⓣ
CM4 0LT (01245) 248946
"A row of pretty little cottages, turned into a gem of a restaurant", which is tipped for its "inventive" cuisine; there are only 30 seats, though (plus a "beautiful" garden), and "the main problem is getting a table".
/ **Details:** www.cuckooradleygreen.co.uk; On the A14 between Ongar and Chelmsford; 8.45 pm, Fri-Sat 9 pm; closed Mon & Sun; no Amex.

RAMSBOTTOM, LANCASHIRE 5–1B

The Venetian House **£49** Ⓣ
18 Market Pl BL0 9HT (01706) 825070
The successor to Ramsons (RIP), one of the North West's most celebrated restaurants, maintains quite a continuity from the former regime – more reports on its new 'cicchetti' (small-plates) formula please!
/ **Details:** www.venetian-hideaway.co.uk.

RAMSGILL-IN-NIDDERDALE, NORTH YORKSHIRE 8–4B

Yorke Arms **£92** 444
HG3 5RL (01423) 755243
Frances Atkins "is an amazingly innovative chef", and produces "exquisite" food – "a good blend of locally sourced, foraged, modern and classic" – at this "indulgent" inn, "beautifully located" in the Dales, which she co-owns with husband Bill.
/ **Details:** www.yorke-arms.co.uk; 4m W of Pateley Bridge; 8.45 pm; no Amex. **Accommodation:** 16 rooms, from £200.

READING, BERKSHIRE 2–2D

Cerise
Forbury Hotel **£63** Ⓣ
26 The Forbury RG1 3EJ (01189) 527770
Surprisingly few reports on this ambitious city centre venue; it' still tipped, though, for is "very good value-for-money" weekday lunch menu.
/ **Details:** www.theforburyhotel.co.uk; @TheForburyHotel; 10 pm. **Accommodation:** 23, 16 apts rooms, from £150.

London Street Brasserie **£55** 343
2-4 London St RG1 4PN (0118) 950 5036
With a "nice canalside location, near the Oracle shopping centre", an "ultra-professional operation" that's become quite an "old favourite" for some reporters; "high-quality" British cooking using "great local ingredients" ensures it's always "popular and rather noisy". / **Details:** www.londonstbrasserie.co.uk; @lsb_reading; 10.30 pm, Fri & Sat 11 pm; booking: max on Sat.

REDHILL, SURREY 10–2D

The Pendleton **£44** 444
RH1 6QF (01737) 760212
"The Coombes are back!"; the popular one-time proprietors of the Westerley (RIP) in Reigate have now relocated their "winning" back-of-/front-of-house partnership; result? – a "welcoming" sort of place, were "London-standard food comes at out-of-town prices!" / **Details:** www.thependleton.co.uk.

REYNOLDSTON, SWANSEA 1–1C

Fairyhill **£65** 554
SA3 1BS (01792) 390139
Feedback on this once-renowned country house hotel, in the wilds of the Gower Peninsular, remains thin on the ground, but it all tends to support the conclusion that this is a gastronomic destination "which couldn't be better", and it's "so friendly too".
/ **Details:** www.fairyhill.net; @Fairyhill_Hotel; 20 mins from M4, J47 off B4295; 9 pm; no Amex; children: 8+ at D. **Accommodation:** 8 rooms, from £180.

RICHMOND, SURREY 3–3A

The Dysart Arms **£61** 443
135 Petersham Rd TW10 7AA (020) 8940 8005
"Beautifully located by Richmond Park", this restaurant in a "refurbished Arts & Crafts house" nowadays offers "an excellent and adventurous menu" (with some emphasis on foraged ingredients).

/ **Details:** www.thedysartarms.co.uk; 9.30 pm; closed Sun D; no Amex; children: 12+ after 8 pm.

RIPLEY, SURREY 3–3A

Drakes £87 543
The Clock Hs, High St GU23 6AQ
(01483) 224777
*"Steve Drake is on top of his game", at this acclaimed venture "in a sleepy Surrey village", where the "memorable" cuisine provides "a real real exploration of textures and flavours"; the modern conversion of its Georgian interior can seem "a bit cold", but even critics found ambience improved this year. / **Details:** www.drakesrestaurant.co.uk; 9.30 pm; closed Mon, Tue L & Sun; no Amex; booking: max 12.*

RIPPONDEN, WEST YORKSHIRE 5–1C

El Gato Negro Tapas £42 553
1 Oldham Rd HX6 4DN (01422) 823070
"Splendid in every way", this renowned family-run venture may have "the last location you would expect", but it elicits rave reviews from all reporters – "no other tapas place comes close!".
*/ **Details:** www.elgatonegrotapas.com; 9.30 pm, Fri & Sat 10 pm, Sun 7.30 pm; closed Mon, Tue, Wed L, Thu L, Fri L & Sun D.*

ROADE, NORTHAMPTONSHIRE 3–1A

Roade House £47 343
16 High St NN7 2NW (01604) 863372
"Always reliable" and "dependable", "just like a local restaurant should be" – this stalwart of the Northants dining scene continues to gather plaudits, not least for its "very good" service.
*/ **Details:** www.roadehousehotel.co.uk; 9.30 pm; closed Mon L, Sat L & Sun D; no shorts.*
***Accommodation:** 10 rooms, from £82.*

ROCK, CORNWALL 1–3B

Dining Room £56 432
Pavilion Buildings, Rock Rd PL27 6JS
(01208) 862622
"An unassuming restaurant, in a modern parade of shops, but oh the cooking...!" – the "appealing and artistically presented" dishes on offer at Fred & Donna Beedle's establishment come as "a pleasant surprise".
*/ **Details:** www.thediningroomrock.co.uk; @TheDiningRmRock; 9 pm; closed Mon, Tue, Wed L, Thu L, Fri L, Sat L & Sun L; no Amex; children: 10+.*

Restaurant Nathan Outlaw
The St Enodoc Hotel £123 553
Rock Rd PL27 6LA (01208) 863394
*"The best UK fish restaurant by far", is, say fans, the hotel dining room where Nathan Outlaw's "extraordinary" dishes "usurp even his former teacher Mr Stein across the water"; the interior is a bit "sterile", but the room has "perfect views of the Camel estuary". / **Details:** www.nathan-outlaw.com; @Nathanoutlaw; 9 pm; D only, closed Mon & Sun; no Amex; no shorts; children: 12+ D. **Accommodation:** 20 rooms, from £130.*

ROCKBEARE, DEVON 1–3D

Jack in the Green Inn £48 454
London Rd EX5 2EE (01404) 822240
*"Going from strength to strength", a gastroboozer where the cooking is often "brilliant", and service is notably "slick" too; if there is a negative, it is that the style of the dining room can seem "very formal". / **Details:** www.jackinthegreen.uk.com; @JackGreenInn; On the old A30, 3 miles east of junction 29 of M5; 9.30 pm, Sun 9 pm; no Amex.*

ROMALDKIRK, COUNTY DURHAM 8–3B

The Rose & Crown £41 444
DL12 9EB (01833) 650213
"Fine locally-sourced fresh fare" from a "no-nonsense" menu that's "sensibly priced" too enables this "lovely" inn to attract "not just many visitors, but the locals too".
*/ **Details:** www.rose-and-crown.co.uk; 6m NW of Barnard Castle on B6277; 9 pm; D only, ex Sun open L & D; children: 7+ in restaurant.*
***Accommodation:** 14 rooms, from £150.*

ROSEVINE, CORNWALL 1–4B

Driftwood Hotel £73 444
TR2 5EW (01872) 580644
"Gorgeous sea views, plus spectacular cooking – what could be more romantic?"; there's not a huge amount of feedback on the dining room of this trendy cliff-top hotel, but it's all extremely positive.
*/ **Details:** www.driftwoodhotel.co.uk; off the A30 to Truro, towards St Mawes; 9.30 pm; D only; booking: max 6; children: 10+. **Accommodation:** 15 rooms, from £170.*

ROWSLEY, DERBYSHIRE 5–2C

The Peacock £79 444
Bakewell Rd DE4 2EB (01629) 733518
This "picturesque Peak District country house hotel" is "a treat for all the senses" and makes "a wonderful venue for a romantic night out" (especially the "delightful" bar); the occasional dish can seem "overwrought", but the general standard of cuisine remains "very high".
*/ **Details:** www.thepeacockatrowsley.com; 9 pm, Sun 8.30 pm; children: 10+ at D.*
***Accommodation:** 15 rooms, from £160.*

RYE, EAST SUSSEX 3–4C

The Ambrette at Rye £42 433
24 High St TN31 7JF (01797) 222 043
"I'd return to Rye to eat here!"; "delicious", "unusual" and "imaginatively-presented" dishes

(and "locally sourced" too) have made quite a hit of this "fairly-priced" spot.
/ **Details:** www.theambrette.co.uk; @the_ambrette; L only; closed Mon.

Landgate Bistro **£44** 4 3 2
5-6 Landgate TN31 7LH (01797) 222829
"Every bit as good as it was 25 years ago"; this "always-reliable" bistro continues to offer "wonderful" British food ("a short menu of local fish, game at meat") at "unbelievably low prices".
/ **Details:** www.landgatebistro.co.uk; 9 pm, Sat 9.15 pm; closed Mon, Tue, Wed L, Thu L, Fri L & Sun D; no Amex.

Webbe's at The Fish Cafe **£44** 5 4 2
17 Tower St TN31 7AT (01797) 222226
Paul Webbe is a "god with fish", say fans of this "creative" town-centre warehouse-conversion, whose coastal location ensures "some of the best" fish possible; there is a "world of difference" between the upstairs restaurant and downstairs café, though both are "fairly unassuming".
/ **Details:** www.thefishcafe.com; @webbesrye; 9.30 pm.

SALFORD, GREATER MANCHESTER 5–2B

Damson **£55** 4 5 4
Orange Building, Media City UK M50 2HF (0161) 751 7020
"Roll on our next visit!"; this "well-spaced" venue, near Media City, is "amazingly good for the price" – it is run with "evident passion", and the cuisine is "generous, strong on presentation, and with great flavours too".
/ **Details:** www.damsonrestaurant.co.uk; @damsonmediacity; Mon-Thu 9.30 pm Fri & Sat 10 pm; closed Sun D.

SALISBURY, WILTSHIRE 2–3C

Anokaa **£42** 4 3 3
60 Fisherton St SP2 7RB (01722) 414142
"A significant cut above the normal Indian"; albeit "tucked away on a rather unpromising street", this innovative venture offers "delicate" and sometimes "spectacular" dishes – "everything is light and beautifully served, and no two sauces are the same". / **Details:** www.anokaa.com; @eatatanokaa; 10.30 pm; no shorts.

SALTAIRE, WEST YORKSHIRE 5–1C

Salts Diner **£34** 2 3 3
Salts Mill, Victoria Rd BD18 3LA (01274) 531163
Judged "very useful" at best – and "consistent" at worst – this gallery café in a UNESCO-listed mill offers "good fresh food, efficiently served" – noise levels, though, "can't be much lower than when the mill was in production!"
/ **Details:** www.saltsmill.org.uk; 2m from Bradford on A650; L & afternoon tea only; no Amex.

SANDSEND, NORTH YORKSHIRE 8–3D

Estbek House **£59** Ⓣ
East Row YO21 3SU (01947) 893424
A seafront restaurant-with-rooms, tipped for its "outstanding" fish choices, and an "excellent" choice of wines too – a formula that can end up a little "pricey" for some tastes.
/ **Details:** www.estbekhouse.co.uk; @estbekhouse; 9 pm; D only; no Amex. **Accommodation:** 5 rooms, from £125.

SAUNDERSFOOT, PEMBROKESHIRE 4–4B

Coast **£55** 4 4 5
SA69 9AJ (01834) 810800
Living up to its name, Will Holland's impressive newly-built restaurant has a "fabulous" location, "right on the beach"; its "very friendly and professional" staff serve up dishes, mostly fish, that are "simple but perfectly prepared".
/ **Details:** www.coastsaundersfoot.co.uk.

SAWLEY, LANCASHIRE 5–1B

The Spread Eagle **£47** Ⓣ
BB7 4NH (01200) 441202
A Ribble Valley coaching inn tipped for "pub food with style"; "in the restaurant, ask for a window table, to see the river and the ducks".
/ **Details:** www.spreadeaglesawley.co.uk; 9.15 pm, Sun 7.15 pm. **Accommodation:** 7 rooms, from £80.

SCARBOROUGH, NORTH YORKSHIRE 8–4D

Lanterna **£54** 5 5 2
33 Queen St YO11 1HQ (01723) 363616
"What a find!"; this "excellent" family-run Italian is a "big favourite" for reporters – a '70s-style temple to Piedmontese dishes, which are "based on the freshest seasonal ingredients"; don't miss the "absolutely delicious" zabaglione, "made at the table". / **Details:** www.lanterna-ristorante.co.uk; 9.30 pm; D only, closed Sun; no Amex.

SCAWTON, NORTH YORKSHIRE 8–4C

Hare Inn **£36** 5 4 4
YO7 2HG (01845) 597769
"High-class dining in a medieval inn"; it may be located "in the middle of nowhere", but this "friendly" family-run establishment is "well worth seeking out" for its "innovative food using high-quality local ingredients"; for top value, go for lunch.
/ **Details:** www.thehare-inn.com; off A170; 9 pm; closed Mon, Tue & Sun D.

SEER GREEN, BUCKINGHAMSHIRE 3–3A

The Jolly Cricketers £49 322
24 Chalfont Rd HP9 2YG (01494) 676308
*A popular rural boozer where the "very well-presented and tasty" fare (including "some top veggie choices") is a hit with most reporters; atmosphere, though, can sometimes prove a touch elusive. / **Details:** www.thejollycricketers.co.uk; @jollycricketers; 11.15 pm, Fri & Sat 11.30, Sun 10.30.*

SHALDON, DEVON 1–3D

Ode £58 342
Fore St TQ14 0DE (01626) 873977
*"A little gem of a restaurant tucked away in this small village" – using "locally-sourced" and "seasonal" ingredients, it "maintains a consistently high standard all year round"; the café offshoot (with sea view) is "above average" too.
/ **Details:** www.odetruefood.com; @odetruefood; 9.30 pm; D only, closed Sun-Tue; no Amex; children: 8+ after 8pm.*

SHEFFIELD, SOUTH YORKSHIRE 5–2C

The Milestone £45 333
84 Green Lane At Ball St S3 8SE (0114) 272 8327
*"In an industrial area, near the canals", this "neighbourhood gastro place" is an "unlikely oasis of good food", and "great beer" too; despite the unpropitious locale, it is often "crowded and noisy". / **Details:** www.the-milestone.co.uk; @TheMilestone; Mon-Sat 10.30 pm, Sun 9.30 pm; no Amex.*

Nonna's £47 332
535-541 Eccleshall Rd S11 8PR
(0114) 268 6166
*There's a "truly Italian experience" to be had at this trendy Eccleshall restaurant, which not only offers "freshly cooked and unusual" fare but "even has its own cycling club with an Italian flavour"; "the noise level is as high as it gets" – "don't take granny!"
/ **Details:** www.nonnas.co.uk; @NonnasCucina; 9.30 pm, Sat & Sun 9.45 pm; no Amex.*

Peppercorn £33 ①
s17 3LB (0114) 2350101
*In "what looks like a bit like a Portakabin from the outside", this "snug" but "pleasant" outfit is tipped as offering some of "the best cooking in Sheffield", in "quirkily British" style.
/ **Details:** www.peppercorn-restaurant.co.uk.*

Rafters £55 444
220 Oakbrook Rd, Nether Grn S11 7ED
(0114) 230 4819
*"This is the tops"; it's 'all change' at this Ranmoor fixture, with the new regime of chef Tom Lawson and front-of-house manager Alistair Myers by all accounts "destined for great things"; "it's amazing that Tom's only in his early 20s and achieving such great things in the kitchen".
/ **Details:** www.raftersrestaurant.co.uk; @rafterss11; 10 pm; D only, closed Tue & Sun.*

Vero Gusto £48 454
S1 2PA (0114) 276 0004
*"The best food in the city-centre"; this dining room of this "excellent little Italian" may be rather "crammed", but "the food and service make up for it", and the "extensive" wine list is "pretty good" too.
/ **Details:** www.gustosheffield.co.uk.*

SHEFFORD, BEDFORDSHIRE 3–1A

Black Horse at Ireland £52 344
Ireland SG17 5QL (01462) 811398
*"Top marks for everything", says one of the fans of this "very good country pub", which offers "enormous portions of well cooked food" and notably "attentive" service too; culinary highlight – "fantastic fish 'n' chips".
/ **Details:** www.blackhorseireland.com; 9.30 pm, Fri & Sat 10 pm; closed Sun D. **Accommodation:** 2 rooms, from £55.*

SHELLEY, WEST YORKSHIRE 5–2C

Three Acres £59 243
Roydhouse HD8 8LR (01484) 602606
*Out on't moors, this long-established inn is a "does-what-it-says-on-the-tin type of place" offering "really great hearty Yorkshire fare"; avoid the "rather soulless" new wing. / **Details:** www.3acres.com; 9.30 pm; no Amex. **Accommodation:** 16 rooms, from £125.*

SHENLEY, HERTFORDSHIRE 3–2B

White Horse £47 323
37 London Rd WD7 9ER (01923) 853054
*This "welcoming" pub – with "log fires in winter, and a terrace for the summer" – offers "good food at moderate cost"; the style, though, can strike critics as slightly "functional".
/ **Details:** www.whitehorseradlett.co.uk; 10 pm, Sat 10.30 pm.*

SHERBORNE, DORSET 2–3B

Eastbury Hotel £49 443
Long St DT9 3BY (01935) 813131
*"A real family-run hotel with an excellent restaurant" that's "ideal for a romantic meal or special occasion"; its tasting menu offers "just enough highs" to make it a "definite attraction", and overnighters can enjoy the "best ever" breakfasts too.
/ **Details:** www.theeastburyhotel.co.uk.*

The Green £50 ①
3 The Grn DT9 3HY (01935) 813821
Well-located in the heart of the town centre, this informal spot is "still the best in the area",

*notwithstanding service that's "inconsistent". / **Details:** www.greenrestaurant.co.uk; @greensherborne; 9.30 pm; closed Mon & Sun.*

SHERE, SURREY 3–3A

Kinghams £53 333
Gomshall Ln GU5 9HE (01483) 202168
*This "attractive old half-timbered cottage" in a "picture-postcard" village may seem stuck in a bit of a "time warp", but almost all reporters agree on the virtues of its "competitively-priced" cuisine. / **Details:** www.kinghams-restaurant.co.uk; off A25 between Dorking & Guildford; 9 pm; closed Mon & Sun D.*

SHINFIELD, BERKSHIRE 2–2D

L'Ortolan £89 443
Church Ln RG2 9BY (0118) 988 8500
*Going out on a high, chef Alan Murchison may be moving on, but has dished up many "sublime" meals this year, accompanied by "superb" wines, at this "welcoming", but slightly "hushed", former rectory, where a new chef is set to take over in early-2015. / **Details:** www.lortolan.com; @lortolan; 8.30 pm; closed Mon & Sun.*

SHIPBOURNE, KENT 3–3B

The Chaser Inn £43 224
Stumble Hill TN11 9PE (01732) 810360
*"An attractive country pub with an interesting and varied menu"; ratings this year were dragged down however by a couple of reports of "average" food and "slow" service – hopefully just a blip! / **Details:** www.thechaser.co.uk; @thechaserinn; 9.30 pm, Sun 9 pm.*

SHIPLAKE, OXFORDSHIRE 2–2D

Orwells £65 423
Shiplake Row RG9 4DP (0118) 940 3673
*"Classy" and "inventive" food in a "great countryside location" is the formula for success at this "wonderful" gastropub, not far from Henley; service, though, "sometimes lacks the finesse you see in the food". / **Details:** www.orwellsatshiplake.co.uk; 9.30 pm; closed Mon, Tue & Sun D.*

SHIPLEY, WEST YORKSHIRE 5–1C

Aagrah £38 444
4 Saltaire Rd BD18 3HN (01274) 530880
*A "consistently good Asian restaurant that sets a benchmark for this type of food" – this "pleasant" HQ of a pre-eminent local chain is a real crowd-pleaser; special feature? – "the upstairs buffet is just amazing for its variety and quality". / **Details:** www.aagrah.com; 11.30 pm; closed Sat L.*

SHIRLEY, DERBYSHIRE 5–3C

The Saracen's Head £31 444
Church Ln DE6 3AS (01335) 360 330
*A "well-regarded country pub" whose "spectacularly good" meat staples are backed up by "good butchery skills" (which are "very evident in the open kitchen") – "go, you'll be amazed"! / **Details:** www.saracens-head-shirley.co.uk; 11 pm, Sun 10.30 pm; no Amex.*

SKENFRITH, MONMOUTHSHIRE 2–1B

The Bell at Skenfrith £52 T
NP7 8UH (01600) 750235
*In a "fabulous location", this remote country inn is tipped as a "super gastropub"; in the wake of a recent change of ownership, however, reports are rather unsettled. / **Details:** www.skenfrith.co.uk; @bellatskenfrith; on B4521, 10m E of Abergavenny; 9.30 pm, Sun 9 pm; no Amex; children: 8+ at D. **Accommodation:** 11 rooms, from £110.*

SKIPTON, NORTH YORKSHIRE 8–4B

The Devonshire Brasserie
The Devonshire Arms £45 433
Bolton Abbey BD23 6AJ (01756) 710710
*In a "lovely country setting", the brasserie of this grand and luxurious ducally-owned country hotel "can be crowded at times, but the food and service are worth it". / **Details:** www.devonshirehotels.co.uk; on A59, 5m NE of Skipton; 9.30 pm, Sun 9 pm. **Accommodation:** 40 rooms, from £200.*

SLAITHWAITE, WEST YORKSHIRE 5–1C

The Handmade Bakery £9 T
HD7 5HA (01484) 842175
*"As the name suggests, a working bakery that happens to offer food"; it's tipped for the "extremely fresh" baked goods you might hope for, as well as some "original and delicious" fruit juices. / **Details:** thehandmadebakery.coop/.*

SLEAT, HIGHLAND 9–2B

Kinloch Lodge £92 435
IV43 8QY (01471) 833333
*"Downton Abbey meets Take the High Road", at the Macdonald of Macdonald's "historic hunting lodge", which has a location that's "out of the way, even for Skye"; "alas Lady Claire has taken a step back", but Marcello Tully's food is "fantastic", and well supported by the "extensive" wine list. / **Details:** www.kinloch-lodge.co.uk; @kinloch_lodge; 9 pm; no Amex. **Accommodation:** 19 rooms, from £99 winter 180 summer pp.*

SNAPE, SUFFOLK 3–1D

The Crown Inn £40 544
Bridge Rd IP17 1SL (01728) 688324
"One evening I heard the landlady say:

I must go and get the goats in" – evidence that they take local sourcing seriously at this "great little place", where the food is often "superb"! / **Details:** *www.snape-crown.co.uk; off A12 towards Aldeburgh; 9.30 pm, Sat 10 pm, Sun 9.30 pm; no Amex.* **Accommodation:** *2 rooms, from £90.*

SNETTISHAM, NORFOLK 6–4B

Rose & Crown £33 [T]

Old Church Rd PE31 7LX (01485) 541382

This "lovely" old moorland pub is "trad at the front" but – "Tardis"-like – conceals multiple dining areas as well as a garden with an "imaginative" playground; it's tipped for "excellent" but "simple" cooking (and puddings which are "better than OK"). / **Details:** *www.roseandcrownsnettisham.co.uk; 9 pm; no Amex.* **Accommodation:** *16 rooms, from £90.*

SOLIHULL, WEST MIDLANDS 5–4C

Spice Club £30 444

B91 3DA (0121) 711 7070

A buzzing South East Asian outfit offering "unusual dishes, cooked perfectly"; those "complimentary ice cream and liqueurs" are a "lovely touch" too! / **Details:** *www.spicecubsolihull.com.*

SONNING-ON-THAMES, BERKSHIRE 2–2D

The French Horn £82 335

RG4 6TN (0118) 969 2204

An "old favourite" of the "old school", which enjoys "a wonderful setting right on the banks of the Thames"; "high-quality" cooking is part of the "very pleasant" overall experience... but it's "so expensive". / **Details:** *www.thefrenchhorn.co.uk; @The_French_Horn; 9.30 pm, Sun 9 pm; booking: max 10.* **Accommodation:** *21 rooms, from £160.*

SOUTH SHIELDS, TYNE AND WEAR 8–2B

Colmans £34 443

182-186 Ocean Rd NE33 2JQ (0191) 456 1202

A classic large-scale chippy (est 1926) that's not the cheapest you'll find, but which continues to offer the highest standards. / **Details:** *www.colmansfishandchips.com; L only; no Amex.*

SOUTHAMPTON, HAMPSHIRE 2–3D

Kuti's £33 [T]

37-39 Oxford St SO14 3DP (023) 8022 1585

"From the doorman to chefs, they get it right here" – especially in a part of the world not over-endowed with decent restaurants, this "very reliable" Indian is a leading local destination well worth knowing about. / **Details:** *www.kutis.co.uk; 11.30 pm.*

SOUTHPORT, MERSEYSIDE 5–1A

Bistrot Vérité £43 443

7 Liverpool Rd PR8 4AR (01704) 564 199

A "cheerful and accommodating" shop-conversion bistro in Birkdale Village, which pleases all who comment on it with its "good honest French cooking" and its "grown-up service" too. / **Details:** *www.bistrotverite.co.uk.*

The Vincent Hotel £42 434

98 Lord St PR8 1JR (01704) 883800

Located in a "trendy modern hotel", this café and sushi bar is "doing things in style and to a very high standard", be it an "excellent traditional afternoon tea" or "surprisingly good Japanese fare". / **Details:** *www.thevincenthotel.com; 10 pm.* **Accommodation:** *60 rooms, from £93.*

SOUTHROP, GLOUCESTERSHIRE 2–2C

The Swan at Southrop £51 [T]

Letchlade GL7 3NU (01367) 850205

"Still a great place to eat"; under new management, this prominent Cotswold boozer is still tipped as a "friendly" sort of place, where the food is "a cut above 'gastropub'". / **Details:** *www.theswanatsouthrop.co.uk; Mon-Thurs 9 pm, Fri-Sat 9.30 pm ; closed Sun D; no Amex.*

SOUTHSEA, HAMPSHIRE 2–4D

Garage Lounge £31 [T]

1 Albert Rd PO5 2SP (023) 9282 8432

"Central Perk comes to PO5!"; this "quirky" and "stylish" hang out occupies an old garage, and serves a "great selection of teas" and coffees, plus food that's a touch "more sophisticated" than your typical café. / **Details:** *@garagelounge1; 11 pm.*

SOUTHWOLD, SUFFOLK 3–1D

The Crown Adnams Hotel £58 233

90 High St IP18 6DP (01502) 722275

This famous Adnams pub continues to divide opinion – fans find the food "wonderful" and sat it's "well supported" by a wine list of some repute... but critics feel it's "coasting along", and that the "cooking standard has dropped". / **Details:** *www.adnams.co.uk/stay-with-us/the-crown; @CrownSouthwold; 9 pm; no Amex.* **Accommodation:** *14 rooms, from £160.*

Sole Bay Fish Company £26 543

22e Blackshore IP18 6ND (01502) 724241

It's all change at this "charming harbourside eatery" which, as of June 2014, has "doubled in size", gaining a bar, al fresco area and "upmarket rustic" décor; the mostly cold seafood menu "now includes chargrilled lobster and chips" – but, muses a fan,

is it all just "a bit too upmarket"?
/ **Details:** *www.solebayfishco.co.uk; closed Mon.*

Sutherland House £52 Ⓣ
56 High St IP18 6DN (01502) 724544
The Bank family's quaint and comfy family-run restaurant-with-rooms is tipped for fairly simple fare prepared to a standard most reporters find "excellent". / **Details:** *www.sutherlandhouse.co.uk; @SH_Southwold; 9.30 pm; closed Mon (winter).* **Accommodation:** *3 rooms, from £150.*

The Swan £52 213
The Market Pl IP18 6EG (01502) 722186
This famous Adnams-owned inn can sometimes seem "a little stuck in the past" nowadays; foodwise, there's "plenty of choice" and some excellent wines and beers, but service – if "friendly" – can seem "half asleep", and the overall experience can sometimes just seem "desultory".
/ **Details:** *www.adnams.co.uk/stay-with-us/the-swan; @swansouthwold; 9 pm; no Amex; no jeans or trainers; children: 5+ at D.* **Accommodation:** *42 rooms, from £185.*

SPARKWELL, DEVON 1–3C

Treby Arms £50 443
PL7 5DD (01752) 837363
MasterChef winner Anton Piotrowski's pub (originally built by Brunel to feed workers on his nearby Royal Albert Bridge) is, by all accounts, "well worth the journey", not least for its "amazing" six- or eight- course tasting menus; on the downside, "tables can be hard to get" nowadays.
/ **Details:** *www.thetrebyarms.co.uk.*

SPARSHOLT, HAMPSHIRE 2–3D

The Plough Inn £47 333
SO21 2NW (01962) 776353
"The best pub food close to Winchester!" – this "reliably good" country gastroboozer inspires impressively consistent reports; you "must book".
/ **Details:** *9 pm, Sun & Mon 8.30 pm, Fri & Sat 9.30 pm; no Amex.*

SPARSHOLT, OXFORDSHIRE 2–2D

Star Inn £44 433
OX12 9PL (01235) 751 873
A "friendly" country pub-with-rooms, primarily of note for the "very talented" cuisine of chef-patron Dave Watts ("who spent eight years as Raymond Blanc's right-hand man").
/ **Details:** *www.thestarsparsholt.co.uk.*

SPELDHURST, KENT 3–4B

George & Dragon £43 324
Speldhurst Hill TN3 0NN (01892) 863125
A "lovely" medieval inn – think oak beams and roaring fires – where the "classy" cooking makes the most of some "outstanding local produce".
/ **Details:** *www.speldhurst.com; @GDSpeldhurst; 9.30 pm; closed Sun D; no Amex.*

ST ALBANS, HERTFORDSHIRE 3–2A

Barrissimo £14 443
28 St Peters St AL1 3NA (01727) 869999
This "lovely, authentic family-run Italian coffee shop" offers "interesting paninis" and "delicious" breakfasts and snacks, all "freshly prepared with love and care". / **Details:** *5.30 pm, Sun 4 pm; L only; no credit cards.*

Cock £35 234
48 St Peters St AL1 3NF (01727) 854 816
This rambling and very popular 16th-century inn – with its handy location between the cathedral and the river, and its log fires too – is well worth knowing about; it serves "good-quality pub food at a very fair price".
/ **Details:** *www.thecockinstalbans.co.uk; 9 pm; no Amex.*

Darcy's £52 Ⓣ
2 Hatfield Rd AL1 3RP (01727) 730777
We reduced this popular local restaurant to 'tip' status simply to reflect a lack of clarity in reports while new chef, Phil Thompson, ex-Auberge du Lac, settles in; early feedback, however, speaks of "improvement" under the new regime.
/ **Details:** *www.darcysrestaurant.co.uk; @thompsonsdarcy; 9 pm, Fri & Sat 10 pm.*

Thompson at Darcy's £59 332
AL1 3RP (01727) 730777
Now owned by the former chef of the Auberge du Lac, this town-centre restaurant wins all-round praise as a "really delightful" destination (even if the odd reporter "expected more of a former Michelin-starred chef").
/ **Details:** *www.thompsonatdarcys.co.uk.*

The Waffle House Kingsbury Water Mill £26 234
St Michael's St AL3 4SJ (01727) 853502
"The only downside to this place are the queues… but it is definitely worth the wait!" – set in a beautiful old watermill, this local institution remains quite a crowd-pleaser, particularly "on a sunny day when you want something sweet".
/ **Details:** *www.wafflehouse.co.uk; 6 pm; L only; no Amex; no booking.*

ST ANDREWS, FIFE 9–3D

Seafood Restaurant £64 435
The Scores, Bruce Embankment KY16 9AB
(01334) 479475
"A stunning 'glass box' overlooking the beach, where a high-quality range of dishes is well served" – one reporter's neat encapsulation of most commentary on this seaside stand-out, which enjoys "fantastic" views.

/ **Details:** www.theseafoodrestaurant.com; @seafoodrestau; 9.30 pm; children: 12+ at D.

Vine Leaf £47 444
131 South St KY16 9UN (01334) 477497
"The best restaurant in St Andrews", in business for a quarter of a century, remains something of a "haven of good food" – a "quirky" but "professional" sort of place, whose hidden-away location can seem quite romantic; warning for first-time visitors, though – allow a bit of extra time so you can find it!
/ **Details:** www.vineleafstandrews.co.uk; 9.30 pm; D only, closed Mon & Sun.

ST AUSTELL, CORNWALL 1–4B

Austells £42 554
10 Beach Rd PL25 3PH (01726) 813888
"If you're anywhere near St Austell, you must pay Brett Camborne-Paynter a visit!"; his "hugely welcoming" restaurant may not inspire a huge number of reports, but all of them pronounce it a "treasure" – "worth a 250-mile round trip to dine here again!". / **Details:** www.austells.co.uk; Tue-Sun 10 pm; closed Mon.

ST DAVIDS, PEMBROKESHIRE 4–4A

Cwtch £46 334
22 High St SA62 6SD (01437) 720491
Fans say this "fabulous" town-centre bistro is "still on the up"; its popularity can affect the service, but, even at peak times, chef Andy Holcroft's food is never less than "very solid".
/ **Details:** www.cwtchrestaurant.co.uk; 9.30 pm; D only.

ST IPPOLYTS, HERTFORDSHIRE 3–2A

The Rusty Gun £34 434
SG4 7PG (01462) 432653
"The local food is impressive… but it's the burgers that make me go back again and again" – whatever the reason, this "great restaurant, attached to a farm shop" is an all-round crowd-pleaser.
/ **Details:** www.therustygun.co.uk.

ST IVES, CAMBRIDGESHIRE 3–1B

PR Massala £29 533
PE27 5DX (01480) 493222 / 493555
Albeit rather "hard to find" ("tucked away in a little back street behind Market Square"), this intimate Bangladeshi venture "rewards persistence", thanks to the consistently high quality of its "spicy" fare (including "very good" vegetarian and vegan options). / **Details:** www.prmassala.co.uk.

ST IVES, CORNWALL 1–4A

Alba Restaurant £43 345
The Old Life Boat Hs, Wharf Rd TR26 1LF
(01736) 797222
An "excellent location and (harbour) views" add to the charms of this comfortable restaurant known for its "creamy" crab linguini in particular, and its "top-class service".
/ **Details:** www.thealbarestaurant.com; @albarestaurant; 10 pm; closed Mon L & Sun L.

Alfresco £51 Ⓣ
Harbourside Wharf Rd TR26 1LF
(01736) 793737
Tipped for its "great location overlooking the harbour", a "friendly" restaurant where "tasty local produce" ("including Cornish wines") are used to good effect. / **Details:** www.alfresco-stives.co.uk; on harbour front; 9.30 pm; no Amex.

The Black Rock £43 Ⓣ
Market Pl TR26 1RZ (01736) 791911
Tipped by fans as "the epitome of what a lovely meal should be", this "ambitious" open-kitchen bistro dishes up some "yummy dishes"; that's not to say that all feedback is perfect – more reports please! / **Details:** www.theblackrockstives.co.uk; 9 pm; D only, closed Sun; no Amex; booking: max 8 in summer.

Porthgwidden Beach Café £42 345
Porthgwidden Beach TR26 1PL
(01736) 796791
It's not just the "inventive and imaginative menu" ("especially for fish and seafood lovers") that makes this seaside café popular – it has a "perfect position overlooking the beach"; "great for breakfast, lunch or dinner". / **Details:** www.porthgwiddencafe.co.uk; 9.30 pm; no Amex; booking: max 10.

Porthmeor Beach Cafe £36 445
Porthmeor Beach TR26 1JZ (01736) 793366
"Right on the beach, with the Atlantic rolling in", and close to the Tate too, this is "just the place for a sunset dinner"; naturally, the "wonderful tapas-style food" majors in "superb fresh fish that doesn't need to be messed about with".
/ **Details:** www.porthmeor-beach.co.uk; 9 pm; D only. Closed Nov-Mar.; no Amex.

Porthminster Café £53 435
Porthminster Beach TR26 2EB
(01736) 795352
"Perched over the beach", and with "wonderful views over St Ives", the location of this "stupendous" favourite is "too beautiful for words"; "the name is misleading, as the food is more gourmet than café" – "beautifully cooked and presented fish, and good wines".
/ **Details:** www.porthminstercafe.co.uk; @PorthBCafe; 10 pm; no Amex.

Tate Cafe Tate Gallery £35 Ⓣ
Porthmeor Beach TR26 1TG (01736) 796226
Tipped as a "wonderful place on a sunny day",

this top-floor gallery café enjoys "great views", and the simple, light fare can be pretty good too; the system, though, doesn't always seem able to cope with the press of customers.
/ ***Details:*** *www.tate.org.uk; L only; no Amex.*

ST LEONARDS-ON-SEA, EAST SUSSEX 3–4C

St Clement's **£48** 442
3 Mercatoria TN38 0EB (01424) 200355
A "lovely" – and perhaps rather surprising – find in the backstreets of this faded seaside town; the dining room itself may be "unremarkable", but Nick Hales's venture is a "welcoming" one, where the menu headlines some "superb locally-caught fish".
/ ***Details:*** *www.stclementsrestaurant.co.uk; closed Mon & Sun D; no Amex.*

ST MAWES, CORNWALL 1–4B

Hotel Tresanton **£67** 445
27 Lower Castle Rd TR2 5DR
(01326) 270055
"A wonderful location by the harbour, and a great food experience too" – Olga Polizzi "has just got it so right" at this fashionable revamp of this longstanding seaside hotel; if you can, dine outside, on one of the terraces overlooking the water.
/ ***Details:*** *www.tresanton.com; @hoteltresanton; 9.30 pm; booking: max 10; children: 6+ at dinner.* ***Accommodation:*** *40 rooms, from £250.*

ST MERRYN, CORNWALL 1–3B

The Cornish Arms **£37** 433
Churchtown PL28 8ND (01841) 520288
Rick Stein's village inn is a "very slick operation which hits the mark on all accounts", from its "good value" but simple British pub grub to its casual atmosphere; naturally it tends to get "crowded in the summer".
/ ***Details:*** *www.rickstein.com; 8.30 pm; no Amex.*

ST MONANS, FIFE 9–4D

Craig Millar
@ 16 West End **£60** 544
16 West End KY10 2BX (01333) 730327
"Fine dining in a beautiful location" – six words which pretty much say it all abut this good-all-round spot, by the harbour.
/ ***Details:*** *www.16westend.com; 9 pm; closed Mon & Tue; children: 5+.*

STADHAMPTON, OXFORDSHIRE 2–2D

The Crazy Bear **£71** 435
Bear Ln OX44 7UR (01865) 890714
"Maximalism" isn't writ much larger than at this "quirky" Anglo/Thai spot (one dining room each); we've traditionally viewed this as an 'atmosphere' recommendation, but reports on the food of late have been very good – even fans, though, can find the package "overpriced" overall.
/ ***Details:*** *www.crazybeargroup.co.uk; @CrazyBearGroup; 10 pm; children: 12+ at Fri & Sat D.* ***Accommodation:*** *16 rooms, from £169.*

STAINES, SURREY 3–3A

Three Horseshoes **£38** Ⓣ
TW18 1SE (01784) 455014
"It looks nothing from the road", but this is tipped as an "excellent gastropub", worth seeking out for its "freshly prepared and healthy fare" – "we could see why it's so busy!"
/ ***Details:*** *www.3horseshoeslalham.co.uk.*

STAMFORD, LINCOLNSHIRE 6–4A

The George Hotel **£68** 345
71 St Martins PE9 2LB (01780) 750750
"A taste of tradition and class"; this huge, historic coaching inn is just the sort of place to seek out for "good roasts" and an "old-fashioned dessert trolley" too, although the "lively" (much cheaper) Garden Room is often preferred to the more sedate main dining room.
/ ***Details:*** *www.georgehotelofstamford.com; @GeorgeStamford; 9.30 pm; jacket and/or tie; children: 8+ at D.* ***Accommodation:*** *47 rooms, from £190.*

The Tobie Norris **£37** Ⓣ
PE9 2BE (01780) 753800
A "beautifully-renovated" ancient building tipped for its "creative" cuisine; a critical reporter, though, would say it's "more a place you're pleased to have stopped off at than a destination in its own right".
/ ***Details:*** *www.tobienorris.com.*

STANLEY, PERTHSHIRE 9–3C

The Apron Stage **£43** 543
5 King St PH1 4ND (01738) 828888
A "delightful, tiny restaurant" (18 covers) in a small village north of Perth; kitchen staff can come and go, but for the most part the local fish and game are cooked to a "fabulous" standard; "booking is essential".
/ ***Details:*** *www.apronstagerestaurant.co.uk; 9.30 pm; D only, closed Mon–Wed & Sun; children: 12+.*

STANTON, SUFFOLK 3–1C

Leaping Hare Vineyard **£44** 234
Wyken Vineyards IP31 2DW (01359) 250287
A "lovely setting" – "a converted barn, tastefully appointed à la Martha Stewart" – and "excellent local wines and bubbly" win plaudits for this vineyard café-restaurant; the food can sometimes be "very good" too, but it is not generally rated the main attraction.
/ ***Details:*** *www.wykenvineyards.co.uk; 9m NE of Bury St Edmunds; follow tourist signs off A143; 5.30 pm, Fri & Sat 9 pm; L only, ex Fri & Sat open L & D.*

STATHERN, LEICESTERSHIRE 5–3D

Red Lion Inn £38 444
2 Red Lion St LE14 4HS (01949) 860868
*"A very welcoming pub" with "excellent" food and a "super range of ales, fruit beers and ciders"; it's externally less picturesque than its sister restaurant, The Olive Branch, but "utterly charming once inside". / **Details:** www.theredlioninn.co.uk; 9.30 pm; closed Sun D; no Amex.*

STAVELEY, CUMBRIA 7–3D

Wilfs Cafe £30 444
Millyard, Back Ln LA8 9LR (01539) 822329
*A "fun" and "quirky" café-bistro offering "lots of different areas to sit, inside and out"; the "wholesome" menu "caters well for vegetarians and allergy sufferers", and "the number of cyclists around makes you feel healthy" too. / **Details:** www.wilfs-cafe.co.uk.*

STEVENAGE, HERTFORDSHIRE 3–2B

Gangnam £18 T
SG1 1DU (01438) 747215
*'The Only Korean Restaurant in Hertfordshire!' (they say) is tipped for its "really good" food, and "very pleasant" service too – "the decor may be a bit sparse, but give it a go". / **Details:** www.gangnamstevenage.co.uk.*

STIRLING, STIRLING 9–4C

Jam Jar Cafe £26 T
FK9 4HR (01786) 831616
*A handy tip for travellers, this newly-refurbished café offers "great food and coffee" in "extremely large portions"; there's a "lovely friendly atmosphere" too. / **Details:** www.jamjarcafe.co.uk.*

STOCKBRIDGE, HAMPSHIRE 2–3D

Clos du Marquis £52 443
London Rd SO20 6DE (01264) 810738
*"An awkward location, but well worth seeking out" – this "slightly quirky" restaurant offers "a South African's take on French cuisine, done very well"; the menu changes daily, and the results can be "really special". / **Details:** www.closdumarquis.co.uk; 2m E on A30 from Stockbridge; 9 pm; closed Mon & Sun D.*

Greyhound £50 444
31 High St SO20 6EY (01264) 810833
*"Raising the bar in a pretty Hampshire town" – the verdict on an inn noted for its "really fun environment", "excellent service" and "delicious menu"; there's been a "huge improvement with the newish (ex-Peat Spade) team", who have "improved the interior considerably". / **Details:** www.thegreyhoundonthetest.co.uk; 9 pm, Fri & Sat 9.30 pm, Sun 9 pm; booking: max 12. **Accommodation:** 7 rooms, from £100.*

Thyme & Tides £32 322
The High St SO20 6HE (01264) 81 01 01
*A "great little deli" which, rather unusually, has a name for "fabulous fish dishes, reasonably priced"; it has recently taken over 'Woodfire', where the Mediterranean-style sarnies get a big thumbs up. / **Details:** thymeandtidesdeli.co.uk/; closed Mon; no Amex.*

STOCKCROSS, BERKSHIRE 2–2D

The Vineyard at Stockcross £85 232
RG20 8JU (01635) 528770
*"The bible of a wine list" – showcasing owner Sir Peter Michael's passion for Californian wine – is the 'Crown Jewel' feature of this contemporary-style ("slightly cold") operation; indeed, it rather eclipses Daniel Galmiche's "enjoyable" but pricey cuisine. / **Details:** www.the-vineyard.co.uk; @VineyardNewbury; from M4, J13 take A34 towards Hungerford; 9.30 pm; no jeans or trainers. **Accommodation:** 49 rooms, from £194.*

STOCKPORT, CHESHIRE 5–2B

The Red Lion £31 T
SK6 8ED (01663) 765 227
*Already tipped for its "lovely" food, a suburban hostelry run by the Damson (Manchester) people; should be one to watch! / **Details:** www.redionhighlane.co.uk.*

STOCKPORT, LANCASHIRE 5–2B

Damson £53 444
113 Heaton Moor Rd SK4 4HY
(0161) 4324666
*"A hidden gem"; thanks to its "excellent" cooking and "friendly" atmosphere, this Heaton Moor spot is decidedly "worth a visit"; special attractions? – an "extensive" wine list, and "bargain" midweek menus. / **Details:** www.damsonrestaurant.co.uk; 9.30 pm, Fri & Sat 10 pm; Mon-Thu D only, Fri-Sun open L & D.*

STOKE ROW, OXFORDSHIRE 2–2D

The Crooked Billet £53 455
Newlands Ln RG9 5PU (01491) 681048
*The food at this "friendly" and "quirky" oak-beamed rural "gem" has been even "better" of late – this is simply an "exemplary" pub-with-food, and one which "really is worth the drive". / **Details:** www.thecrookedbillet.co.uk; off the A4130; 10 pm, Sat 10.30 pm.*

STOKE-BY-NAYLAND, SUFFOLK 3–2C

The Crown **£43** 344
Park St CO6 4SE (01206) 262346
*The owners "seem to have it got it right all round" at this "always-buzzy" village pub and boutique hotel; not only does its "varied" menu achieve "London standards", but there's also an "amazing" wine list. / **Details:** www.crowninn.net; @CrownInnSuffolk; on B1068; 9.30 pm, Fri & Sat 10 pm, Sun 9 pm. **Accommodation:** 11 rooms, from £130.*

STONE IN OXNEY, KENT 3–4C

Crown **£40** Ⓣ
TN30 7JN (01233) 758302
*A village inn, whose surprise feature is "the best pizzas outside Italy" (well almost)! / **Details:** www.thecrowninnstoneinoxney.co.uk; 9 pm; closed Mon & Sun D; no Amex; children: 12+ evening.*

STONEHAVEN, ABERDEENSHIRE 9–3D

Muchalls Bistro **£36** 442
AB39 3RP (01569) 730393
*"A little gem"; "tucked away off the A90 in a fishing village", a "very good and well priced bistro"; the decor may not be a highpoint, but fans say the place offers "an excellent meal every time". / **Details:** www.muchallsbistro.co.uk.*

STONOR, OXFORDSHIRE 2–2D

Quince Tree **£44** 434
RG9 6HE (01491) 639039
*Comprising a "pub, café and shop", this "chic" rural rendezvous is unanimously praised for its "fresh and interesting" food from "top-quality ingredients", and in a "lovely location" too. / **Details:** www.thequincetree.com/; 9.30 pm; closed Sun D.*

STOW ON THE WOLD, GLOUCESTERSHIRE 2–1C

The Old Butchers **£45** Ⓣ
Park St GL54 1AQ (01451) 831700
*Still few reports on this relaunched outfit, which does indeed occupy a former butcher's shop; it is, however, tipped as a top destination for a "really good cheap and cheerful lunch". / **Details:** www.theoldbutchers.com; on the main road heading out of Stow on the Wold towards Oddington; 9.30 pm, Sat 10 pm; closed Mon & Sun; booking: max 12.*

STOWMARKET, SUFFOLK 3–1C

The Shepherd & Dog **£42** Ⓣ
IP14 5HN (01449) 711685
*"The new owners have made a big impact", says one of the fans of this revamped rural boozer, tipped for the "superb" quality of its food, both at the bar and in the restaurant. / **Details:** www.theshepherdanddog.com.*

STRACHUR, ARGYLL AND BUTE 9–4B

Inver Cottage Restaurant **£47** Ⓣ
Stracthlachlan PA27 8BU (01369) 860537
*Beside Loch Fyne, a small cottage-restaurant, tipped for "great food" (including "fresh lobsters" from the loch) and "tons of charm" too. / **Details:** www.invercottage.com; 8.30 pm; closed Mon & Tue; no Amex.*

STRATFORD UPON AVON, WARWICKSHIRE 2–1C

The Fuzzy Duck **£48** 344
CV37 8DD (01608) 682635
*"Beautiful decor, a lovely menu and superb quality food" – this recently-launched restaurant-with-rooms is already attracting high praise for its "excellent varied menu", and "very good value" too; "good al fresco seating". / **Details:** www.fuzzyduckarmscote.com/.*

Lambs **£45** 223
12 Sheep St CV37 6EF (01789) 292554
*An "always-reliable" city-centre stalwart, which fans claim is a "bit cheaper" and "more fun" than its rivals; "it's sometimes a victim of its own success" though, and service can be "erratic" at busy times. / **Details:** www.lambsrestaurant.co.uk; @lambsrestaurant; 8.30 pm, Fri & Sat 9 pm; closed Mon L; no Amex.*

No. 9 **£46** 442
9 Church St CV37 6HB (01789) 415 522
*"Always good food, possibly the best in town" – this is perhaps not so much an 'ambience' choice as some of the local competitors, but its "well prepared" (and "occasionally creative") dishes have many admirers. / **Details:** no9churchst.com; 9.15 pm; no Amex.*

The Oppo **£46** 242
13 Sheep St CV37 6EF (01789) 269980
*A contemporary-styled bistro of twenty years' standing, near the RSC, whose pre-theatre menu is "a real bargain"; "the service really makes this restaurant", says one fan, and "if you are going to a show they always make sure you get fed in time". / **Details:** www.theoppo.co.uk; 10 pm, Sun 9.30 pm; closed Sun L; no Amex; booking: max 12.*

Rooftop Restaurant Royal Shakespeare Theatre **£41** 113
Waterside CV37 6BB (01789) 403449
"Sited in what used to be the gods of the old theatre", this rooftop restaurant is – insist fans – a "great hideaway" that offers a "wonderful dining experience from start to finish"; critics, though,

say it's too pricey, or speak of "a steady decline ever since the first night". / **Details:** *www.rsc.org.uk/eat; 9.45 pm; no Amex.*

The Vintner **£41** **344**
4-5 Sheep St CV37 6EF (01789) 297259
Housed in an "atmospheric" medieval building, a "reliable" town centre fixture, with "smiling" staff. / **Details:** *www.the-vintner.co.uk; 9.30 pm, Fri & Sat 10 pm, Sun 8.30 pm; no Amex.*

STUCKTON, HAMPSHIRE 2–3C

The Three Lions **£53** **432**
Stuckton Rd SP6 2HF (01425) 652489
It may "look like an ordinary country pub-restaurant", but this New Forest venture is a "real gem", offering "absolutely amazing" food and a "nicely judged wine list"; "comfortable accommodation too".
/ **Details:** *www.thethreelionsrestaurant.co.uk; off the A338; 9 pm, Fri & Sat 9.30 pm; closed Mon & Sun D; no Amex.* **Accommodation:** *7 rooms, from £105.*

STUDLAND, DORSET 2–4C

Shell Bay **£46** **345**
Ferry Rd BH19 3BA (01929) 450363
The location – "looking out over Poole Harbour, especially at sunset" – is the "main draw" to this minimalist venture, but it is also praised for its "consistent" cooking which "makes great use of the local catch". / **Details:** *www.shellbay.net; near the Sandbanks to Swanage ferry; 9 pm.*

SUMMERHOUSE, COUNTY DURHAM 8–3B

Raby Hunt **£75** **545**
DL2 3UD (01325) 374237
"Best food we'd eaten anywhere this year!"; James Close's restaurant-with-rooms dishes up "wonderful combinations of taste and texture", winning unanimous rave reviews for this "emerging star" – "off the beaten track, but worth a trip".
/ **Details:** *www.rabyhuntrestaurant.co.uk/; 9.30 pm; closed Mon, Tue & Sun.* **Accommodation:** *2 rooms, from £125.*

SUNBURY ON THAMES, SURREY 3–3A

Indian Zest **£43** **544**
21 Thames St TW16 5QF (01932) 765 000
"Can't fault it" – the majority verdict on Manoj Vasaikar's "very original" colonial-style venture, in a rambling villa; it offers "highly exotic" nouvelle Indian fare, which is ably served by "very knowledgeable" staff. / **Details:** *www.indianzest.co.uk; 11 pm.*

SUNNINGDALE, BERKSHIRE 3–3A

Bluebells **£64** **453**
Shrubs Hill SL5 0LE (01344) 622 722
For its small army of fans, this roadside fixture offers "fab food" in attractive surroundings (with open fires in winter and outside tables in summer) and the "friendly staff never disappoint"; the set lunch is "a real steal".
/ **Details:** *www.bluebells-restaurant.com; 9.45 pm; closed Mon & Sun D.*

SUNNINGHILL, BERKSHIRE 3–3A

Carpenter's Arms **£56** **544**
78 Upper Village Rd SL5 7AQ
(01344) 622763
Run by Gallic expats, this "traditional British pub", near Windsor Great Park, is home to a "very traditional French kitchen", and wins nothing but praise for its "superb" cuisine.
/ **Details:** *www.lalochepub.com/carpenters.*

SURBITON, SURREY 3–3A

The French Table **£56** **443**
85 Maple Rd KT6 4AW (020) 8399 2365
"The best for miles around"; with its "good Gallic cooking" and "charming" service, this much commented-on suburban all-rounder is a "real treat" (if a "noisy" one); "it now has a spin-off café next door, which is also worth a visit".
/ **Details:** *www.thefrenchtable.co.uk; 10.30 pm; closed Mon & Sun.*

Pickled Pantry **£14** ⓣ
KT6 4PJ (020) 8399 4694
A "fantastic friendly café" all the more welcome in a "poorly-served area"; an "ideal local breakfast and brunch spot", it can become "overrun with buggies".
/ **Details:** *www.pickledpantry.co.uk.*

SUTTON GAULT, CAMBRIDGESHIRE 3–1B

The Anchor **£46** **444**
Bury Ln CB6 2BD (01353) 778537
"A true gem in the middle of nowhere"; this Fenland inn attracts only positive reports, not least for food that's "consistently way above average"; this makes an "excellent place to stay", too, in "unique surroundings".
/ **Details:** *www.anchorsuttongault.co.uk; @TheanchorinnSG; 7m W of Ely, signposted off B1381 in Sutton; 9 pm, Sat 9.30 pm, Sun 8.30 pm; no Amex.*
Accommodation: *4 rooms, from £79.5 - 135.*

SUTTON ON THE FOREST,
NORTH YORKSHIRE 8–4C

Park Restaurant **£69** **443**
YO61 1DP (01347) 810 852
"Recently opened and going from strength to strength", this fine-dining venture offers local chef Adam Jackson's "highly accomplished" cooking; "it's not a quick dining experience" (five- or eight-course set menus, with "amazing wine flights") but, on all accounts, your time will not be wasted.
/ **Details:** *www.theparkrestaurant.co.uk.*

SWANSEA VALLEY, POWYS 4–4D

Pen y Cae Inn **£40** 444
Brecon Rd SA9 1FA (01639) 730100
"Excellent food, very friendly proprietor, lovely surroundings…" – reports on this elegant 'restaurant and gallery', in a former inn, remain extremely positive all-round.
*/ **Details:** www.penycaeinn.com/; @penycaeinn; 9 pm; no Amex.*

SWANSEA, SWANSEA 1–1C

Castellamare **£55** 444
Bracelet Bay, Mumbles Rd SA3 4JT
(01792) 369408
A large, glass-fronted Italian venue, overlooking the Mumbles lighthouse; consistently high ratings from local reporters indicate a very high degree of continuing satisfaction.
*/ **Details:** www.castellamare.co.uk; 9.30 pm.*

Didier And Stephanie **£39** 443
56 Saint Helen's Rd SA1 4BE (01792) 655603
*"Really fresh fish" is a highlight of the "great French food" on offer at this small city-centre restaurant; reports, though relatively few, suggest the place is "under-appreciated". / **Details:** 9.15 pm; closed Mon & Sun; no Amex.*

Hanson's **£45** 444
Pilot House Whf, Trawler Rd SA1 1UN
(01792) 466200
"Small and consistent", this "innovative" fish restaurant is – on all reports – "well worth a visit" for cooking that's not only "delicious" but "good value" too.
*/ **Details:** www.hansonatthechelsea.co.uk; 9.30 pm; no Amex.*

TAPLOW, BERKSHIRE 3–3A

André Garrett At Cliveden
Cliveden House **£100** 444
Cliveden Rd SL6 0JF (01628) 668561
"Such an improvement since we last dined here!"; if you're looking for "fantasyland-perfect" grandeur, the dining room of this famous Thames-view palazzo is hard to beat, and – under the new chef, who used to work for the Galvin brothers' empire – the food is beginning to measure up.
*/ **Details:** www.clivedenhouse.co.uk; 9.30 pm; no trainers. **Accommodation:** 38 + cottage rooms, from £252.*

TATTENHALL, CHESHIRE 5–3A

The Pheasant Inn **£44** 444
Higher Burwardsley CH3 9PF (01829) 770434
Just off the Sandstone Trail, this recently revamped inn makes a "fantastic" pit stop for walkers (offering "stunning" views of the Cheshire Plain); its charms are rounded out by an "interesting" menu of food that's "well-cooked" and "tasty".
*/ **Details:** www.thepheasantinn.co.uk.*

TAUNTON, SOMERSET 2–3A

Augustus **£46** 453
3 The Courtyard, St James St TA1 1JR
(01823) 324 354
"What a wonderful find"; this "small but beautifully formed" bistro, run by an ex-Castle Hotel team, offers "well judged" cuisine and a "friendly welcome"; "unexpectedly good" wines too.
*/ **Details:** www.augustustaunton.co.uk; @augustustaunton; 9.30 pm; closed Mon & Sun; no Amex.*

Brazz
Castle Hotel **£39** 222
Castle Bow TA1 1NF (01823) 252000
*"A good standby"; this "always-busy" town-centre brasserie doesn't excel in any particular, but its "consistent" performance wins it enduring popularity. / **Details:** www.brazz.co.uk; 10 pm.*
***Accommodation:** 44 rooms, from £230.*

The Willow Tree **£51** 543
3 Tower Ln TA1 4AR (01823) 352835
"Never fails to offer excellent food"; it may be "difficult to find, down a pedestrian alleyway", but this "reliable favourite" is worth seeking out for Darren Sherlock's "inventive" Gallic cooking.
*/ **Details:** www.thewillowtreerestaurant.com; 9.15 pm; D only, closed Sun & Mon; no Amex; booking: max 6.*

TEDDINGTON, MIDDLESEX 3–3A

Imperial China **£40** 412
196-198 Stanley Rd TW11 8UE
(020) 8977 8679
"In the middle of nowhere", this ever-"heaving" spot is a real "diamond", offering "top-class" and "authentic" Chinese food, and the particular attraction of dim sum that's "right up there with the best"; just "don't expect good service".
*/ **Details:** www.imperialchinalondon.co.uk; 11 pm, Fri & Sat 11.30 pm, Sun 10 pm.*

Retro **£59** 454
114-116 High St TW11 8JB (020) 8977 2239
"The manager Vincent is a great performer", and his "very French" and "engaging" service adds to the "very jolly" atmosphere of this informal bistro; the cooking is "delicious" too.
*/ **Details:** www.retrobistrot.co.uk; @retrobistrot; Tue-Sat 11 pm; closed Mon & Sun D.*

TEIGNMOUTH, DEVON 1–3D

Crab Shack **£28** 543
3 Queen St TQ14 9HN (01626) 777956
Fish comes "straight off the boat into the kitchen" at this "busy" but "relaxed" family-run beachside shack; it's "really popular with locals and tourists",

*though... "half the battle is getting a table". / **Details:** www.crabshackonthebeach.co.uk/; 9 pm; closed Mon & Tue; no Amex.*

TENTERDEN, KENT 3–4C

The Raja Of Kent **£36** Ⓣ
Bibbenden Rd TN30 6SX (01233) 851191
*A roadside rural restaurant, tipped for its unusually "interesting" Bangladeshi menu, and its "good food and service too". / **Details:** www.therajaofkent.com; midnight.*

TETBURY, GLOUCESTERSHIRE 2–2B

Calcot Manor **£65** 332
GL8 8YJ (01666) 890391
*The main conservatory-restaurant of this family-friendly country house hotel has "recently simplified" its menu to offer "more brasserie-style food than fine dining", but standards remain "very good". / **Details:** www.calcotmanor.co.uk; @Calcot_Manor; junction of A46 & A4135; 9.30 pm, Sun 9 pm. **Accommodation:** 35 rooms, from £280.*

Gumstool Inn Calcot Manor **£45** 333
GL8 8YJ (01666) 890391
*Even those who find this "pub-style restaurant attached to a large hotel" a "little expensive for what it is" concede it's a "reliable" spot with "a good selection of dishes and professional service"; brace yourself though for a "high hooray Henry count". / **Details:** www.calcotmanor.co.uk; @Calcot_Manor; crossroads of A46 & A41345; 9.30 pm, Sun 9 pm; no jeans or trainers; children: 12+ at dinner in Conservatory. **Accommodation:** 35 rooms, from £240.*

The Royal Oak **£32** Ⓣ
GL8 8EY (01666) 500021
*Recently refurbished, a classic Cotswold inn with a "great courtyard for sunny days and evenings", and tipped for its "well thought-out and reasonably priced" food menu. / **Details:** www.theroyaloaktetbury.co.uk.*

TEWKESBURY, GLOUCESTERSHIRE 2–1B

My Great Grandfathers **£55** Ⓣ
GL20 5RX (01684) 292687
This town-centre fixture just celebrated a decade in business, and wins praise for its "romantic" style and quality cooking, with steaks a speciality.

THELWALL, CHESHIRE 4–2B

Little Manor **£44** Ⓣ
Bell Ln WA4 2SX (01925) 261703
*With its dependable food and beer, and pleasant service too, this large village inn has many of the typical virtues of the Brunning & Price gastropub chain. / **Details:** www.brunningandprice.co.uk/littlemanor/.*

THORNBURY, GLOUCESTERSHIRE 2–2B

Ronnie's **£46** 443
11 St Mary St BS35 2AB (01454) 411137
*"Never had a disappointing meal" – invariably the theme of commentary on Ronnie Faulkner's "careful" and "imaginative cuisine", served up in his 17th-century barn; "the set lunch menus are exceptionally good value, but even the three course dinner is a steal!" / **Details:** www.ronnies-restaurant.co.uk; @ByRonnie; Tue-Thu 9.30 pm, Fri & Sat 10.30 pm; closed Mon & Sun D; no Amex.*

THORNHAM, NORFOLK 6–3B

The Orange Tree **£47** 322
High St PE36 6LY (01485) 512 213
*In a "very competitive market", this "lovely" coastal gastropub-with-rooms stands out from the crowd, thanks not least to its "imaginative" cuisine. / **Details:** www.theorangetreethornham.co.uk; 9.30 pm; no Amex. **Accommodation:** 6 rooms, from £89.*

TILLINGTON, WEST SUSSEX 3–4A

The Horse Guards Inn **£41** 335
Upperton Rd GU28 9AF (01798) 342 332
*A "smashing shabby-chic pub", offering "better-than-average" cooking of "superb local produce" in an ambience of relaxed informality; you can stay here too – "it's worth it just for the home-made muesli!" / **Details:** www.thehorseguardsinn.co.uk; 9 pm, Fri & Sat 9.30 pm; no Amex.*

TITCHWELL, NORFOLK 6–3B

Titchwell Manor **£50** Ⓣ
PE31 8BB (01485) 210 221
*A "wonderful, small family-run hotel on a beautiful part of the north Norfolk coast", owned by the Snaiths for a quarter of a century; it's tipped for some "very imaginative cooking, including lovely fresh seafood". / **Details:** www.titchwellmanor.com; @TitchwellManor; 9.30 pm. **Accommodation:** 29 rooms, from £95.*

TITLEY, HEREFORDSHIRE 2–1A

Stagg Inn **£51** 433
HR5 3RL (01544) 230221
*"A splendid pub meal in one of the most quintessential country inns" – an enduring formula for success for Steve Reynold's "rustic" hostelry, where, on most accounts, the cooking is "always delicious and very original". / **Details:** www.thestagg.co.uk; @TheStaggInn; on B4355, NE of Kington; 9 pm; closed Mon & Tue. **Accommodation:** 7 rooms, from £100.*

TOBERMORY, ARGYLL AND BUTE 9–3A

Café Fish **£45** 5 4 3
The Pier PA75 6NU (01688) 301253
*"Perfect seafood in a relaxed café atmosphere", and "right on the harbour too" – those who've made the schlep to this pretty town find ample reward in the "outstanding range of fish dishes" and "wonderful views (even on a rainy day)" at this "lovely" spot. / **Details:** www.thecafefish.com; 10 pm; Closed Nov-Mar; no Amex; children: 14+ after 8 pm.*

TOPSHAM, DEVON 1–3D

The Galley **£49** 4 5 3
41 Fore St, Topsham EX3 0HU
(01392) 876078
*"An excellent and consistent fish restaurant", in a "picturesque" town, where the menu consists of "good mix of specials and staples"; there's a "good wine list" too ("including from down the road"). / **Details:** www.galleyrestaurant.co.uk; closed Mon & Sun; children: 12+.*

TORCROSS, DEVON 1–4D

Start Bay Inn **£34** 4 3 4
TQ7 2TQ (01548) 580553
*"Amazing standards of deep-fried fish" is the main draw to this ever-popular beachside pub, where the food is "always good".
/ **Details:** www.startbayinn.co.uk; on beach front (take A379 coastal road to Dartmouth); 10 pm; no Amex; no booking.*

TORQUAY, DEVON 1–3D

Elephant Restaurant & Brasserie **£60** 5 4 4
3-4 Beacon Ter, Harbourside TQ1 2BH
(01803) 200044
*"One of the best in the West Country", say fans of Simon Hulstone's first-floor restaurant where, of late, "ingredients from their own farm have really changed the dynamic"; the downstairs brasserie offers "great value and atmosphere".
/ **Details:** www.elephantrestaurant.co.uk; 9 pm; closed Mon & Sun; children: 14+ at bar.*

No 7 Fish Bistro **£52** 5 5 4
7 Beacon Terrace TQ1 2BH (01803) 295055
*"Other places are fancier but this place does what matters – food (especially), service and atmosphere really well"; the highlight, of course, is the "fantastic range of great fish, simply cooked".
/ **Details:** www.no7-fish.com; @no7fishbistro; 9.45 pm.*

TOTNES, DEVON 1–3D

The Vineyard Cafe **£37** 5 4 5
TQ9 7UT (01803) 732178
*Open in summer only, a "quirky" al fresco bistro on the Sharpham Wine Estate, praised in all reports for its "delicious" cooking (and "surprisingly good" wines too); "booking ahead is essential".
/ **Details:** www.vineyardcafe.co.uk.*

TREEN, CORNWALL 1–4A

Gurnards Head **£45** 4 5 5
TR26 3DE (01736) 796928
*"A very special inn in a very special place"; "from the simple, rustic flagstone-floored bar to the more formal dining room", everything at this cliff-top pub "shows care and consideration", and it is also praised for its "inspired seasonal cooking"; afterwards, head "straight out on to the coast path to blow away the Armagnac fumes".
/ **Details:** www.gurnardshead.co.uk; @gurnardshead; on coastal road between Land's End & St Ives, near Zennor B3306; 9.15 pm; no Amex.
Accommodation: 7 rooms, from £105.*

TRING, HERTFORDSHIRE 3–2A

Olive Limes **£37** Ⓣ
60 High St HP23 5AG (01442) 828283
*Tipped for its "unusual" and "consistently good" North Indian menu, a restaurant by Tring Park; "visit at the weekend, when the nicer room upstairs is open". / **Details:** www.olivelimes.co.uk; 11 pm, Fri & Sat 11.30 pm.*

TROON, SOUTH AYRSHIRE 9–4B

MacCallum's Oyster Bar **£39** Ⓣ
The Harbour, Harbour Rd KA10 6DH
(01292) 319339
*Much more a restaurant than a bar, a local institution tipped, as you'd hope, for "great seafood and fish"; prior notice of non-fishy orders is required.
/ **Details:** www.maccallumsoftroon.co.uk.*

TROUTBECK, CUMBRIA 7–3D

Queen's Head **£47** 4 4 4
Townhead LA23 1PW (01539) 432174
*"Hidden away, but worth seeking out", this "rambling" and "comfortable" inn produces "varied" dishes from "excellent local produce", and it's "reasonably priced" too ("by Lakeland standards"). / **Details:** www.queensheadhotel.com; A592 on Kirkstone Pass; 9 pm; no Amex.
Accommodation: 15 rooms, from £120.*

TRURO, CORNWALL 1–4B

Hub Box **£22** Ⓣ
116 Kenwyn St TR1 3DJ (07742) 875468
*"Dirty burgers the way we like 'em, served by zealots!" – it may have started life in a "modified shipping container", but fans insist the food at this trendy operation (nowadays in a converted chapel) is "great". / **Details:** www.hubbox.co.uk.*

TUDDENHAM, SUFFOLK 3–1C

Tuddenham Mill
Tuddenham Mill Hotel £60 444
High St IP28 6SQ (01638) 713 552
"A friendly, well-run restaurant in a beautiful old mill", and in "the middle of nowhere" too; it used to attract very mixed reviews, but the new chef seems to have brought much greater consistency – the "reasonably-priced prix-fixe" is especially worth seeking out. / ***Details:*** *www.tuddenhammill.co.uk; @Tuddenham_Mill; 9.15 pm.* ***Accommodation:*** *15 rooms, from £205.*

TUNBRIDGE WELLS, KENT 3–4B

The Black Pig £40 232
18 Grove Hill Rd TN1 1RZ (01892) 523030
Handily located for the railway station, a "good gastropub" that "as the name suggests, specialises in pork"; there's a feeling among reporters, though, that it's becoming "rather expensive". / ***Details:*** *www.theblackpig.net; @BlackPigTW; 9 pm, Fri & Sat 9.30 pm; no Amex.*

Hotel du Vin et Bistro £56 T
Crescent Rd TN1 2LY (01892) 526455
With its impressive Victorian-club-style premises, this outpost of the Gallic hotel-bistro chain is tipped as a "good business lunch venue"; even fans, though, concede that the food can be "a bit hit-and-miss". / ***Details:*** *www.hotelduvin.com; 10 pm, Fri & Sat 10.30 pm; booking: max 10.*
Accommodation: *34 rooms, from £120.*

Mount Edgcumbe £41 T
TN4 8BX (01892) 618854
Billing itself a 'bar – restaurant – lounge – cave – garden', this recently revamped pub "looks great" and enjoys a "beautiful location on the common"; it wins a 'tip' for its "fine" cooking.
/ ***Details:*** *www.themountedcumbe.com.*

Rendez-Vous £35 T
TN1 2QP (01892) 525830
Recently re-opened on the site once known as Chez JJ, a "delightful" establishment, tipped for its "plentiful bistro-style food", imaginatively served.
/ ***Details:*** *www.rendezvoustw.co.uk.*

Signor Franco £44 343
5a High St TN1 1UL (01892) 549199
"A welcome family feel" to the whole operation helps underpin the appeal of this "traditional Italian with its old-style menu", as does the quality cooking and decor.
/ ***Details:*** *www.signorfrancorestaurant.com; 10.45 pm; closed Mon & Sun D; no Amex.*

Thackeray's £69 433
85 London Rd TN1 1EA (01892) 511921
This "beautiful" Regency villa, near the town centre, is "a great place to take someone to make them feel special" – "the modern Anglo-French cooking showcases top local produce" and "can be outstanding", although it's "let down a little" by sometimes "rather random" service.
/ ***Details:*** *www.thackerays-restaurant.co.uk; @Thackeraysrest; 10.30 pm; closed Mon & Sun D.*

Zagatos Bar & Brasserie £55 T
TN4 8XJ (01892) 520331
The "less formal" of the two restaurants at the hotel, tipped as as "an excellent venue for romantic meals or family gatherings"; "ask for a window table".

TUNSTALL, LANCASHIRE 7–4D

Lunesdale Arms £38 T
LA6 2QN (01524) 274203
A recent change of ownership appears to have done "nothing to dent the charms" of this smart village inn; of late, however, reports have been few, so this is just a 'tip' for the moment.
/ ***Details:*** *www.thelunesdale.co.uk; 15 min from J34 on M6 onto A683; 9 pm; closed Mon.*

ULLSWATER, CUMBRIA 7–3D

Sharrow Bay £101 324
CA10 2LZ (01768) 486301
Now under new owners, this newly refurbished country house hotel has "not lost its local reputation" or its wonderful views – "get a table in an alcove overlooking Lake Ullswater"; let's hope it goes on to re-establish a national reputation too!
/ ***Details:*** *www.sharrowbay.co.uk; @sharrowbay; on Pooley Bridge Rd towards Howtown; 8 pm; no jeans or trainers; children: 8+.* ***Accommodation:*** *17 rooms, from £355 (B&B).*

UPPER BUCKLEBURY, BERKSHIRE 2–2D

Bladebone Inn £43 443
Chapel Row RG7 6PD (0118) 971 2326
"A favourite of the county set" – this country inn is a "good all-rounder" with "solid pub fare, prepared, cooked and presented beautifully, and with really friendly staff too".
/ ***Details:*** *www.thebladeboneinn.com/; 9 pm; closed Mon & Sun D; no Amex.*

UPPER SLAUGHTER, GLOUCESTERSHIRE 2–1C

Lords of the Manor £90 434
GL54 2JD (01451) 820243
In a famously pretty Cotswolds village, a "friendly" and "romantic" hotel that's ideal "for a lovely weekend break"; prices are far from give-away, but the dining room here is consistently highly rated.
/ ***Details:*** *www.lordsofthemanor.com; @CotswoldLords; 4m W of Stow on the Wold; 8.45 pm; D only, ex Sun open L & D; no jeans or trainers; children: 7+ at D in restaurant.*
Accommodation: *26 rooms, from £199.*

UPPINGHAM, RUTLAND 5–4D

The Lake Isle £52 Ⓣ
16 High Street East LE15 9PZ (01572) 822951
A "simple" restaurant-with-rooms of long standing, cutely positioned in this small market town, and known for its extensive wine list as much as its "unfailing" cuisine. / ***Details:*** *www.lakeisle.co.uk; @LakeIsleHotel; past the Market place, down the High Street; 9 pm, Fri & Sat 9.30 pm; closed Mon L & Sun D; no Amex.* ***Accommodation:*** *12 rooms, from £85.*

VENTNOR, ISLE OF WIGHT 2–4D

The Hambrough £72 544
Hambrough Road PO38 1SQ (01983) 856333
A rejuvenated hotel dining room by the sea that's now "well on the way back to its former heights"; it makes "a fantastic setting for a romantic dinner", especially if you like "really fresh fish", served "with just the right amount of fuss!"
/ ***Details:*** *www.robert-thompson.com; @TheHambrough; 9.30 pm; closed Mon & Sun; no Amex.* ***Accommodation:*** *7 rooms, from £170.*

WADDINGTON, LANCASHIRE 5–1B

The Higher Buck £42 444
BB7 3HZ (01200) 423226
"The new venture for Michael Heathcote of Duke of York at Grindleton fame"; it's already winning acclaim for its "proper pub food, served in classy surroundings". / ***Details:*** *www.higherbuck.com.*

WADEBRIDGE, CORNWALL 1–3B

Bridge Bistro £41 442
4 Molesworth St PL27 7DA (01208) 815342
"Most enjoyable, and a real bonus for the town" – this husband-and-wife-run restaurant remains an all-round crowd-pleaser; at least it must be doing something right – they've now expanded next door!
/ ***Details:*** *www.bridgebistro.co.uk/; 9 pm; closed Mon & Sun; no Amex.*

WAKEFIELD, WEST YORKSHIRE 5–1C

Bar Biccari £43 Ⓣ
WF4 5LU (01924) 263 626
In the handsome village of Horbury, a "lovely family-run Italian", tipped for its "authentic" pizzas, as well as a menu of other fare that's "always changing and interesting". / ***Details:*** *www.barbiccari.co.uk.*

WALBERSWICK, SUFFOLK 3–1D

The Anchor £43 334
Main St IP18 6UA (01502) 722112
An "excellent" village inn ("dogs welcome") where you can "eat some cracking fish and chips, and then walk it all off on the blissfully quiet Suffolk coast"; also noted for its "great range of beers".
/ ***Details:*** *www.anchoratwalberswick.com; 9 pm.* ***Accommodation:*** *10 rooms, from £110.*

WARLINGHAM, SURREY 3–3B

Chez Vous £41 432
432 Limpsfield Rd CR6 9LA (01883) 620451
Established in 2011, a hotel-restaurant that's "well worth a visit", thanks to its "top-quality" cooking; "wines are not numerous, but the selection is good and well priced".
/ ***Details:*** *www.chezvous.co.uk.*

WARWICK, WARWICKSHIRE 5–4C

The Art Kitchen £44 443
7 Swan St CV34 4BJ (01926) 494303
"Consistently good" food, and "beautifully presented" too, has made quite a name for this town-centre Thai; the set lunch is particularly worth seeking out for its "very good value".
/ ***Details:*** *www.theartkitchen.com; 10 pm.*

Micatto £47 Ⓣ
CV34 4SD (01926) 403053
In the heart of the town, a smart but "friendly" Italian of recent vintage, which fans tip as a great all-rounder; more reports please.
/ ***Details:*** *www.micatto.com.*

The Saxon Mill £43 Ⓣ
Coventry Rd, Guys Cliffe CV34 5YN
(01926) 492255
Tipped in particular for its charming view of the mill race from the terrace – "the food's always pleasant, but you go for the ambience".
/ ***Details:*** *www.saxonmill.co.uk; 9.30 pm, Fri & Sat 10 pm, Sun 9 pm.*

Tailors £55 554
22 Market place CV34 4SL (01926) 410590
"Consistently the best restaurant around here"; fans are full of praise for the "cracking cooking" and "inventive menu", at this "intimate and comfortable" venture, which occupies a former tailoring shop in the town centre; "the secret is out", though, so "book early".
/ ***Details:*** *www.tailorsrestaurant.co.uk; 9 pm; closed Mon & Sun; no Amex; children: 12+ for dinner .*

WATERGATE BAY, CORNWALL 1–3B

The Beach Hut
Watergate Bay Hotel £46 335
On The Beach TR8 4AA (01637) 860543
"A CA-style eatery on the beach serving modern Cali-classics"; it's a "bustling", "bright" and "friendly" sort of place, offering "great sea views" too.
/ ***Details:*** *www.watergatebay.co.uk; 9 pm; no Amex.*
Accommodation: *69 rooms, from £105.*

Fifteen Cornwall
Watergate Bay Hotel **£81** [2][3][5]
TR8 4AA (01637) 861000
*"A stunning location with fabulous sea views" provides the "stunning" location for Jamie O's "heavily-booked" destination; the food is no more than "adequate", though, and all at prices so "eye-watering" that cynics think they're just "taking the p**s". / **Details:** www.fifteencornwall.co.uk; @fifteencornwall; on the Atlantic coast between Padstow and Newquay; 9.15 pm; children: 4+ at D.*

WATERNISH, HIGHLAND 9–2A

Loch Bay **£46** Ⓣ
Stein IV55 8GA (01470) 592235
A lochside bistro tipped for its "great use of locally landed fish and delicious cooking", all at very reasonable prices; in past surveys, the chips have also been particularly approved.
*/ **Details:** www.lochbay-seafood-restaurant.co.uk; 22m from Portree via A87 and B886; 8m from Dunvegan; 8.30 pm; closed Mon, Tue L, Wed L, Thu L, Fri L, Sat & Sun; no Amex; children: 8+ at D.*

WATH-IN-NIDDERDALE, NORTH YORKSHIRE 8–4B

Sportsman's Arms **£50** [3][4][4]
HG3 5PP (01423) 711306
*"Traditional British" recipes served in a "beautiful" Victorian dining room – or a "cosy bar area with a roaring fire" – establish this Dales village inn as "one of the best Yorkshire country pubs". / **Details:** www.sportsmans-arms.co.uk; take Wath Road from Pateley Bridge; 9 pm, Sun 8 pm; no Amex. **Accommodation:** 11 rooms, from £120.*

WEDMORE, SOMERSET 2–3A

The Swan **£44** Ⓣ
Cheddar Rd BS28 4EQ (019) 3471 0337
*Shame we haven't got more feedback on this "fantastic" trendified inn, tipped not least for the "hefty" portions of "high-quality" dishes. / **Details:** www.theswanwedmore.com; @theswanwedmore; 10 pm, Sun 9 pm; closed Sun D; no Amex. **Accommodation:** 6 rooms, from £85.*

WELLS NEXT THE SEA, NORFOLK 6–3C

Globe **£41** [4][3][3]
The Buttlands NR23 1EU (01328) 710206
*Only positive reports on the new regime at this "lovely friendly inn", not least for "hearty" food that's of "good quality", and with some "interesting twists" too. / **Details:** www.holkham.co.uk/globe; 9 pm; no Amex. **Accommodation:** 7 rooms, from £100.*

WELLS, SOMERSET 2–3B

Goodfellows **£55** Ⓣ
5 Sadler St BA5 2RR (01749) 673866
*Adam Fellows's compact restaurant (with neighbouring café) is tipped as a "real gem", and hailed in particular for its "French/Mediterranean-inspired fish dishes". / **Details:** www.goodfellowswells.co.uk; @goodfellowswest; 9.30 pm; closed Mon, Tue D & Sun.*

Old Spot **£47** Ⓣ
12 Sadler St BA5 2SE (01749) 689099
*Up-and-down reports of late on this potentially "lovely" pub, which has a "wonderful" location, by the cathedral; it's still tipped for its "dependable" cooking, but even fans can find the ambience a bit "canteen-like". / **Details:** www.theoldspot.co.uk; 9.15 pm; closed Mon, Tue L & Sun D.*

WELWYN, HERTFORDSHIRE 3–2B

Auberge du Lac
Brocket Hall **£92** [3][2][3]
AL8 7XG (01707) 368888
*"Wonderful surroundings" – by a lake on the Brocket Hall estate – make this well-established venue "superb for a sunny day al fresco lunch"; most reports applaud its "top wine" and "inventive" cuisine too, but service can be "slapdash" and "the interior needs a refurb to match the setting". / **Details:** www.brocket-hall.co.uk; on B653 towards Harpenden; 9.30 pm; closed Mon & Sun L; no jeans or trainers; children: 12+. **Accommodation:** 16 rooms, from £175.*

The Wellington **£45** Ⓣ
1 High St AL6 9LZ (01438) 714036
*The cooking is certainly "tasty", but it's as a tip for oenophiles that this large town-centre inn most obviously standards out – "the range of d'Arenberg wines from McLaren Vale district in Australia never fails to amaze the palate". / **Details:** www.wellingtonatwelwyn.co.uk; 10 pm; no Amex. **Accommodation:** 6 rooms, from £100.*

WEST BRIDGFORD, NOTTINGHAMSHIRE 5–3D

Larwood And Voce **£44** [4][3][4]
Fox Rd NG2 6AJ (0115) 981 9960
*"Great English pub food" – with "brilliant beers" too – draws many admirers to this "simple" but notably consistent boozer, next to Trent Bridge cricket ground; it's a "child-friendly" destination too. / **Details:** www.larwoodandvoce.co.uk; @larwoodvocepk; 9 pm, Sun 5 pm; closed Sun D.*

WEST CLANDON, SURREY 3–3A

The Onslow Arms **£45** [3][2][3]
The St GU4 7TE (01483) 222447
"A well-heeled pub in a pretty village, trying a bit

harder than many", and whose food is "robust and attractive"; the "always-packed and buzzing" atmosphere may help explain a few reports of "slow service".
*/ **Details:** www.onslowarmsclandon.com; 10 pm, Fri & Sat 10.30 pm; children: 18+ after 7.30pm.*

WEST HOATHLY, WEST SUSSEX 3–4B

The Cat Inn **£45** 344
Queen's Sq RH19 4PP (01342) 810369
"A great pub with good food and friendly, 'local' service" – the all-round attractions of this village boozer can come as a "real surprise" to first-timers.
*/ **Details:** www.catinn.co.uk; 9 pm, Fri-Sun 9.30 pm; closed Sun D; no Amex; children: 7+.*
***Accommodation:** 4 rooms, from £110.*

WEST LINTON, SCOTTISH BORDERS 9–4C

The Old Bakehouse **£35** Ⓣ
Main St EH46 7EA (0196) 8660830
TV chef Tony Singh, ex-Oloroso (RIP) has headed off down the A702 to this West Linton venue, now offering ambitious Scottish-Indian fusion fare (think haggis pakora); it opened too late for survey commentary, and we tip it on the basis of positive press reviews.
*/ **Details:** www.theoldbakehouserestaurant.com.*

WEST MALLING, KENT 3–3C

The Swan **£55** 233
35 Swan St ME19 6JU (01732) 521910
Limited and rather mixed feedback of late for this brasserie with vintage fixtures and an equally design-heavy garden; fans praise its "innovative" dishes from "really fresh ingredients", but doubters find standards "mediocre".
*/ **Details:** www.theswanwestmalling.co.uk; @swanwm; 11 pm, Sun 7 pm.*

WEST MEON, HAMPSHIRE 2–3D

The Thomas Lord **£44** 344
High St GU32 1LN (01730) 829244
This "lovely" village inn, in the South Downs National Park, is a "dependable" place, offering food "of very good quality"; the occasional off-day, however, is also reported.
*/ **Details:** www.thethomaslord.co.uk; @ThomasLordPub; 9 pm, Sat 9.30 pm.*

WEST MERSEA, ESSEX 3–2C

The Company Shed **£33** 523
129 Coast Rd CO5 8PA (01206) 382700
"Its rustic charms border on the basic" ("this is literally a shed with a BYO wine and bread policy"), but it's the "incredible seafood" ("none fresher") which is the reason to seek out this seaside legend; arrive early if you want to be sure of a table.
*/ **Details:** www.the-company-shed.co.uk; 4 pm; L only, closed Mon; no credit cards; no booking.*

West Mersea Oyster Bar **£38** 433
Coast Rd CO5 8LT (01206) 381600
"You do not go here for the (IKEA-style) decor or setting" – a very different ambience from the famous nearby 'Shed' – but rather for the "wonderful" fish 'n' chips and oysters.
*/ **Details:** www.westmerseaoysterbar.co.uk; 8.30 pm; Sun-Thu closed D; no Amex; no shorts.*

WEST STOUR, DORSET 2–3B

The Ship Inn **£37** Ⓣ
SP8 5RP (01747) 838 640
Tipped for its "really excellent pub food", a "pleasant" village inn (with rooms), recently given a modern makeover.
*/ **Details:** www.shipinn-dorset.com.*

WEST WITTON, NORTH YORKSHIRE 8–4B

The Wensleydale Heifer **£60** 333
Main St DL8 4LS (01969) 622322
*"An excellent fish restaurant, tucked away in the Yorkshire Dales!"; most reports continue to praise the "wonderful" dishes on offer at this "beautiful old inn", but this year's reports also included a few 'off' nights. / **Details:** www.wensleydaleheifer.co.uk; @wensleyheifer; 9.30 pm. **Accommodation:** 13 rooms, from £130.*

WESTCLIFF-ON-SEA, ESSEX 3–3C

Toulouse **£50** Ⓣ
Western Esplanade SS0 8FE (01702) 333731
*"A beacon in a gastronomic wasteland", this former public convenience is tipped for its "fantastic location right on the seafront"; "it's perhaps a bit over-ambitious, but there's nowhere else of this standard for miles around – believe me, I've looked"! / **Details:** www.toulouserestaurant.co.uk; 9.30 pm, Sat 9.30, Sun 7 pm; closed Mon L.*

WESTERHAM, KENT 3–3B

Food For Thought **£30** Ⓣ
TN16 1AX (01959) 569888
"Hearty, good-value lunches" and "excellent afternoon teas" make this "really good café on the green" something of a top tip locally.
*/ **Details:** www.foodforthought.eu.*

WESTFIELD, EAST SUSSEX 3–4C

The Wild Mushroom **£46** 553
Westfield Ln TN35 4SB (01424) 751137
*Paul Webbe's comfortable country venue is "still ahead of the competition in this part of Sussex" – "go for the real wild mushrooms gathered by the owner in autumn", or the set menus (which offer "outstanding value with no compromise on quality"). / **Details:** www.webbesrestaurants.co.uk; 9.30 pm; closed Mon, Tue & Sun D.*

WESTLETON, SUFFOLK 3–1D

The Westleton Crown **£45** ⓣ
IP17 3AD (01728) 648777
*"A find"; this "friendly" and "pleasant" inn is tipped for its "good standard" of cuisine, and its "pleasant" service. / **Details:** www.westlecrown.co.uk.*

WEYBRIDGE, SURREY 3–3A

Osso Buco **£36** 354
KT13 8DE (01932) 849949
*"A passionate Italian-family-owned restaurant"; reports all suggest it's a good all-rounder, but it's the service – for which "nothing is too much trouble" – which attracts particular praise.
/ **Details:** www.ossobuco.co.uk.*

WEYMOUTH, DORSET 2–4B

Crab House Café **£44** 434
Ferrymans Way, Portland Rd DT4 9YU
(01305) 788867
*"Seafood cooked with no frills" ("just how it should be") and at "good prices" are the order of the day at this "unpretentious" shack – a "fun" and "efficient" venue, by Chesil Beach.
/ **Details:** www.crabhousecafe.co.uk; overlooking the Fleet Lagoon, on the road to Portland; 9 pm, Sat 9.30 pm, Sun 8.30 pm; closed Mon L & Tue L; no Amex; to book 8+ deposit of £10 per head.*

WHALEY BRIDGE, DERBYSHIRE 5–2C

Zayka **£33** ⓣ
SK23 7AA (01663) 719555
*Top tip locally for "authentic, Punjabi-style cuisine", with "particularly impressive lamb dishes"; it can seem "quite pricey" by local standards, but inspires only very positive reports.
/ **Details:** www.zaykafinedining.co.uk.*

WHALLEY, LANCASHIRE 5–1B

Food by Breda Murphy **£39** 554
41 Station Rd BB7 9RH (01254) 823446
*A Ribble Valley favourite with "two small dining areas and a good deli counter", where the Ballymaloe-trained owner offers an "excellent Irish welcome"; it's particularly rated for fish pie and "unfailingly good" puddings; "shame it's not open regularly in the evenings".
/ **Details:** www.foodbybredamurphy.com; 5.30 pm; closed Mon & Sun, Tue-Sat D; no Amex.*

The Three Fishes **£41** 444
Mitton Rd BB7 9PQ (01254) 826888
*The first of the Ribble Valley Inns (gastropub offshoots of Northcote, Langho) "has had a facelift", and now benefits from a "smarter and and more engaging" ambience in which to enjoy "simple, classic British fare", based on "wonderful locally-sourced produce" – highlights include the "best fish pie around". / **Details:** www.thethreefishes.com; 8.30 pm, Fri & Sat 9 pm, Sun 8 pm.*

WHEATHAMPSTEAD, HERTFORDSHIRE 3–2A

L'Olivo **£59** 342
135 Marford Rd AL4 8NH (01582) 834 145
*"A great place, so long as you don't mind it being rather noisy" – this "authentic" Italian ("enormous pepper grinders") provides "attentive" service and food that's a "step up".
/ **Details:** www.lolivo-restaurant.com; 9.30 pm; D only, closed Mon & Sun.*

WHITBY, NORTH YORKSHIRE 8–3D

Magpie Café **£41** 542
14 Pier Rd YO21 3PU (01947) 602058
*"Still the best battered fish in the UK" continues to establish this "old fashioned café with lovely views of the harbour" as one of the nation's best-known eateries – "the queue can stretch a long way out of the door!" / **Details:** www.magpiecafe.co.uk; 9 pm; no Amex; no booking at L.*

Trenchers **£40** 443
New Quay Rd YO21 1DH (01947) 603212
*"Posh fish 'n' chips that beat the rest"; "the booths are comfortable" and "the chrome, mirrors and tiles give a fresh clean feel" to this elegant venue – "part of Whitby's triumvirate of great fish restaurants... and a bit cheaper than the other two!" / **Details:** www.trenchersrestaurant.co.uk; 8.30 pm; need 7+ to book.*

WHITEBROOK, MONMOUTHSHIRE 2–2B

The Crown at Whitebrook **£79** 523
NP25 4TX (01600) 860254
*"As good as ever under new ownership", this celebrated restaurant-with-rooms, with a "heavenly" location in the Wye Valley, is back with a bang – service still seems to be settling in, but the "intricate and very well balanced" cooking is "stunningly good".
/ **Details:** www.crownatwhitebrook.co.uk; 2m W of A466, 5m S of Monmouth; 9 pm; closed Mon; children: 12+ for D. **Accommodation:** 8 rooms, from £145.*

WHITSTABLE, KENT 3–3C

Crab & Winkle **£45** 433
South Quay, Whitstable Harbour CT5 1AB
(01227) 779377
With its "amazing" view over the harbour, it is appropriate that this café-like venue is highly rated for fish – "Cornish crab and half-lobster hit the mark on all fronts"; it pleases most reporters, although even fans can't "see the point of the background tape of '60s hits… or any Muzak come to that!"

/ **Details:** *www.crabandwinklerestaurant.co.uk; 9.30 pm; closed Mon & Sun D; no Amex.*

East Coast Dining Room £49 332
101 Tankerton Rd CT5 2AJ (01227) 281180
"A treasure, hidden in a mediocre line of shops"; despite its slightly off-piste Tankerton location, this new venture (run by a team with local pedigree) wins praise for "fine cooking" in general, and a "very reasonable" weekday set lunch in particular.
/ **Details:** *www.eastcoastdiningroom.co.uk; 9 pm; closed Mon, Tue, Wed D & Sun D.*

JoJo £32 554
2 Herne Bay Rd CT5 2LQ (01227) 274591
"Wonderful food, exceptional service, and a perfect candlelit seaside setting"; with its succession of "delicious tapas-style dishes", this 'Mezze, Meat & Fish Restaurant' impresses all who comment on it; only two reservations – i) the recent withdrawal of lunchtime BYO, and ii) "the DFLs!"
/ **Details:** *www.jojosrestaurant.co.uk; 8.30 pm; closed Mon, Tue, Wed L & Sun D; no credit cards.*

Pearson's Arms £49 444
The Horsebridge, Sea Wall CT5 1BT (01227) 272005
In a "fabulous" location ("ask for a window table upstairs for a fine sea view"), Richard Phillips's "very relaxed" pub and fine dining venture has upped its game of late; "menus have improved to be more seasonal" and service is "attentive" too; "excellent-value set lunch".
/ **Details:** *www.pearsonsarmsbyrichardphillips.co.uk; @pearsonsarms; 9 pm, Fri & Sat 9.30 pm, Sun 8.30 pm; closed Mon D.*

Samphire £46 332
4 High St CT5 1BQ (01227) 770075
"Consistently good-value food and service" draw fans to this informal all-day eatery, just outside the town-centre – a "friendly" place that's "always very busy". / **Details:** *www.samphirerestaurant.co.uk; @samphirewhit; 10 pm; no Amex.*

The Sportsman £50 554
Faversham Rd, Seasalter CT5 4BP (01227) 273370
It's "one of the UK's standout places to eat", yet Stephen Harris's "rather run-down-looking" coastal pub puts on "no airs and graces", and delivers "really honest, beautiful and carefully prepared" food, "with real heart".
/ **Details:** *www.thesportsmanseasalter.co.uk; @sportsmankent; 9 pm, Sun 2.30 pm; closed Mon & Sun D; no Amex; children: 18+ in main bar.*

Wheelers Oyster Bar £45 554
8 High St CT5 1BQ (01227) 273311
"Everyone should have a meal at least once", at this "tiny" (16 seats), "quirky" and "utterly unbeatable" institution, established in 1856; the style is "homely (in a good way"), and the "amazing" seafood is "a fishlover's dream come true"; no licence but BYO with no corkage.
/ **Details:** *www.seewhitstable.com/Wheelers-Whitstable-Restaurant.html; @WheelersOB; 7.30 pm, Sun 7 pm; closed Wed; no credit cards.*

Whitstable Oyster Fishery Co. £58 434
Royal Native Oyster Stores, Horsebridge CT5 1BU (01227) 276856
"Wonderful, but best during the week when there are fewer tourists about"; this "vast and vastly popular" institution – "in a beautiful restored warehouse right on the beach" – "does what it says on the tin", with "the main focus on oysters and seafood".
/ **Details:** *www.whitstableoystercompany.com; 8.45 pm, Fri 9.15 pm, Sat 9.45 pm, Sun 8.15 pm.*

WILLIAN, HERTFORDSHIRE 3–2B

The Fox £48 212
SG6 2AE (01462) 480233
An "edge-of-town gastropub" offering "excellent food and beers" and "consistently good" fish; it has a strong local fan base, but there are a few sceptics, too, who feel that it's "only on the borderline of good", having been let down of late by "snooty and slow" service. / **Details:** *www.foxatwillian.co.uk; @FoxAtWillian; 1 mile from junction 9 off A1M; 9 pm; closed Sun D; no Amex.*

WINCHCOMBE, GLOUCESTERSHIRE 2–1C

5 North Street £65 442
5 North St GL54 5LH (01242) 604566
An "intimate" venture, run by Marcus & Kate Ashenford, which offers "knock-out" food that's "fully deserving of the (Michelin) acclaim"; the "simple café-style setting", in a former tea-room, is a tad "provincial" in style for some tastes, but there's no doubting the "outstanding gastronomy".
/ **Details:** *www.5northstreetrestaurant.co.uk; 9 pm; closed Mon, Tue L & Sun D; no Amex.*

WINCHESTER, HAMPSHIRE 2–3D

Bangkok Brasserie £38 444
33 Jewry St SO23 8RY (01962) 869 966
An "outstanding" establishment "with a bit more about it than your usual high street Thai" (including a menu which offers a "good selection of vegetarian options"); "its success is obvious from the fact it's so busy". / **Details:** *www.bangkokbrasserie.co.uk; 10.30 pm.*

The Bengal Sage £37 443
72-74 St George's St SO23 8AH (01962) 862 173
With its "innovative, fresh-tasting and fragrant" cuisine, this "unusual" curry house "continues to be a stand-out eatery, even amongst Winchester's

numerous quality Indians"; it's a small place, and fans say its "intimate" vibe is "perfect for dates". / **Details:** *www.thebengalsage.co.uk; 10.30 pm; no Amex.*

The Black Rat £53 443
88 Chesil St SO23 0HX (01962) 844465
With its "very interesting modern cooking" and "unpretentious" atmosphere, this "quirky" former pub, is promoted by its many fans as "easily Winchester's best restaurant"; only gripe? – "almost London prices!"
/ **Details:** *www.theblackrat.co.uk; @the_black_rat; 9.30 pm; closed weekday L; children: 18+ except weekend L.*

The Chesil Rectory £55 445
1 Chesil St S023 0HU (01962) 851555
"In an ancient beamed building in the heart of the city", this "gem" of a restaurant has "bags of atmosphere", and – with its "good" and "interesting" cuisine – most reporters find it "an absolute delight" all-round.
/ **Details:** *www.chesilrectory.co.uk; @ChesilRectory; 9.30 pm, Sat 10 pm, Sun 9 pm; children: 12+ at D .*

The Chestnut Horse £47 234
Easton Village SO21 1EG (01962) 779257
"A charming old 'mind-your-head' pub", serving "outstanding bar food" – that's the majority view on this "relaxed" destination… although there's also the odd gripe that it's "resting on its laurels" a bit.
/ **Details:** *www.thechestnuthorse.com; @CHESTNUT_HORSE; Junction M3 Newbury exit right hand lane; 9.30 pm, Sun 8 pm; no Amex.*

Hotel du Vin et Bistro £53 222
14 Southgate St SO23 9EF (01962) 841414
On a good day, the potentially "romantic" original branch of the Hotel du Vin chain dishes up "good, reasonably-priced French brasserie-style food"; standards are not consistent, though, and those who complain of "dull" food in a "noisy" environment may just feel that it has "lost the plot".
/ **Details:** *www.hotelduvin.com; @HdV_Winchester; 9.45 pm; booking: max 12.* **Accommodation:** *24 rooms, from £145.*

Kyoto Kitchen £35 443
70 Parchment Street SO23 8AT
(01962) 890895
On almost all accounts, this two-year-old restaurant is an "exceptional" place to eat, offering "delicious and authentic" Japanese cuisine – "wow, not many places in Hampshire serve sashimi like this!"
/ **Details:** *www.kyotokitchen.co.uk/; 10.30 pm.*

The Avenue
Lainston House Hotel £82 232
Woodman Ln SO21 2LT (01962) 776088
"Overall good cooking, great service but great cost" – the majority verdict on this "stuffy" but "impressive" country house hotel; optimists, though, claim the "food is on the up since Olly Rouse (ex-Coworth Park) took over", in late-2013.
/ **Details:** *www.lainstonhouse.com; @lainstonhouse; 9.30 pm, Fri & Sat 10 pm.* **Accommodation:** *50 rooms, from £245.*

The Old Vine £42 233
8 Great Minster St SO23 9HA
(01962) 854616
It's "always a pleasure" to visit this very popular pub and dining room, near the cathedral; reports suggest the food is variable – "some good dishes, some average" – but this is a good-value venue overall, with an "excellent and frequently-changing range of beers".
/ **Details:** *www.oldvinewinchester.com; @oldvinewinch; 9.30 pm, Sun 9 pm; children: 6+.*
Accommodation: *5 rooms, from £100.*

Wykeham Arms £49 335
75 Kingsgate St SO23 9PE (01962) 853834
The "time warp" charm of this "unique" and hugely popular institution near the cathedral cannot be doubted; on the food front, though, opinions range from "excellent" to "not what it was".
/ **Details:** *www.wykemarmswinchester.com; @WykehmarmsLL; between Cathedral and College; 9.15 pm; children: 14+.* **Accommodation:** *14 rooms, from £139.*

WINDERMERE, CUMBRIA 7–3D

First Floor Café
Lakeland Limited £33 443
Alexandra Buildings LA23 1BQ
(015394) 47116
"Always reliable", the "very nice coffee shop" above the famous kitchenware shop ("full of all those things you never realised you needed") always impresses with its "high-quality lunches and snacks" (presided over by an ex-Gavroche chef Steven Doherty); "you may have to queue".
/ **Details:** *www.lakeland.co.uk; 6 pm, Sat 5 pm, Sun 4 pm; no Amex.*

Gilpin Lodge £51 545
Crook Rd LA23 3NE (01539) 488818
It's hard to criticise the "luxurious" dining room at this "friendly" hotel, whose "fine position" in "lovely countryside" is "perfect for a romantic weekend"; the cuisine is "faultless", and there's some "really interesting wine" on offer too.
/ **Details:** *www.thegilpin.co.uk; @chef_keller; 9.15 pm; no jeans; children: 7+.*
Accommodation: *20 rooms, from £255.*

Holbeck Ghyll £94 424
Holbeck Ln LA23 1LU (01539) 432375
"The views are just amazing", from this "sumptuous" former hunting lodge, overlooking Windermere; for the most part, reports are a hymn of praise to its "superb" cuisine and "professional" style, but some reporters do find the style "a little

starchy and traditional".
/ **Details:** *www.holbeckghyll.com; @HolbeckGhyll; 3m N of Windermere, towards Troutbeck; 9.30 pm; no jeans or trainers; children: 7+ at D.* ***Accommodation:*** *33 rooms, from £190.*

Linthwaite House **£75** Ⓣ
Crook Rd LA23 3JA (015394) 88600
Still fewer reports than we would like, but this hotel above Windermere is tipped as an "enjoyable" destination in "traditional" style, where the cooking is of a "very high standard".
/ **Details:** *www.linthwaite.com; near Windermere golf club; 9 pm; no jeans or trainers; children: 7+ at D.* ***Accommodation:*** *30 rooms, from £180.*

The Samling **£88** 223
Ambleside Rd LA23 1LR (01539) 431922
It has "tremendous views", and fans say Ian Swainson "deserves a second Michelin star" for his cooking at this contemporary-style country house hotel; even they can feel "ripped off" by the prices, though, and critics see "a chef trying too hard to impress" (or, perhaps, get that second star!).
/ **Details:** *www.thesamlinghotel.co.uk; @theSamlingHotel; take A591 from town; 9.30 pm.* ***Accommodation:*** *11 rooms, from £300.*

WINDSOR, BERKSHIRE 3–3A

Al Fassia **£40** 432
27 St Leonards Rd SL4 3BP (01753) 855370
"Traditional Moroccan food cooked to perfection and reasonably priced" (and in "great sized portions" too) helps ensure this "welcoming" spot "still delivers all-round".
/ **Details:** *www.alfassiarestaurant.com; 10.15 pm, Fri & Sat 10.30 pm, Sun 9.45 pm; closed Mon L.*

The Greene Oak **£46** Ⓣ
Deadworth Rd, Oakley Grn SL4 5UW (01753) 864294
Somewhat removed from the tourist throng, a non-central gastropub tipped as an "enjoyable lunch venue"; even here, though, standards can be "hit-and-miss". / **Details:** *www.thegreeneoak.co.uk; 9.30 pm.*

WINSLEY, WILTSHIRE 2–3B

The Seven Stars **£34** Ⓣ
BA15 2LQ (01225) 722204
"Great for lunch after a walk along the Kennet & Avon Canal", this "very pretty" dining pub boasts a "large and well-staffed kitchen", and is strongly tipped as an all-round quality production.
/ **Details:** *www.sevenstarswinsley.co.uk.*

WINTERINGHAM, LINCOLNSHIRE 5–1D

Winteringham Fields **£100** 433
1 Silver St DN15 9ND (01724) 733096
Colin McGurran's "clever" cuisine is helping to re-establish this lavishly appointed restaurant-with-rooms as a major hit for many reporters; even fans can find prices "daft", though, and some reporters with longer memories still make unfavourable comparisons with days of yore.
/ **Details:** *www.winteringhamfields.co.uk; @winteringhamf; 4m SW of Humber Bridge; 9 pm; closed Mon & Sun; no Amex.* ***Accommodation:*** *11 rooms, from £180.*

WISWELL, LANCASHIRE 5–1B

Freemasons at Wiswell **£56** 554
8 Vicarage Fold Clitheroe BB7 9DF (01254) 822218
"An almost hidden little restaurant – not really a pub any more – which offers some cracking food"; all reports testify to its remarkable "consistency"… and in a "fantastic" setting too!
/ **Details:** *www.freemasonswiswell.co.uk; @wiswellchef; Tue-Thu 9 pm, Fri & Sat 9.30 pm, Sun 8 pm; closed Mon & Tue; no Amex; to book 8+ have to pre-order.*

WITHERNWICK, EAST YORKSHIRE 6–1A

The Falcon Inn **£–** Ⓣ
Main St HU11 4TA
A newly revamped Yorkshire country inn now under the ownership of Richard and Lindsey Johns, formerly of the well-regarded Artisan in Hessle – we tip it purely as an interesting novelty which, given its ownership, should be worth checking out.

WIVETON, NORFOLK 6–3C

Wiveton Bell **£45** 334
Blakeney Rd NR25 7TL (01263) 740 101
Next to the church, and with a "delightful" garden, a pub where the cooking, with its "emphasis is on local ingredients", generally pleases; given the "almost-London prices", though, not everyone is convinced. / **Details:** *www.wivetonbell.co.uk; @wivetonbell; 9 pm; no Amex.* ***Accommodation:*** *4 rooms, from £75.*

WOBURN SANDS, BUCKINGHAMSHIRE 3–2A

Purple Goose **£47** 444
61 High St MK17 8QY (01908) 584385
"Fab decor, thoughtful but unobtrusive service…" – it doesn't inspire a huge volume of commentary, but all reports on this "elegant" high street restaurant are notably positive, including about the very good cooking.
/ **Details:** *www.thepurplegoose.co.uk/; 9.30 pm; closed Mon, Tue L, Wed L & Sun D; no Amex.*

WOBURN, BUCKINGHAMSHIRE 3–2A

Birch **£48** Ⓣ
20 Newport Rd MK17 9HX (01525) 290295
Little in the way of actual commentary from reporters on this busy gastropub; the survey ratings

they award, however, confirm its continuing all-round attractions. / **Details:** *www.birchwoburn.com; between Woburn and Woburn Sands on the Newport rd; 9.30 pm; closed Sun D; booking: max 12, Fri & Sat.*

The Black Horse £50 ⓣ
1 Bedford St MK17 9QB (01525) 290210
A "comfy" old inn, tipped for its "consistently good food"; "cheerful" service too.
/ **Details:** *www.blackhorsewoburn.co.uk; 9.45 pm, Sun 9 pm.*

Paris House £116 334
London Rd MK17 9QP (01525) 290692
"Top-notch cooking, interesting flavour combinations, beautifully presented food… and all in a magnificent parkland setting" – most reporters can find very little to fault at Phil Fanning's "inventive" restaurant, in a Tudor house on the Woburn Estate; no surprise, then, that it's quite "expensive". / **Details:** *www.parishouse.co.uk; @ParisHousechef; on A4012; 9 pm; closed Mon, Tue & Sun D.*

WOLVERCOTE, OXFORDSHIRE 2–2D

The Trout Inn £43 224
195 Godstow Rd OX2 8PN (01865) 510930
This "lovely riverside pub-restaurant", a favourite haunt of Inspector Morse, offers "honest" food, and it can get "very crowded with the locals" when the sun shines; critics, though, do find the style rather "corporate" nowadays.
/ **Details:** *www.thetroutoxford.co.uk; @TheTroutOxford; 2m from junction of A40 & A44; 10 pm, Fri & Sat 10.30 pm, Sun 9 pm.*

WOLVERHAMPTON, WEST MIDLANDS 5–4B

Bilash £51 544
2 Cheapside WV1 1TU (01902) 427762
"Consistently the best food from the subcontinent in this part of the Midlands"; Sitab Khan's "very stylish and upmarket" city-centre Indian elicits a flurry of superlatives from all who comment on it.
/ **Details:** *www.thebilash.co.uk; @thebilash; 10.30 pm; closed Sun.*

WOODBRIDGE, SUFFOLK 3–1D

The Table £34 ⓣ
IP12 1BX (01394) 382428
A town-centre "mainstay", tipped for its "buzzing candlelit atmosphere" and "clever" food; "interesting streetfood parties on Sunday night" are worth seeking out.

WOODHOUSE EAVES, LEICESTERSHIRE 5–3D

Paul Leary @ The Woodhouse £53 ⓣ
LE12 8RG (01509) 890318
"A splendid find" – hidden away in a small village ("thank goodness for SatNav"), this "elegant" dining room is tipped for its "fine and eclectic" cooking; a "really excellent-value" set lunch is a highlight.
/ **Details:** *www.thewoodhouse.co.uk.*

WOODLANDS, HAMPSHIRE 2–4C

Terravina Hotel Terravina £59 353
174 Woodlands Rd, Netley Marsh, New Forest SO40 7GL (023) 8029 3784
The "strong wine list you would expect from the pedigree" is the stand-out feature at Hotel du Vin-founder Gerard and Nina Basset's New Forest dining room; service is "assiduous" too, but unfortunately the "pleasant" cooking "lacks the wow-factor to match the liquid refreshment".
/ **Details:** *www.hotelterravina.co.uk; @Hotel_TerraVina; 9.30 pm.* **Accommodation:** *11 rooms, from £165.*

WOOTTON, OXFORDSHIRE 2–1D

The Killingworth Castle £48 454
OX20 1EJ (01993) 811 401
Hugely positive feedback for this "tastefully restored" 17th-century coaching inn, opened in late-2012 by the owners of the Ebrington Arms, near Chipping Campden, where Andrew Lipp's "wonderful" grub is brilliantly set off by locally brewed ales; there's a "lovely" garden too.
/ **Details:** *www.thekillingworthcastle.com.*

WORTHING, WEST SUSSEX 3–4A

The Fish Factory £39 443
51-53 Brighton Rd BN11 3EE (01903) 207123
"Always a treat" – this "relaxed" chippy garners survey praise for its "super-fresh" catch and "crisp" batter; also in Littlehampton.
/ **Details:** *www.protorestaurantgroup.com; 10 pm.*

WRINEHILL, CHESHIRE 5–2B

The Hand & Trumpet £46 ⓣ
Main Rd CW3 9BJ (01270) 820048
"Probably the best place to eat in a culinary desert", this Brunning & Price gastroboozer serves "good food in generous portions"; by the group's generally consistent standards, though, feedback is rather up-and-down.
/ **Details:** *www.brunningandprice.co.uk/hand; 10 pm, Sun 9.30 pm; no Amex.*

WRINGTON, SOMERSET 2–2B

Ethicurean £47 434
Barley Wood Walled Garden, Long Ln BS40 5SA (01934) 863713
"Set in a restored orangery in a lovely walled garden, with views across the valley to the Mendip Hills", this 'ethical' restaurant "uses only local produce, a lot of it from their own garden"; no good

if the food doesn't measure up, of course, but all reports say it's "original", with "vivid flavours", and "served with love".
/ **Details:** *www.theethicurean.com; Fri & Sat 11.30 pm, Sun 2.30 pm; closed Mon, Tue D, Wed D & Thu D.*

WYMONDHAM, LEICESTERSHIRE 5–3D

The Berkeley Arms **£45** 554
59 Main St LE14 2AG (01572) 787 587
This "charming" inn, run by a "very able" husband-and-wife team, may attract foodies with its "innovative, top-notch" cooking but it's also a hit with "normal drinkers having a pint"; it's "not all Farrow & Balled either", which may or may not be a further recommendation.
/ **Details:** *www.theberkeleyarms.co.uk; @TheBekeleyArms; 9 pm, Fri & Sat 9.30 pm; closed Mon & Sun D; no Amex.*

YEADON, WEST YORKSHIRE 5–1C

Murgatroyds **£35** T
Harrogate Rd LS19 7BN (0113) 250 0010
"If there's a better chippy in the UK, I've yet to find it" – "the queues out of the door testify to its quality!" / **Details:** *www.murgatroyds.co.uk; 9.30 pm.*

YORK, NORTH YORKSHIRE 5–1D

Bettys **£46** 344
6-8 St Helen's Sq YO1 8QP (01904) 659142
Offering a return "to the charm of the early 20th century", this "totally traditional" tearoom offers "delicious" cakes and some more substantial "Swiss-influenced dishes" too, the enjoyment of which underpins many visits to York – "you may well have to queue to get in". / **Details:** *www.bettys.co.uk; 9 pm; no Amex; no booking, except Sun.*

Café Concerto **£44** 222
21 High Petergate YO1 7EN (01904) 610478
"Conveniently placed for the Minster", this classic café is a "great place for an unpretentious meal" (particularly at lunch); "at busy times, though, service can collapse".
/ **Details:** *www.cafeconcerto.biz; 9.30 pm; booking: max 6-8.* **Accommodation:** *1 room, at about £175.*

Cafe No. 8 Bistro **£46** 343
8 Gillygate YO31 7EQ (01904) 653074
"Small but superb", this venue near the Minster is "one of the city's best, most casual eateries", offering an "interesting menu" that's often "superbly cooked"; "friendly atmosphere" too.
/ **Details:** *www.cafeno8.co.uk; 9.30 pm; no Amex.*

Le Cochon Aveugle **£51** T
YO1 9TX (01904) 640222
Risen from the ashes of the short-lived Blind Swine, this "intimate" (7-table) Walmgate bistro, from chef-patron Josh Overington (ex-Waterside Inn), "now appears to be morphing into a serious restaurant in its own right"; its tasting menus are a top tip for "foodies wanting to try something innovative". / **Details:** *www.lecochonaveugleyork.com.*

Il Paradiso Del Cibo **£36** 434
40 Walmgate YO1 9TJ (0190) 461 1444
"Genuine Sardinian food" and a "welcoming atmosphere" ensure that this "very busy" spot is reassuringly "well patronised by the local Italians"; on the menu, "perfect" pizzas with "plenty of topping". / **Details:** *www.ilparadisodelcibo.com; 10 pm.*

Le Langhe **£50** 523
The Old Coach Hs, Peasholme Grn YO1 7PW (01904) 622584
"The best Italian outside London by far" – "top-quality" ingredients are used "with imagination", at this "surprising" restaurant, behind a deli, and it offers "endless fine Italian wines to suit every budget" too; service, though, can be a touch "erratic". / **Details:** *www.lelanghe.co.uk; @lelanghe; midnight; closed Mon, Tue, Wed, Thu & Sun; no Amex.*

Melton's **£52** 442
7 Scarcroft Rd YO23 1ND (01904) 634 341
"A consistently good-value performer for many years" – this slightly out-of-the-way stalwart "is worth seeking out" for its "first-class food" (with "much emphasis on local sourcing"); "the only let-down is the layout, which doesn't create any sort of special atmosphere".
/ **Details:** *www.meltonsrestaurant.co.uk; @Meltons1; 9.30 pm; closed Mon & Sun; no Amex.*

Melton's Too **£40** 231
25 Walmgate YO1 9TX (01904) 629 222
It may be "unpretentious", but fans say that Melton's "informal" spin-off is "worth a visit" for its often "imaginative" dishes; the setting, though – which strikes critics as "shabby and uninviting" – can let the whole show down.
/ **Details:** *www.meltonstoo.co.uk; 10.30 pm, Sun 9.30 pm; no Amex.*

Middlethorpe Hall **£70** 444
Bishopthorpe Rd YO23 2GB (01904) 641241
It's not just the charm of this National Trust-owned country house hotel, in 200 acres on the edge of the city, that makes it worth seeking out – the "very accomplished" cuisine is "some of the best in Yorkshire", and the service is "very good" too. / **Details:** *www.middlethorpe.com; 9.30 pm; no shorts; children: 6+.* **Accommodation:** *29 rooms, from £199.*

Mumbai Lounge **£32** 333
47 Fossgate YO1 9TF (01904) 654 155
"Slightly better-than-average" food (with "extremely good naans and chapatis") still makes this "large and bustling" Indian a popular city-centre choice; this year, however, also saw the occasional below-par

experience. / **Details:** *www.mumbailoungeyork.co.uk; 11.30 pm, Fri & Sat midnight; closed Fri L.*

Rice Style **£42** ①

YO23 1NA (01904) 848927

"The only problem is that it's a bit small!" – otherwise, this "great" Thai restaurant is consistently praised by reporters, not least for its "short" but "perfectly considered" menu, which includes "dishes you don't normally find".

/ **Details:** *www.ricestyle.co.uk.*

Star in the City **£52** 234

YO1 7DR (01904) 619208

It's "a great addition to York", say fans, but in truth this "pricey" riverside offshoot of the fabled Star at Harome has had a very mixed reception – fans find the style "big, bold and brilliant", but for critics its's all just rather "gimmicky".

/ **Details:** *www.starinnthecity.co.uk.*

The Whippet Inn **£36** 454

YO1 6JD (01904) 500660

"A gorgeous gastropub, hidden away in the centre of the city"; with its "varied" menu, "quality range of gins, whiskies and wine" and "fantastic" service, this newish 'steak and ale house' (as it calls itself) is hailed by all reporters for its impressive all-round standards. / **Details:** *www.thewhippetinn.co.uk.*

UK MAPS

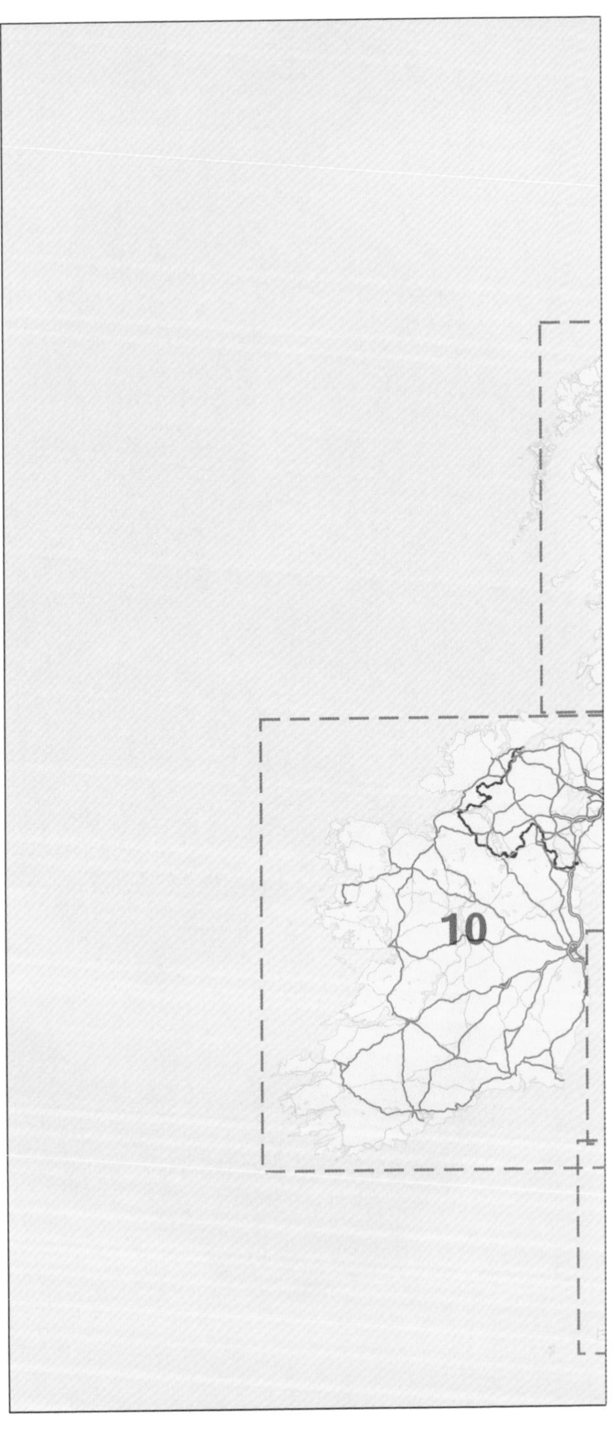
10

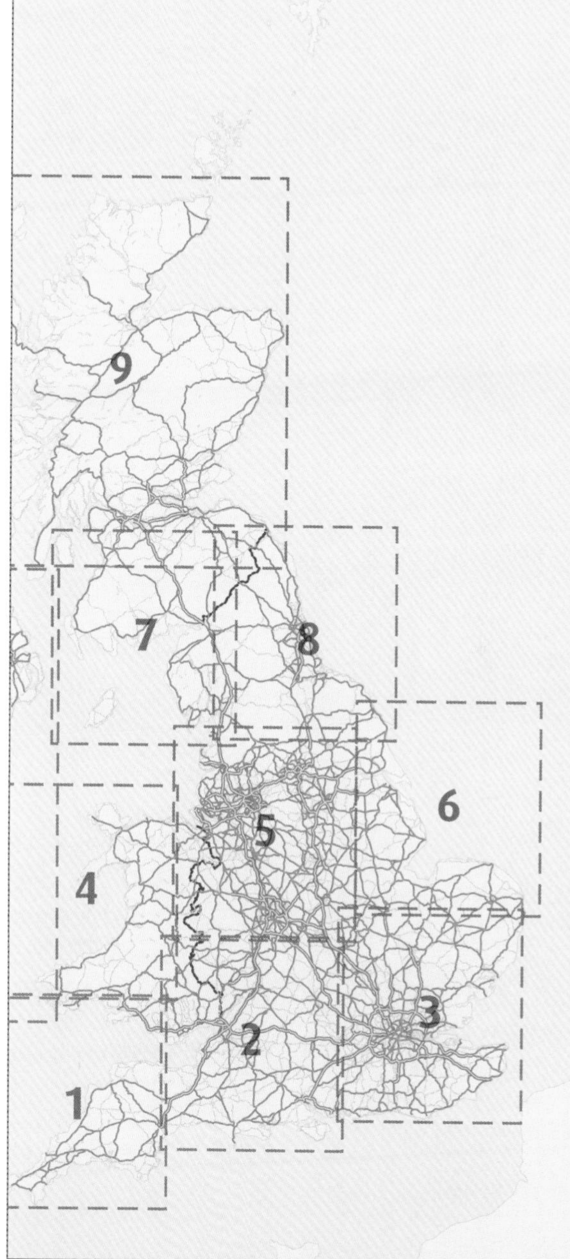
9
7
8
6
5
4
3
2
1

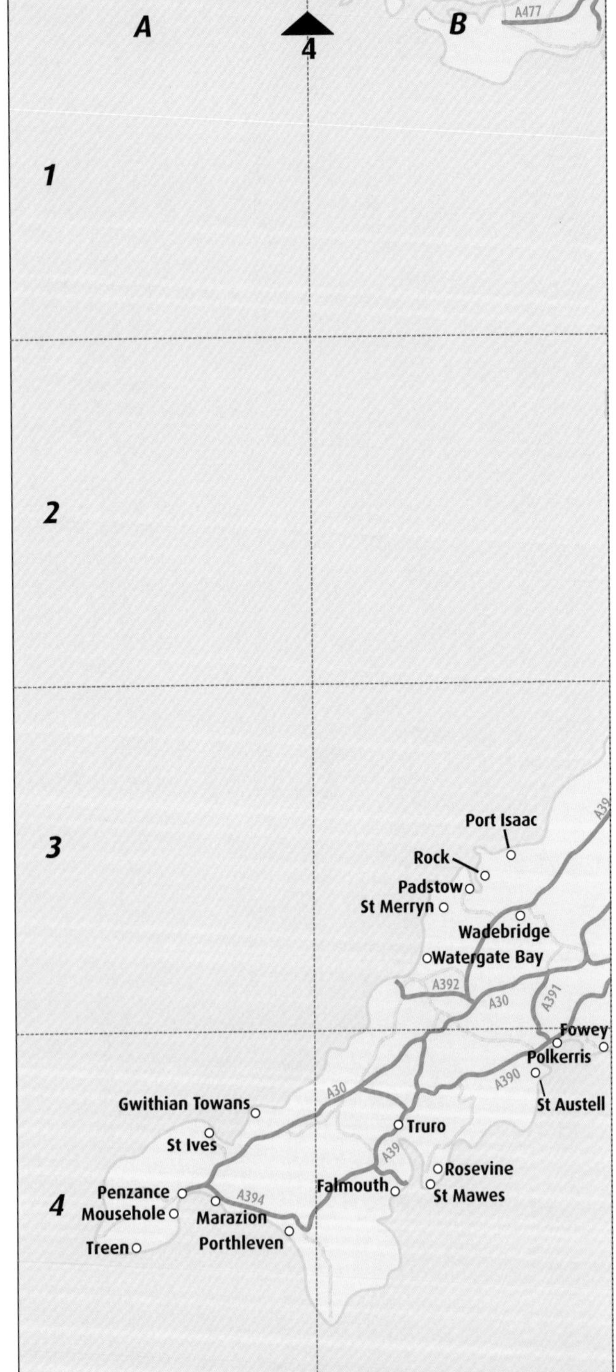
A
B
4
A477
1
2
3
4
Port Isaac
Rock
Padstow
St Merryn
Wadebridge
Watergate Bay
A392
A30
A391
A39
Fowey
Polkerris
A390
St Austell
Gwithian Towans
A30
St Ives
Truro
A39
Rosevine
Penzance
Falmouth
St Mawes
Mousehole
A394
Marazion
Treen
Porthleven

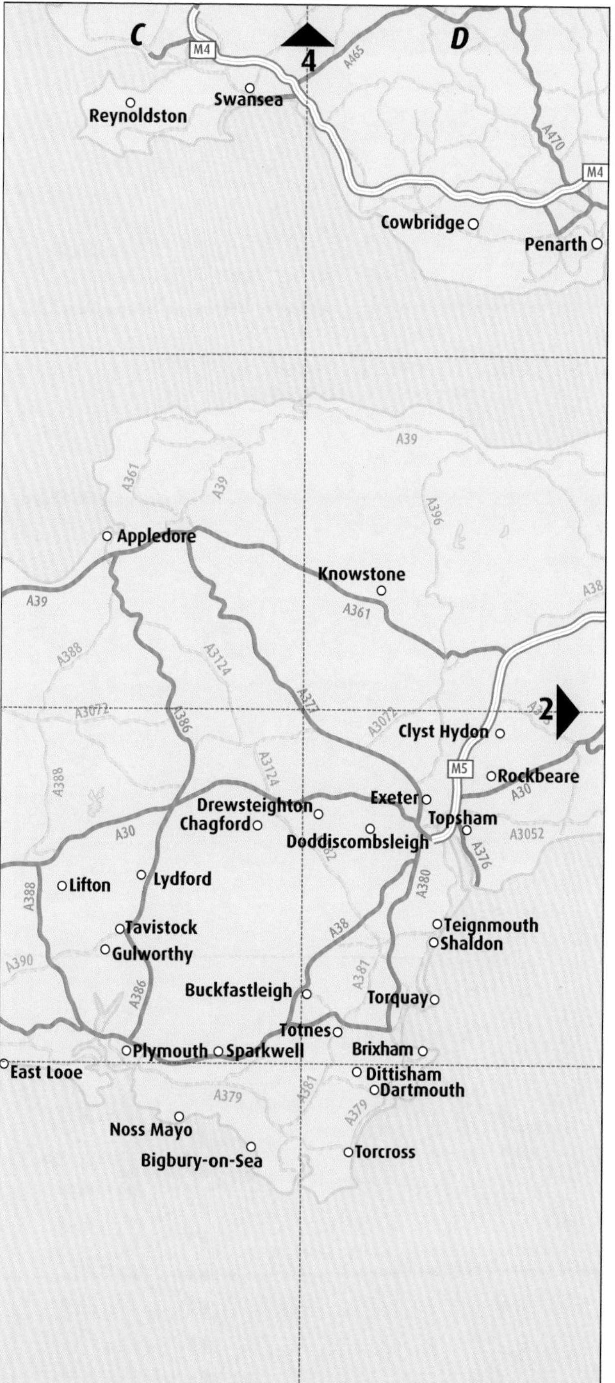

C
D
4
M4
A465
Swansea
Reynoldston
A470
M4
Cowbridge
Penarth
A39
A361
A39
A396
Appledore
Knowstone
A38
A39
A361
A388
A3124
A377
A3072
A3072
A386
2
Clyst Hydon
M5
Rockbeare
A3124
A388
A30
Exeter
Drewsteighton
Chagford
Topsham
A3052
A30
Doddiscombsleigh
A376
Lifton
Lydford
A388
A380
Tavistock
Teignmouth
Shaldon
A38
Gulworthy
A390
A381
Buckfastleigh
A386
Torquay
Totnes
Brixham
Plymouth
Sparkwell
East Looe
Dittisham
Dartmouth
A379
A381
A379
Noss Mayo
Bigbury-on-Sea
Torcross

MAP 1

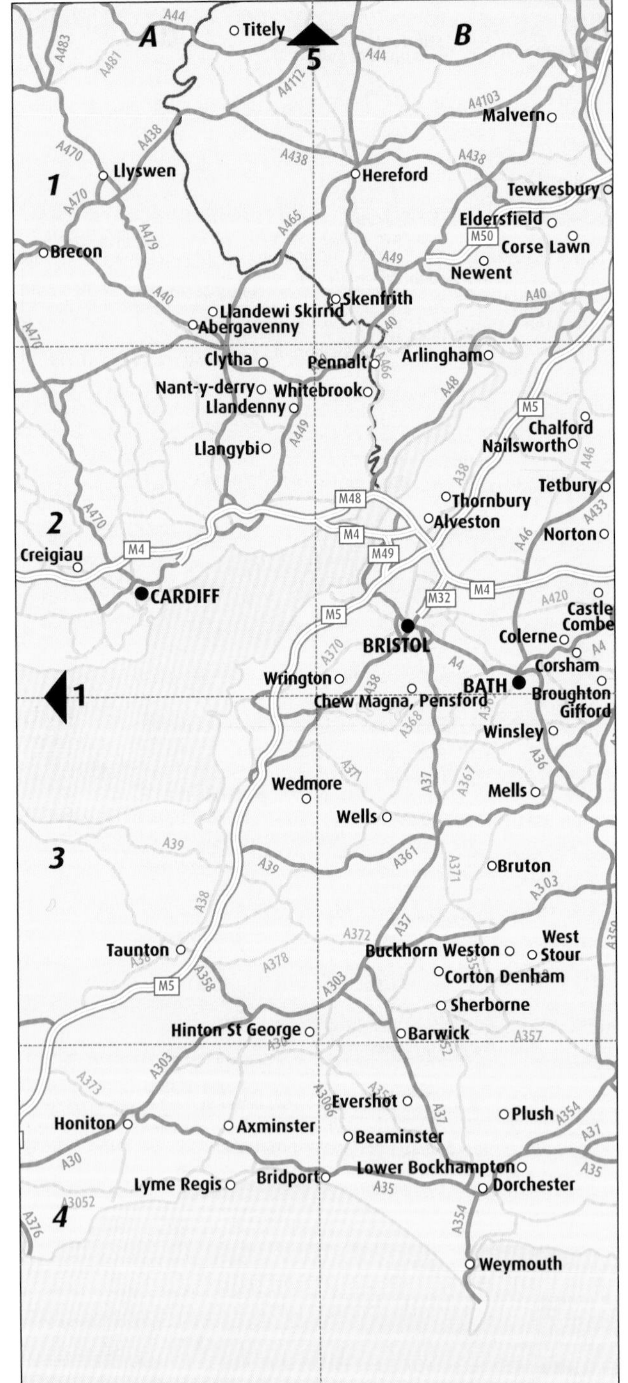
A
B
5
1
2
3
4
Titely
Malvern
Llyswen
Hereford
Tewkesbury
Eldersfield
Corse Lawn
Brecon
Newent
Skenfrith
Llandewi Skirrid
Abergavenny
Clytha
Pennalt
Arlingham
Nant-y-derry
Whitebrook
Llandenny
Chalford
Nailsworth
Llangybi
Tetbury
Thornbury
Alveston
Norton
Creigiau
CARDIFF
BRISTOL
Castle Combe
Colerne
Corsham
Wrington
BATH
Chew Magna, Pensford
Broughton Gifford
Winsley
Wedmore
Mells
Wells
Bruton
Taunton
Buckhorn Weston
West Stour
Corton Denham
Sherborne
Hinton St George
Barwick
Evershot
Plush
Honiton
Axminster
Beaminster
Lower Bockhampton
Lyme Regis
Bridport
Dorchester
Weymouth
M4
M48
M49
M32
M5
M50
A44
A483
A481
A4112
A4103
A438
A470
A479
A465
A49
A40
A466
A48
A449
A38
A46
A433
A420
A4
A370
A368
A367
A36
A371
A37
A39
A361
A303
A372
A378
A358
A357
A352
A354
A3066
A373
A31
A35
A30
A3052
A376

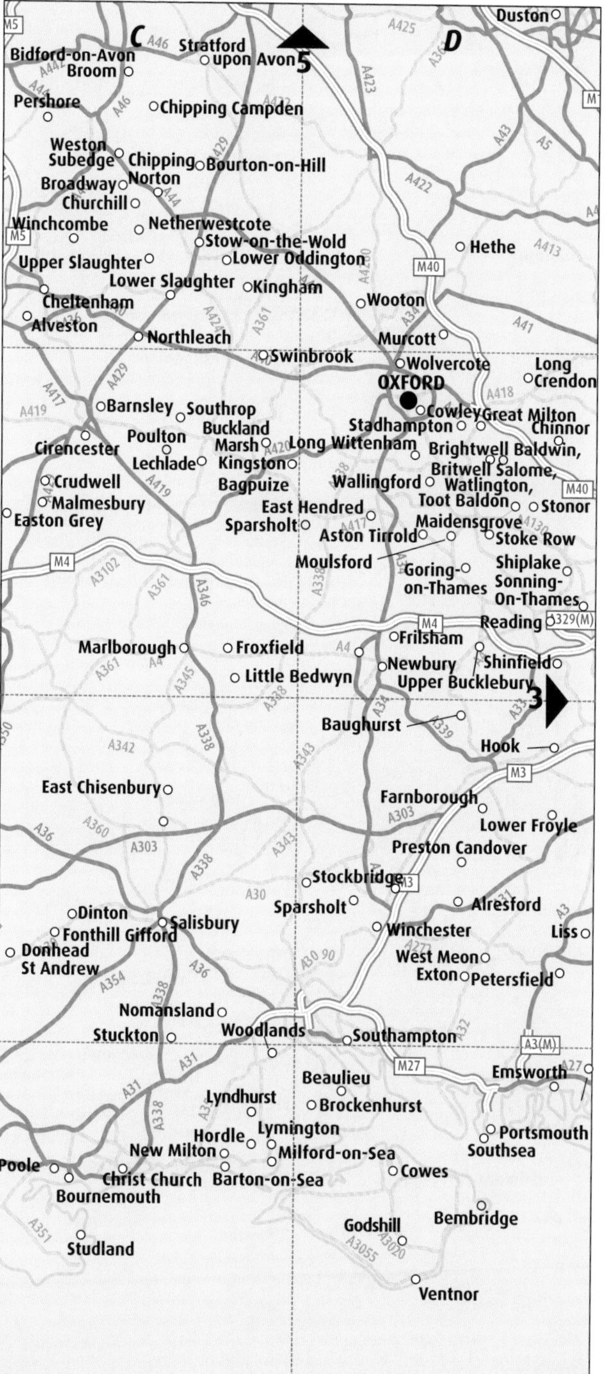
Bidford-on-Avon
Broom
Stratford upon Avon
Duston
Pershore
Chipping Campden
Weston Subedge
Chipping Norton
Bourton-on-Hill
Broadway
Churchill
Winchcombe
Netherwestcote
Stow-on-the-Wold
Upper Slaughter
Lower Oddington
Lower Slaughter
Kingham
Hethe
Cheltenham
Wooton
Alveston
Northleach
Murcott
Swinbrook
Wolvercote
Long Crendon
OXFORD
Barnsley
Southrop
Cowley
Great Milton
Chinnor
Stadhampton
Poulton
Buckland Marsh
Long Wittenham
Brightwell Baldwin,
Britwell Salome,
Watlington,
Cirencester
Lechlade
Kingston Bagpuize
Wallingford
Toot Baldon
Stonor
Crudwell
Malmesbury
Easton Grey
East Hendred
Sparsholt
Maidensgrove
Aston Tirrold
Stoke Row
Moulsford
Goring-on-Thames
Shiplake
Sonning-On-Thames
Reading
Frilsham
Marlborough
Froxfield
Newbury
Shinfield
Little Bedwyn
Upper Bucklebury
Baughurst
Hook
East Chisenbury
Farnborough
Lower Froyle
Preston Candover
Stockbridge
Sparsholt
Alresford
Dinton
Salisbury
Fonthill Gifford
Winchester
Liss
Donhead St Andrew
West Meon
Exton
Petersfield
Nomansland
Stuckton
Woodlands
Southampton
Emsworth
Beaulieu
Lyndhurst
Brockenhurst
Hordle
Lymington
Portsmouth
Southsea
New Milton
Milford-on-Sea
Poole
Christ Church
Barton-on-Sea
Cowes
Bournemouth
Godshill
Bembridge
Studland
Ventnor

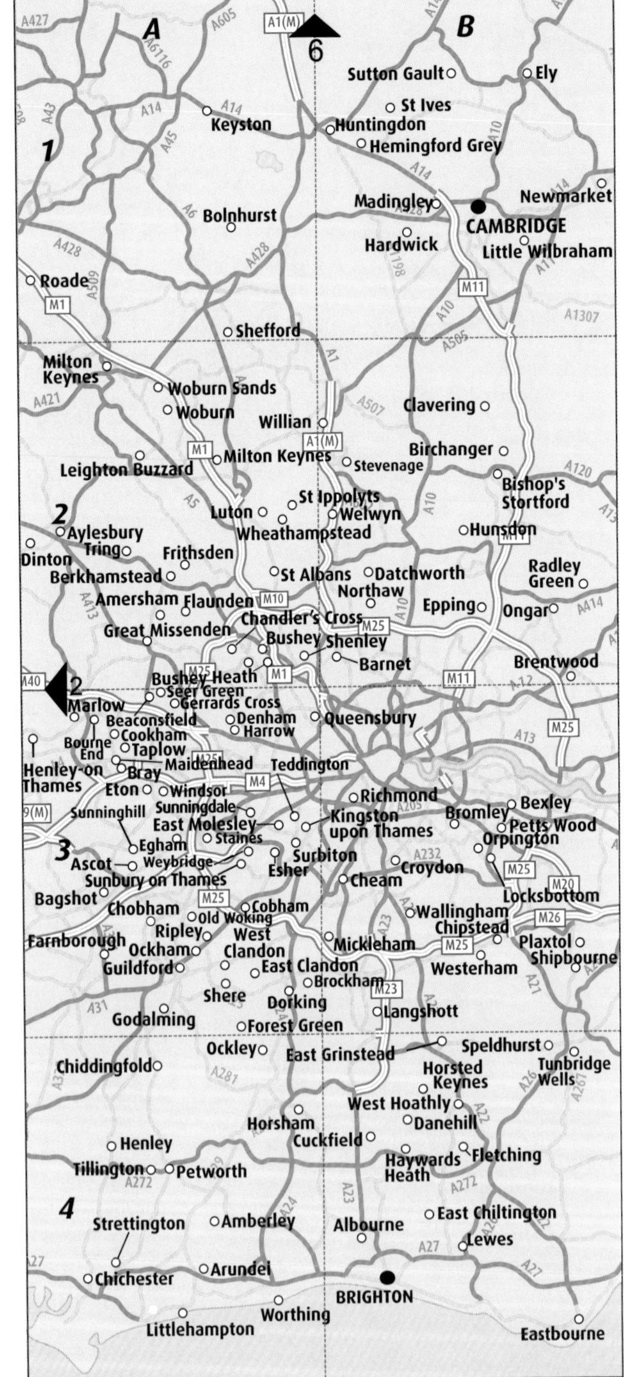
A
B
1
2
3
4
6
2
A1(M)
Sutton Gault
Ely
St Ives
Keyston
Huntingdon
Hemingford Grey
Madingley
Newmarket
CAMBRIDGE
Bolnhurst
Hardwick
Little Wilbraham
Roade
M1
M11
Shefford
Milton Keynes
Woburn Sands
Woburn
Willian
Clavering
A1(M)
Birchanger
Leighton Buzzard
Milton Keynes
Stevenage
Bishop's Stortford
St Ippolyts
Luton
Welwyn
Wheathampstead
Hunsdon
Aylesbury
Dinton
Tring
Frithsden
Berkhamstead
St Albans
Datchworth
Radley Green
Northaw
Amersham
Flaunden
M10
Epping
Ongar
Chandler's Cross
Great Missenden
M25
Bushey
Shenley
Barnet
Brentwood
Bushey Heath
M1
M11
Seer Green
Marlow
Gerrards Cross
Beaconsfield
Denham
Queensbury
Harrow
Cookham
Bourne End
Taplow
M25
Maidenhead
Teddington
Henley-on Thames
Bray
Eton
Windsor
M4
Richmond
Sunninghill
Sunningdale
Bromley
Bexley
East Molesley
Kingston upon Thames
Petts Wood
Egham
Staines
Orpington
Ascot
Weybridge
Surbiton
Esher
Croydon
M25
Sunbury on Thames
Cheam
M20
Locksbottom
Bagshot
M25
Chobham
Cobham
Wallingham
Old Woking
Chipstead
M26
Ripley
West Clandon
Farnborough
Mickleham
M25
Plaxtol
Ockham
Westerham
Shipbourne
Guildford
East Clandon
Brockham
M23
Shere
Dorking
Godalming
Langshott
Forest Green
Ockley
East Grinstead
Speldhurst
Chiddingfold
Horsted Keynes
Tunbridge Wells
West Hoathly
Danehill
Horsham
Cuckfield
Henley
Fletching
Haywards Heath
Tillington
Petworth
East Chiltington
Strettington
Amberley
Albourne
Lewes
Arundel
Chichester
BRIGHTON
Worthing
Littlehampton
Eastbourne
A427
A605
A6116
A14
A43
A45
A10
A6
A428
A1198
A509
A1307
A505
A1
A421
A507
A120
A5
A10
A413
A414
A12
A13
A205
A232
A31
A281
A272
A24
A23
A22
A26
A27
A21
M40
M25

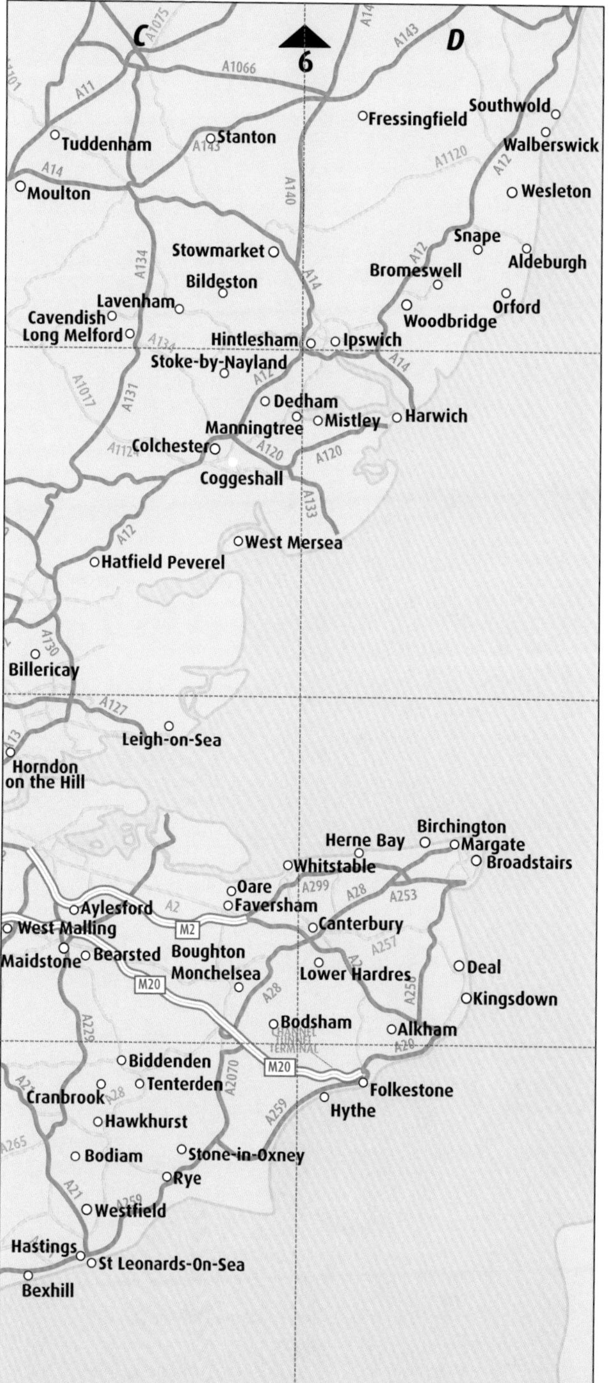
C
D
6
A1066
A143
A11
A14
A1120
A12
A140
A134
A131
A1017
A1124
A120
A133
A130
A127
A2
M2
M20
A299
A28
A253
A257
A258
A20
A229
A2070
A259
A21
A265
Fressingfield
Southwold
Walberswick
Tuddenham
Stanton
Moulton
Wesleton
Stowmarket
Snape
Aldeburgh
Bromeswell
Bildeston
Orford
Woodbridge
Lavenham
Cavendish
Long Melford
Hintlesham
Ipswich
Stoke-by-Nayland
Dedham
Mistley
Harwich
Manningtree
Colchester
Coggeshall
West Mersea
Hatfield Peverel
Billericay
Leigh-on-Sea
Horndon
on the Hill
Birchington
Herne Bay
Margate
Broadstairs
Whitstable
Oare
Faversham
Aylesford
West Malling
Canterbury
Maidstone
Bearsted
Boughton
Monchelsea
Lower Hardres
Deal
Kingsdown
Bodsham
Alkham
CHANNEL
TUNNEL
TERMINAL
Biddenden
Tenterden
Folkestone
Cranbrook
Hythe
Hawkhurst
Bodiam
Stone-in-Oxney
Rye
Westfield
Hastings
St Leonards-On-Sea
Bexhill

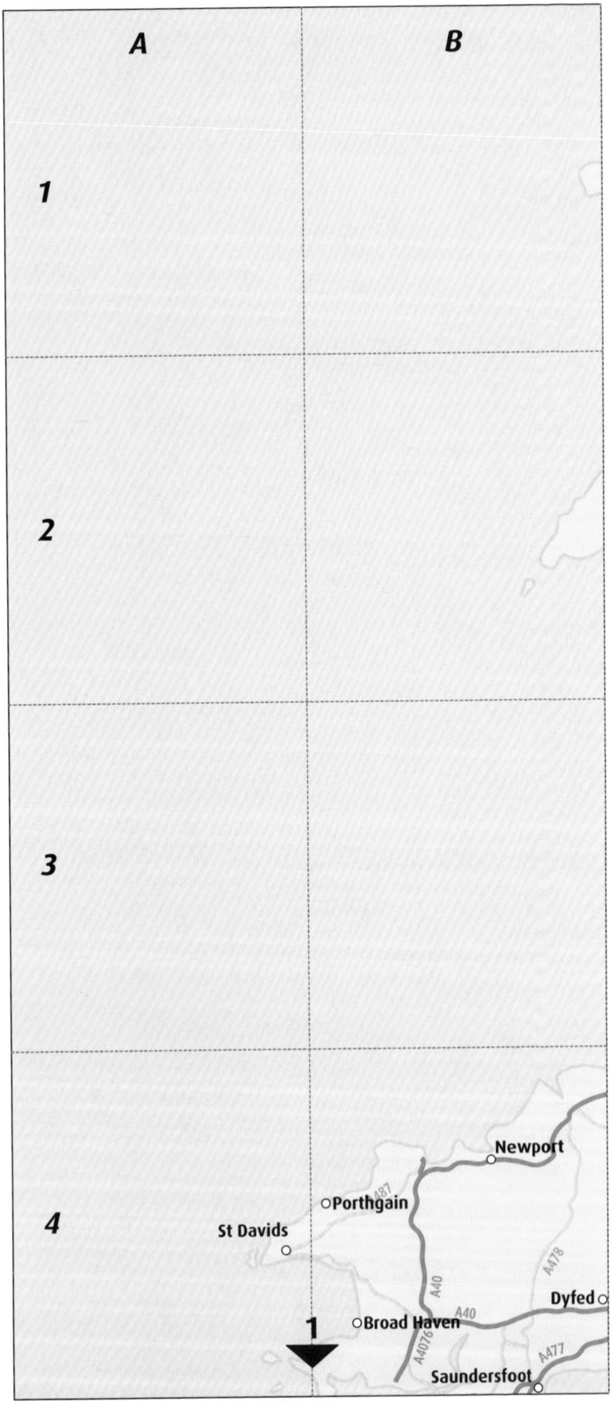

A
B
1
2
3
4
Newport
A487
Porthgain
St Davids
A478
A40
Dyfed
A40
Broad Haven
1
A4076
A477
Saundersfoot

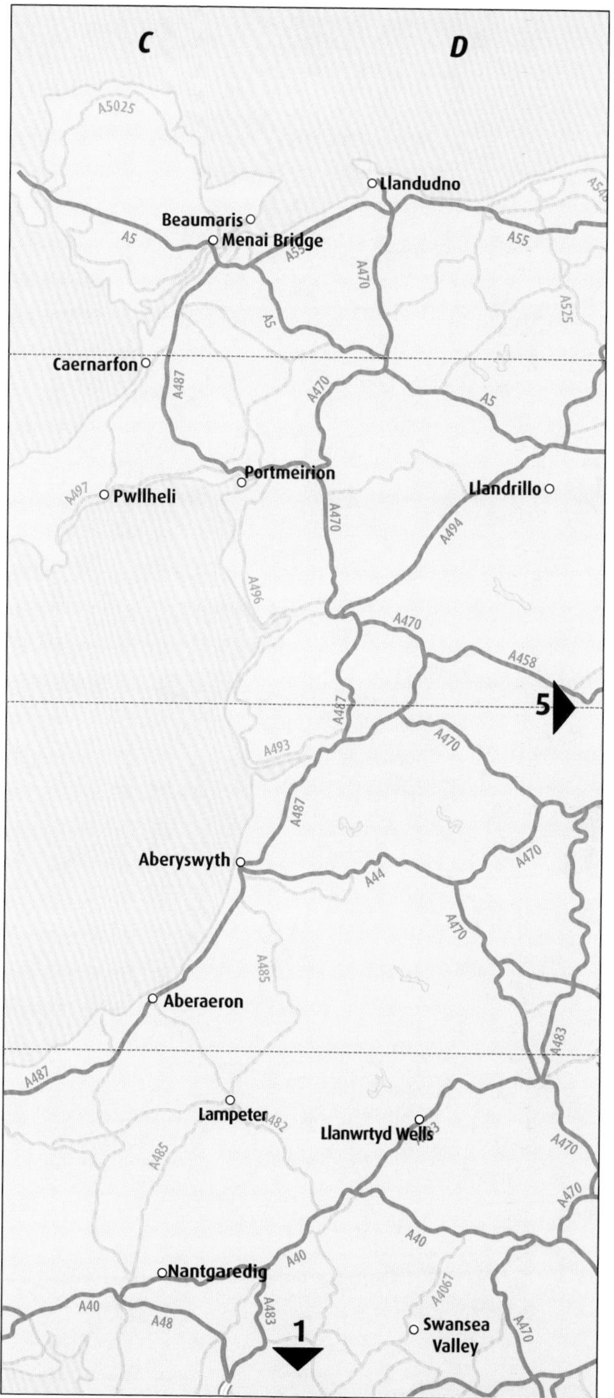
C
D
A5025
Llandudno
Beaumaris
Menai Bridge
A5
A55
A470
A55
A525
A5
Caernarfon
A487
A470
A5
Portmeirion
Pwllheli
A497
Llandrillo
A470
A494
A496
A470
A458
5
A487
A493
A470
A487
Aberyswyth
A44
A470
A470
A485
Aberaeron
A483
A487
Lampeter
A482
Llanwrtyd Wells
A485
A470
A470
A40
Nantgaredig
A40
A4067
A40
A48
A483
1
Swansea
Valley
A470

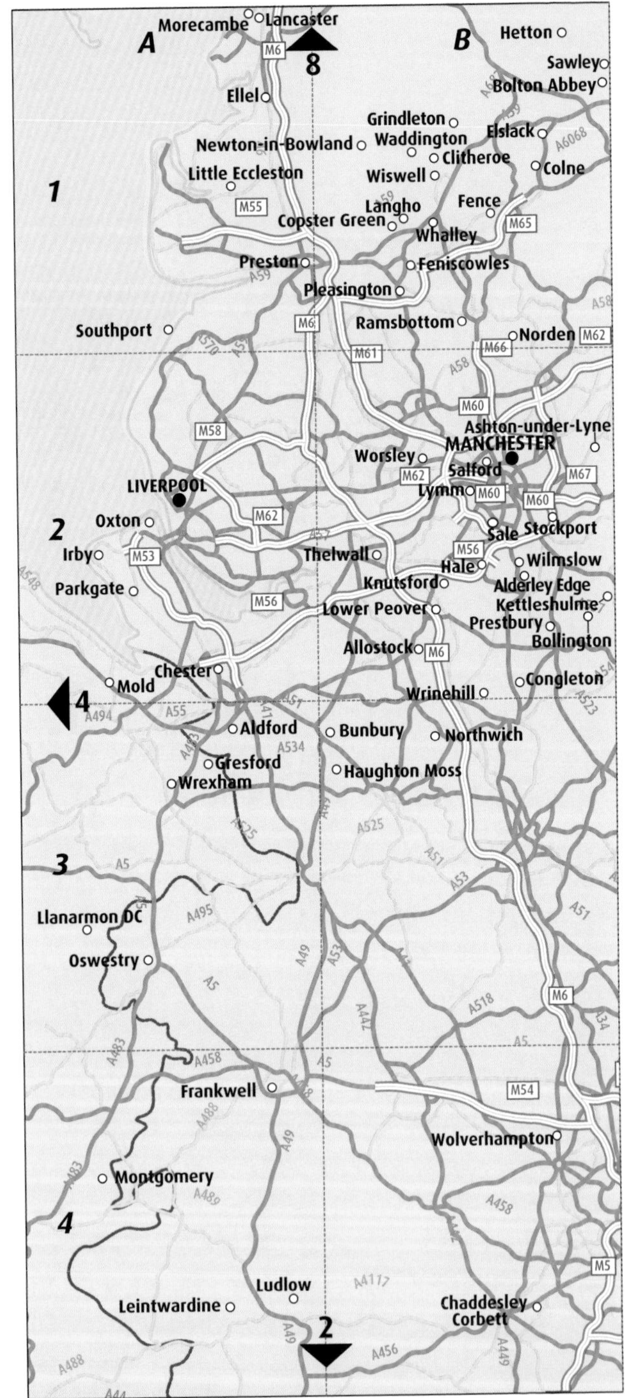

A
B
1
2
3
4
8
4
2
Morecambe
Lancaster
Hetton
Sawley
Bolton Abbey
Ellel
Grindleton
Waddington
Elslack
Newton-in-Bowland
Clitheroe
Colne
Little Eccleston
Wiswell
Langho
Fence
Copster Green
Whalley
Preston
Feniscowles
Pleasington
Ramsbottom
Southport
Norden
Ashton-under-Lyne
MANCHESTER
Worsley
Salford
LIVERPOOL
Lymm
Oxton
Sale
Stockport
Irby
Thelwall
Wilmslow
Hale
Parkgate
Knutsford
Alderley Edge
Kettleshulme
Lower Peover
Prestbury
Bollington
Allostock
Chester
Mold
Congleton
Wrinehill
Aldford
Bunbury
Northwich
Gresford
Haughton Moss
Wrexham
Llanarmon DC
Oswestry
Frankwell
Wolverhampton
Montgomery
Ludlow
Leintwardine
Chaddesley Corbett
M6
M55
M65
M61
M66
M62
M60
M58
M67
M53
M56
M54
M5
A59
A6068
A570
A58
A57
A548
A494
A55
A483
A41
A51
A534
A525
A49
A5
A495
A53
A442
A518
A458
A488
A489
A4117
A456
A449
A523
A34
A44

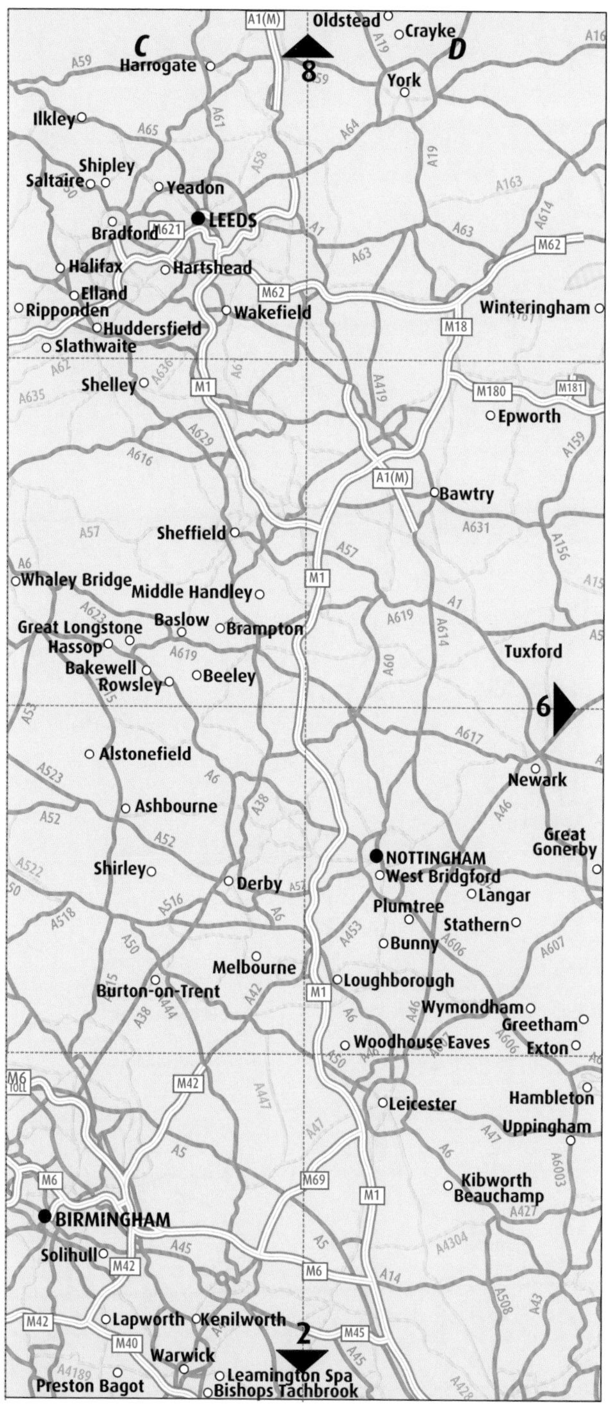
C
D
8
Oldstead
Crayke
Harrogate
York
Ilkley
Shipley
Saltaire
Yeadon
LEEDS
Bradford
Halifax
Hartshead
Elland
Ripponden
Wakefield
Huddersfield
Slathwaite
Winteringham
Shelley
Epworth
Bawtry
Sheffield
Whaley Bridge
Middle Handley
Great Longstone
Baslow
Brampton
Hassop
Bakewell
Rowsley
Beeley
Tuxford
6
Alstonefield
Newark
Ashbourne
Great Gonerby
NOTTINGHAM
West Bridgford
Shirley
Derby
Langar
Plumtree
Stathern
Bunny
Melbourne
Loughborough
Burton-on-Trent
Wymondham
Greetham
Woodhouse Eaves
Exton
Hambleton
Leicester
Uppingham
Kibworth Beauchamp
BIRMINGHAM
Solihull
Lapworth
Kenilworth
2
Warwick
Leamington Spa
Preston Bagot
Bishops Tachbrook

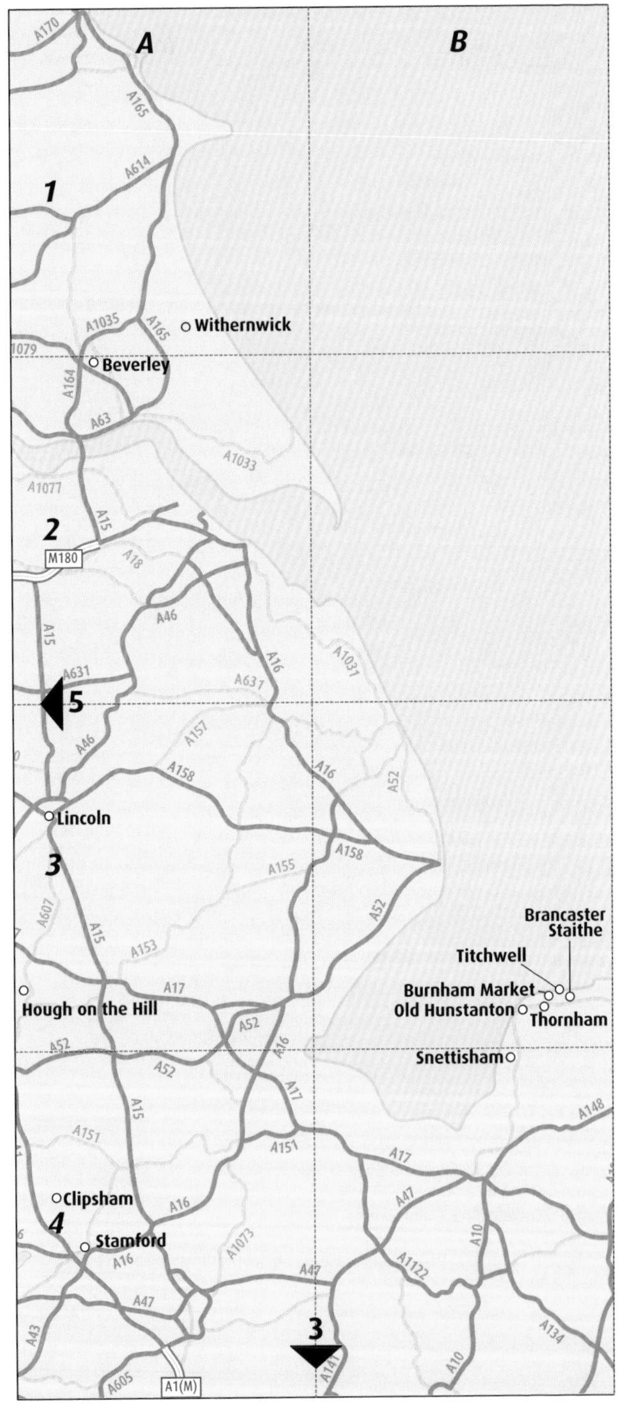
A
B
1
2
3
4
5
3
Withernwick
Beverley
Lincoln
Hough on the Hill
Clipsham
Stamford
Brancaster Staithe
Titchwell
Burnham Market
Old Hunstanton
Thornham
Snettisham
M180
A1(M)

C
D
Morston
Blakeney
Wiveton
Holt
Cromer
A148
Wells-next-the-Sea
A140
A149
A1067
A47
Norwich
Brundall
A47
Darsham
A146
A143
A11
3
A140
A1075
A143

MAP 6

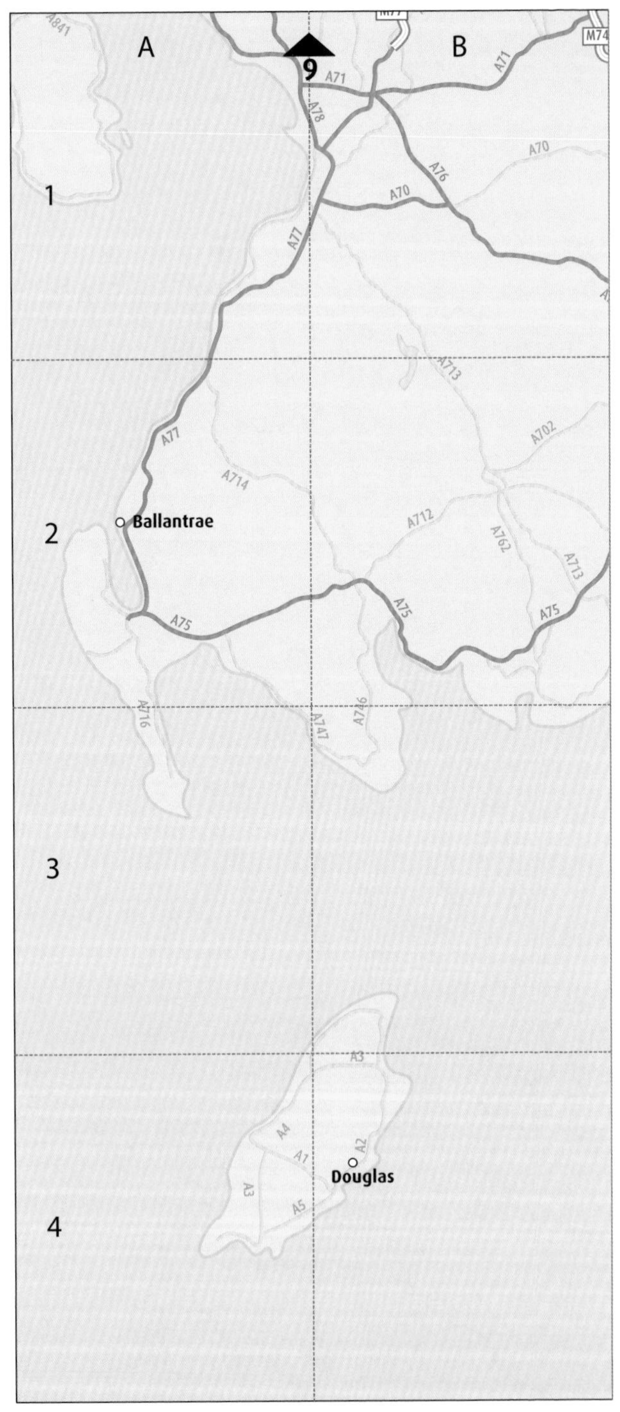

A
B
1
2
3
4
9
A841
M77
M74
A71
A78
A70
A76
A77
A713
A702
A714
Ballantrae
A712
A762
A75
A716
A747
A746
A3
A4
A1
A2
Douglas
A5

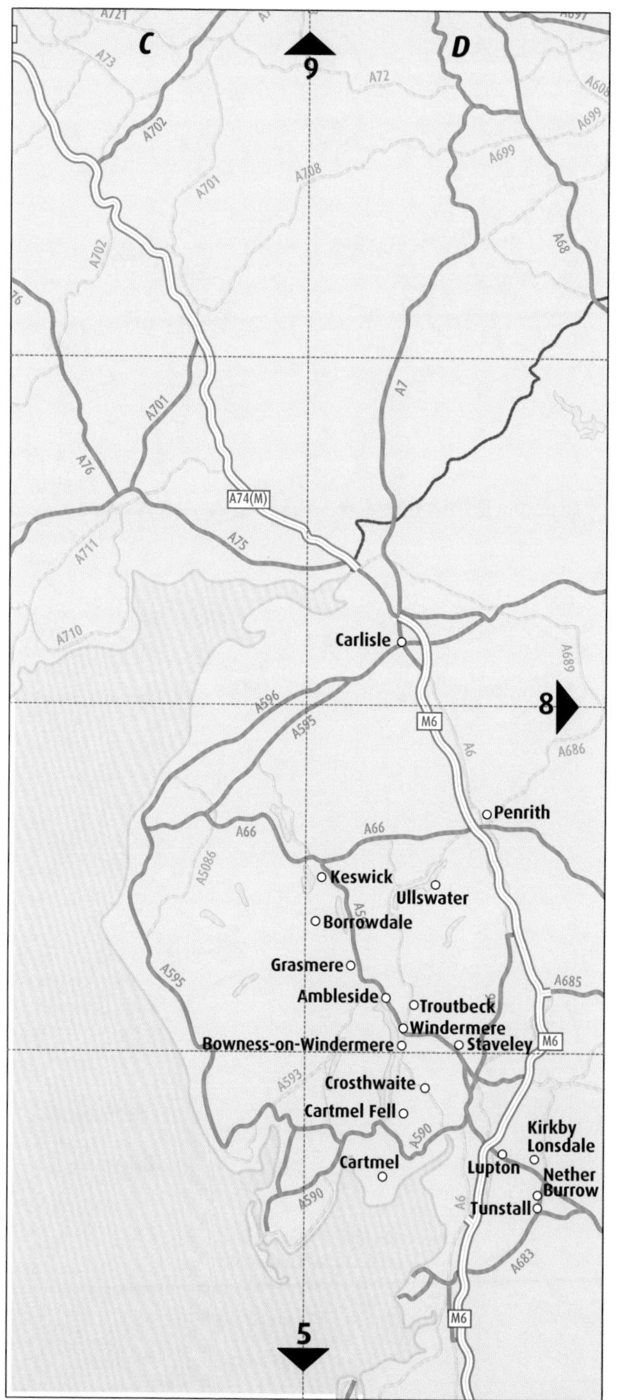
C
D
9
A721
A73
A72
A608
A699
A702
A701
A708
A68
A76
A7
A74(M)
A75
A711
A710
Carlisle
A689
A596
A595
M6
A6
8
A686
Penrith
A66
A5086
Keswick
Ullswater
Borrowdale
Grasmere
Ambleside
Troutbeck
Windermere
Bowness-on-Windermere
Staveley
A685
A593
Crosthwaite
Cartmel Fell
A590
Cartmel
Kirkby
Lonsdale
Lupton
Nether
Burrow
Tunstall
A683
5

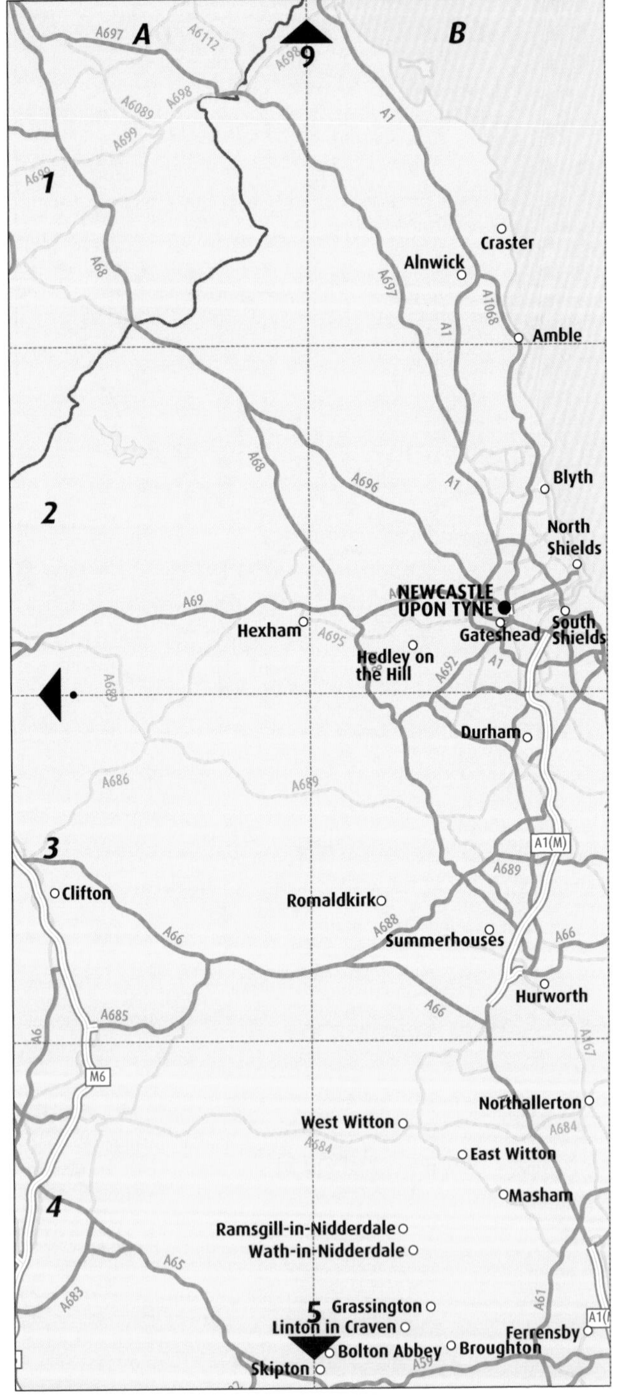

A
B
9
1
2
3
4
5
A697
A6112
A698
A6089
A699
A68
A1
A697
A1068
Craster
Alnwick
Amble
A696
Blyth
North
Shields
NEWCASTLE
UPON TYNE
South
Shields
Gateshead
A69
Hexham
A695
Hedley on
the Hill
A692
Durham
A686
A689
A1(M)
Clifton
Romaldkirk
A688
Summerhouses
A66
Hurworth
A685
A6
M6
A167
Northallerton
West Witton
A684
East Witton
Masham
Ramsgill-in-Nidderdale
Wath-in-Nidderdale
A65
A683
Grassington
Linton in Craven
Bolton Abbey
Broughton
Ferrensby
Skipton
A59
A61

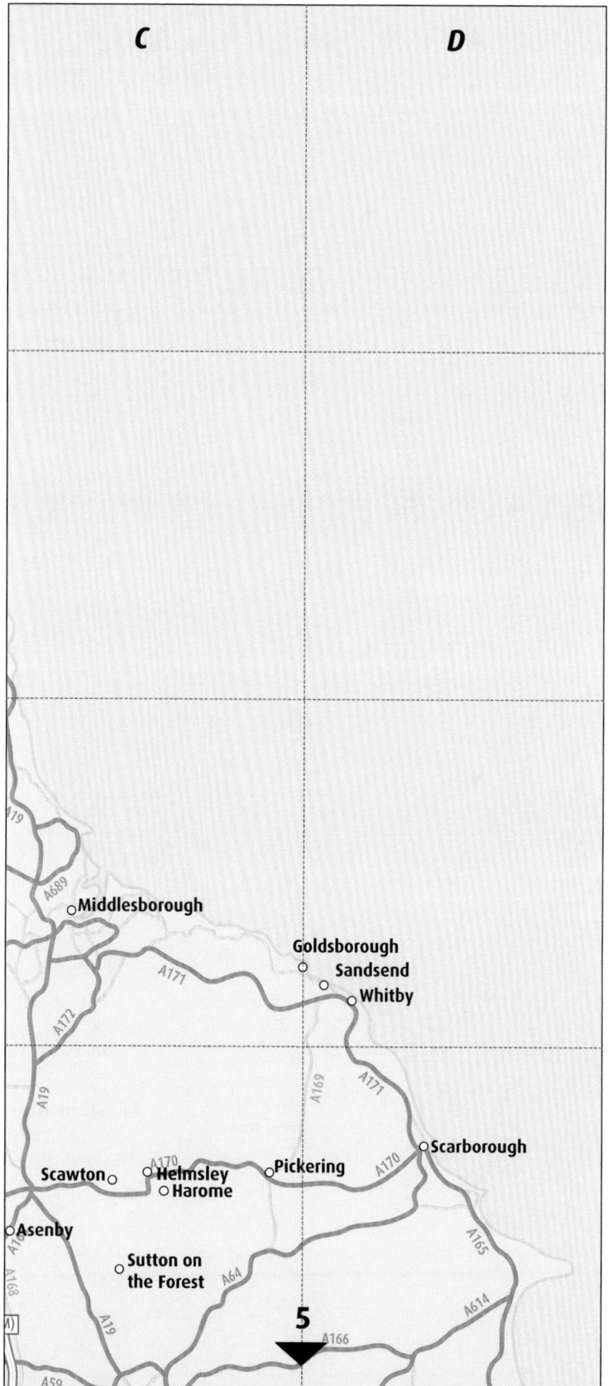
C
D
A19
A689
Middlesborough
Goldsborough
Sandsend
Whitby
A171
A172
A169
A171
A19
Scarborough
Scawton
A170
Helmsley
Harome
Pickering
A170
Asenby
A168
Sutton on
the Forest
A64
A165
A19
5
A614
A166
A59

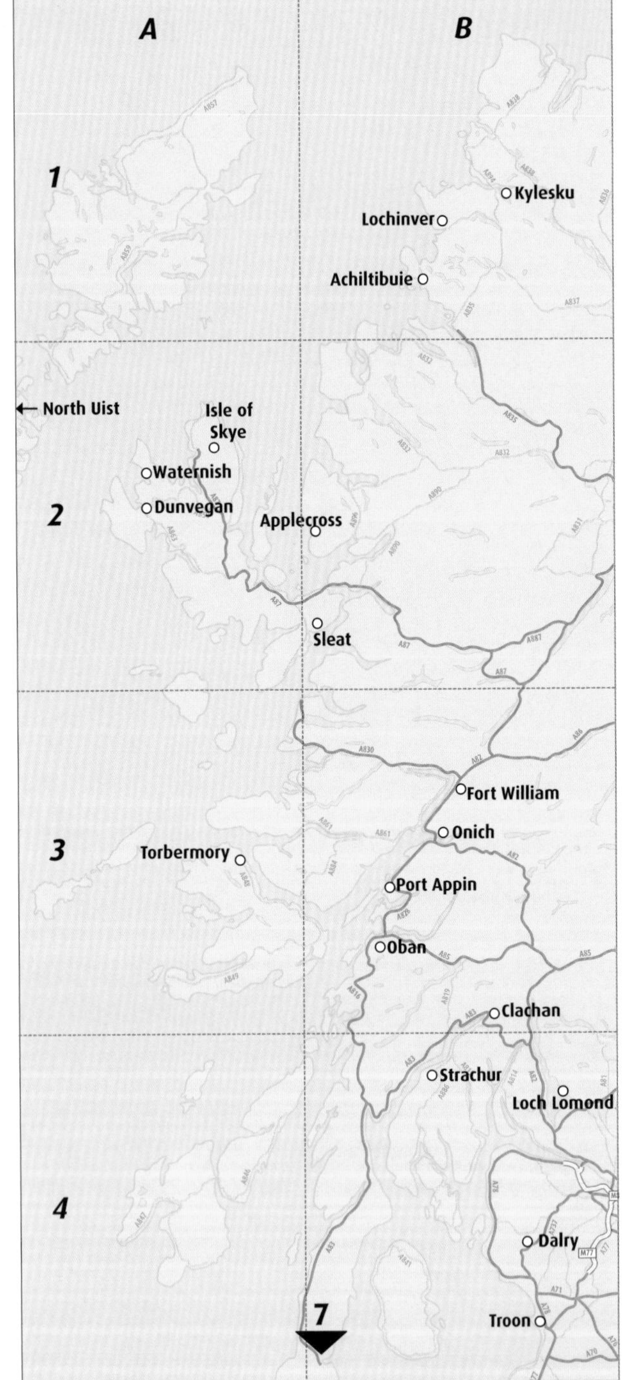
A
B
1
2
3
4
Kylesku
Lochinver
Achiltibuie
North Uist
Isle of Skye
Waternish
Dunvegan
Applecross
Sleat
Fort William
Onich
Torbermory
Port Appin
Oban
Clachan
Strachur
Loch Lomond
Dalry
Troon
7

MAP 9

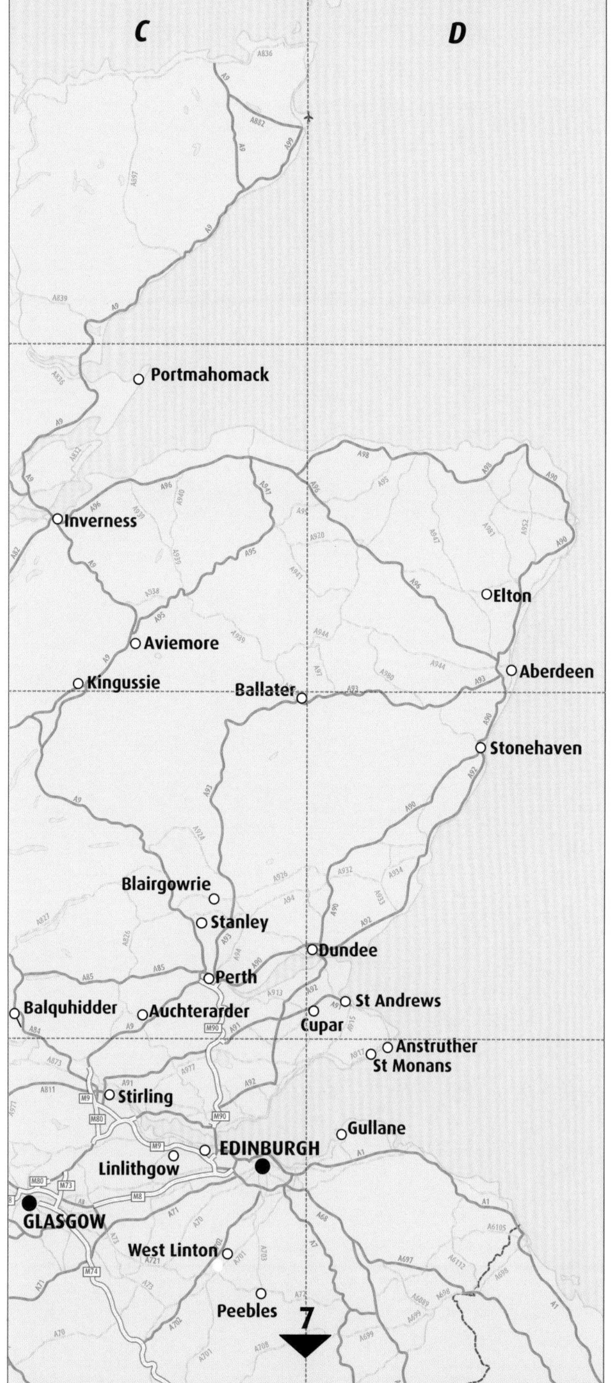
C
D
Portmahomack
Inverness
Elton
Aviemore
Kingussie
Ballater
Aberdeen
Stonehaven
Blairgowrie
Stanley
Dundee
Perth
St Andrews
Balquhidder
Auchterarder
Cupar
Anstruther
St Monans
Stirling
Gullane
EDINBURGH
Linlithgow
GLASGOW
West Linton
Peebles
7

A
B
1
2
3
4

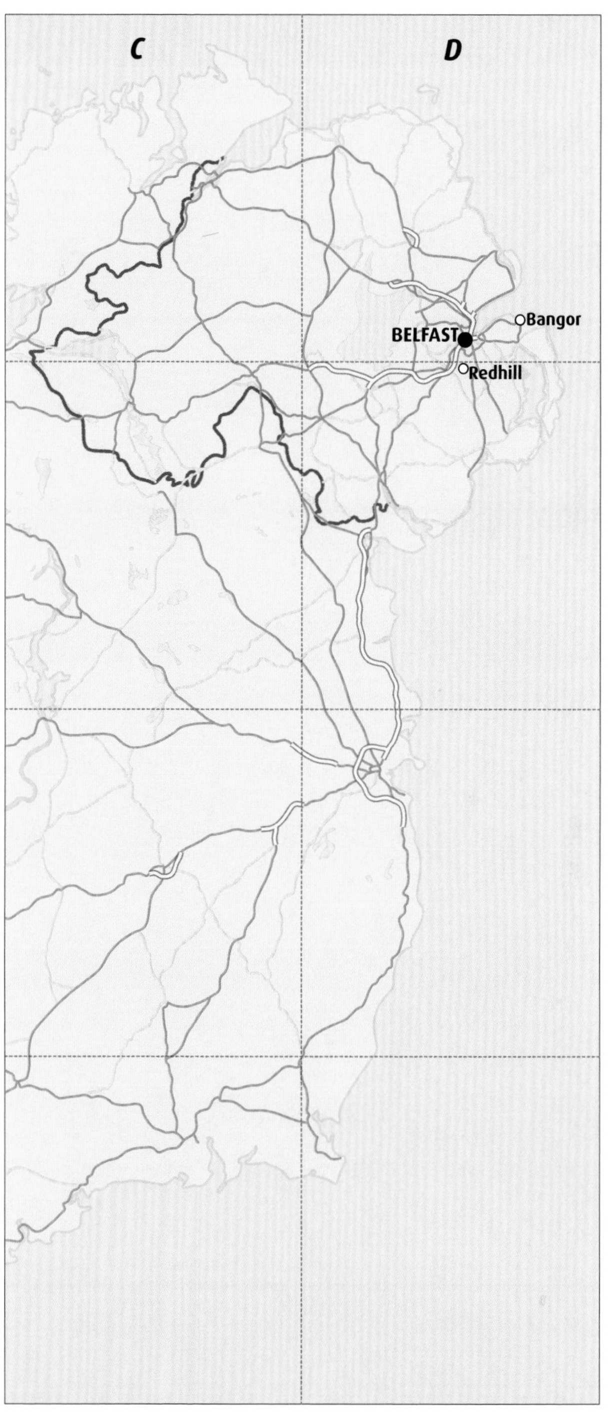
C
D
Bangor
BELFAST
Redhill

ALPHABETICAL INDEX

ALPHABETICAL INDEX

ALPHABETICAL INDEX

ALPHABETICAL INDEX

ALPHABETICAL INDEX

ALPHABETICAL INDEX

ALPHABETICAL INDEX

ALPHABETICAL INDEX

ALPHABETICAL INDEX